CHRIS RIGBY
WARTON England
A694
3—

The GOLF COURSE *Guide*
TO BRITAIN & IRELAND

The GOLF COURSE Guide
TO BRITAIN & IRELAND
BY DONALD STEEL OF THE SUNDAY TELEGRAPH

First published 1968
Eighth revised edition 1988

© Daily Telegraph and Sunday Telegraph
© Maps, BTA 1988

Maps produced by ESR Ltd, West Byfleet, Surrey.

ISBN 0 – 00 – 434153 – 8

Designed and typeset by Arthur Brown & Peter Cooling, Hersham, Surrey.
Printed in Great Britain by Redwood Burn, Trowbridge, Wilts.

Contents

T.J.A. MACAULEY
GOLF COURSE ARCHITECT
Bachelor of Science, Master of Science

MEMBER: British Association of Golf Course Architects
Association Francais des Architectes de Golf
Sports Turf Research Institute
The Association of Consulting Engineers

FELLOW: The Institution of Civil Engineers
The Institution of Structural Engineers

STUDIES: Noise Attenuation
Flood Plain Utilisation
Market Research
Environmental Impact Appraisal

CLIENTELE: Public Courses, Private and Country Clubs,
Leisure Hotels and Golf/Housing.

UNITED KINGDOM
38 Moira Drive Bangor
County Down BT20 4RW
Tel: 0247 465953
Fax: 0247 452863
Telex: 74195

FRANCE
113 Boulevard Pereire
75017 Paris
Tel: 1 47 63 04 49
Telex: 643 585F

Foreword

It is twenty years since the first edition of the Golf Course Guide was published. In that period, something like a million new golfers have taken up the game in Great Britain and Ireland; so you might say that the need for a catalogue of courses is greater than ever.

If they haven't already done so, now is the time for new golfers to go in search of the incomparable variety of courses which lie within these shores. Golf is so much more fortunate than other sports where one football pitch, tennis court or swimming pool is much the same as another. They lack the aesthetic delights that mean so much to golfers, good and bad.

The purpose of the Guide is to allow readers to know where they will be welcome and how much a round might cost. And it also provides help in getting to the courses.

I see from the first edition in 1968 that 18 holes at Ganton cost £1 while a weekly ticket at Turnberry set you back 50 shillings. Nowadays, a new golf ball costs something in between. The pound in your pocket is not what it was but it certainly hasn't checked the surge in the popularity of the game and I hope that, in its own way, this Guide will add to that popularity.

Finally, my grateful thanks to club secretaries for filling in our forms and for supplying the information. Without them there would be no Guide.

Donald Steel
March 1988

Golf Courses and their Design Oddities

There is a modern belief that all championship courses must have a par of 72, contain four par 5s and four par 3s, and be not less than 7000 yards long. It is as crazy a notion as maintaining that all loaves of bread should be the same size and shape. Choice is a matter of personal taste. However, the chief fault, where courses are concerned, lies in the overworked and misused word 'championship'.

A definition of a championship course is one on which a championship has been played. Not will be, may be, or should have been — and not just a tournament either. A common phrase describing new courses is 'championship standard'; but who decides? On the other hand, it can be argued that the Wiltshire Girls championship is as much a championship as the US Open and that it is misleading to apply the same cachet.

To some extent that is true, but every course in the world, indeed every hole on every course, is different and it is the lack of any set pattern in their layout which makes them so. For example, the Old course at St Andrews, the most famous of all, has only two par 5s and two par 3s; and you play seven holes before reaching the first short hole. Some longish courses have no par 5s. Many courses begin or end with a short hole. A few begin and end with a short hole; others may have a total of five or six. The Red course at the Berkshire is made up of six threes, six fours and six fives.

Largely to illustrate these inconsistencies, and largely for my own amusement, I have prepared a list of some of the courses covered by this Guide which may help to explode a few myths. It is not claimed to be a complete list and readers may wish to prepare their own categories next time they are flying the Atlantic, tossing and turning at night, under the hair dryer or bored with a lecture.

18-hole courses over 5800 yards beginning with a par 3 Royal Lytham and St Annes, Royal Mid- Surrey, Berkshire (Blue), Liphook, Hayling Island, Addington, Southport and Ainsdale, West Cornwall, Longcliffe, Ashburnham, Churston, Huntercombe, Purley Downs, City of Derry, Peebles, Dartford, West Bowling, Wearside, Llandudno (Maesdu), Livingston, Royal Norwich, Skips, Colville Park, Houldsworth, Llanymynech, Whitchurch (Cardiff), Withington, Knole Park.

18-hole courses over 5800 yards ending with a par 3 Berkshire (Red), Moor Park (High), Royal St David's, St Pierre, Killarney, Lindrick, Sandy Lodge, Goodwood, Piltdown, Sandiway, Parkstone, Chelmsford, Boyce Hill, Brora, Kirkcaldy, Dunwood Manor, Nottingham City, Glamorganshire (Penarth), Mount Oswald, Airdrie, Downes Crediton, Dougalston, Dunstable Downs, Erewash Valley, Louth, Saffron Walden, Fortrose and Rosemarkie, Sickleholme, Bremhill Park, Cold Ashby, Ellesmere, Ashford (Kent), Milford Haven, Alloa, Carlyon Bay, West Lothian, Royal Eastbourne, Howley Hall, Northcliffe, Wallsend, Barnard Castle, Kilsyth Lennox, Chapel-en-le-Frith, Worksop, Hoebridge, Padeswood and Buckley, Stoke by Nayland (both courses), Breightmet, Great Barr, Dewsbury, Wetherby, Tredegar Park, Courtown, Bandon, Cawder, Prestwick St Nicholas, Old Padeswood, Ryton, Langley Park, Royal Guernsey.

18-hole courses beginning and ending with a par 3 Hawick, Didsbury, Bingley St Ives, Southwood, Bearsted.

18-hole course with four consecutive par 3s Clober

18-hole courses with three consecutive par 3s Chipstead, Callander, Ilfracombe, Betws- y-coed (twice)

18-hole courses over 5800 yards with consecutive par 3s Cruden Bay, Machrihanish, West Sussex, Sandy Lodge, Elgin, Brancepeth Castle, Stoneham, North Oxford, Potters Bar, Haywards Heath, Glamorganshire (Penarth), Consett and District, Birr, Barnard Castle, Erewash Valley, Bandon, Royal Jersey, Knott End, Linlithgow, Harburn, Tain , Waterlooville, Tredegar Park, Kidderminster, Royal Epping Forest, Brough, Burntisland, Royal Eastbourne, Balmoral, Willesley Park, Bishop Auckland.

Courses over 6000 yards with more than five par 3s Berkshire (Red) (6), Sandy Lodge (6), Darlington (6).

18-hole courses with less than three par 3s St Andrews (Old), Elie.

Courses over 6000 yards with no par 5s Aldeburgh, Elie.

Courses where first short hole comes at the 9th Blyth, Royal Cromer, Torquay, Maryport, Breightmet, Bremhill Park, **8th** St Andrews (Old), Ratho Park, Sand Moor, Royal Eastbourne, Shandon Park, Blainroe, West Kent, **7th** Wells, Western Gailes, Cork (Little Island), Great Lever and Farnworth, Shifnal.

Courses where last short hole comes at 10th Furness, **11th** St Andrews (Old), Elie, **12th** Royal Dublin, Bishop Auckland, Bishop's Stortford, Woodhall Spa and Royal Lytham and St Annes.

Open, Amateur or national championship courses with only two par 5s St Andrews (Old), Turnberry, Southerness, Royal Aberdeen, Royal Dornoch, Prestwick, Western Gailes, Ganton, Moortown, Royal St George's, Sunningdale (Old).

Courses with three successive par 5s Bishop Auckland (2nd to 4th), West Berkshire (13th to 15th), Sutton Coldfield (5th to 7th), Cleckheaton and District (6th to 8th), Whitburn (7th to 9th), Monmouthshire (6th to 8th).

Courses over 7000 yards West Berkshire, The Belfry (Brabazon), Thorpe Wood, West Malling.

Holes under 100 yards Erewash Valley (4th, 89 yards), Bridport and West Dorset (2nd, 93 yards), Dun Laoghaire (7th, 95 yards), Ilfracombe (4th, 81 yards).

Publisher's note

For easy reference the country has been divided into 28 areas and each area has been given an identifying letter from A to Z, then AA and BB. Within these areas the courses are arranged alphabetically and numbered, starting from 1 in each new area. There is a map at the start of each section which shows the location of the golf courses within that section identified by the number given to each course. The outline map opposite shows the 28 areas within the book and the index at the back of the book (page 299) lists each golf course and gives its identifying letter and number for any reference in case of doubt.

All the information in this book has been compiled with the help of club secretaries. Information on subjects such as green fees is liable to change quickly and the publishers would welcome letters from club secretaries or golfers finding any discrepancy between details given in the guide and their own experiences. It should be noted that many green fees are subject to VAT and that weekend rates usually apply on public holidays also.

The distribution of golf courses into grouped county areas has generally been done on the basis of the address. This has resulted in some courses, particularly around London and other major cities, being included in 'wrong' areas. Reference to the index will clear up any confusion and show the identifying letter and number under which each course is located.

Area Map Reference

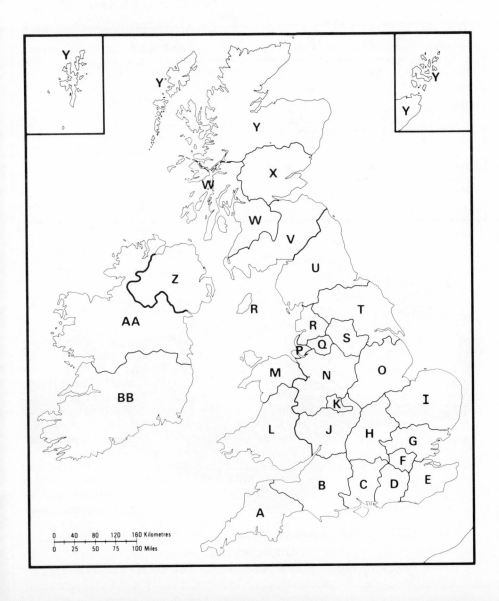

A Cornwall, Devon and Channel Islands

Everybody has heard of Westward Ho! but not everyone who ought to has played there. Modern championships at national level have passed it by more on the grounds of its inaccessibility and a lack of accommodation than any lack of quality as a test of golf. Westward Ho! is the oldest seaside course in England and, as such, is worthy of special recognition.

It is no ordinary place. In fact, a visit there is something of a pilgrimage. It was at the Royal North Devon Club that Horace Hutchinson and J. H. Taylor learned their golf and it is interesting that, on leaving school at the age of 11, one of Taylor's first jobs was as a boot boy in the home of Horace Hutchinson's father. Later, Taylor became one of the world's leading players and ended his days as President of the Club. He described the view from his cottage in Northam as 'the finest in Christendom'.

It may be thought that much has changed in over 120 years of the Club's history but Westward Ho! was a design of nature and nowhere, except perhaps St Andrews or Prestwick, is there a more natural setting for the game.

One of its charms is that nobody has attempted to up-date it and, in the memorable match played to celebrate the Club's centenary in 1964, Max Faulkner and Christy O'Connor looked thoroughly at home wearing the costume and using the equipment familiar to Taylor in his early days.

The area abounds in splendid holiday golf and there is much rewarding exploring to be done. In talking about Saunton, Westward Ho!'s distinguished neighbour across the water, one has to use the most exalted terms. It is the finest course in the south-west, one of the finest in the country — an Open championship course in any other region.

It has hosted several notable occasions but it is also a paradise for botanists, bird watchers and, when the sun shines, bathers. The beach, fringed by the golfing dunes, is superb and, as such, is ideal for a short stay or simply as a stopping place en route for Cornwall.

The journey over the county border into Cornwall is much easier to attempt in the imagination than on crowded summer roads, Cornwall has many pleasant courses including St Enodoc, Trevose, a wonderful holiday centre immensely popular with families, Bude, Newquay, Lelant and Carlyon Bay.

Most have a seaside setting, but for lovers of inland golf there is little better than the Manor House Hotel course at Moretonhampstead on the edge of Dartmoor in Devon, especially the treacherous charm of the first nine holes. With a fine hotel right on the doorstep there is no urge to move far, but the East Devon Club at Budleigh Salterton is excellent and praise, too, for Thurlestone, Torquay and Churston with its lovely views of Torbay.

The Jersey courses are well known to me, Royal Jersey and La Moye making a splendid foil for each other, La Moye on its western headland and Royal Jersey much closer to sea level at the other end of the island.

With nine holes at St Clements, Jersey is better served numerically than Guernsey but Royal Guernsey, described elsewhere, is highly popular. My late partner, Frank Pennink, was responsible for the nine holes on Alderney and was very pleased with the way they turned out, a view supported by many who have sampled their charm.

A1 Alderney

☎ Alderney (048 182) 2835
Routes des Carriers, Alderney,
Channel Islands.
1 mile E of St Annes.
Undulating seaside course.
9 holes, 2528 yards, S.S.S.32
Double rounds for 18 S.S.S.65
Course designed by Frank Pennink.
Visitors: welcome at all times,
except competition days.
Green fees: weekdays £7 per day,
weekends and Bank Holidays £8;
weekly rates on application.
Society meetings: catered for on
weekdays by arrangement and
weekends for special events.
Catering: bar foods served on
weekdays,Sun lunch, special parties
or lunches by arrangement.
Hotels: Devereux House; Sea View.

A2 Axe Cliff

☎ Seaton (0297) 20499
Axmouth, Seaton, Devon EX12 4AB
Off A35, 1 mile from Seaton.
Undulating seaside course.
18 holes, 5000 yards, S.S.S.64
Club founded in 1892
Visitors: welcome Mon to Sat.
Green fees: weekdays £7; Sat and
Bank Holidays £8.

Catering: snacks and meals.
Hotels: Hawkes Hyde; Bay.

A3 Bigbury

☎ Bigbury (0548) 810207
Bigbury-on-Sea, Kingsbridge, Devon
TQ7 4BB.
Take A379 Plymouth to Kingsbridge
road; turn right 2 miles from Modbury
at Harraton Cross, signposted
Bigbury-on-Sea. Golf Club is a
further 5 miles from here.
Undulating seaside course.
18 holes, 6076 yards, S.S.S.69
Course designed by J.H. Taylor.
Club founded in 1926.
Visitors: welcome.
Green fees: £10 per day,
half price after 5pm.
Society meetings: welcome by
arrangement.
Catering: full catering and bar
facilities.
Hotels: Seagulls, Bigbury-on-Sea;
Thurlestone, Thurlestone.

A4 Bude and N Cornwall

☎ Bude (0288) 2006 Sec and
Steward, 3635 Pro.
Burn View, Bude, Cornwall
EX23 8DA.
A39, 1 minute from Bude town

centre.
Seaside links course.
18 holes, 6202 yards, S.S.S.70
Course designed by Tom Dunn.
Club founded in 1891.
Visitors: 1st tee reserved for
members 8.00am-9.30am, 12.30pm-
2.00pm, 5pm-6pm.
Green fees: £9 per round/day.
Society meetings: welcome. 1st tee
can be reserved (Mon-Fri).
Catering: wide selection of meals
lunchtime and evenings.
Hotels: Camelot; Grosvenor;
Penarvor; Burn Court.

A5 Budock Vean

☎ Falmouth (0326) 250288
Mawnan Smith, Falmouth, Cornwall
TR11 5LG.
On main road between Falmouth and
Helston, 7 miles from Helston.
Undulating parkland course.
9 holes, 5222 yards, S.S.S.65
Course designed by James Braid,
D. Cook and P.H. Whiteside.
Club founded in 1932.
Visitors: welcome any time.
Green fees: on application.
Society meetings: catered for all
year on application, except Sun.
Catering: snacks, lunch and table

There is life after golf.

Set aside, for a moment, Turnberry's two championship courses.

Consider, instead, the tranquil elegance of the lounges, with their views of shore, sea and islands.

Ponder the pleasures of the heated indoor pool, the sauna, solarium and gym. Weigh up the attractions of billiards or tennis. Imagine French and Scottish cuisine which reflects the hotel's five-star status.

It all exists. For proof of this phenomenon, contact Turnberry today.

TURNBERRY HOTEL AND GOLF COURSES
Turnberry, Ayrshire KA27 9LT, Scotland.
Telephone: 06553 1000. Telex: 777779. Fax: 06553 1706

d'hôte or à la carte dinner.
Hotels: Budock Vean.

A6 Carlyon Bay Hotel

☎Par (072 681) 2304
Carlyon Bay, St Austell, Cornwall
PL25 3RD.
Main Plymouth to Truro road 1 mile
W of St Blazey.
Clifftop/parkland course.
18 holes, 6463 yards, S.S.S.71
Course designed by Hamilton Stutt.
Club founded in 1926.
Visitors: ring for starting times (072
681) 4228.
Green fees: on application.
Society meetings: welcome by
reservation with Pro.
Catering: Lunch 12am-2pm, dinner
from 6pm.
Hotels: Carlyon Bay.

A7 Chulmleigh

☎(0769) 80519
Leigh Road, Chulmleigh, North
Devon EX18 7BL.
1 mile off A377 midway between
Exeter and Barnstaple.
Meadowland course.
18 holes, 1450 yards, S.S.S.54
Winter: Dec to Mar: 9 holes,
2360 yards, S.S.S.56
Course designed by J.W.D.
Goodban OBE.
Club founded in 1976.
Visitors: welcome.
Green fees: £2.75 per round; £3.75
per day.
Society meetings: welcome by prior
arrangement.
Catering: light snacks, licensed bar.
Hotels: Northcote Manor; Fox &
Hounds, Eggesford.

A8 Churston

☎Churston (0803) 842751 Sec,
842128 Clubhouse, 842894 Pro.
Churston, nr Brixham, Devon.
On A379 3 miles from Paignton.
Downland course.
18 holes, 6201 yards, S.S.S.70
Course designed by H.S. Colt.
Club founded in 1890.
Visitors: members of recognised
golf clubs only, proof required.
Green fees: on application.
Society meetings: by arrangement.
Catering: available each day during
summer, opening hours depend on
time of year.
Hotels: numerous hotels in area.

A9 Downes Crediton

☎Crediton (036 32) 3991,
3025 Sec.
Hookway, Crediton, Devon
EX17 3PT.
Off A377 Exeter-Crediton road,
8 miles NW of Exeter. Turn off at
Crediton railway.
Parkland/Meadowland course.
18 holes, 5858 yards, S.S.S.68
Club founded in 1976.
Visitors: welcome, telephone Sec or
club.
Green fees: £8 weekdays; £10
weekends.
Society meetings: welcome
weekdays.
Catering: coffee, lunch, dinners
available.
Hotels: Rosemont.

A10 East Devon

☎Budleigh Salterton (039 54) 3370
North View Rd, Budleigh Salterton,
Devon.
5 miles E of Exmouth on A376.
Heathland seaside course.
18 holes, 6214 yards, S.S.S.70
Club founded in 1902.
Visitors: welcome with letter of
introduction.
Green fees: £12.
Society meetings: by arrangement.
Catering: every day from 10am.
Hotels: Southlands; Rosemullion.

A11 Elfordleigh G & CC

☎Plymouth (0752) 336428
Plympton, Plymouth, Devon
PL7 5EB.
Off A38. 5 miles NE of Plymouth.
Undulating parkland course.
9 holes, 5609 yards, S.S.S.67
Course designed by J.H. Taylor.
Club founded in 1932.
Visitors: weekdays unrestricted,
weekends telephone first.
Green fees: £7 weekdays, £8
weekends.
Society meetings: welcome,
telephone first.
Catering: bar meals, sit down meals
by arrangement.
Hotels: Elfordleigh.

A12 Exeter G & CC

☎Topsham (039 287) 4139
Countess Wear, Exeter, Devon
EX2 7AE.
On A377 to Exmouth.
Parkland course.
18 holes, 6061 yards, S.S.S.69
Course designed by James Braid.
Visitors: welcome on weekdays.

Green fees: £12 per day everyday.
Society meetings: Thurs only.
Catering: lunch and evening meals
all week.
Hotels: Moat House; Countess
Wear, Exeter.

A13 Falmouth

☎Falmouth (0326) 311262, 40525
Sec.
Swanpool Rd, Falmouth, Cornwall
TR11 3BQ.
1 mile W of Swanpool Beach,
Falmouth.
Seaside parkland course.
18 holes, 5581 yards, S.S.S.67
Club founded in 1928.
Visitors: welcome.
Green fees: £8 per round; £10 per
day; Juniors under 18 half price, all
week.
Catering: lunch and tea all week,
evening meals by arrangement.
Hotels: Royal Duchy; St Michael's;
Penmere Manor; Greenlawns;
Somerdale; Meudon Vean.

A14 Great Torrington

☎ Torrington (0805) 22229
Weare Trees, Torrington, North
Devon EX38 7EZ.
1 mile N of Torrington on Weare
Giffard road.
Undulating commonland course.
9 holes, 4418 yards, S.S.S.62
Club founded in 1932.
Visitors: welcome except Sun
mornings.
Green fees: Adults £6 per round/
day; Juniors £3 per round/day at all
times.
Society meetings: welcome by ar-
rangement.
Catering: light meals by arrange-
ment.
Hotels: Castle Hill, Torrington.

A15 Holsworthy

☎Holsworthy (0409) 2531 Sec,
Holsworthy, N Devon.
1.5 miles W of Holsworthy on A3072.
Parkland course.
18 holes, 5894 yards, S.S.S.68
Club founded in 1937.
Visitors: welcome except Sun
mornings.
Green fees: £6 daily; £24 weekly.
Society meetings: welcome by
arrangement.
Catering: by arrangement.
Hotels: Coles Mill.

A16 Honiton

☎Honiton (0404) 44422 Sec,

2943 Pro.
Middlehills, Honiton, Devon
EX14 8RT.
2 miles S of Honiton.
Parkland course.
18 holes, 5931 yards, S.S.S.68
Club founded in 1896.
Visitors: members of a recognised
Golf Club welcome any time except
prior reservation for competition.
Green fees: £8 per day; £10
weekends and Bank Holidays
Society meetings: limited number
catered for usually on Thurs.
Catering: lunch, high tea and dinner,
except Sun.
Hotels: Dolphin; Angel; Deer Park.

A17 Ilfracombe
☎Ilfracombe (0271) 62176
Hele Bay, Ilfracombe, North Devon.
On A399 Ilfracombe to Combe
Martin road, 2 miles from Ilfracombe.
Undulating course.
18 holes, 5857 yards, S.S.S.68
Club founded in 1892.
Visitors: welcome. Starting sheets
at weekends.
Green fees: £9 per round/day (Sat
and Sun inclusive); £27 per 5 day
ticket (Mon-Fri).
Society meetings: by arrangement.
Catering: bar and dining room.
Hotels: Collindale; St Hellier.

A18 Isles of Scilly
☎Scillonia (0720) 22692
St Mary's, Isles of Scilly TR21 0NF.
1.5 miles from Hugh Town in St
Mary's.
Moorland course.
9 holes, 5974 yards, S.S.S.69
Course designed by Horace
Hutchinson.
Club founded in 1904.
Visitors: welcome Mon-Sat.
Green fees: £7 per day; £18 per
week; £27 per two weeks.
Catering: lunch and evening meals
served.
Hotels: Godolphin; Tregarthen's.

A19 La Moye
☎Jersey (0534)43401
La Moye, Jersey.
From Airport, follow main road,
turning right at main traffic lights at
junction. Sign indicating the club will
be seen on right-hand side of road
about a mile down.
Links course.
18 holes, 6741 yards, S.S.S.72
Club founded in 1902.
Visitors: welcome except

competition days.
Green fees: on application.
Society meetings: by arrangement
with Sec.
Catering: full restaurant facilities.
Hotels: Atlantic; L'Horizon; Silver
Springs; Mermaid.

A20 Launceston
☎Launceston (0566) 3442
St Stephens, Launceston, Cornwall.
Take Bude road from Launceston, 1
mile N of town turn left opposite St
Stephen's church. Club is 300 yards
on right.
Undulating parkland course.
18 holes, 6454 yards, S.S.S.71
Course designed by Hamilton Stutt.
Club founded in 1927.
Visitors: welcome - with handicap.
Green fees: £8.
Society meetings: by arrangement -
weekdays.
Catering: by arrangement. Bar
snacks lunchtime.
Hotels: White Hart; Lantegloo.

A21 Looe Bin Down
☎Widegates (050 34) 247
Widegates, Looe, Cornwall.
Midway between Liskeard and Looe.
Moorland/meadowland course.
18 holes, 6104 yards, S.S.S.69
Course designed by Harry Vardon.
Club founded in 1934.
Visitors: 7 days per week.
Green fees: £8 per day.
Society meetings: by arrangement.
Catering: bar snacks, meals to
order.
Hotels: Commonwood Manor, Looe.

A22 Manor House Hotel
☎Moretonhampstead (0647) 40355
Moretonhampstead, Newton Abbot
TQ13 8RE.
12 miles from Exeter and Newton
Abbot on Princetown road.
Parkland course.
18 holes, 6016 yards, S.S.S.69
Course designed by
J.W. Abercrombie.
Visitors: welcome by arrangement.
Green fees: £11 per round; £14 per
day.
Society meetings: catered for 7
days.
Catering: breakfast, dinner, cream
teas, lunch.
Hotels: Manor House.

A23 Mullion
☎Mullion (0326) 240685
Cury, Helston, Cornwall. 5 miles from

Helston on A3083 Lizard road.
Undulating course.
18 holes, 5616 yards, S.S.S.67
Visitors: welcome (handicap
required)
Green fees: £8 per day; £28 per 5
days.
Society meetings: welcome, fee £5.
Catering: bar snacks, restaurant.
Hotels: Polurrian; Mullion Cove.

A24 Newquay
☎Newquay (0637) 874354
Tower Road, Newquay TR17 1LT.
Half mile from town centre in the
direction of Fistral beach.
Seaside course.
18 holes, 6140 yards, S.S.S.69
Course designed by H.S. Colt.
Club founded in 1890.
Visitors: welcome at all times.
Green fees: £10 weekdays; £12
weekend.
Society meetings: catered for
weekdays.
Catering: lunch served 7 days.
Hotels: Bristol; Windsor.

A25 Newton Abbot (Stover)
☎Newton Abbot (0626) 52460 Sec,
65472 Club. Bovey Rd, Newton
Abbot, S Devon TQ12 6QQ.
On A382 Newton Abbot to Bovey
Tracey road, N of Newton Abbot.
Parkland course.
18 holes, 5834 yards, S.S.S.68
Course redesigned by James Braid
in 1931.
Club founded in 1899.
Visitors: must be introduced or have
proof of membership of recognised
club.
Green fees: £10.
Society meetings: Thursdays only -
minimum 24.
Catering: full catering 7 days.
Hotels: Globe, Newton Abbot.

A26 Okehampton
☎Okehampton (0837) 2113
Okehampton, Devon EX20 1EF.
Take A30 to Okehampton town
centre from where the club is clearly
signposted.
Turn towards Dartmoor at the traffic
lights, take the third right then the
right fork and club is second on the
right; the name is on the entrance
post.
Undulating moorland course.
18 holes, 5307 yards, S.S.S.67
Club founded in 1913.
Visitors: welcome but no athletes
shorts, ankle socks or denim.

Royal Guernsey

One of Royal Guernsey's most celebrated claims to fame is that it was the first course Henry Cotton ever saw. He used to be taken for walks over it by his mother, herself a Guernsey woman, although the family had moved to London by the time Cotton was four years old. So the course was denied added lustre by being, in part, responsible for the golfing development of the great man, but for almost a century it has served the needs of local golfers and hundreds of visitors alike.

There have been two or three versions of the layout, the most recent caused principally by the occupation of the Germans whose idea of bunkers consisted of solid stone rather than sand. The difficulty of demolishing these emplacements means they survive as reminders of darker days, but golfers have never been easily suppressed and L'Ancresse Common on the island's northern shores has maintained the defiant spirit and noble traditions of Channel Island golf to perfection.

It has a seaside flavour with a variety of spectacular views of beach, bathers and boats although there is no hint of dunes. The major hazard on the front nine is a dense crop of gorse which makes accurate driving an integral part of success, together with the more unusual feature of Guernsey cows munching at intervals along the rough with an air of relaxed contentment that is the envy of players. Under Guernsey law they must be tethered, which may be to spare them the fate of the young bullock in a field near Headingly GC which, as the **Golfer's Handbook** used to relate, was found on slaughter to have had 56 golf balls in its five stomachs.

Royal Guernsey's first hole, curving round the hill in front of the clubhouse, makes a pleasant start even if the pitch to a small green must be precisely struck. The 2nd immediately calls for higher skills. It recalls the story of a newcomer to Walton Heath playing one foggy morning and enquiring of James Braid, with whom he was paired, the line on a certain hole. 'It's on the spire of yon' church', replied Braid, 'You canna see it this morning but that's the line.' Well, the line on the 2nd from the back tee is on Vale Church and there is little room for error. A narrow ribbon of fairway fringes the gorse on the left and the first sight of the sea on the right in the shape of Grand Havre, but the labyrinth of gorse weaves an ever more constant pattern all the way to the turn, notably at the 9th, the hardest hole of all, at 460 yards.

Before that point is reached, the 4th is not much shorter although the 6th, the only par five on the first nine, and the 5th and 8th introduce welcome variety of length. The second nine, running at right angles to the first, makes a fine study in the shapes of its greens, the downhill approach to a sunken 10th contrasting with the new 12th, the raised 13th and the clever angling of the 14th — the second par 5.

The 14th green is the limit of the course in an easterly direction and the 15th and 16th, running parallel to the best example of Guernsey's beaches, head for home — the 15th in the form of an excellent two shotter. The 17th, in a slight dogleg, climbs the hill while the short 18th, plunging down again, completes the circuit which combines so many admirable qualities. It tests the good players without plaguing the weak, giving enjoyment to all in a setting that, seen at its best, is a glorious place to play. What more could you ask?

Green fees: on application.
Society meetings: welcome by prior arrangement; £4 per person if number 12 or more.
Catering: full lunch served, other meals by arrangement.
Hotels: White Hart; Manor; Oxenham Arms.

A27 Perranporth

☎Perranporth (0872) 573701 and 572454
Budnick Hill, Perranporth TR6 0AB.
A3075 from Newquay then B3285.
Club is on fringe of town adjacent to beach.
Links course.
18 holes, 6208 yards, S.S.S.71
Course designed by James Braid.
Club founded in 1929.
Visitors: welcome but ring before arrival.
Green fees: on application.
Society meetings: welcome.
Catering: resident steward and stewardess.
Hotels: Beach Dunes; Dunsmore.

A28 Praa Sands

☎Penzance (0736) 763445
Germoe Crossroads, Penzance, Cornwall T20 9RB.
Off A394, halfway between Helston and Penzance.
Parkland course.
9 holes, 4036 yards, S.S.S.60
Club founded in May 1971.
Visitors: welcome except Fri from 5pm and Sun morning.
Green fees: £5 per day/round; (£3 with member), Juniors £3.
Society meetings: welcome by prior arrangement.
Catering: breakfast, lunch and dinner.
Hotels: Praa Sands; Lesceave Cliff; Mount Haven; Mount Prospect.

A29 Royal Guernsey

☎Guernsey (0481) 47022
L'Ancresse Vale, Guernsey, Channel Islands.
3 miles from St Peter Port.
Seaside course.
18 holes, 6206 yards, S.S.S.70
Course designed by Mackenzie Ross. Club founded in 1890.
Visitors: Not after 12 noon Thurs and Sat. Not Sun. Must produce handicap certificates.
Green fees: £8.50 per round; £10.50 per day; £35 per week; £52 per 2 weeks.
Society meetings: small societies on application.

Catering: Morning coffee, afternoon tea, lunch, evening meals Tue, Wed, Thurs, Fri, Sat.
Hotels: Pembroke; L'Ancresse Lodge.

A30 Royal Jersey

☎Jersey (0534) 54416, 51042 Sec.
Steward and members.
Grouville, Jersey, Channel Islands.
4 miles E of St Helier on road to Gorey.
Seaside course.
18 holes, 6097 yards, S.S.S.69
Club founded in 1878.
Visitors: welcome weekdays after 10am, weekends and Bank Holidays after 2.30pm (BST) or 12.30 (whites).
Green fees: on application.
Society meetings: small parties only.
Catering: full facilities by prior arrangement with Steward.
Hotels: Beachcomber, Grouville; Grouville Bay.

A31 Royal North Devon

☎Bideford (023 72) 73817 Sec, 73824 Clubhouse.
Westward Ho! Bideford, Devon EX39 1HD. From Northam village take the road down Bone Hill past the P.O., keeping left. The club house is visible as you come down the hill.
Links course.
18 holes, 6449 yards, S.S.S.72
Course laid out by Tom Morris.
Club founded in 1864.
Visitors: welcome
Green fees: £10 per round; £12 per day; weekends £12 per round.
Society meetings: by booking.
Catering: full facilities.
Hotels: Culloden House; Durrant House.

A32 St Austell

☎St Austell (0726) 74756 Sec, 72649 Clubhouse.
Tregongeeves Lane, St Austell, Cornwall PL26 7DS.
On A390 St Austell – Truro road 1 mile W of St Austell. The Tregon-geeves Lane junction is clearly signposted just below the St Mewan school.
Heathland/parkland course.
18 holes, 5725 yards, S.S.S.68
Club founded in 1911.
Visitors: welcome with reservation, must be club members and hold handicap certificates.
Green fees: £9 per round/day; £12 weekends.
Society meetings: catered for

weekdays by arrangement.
Catering: full service; hot meals, bar snacks, noon - 2pm daily. Evening meals available ring first.
Hotels: Cliff Head Hotel, Carlyon Bay.

A33 St Enodoc

☎Trebetherick (020 886) 3216
Rock, Wadebridge, Cornwall PL27 6LB.
From Wadebridge take B3314 Port Isaac road for 3 miles and then turn left to Rock.
Links course.
18 holes, 6207 yards, S.S.S.70 (Church course).
16 holes, 4166 yards, S.S.S.61 (Holywell course).
Visitors: handicap certificate required for Church course.
Green fees: on application.
Society meetings: limited to out of holiday season.
Catering: Cornish Arms, Pendogget. Lunch every day except Fri.
Hotels: St Enodoc; St Moritz; Bodare; Port Gaverne.

A34 St Mellion CC

☎Liskeard (0579) 50101
St Mellion, Saltash, Cornwall PL12 6SD.
3 miles S of Callington on A388.
Parkland course.
International course - 18 holes, 6626 yards, S.S.S.72
Resort course - 18 holes, 5927 yards, S.S.S.68
International course designed by Jack Nicklaus
Resort course designed by J. Hamilton Stutt.
Club founded in 1976.
Visitors: welcome.
Green fees: per round Nicklaus course £25; Resort course £12.
Society meetings: welcomed.
Catering: restaurant, coffee shop grill room.
Hotels: St Mullion.

A35 Saunton

☎Braunton (0271) 812436
Saunton, nr Braunton, N.Devon EX33 1LG.
On B3231 from Braunton to Croyde, 7 miles from Barnstaple.
Traditional links course.
East-18 holes, 6703 yards, S.S.S.73
West-18 holes, 6322 yards, S.S.S.71
E course designed by Herbert Fowler
W course designed by Frank Pennink.
Club founded in 1897.

Visitors: welcome.
Green fees: £12 per day on E course Mon-Fri; £14 per day weekends and public hols. On W course £10 per day at all times.
Society meetings: any time booked in advance.
Catering: full restaurant all day.
Hotels: Saunton Sands; Lee Bay; Kittiwell House.

A36 **Sidmouth**
☎Sidmouth (0395) 3451 Sec, 3023 Club.
Peak Hill, Cotmaton Rd, Sidmouth EX10 8SZ.
Take Exeter Station Rd, to Woodlands Hotel, then turn right on Cotmaton Rd.
Undulating parkland course.
18 holes, 5188 yards, S.S.S.66
Club founded in 1898.
Visitors: welcome.
Green fees: on application.
Society meetings: welcome.
Catering: meals served except Tues.
Hotels: numerous in Sidmouth.

A37 **Staddon Heights**
☎Plymouth (0752) 402475
Staddon Heights, Plymstock, Plymouth, Devon PL9 9SP.
Leave Plymouth city on the Plymstock Rd.
Clubhouse is 5 miles S of city near Royal Navy aerial towers.
Links course.
18 holes, 5861 yards, S.S.S.68
Club founded in 1895.
Visitors: welcome on weekdays.
Green fees: £8 weekdays, (£5 with member).
Society meetings: catered for weekdays.
Catering: every day.
Hotels: Highlands, Plymstock.

A38 **Tavistock**
☎Tavistock (0822) 612049 Sec, 612344.
Down Rd, Tavistock, Devon PL19 9AQ.
Take the Whitchurch Rd, turning into Down Rd and onto Whitchurch Down.
Moorland course.

18 holes, 6250 yards, S.S.S.70
Club founded in 1891.
Visitors: welcome, but telephone in advance.
Green fees: £8 weekdays (with member); £10 weekends/Bank Holidays.
Society meetings: by arrangement.
Catering: lunch, bar snack, evening meals every day.
Hotels: Bedford; Moorland Links; Arundel Arms.

A39 **Tehidy Park**
☎Portreath (0209) 842208
Camborne, Cornwall TR14 0HH.
Off A30 2 miles NE of Camborne on the Portreath road.
Parkland course.
18 holes, 6222 yards, S.S.S.70
Club founded in 1922.
Visitors: unrestricted.
Green fees: £10 weekdays; £15 weekends.
Society meetings: by arrangement.
Catering: full range bar snacks, à la carte restaurant mornings/ evenings.

Saunton

Name the courses worthy of the Open championship if they were more strategically located, and Saunton would be top of many lists. A strange fact because in some ways Saunton's setting is its prime asset. It is best appreciated from the terrace of the magnificent Saunton Sands Hotel which is as well situated as any hotel you could find.

It is hard to avoid sounding like a travel brochure when describing the vast, wide stretch of golden sand, the estuaries of the Taw and the Torridge, the botanic delights of the Burrows and the mountainous dunes that divide the golf from the sea. A keen eye quickly spots the Pebble Ridge and the links of Westward Ho! across the estuary, which are the oldest seaside links in England.

To complete the geography lesson, there is Hartland Point and Lundy Island but this is a part of the world where history and geography intermingle.

It is entirely understandable that, in his wonderful book 'The Golf Courses of the British Isles' published in 1910, Bernard Darwin felt it would be 'unbecoming to treat the western and south-western courses in strict geographical order because there is one honoured name that must come first — that of Westward Ho!'.

He described a visit to Westward Ho! as a 'reverent pilgrimage', blossoming forth into seven or eight pages of ecstatic detail and eventually glossing over Saunton in a few lines. 'Saunton', he wrote, 'looks at first glance like a fine golf course'. Nonetheless he quoted Herbert Fowler as rating Saunton 'almost, if not quite, as highly as Westward Ho!' and Harry Vardon as saying he would like to retire to Saunton and do nothing but play golf for pleasure'.

In fairness to Darwin, Saunton had scarcely come of age when he wrote those words but I am sure that, had he had occasion to re-assess his judgements, he would have indulged in a purple passage or two on the subject of Saunton. It was, after all, one of the very few seaside links laid out for the modern ball, which is why

it has withstood the recent advancements in the manufacture of clubs and bails better than any.

As John Goodban's excellent history of the Club — 'The First 90 Years' — relates, the changes that have been necessary were mostly caused by the upheaval during the Second World War. The clubhouse became the headquarters of the Coast Defence Unit and the courses a battle training school with the sandhills mined against possible invasion.

Three years earlier, Saunton had reached a deserved peak of eminence by staging the English championship in which Frank Pennink defeated Leonard Crawley in the final. Pre-war Saunton had two fine courses and an assured future.

Following the war however, Saunton arose phoenix-like from the ashes although it involved a period of uncertainty when its survival might be said to have been 'a close run thing'. Until 1960, the management of the Club had been in the hands of its owners, the Christie Estate — the Christie family being amongst other things, the owners of Glyndebourne — but the architectural saviour of the old Old course was Ken Cotton.

He was able to restore most of it in 1950 with the only radical change being to the first two and last two holes. From a tee on the high ridge near the clubhouse, he made a new 1st hole which, with the addition of the new 2nd, stretched the first four holes (all par 4s) to nigh on a mile. However, one of the charms of Saunton is that two of its three short holes really are short.

The 5th and 13th are classic examples of how short holes need not be a long iron or a wood but still demand plenty of stout hitting. Cotton's other amendment was to cut a gap in the hills at the 8th and to turn the 17th into a downhill short hole and the 18th into a fine par 4 which curves right-handed to a green outside the clubhouse windows.

Saunton's demand for the best championships and other important events is illustrated by its selection for three English strokeplay championships, the 1984 St Andrews Trophy match between Great Britain, Ireland and the Continent of Europe, countless county events and the alternate staging with Royal North Devon of the West of England strokeplay championship — inaugurated in 1968. Lovers of Saunton hope it will one day house the Amateur championship. It is worthy of any occasion but a significant development came in 1974 with the opening of the new West course. Instead of the pre-war Old and New courses came the East and West and, with the decision in 1987 to re-model the greens, there is no doubt that the two courses will be as fine as any in Britain. Saunton's glories are infinite.

Hotels: Penventon; Glenfeadon; Old Shire Inn; Tyacks.

A40 **Teignmouth**
☎Teignmouth (062 67) 4194 Sec, 3614 Clubhouse, 2894 Pro.
Exeter Rd, Teignmouth, Devon TQ14 9NY.
2 miles from Teignmouth on B3192 to Exeter. 900 feet above Teignmouth on Haldon Moor. Moorland course.
18 holes, 6142 yards, S.S.S.69
Course designed by Dr Alister Mackenzie.
Club founded in 1924.
Visitors: must be members of a club and have handicap certificate.
Green fees: £12 weekdays; £15 weekends.
Society members: by appointment, not weekends or Wednesday.
Catering: full service every day.
Hotels: London; Venn Farm.

A41 **Thurlestone**
☎Kingsbridge (0548) 560405
Thurlestone, nr Kingsbridge, S Devon TQ7 3NZ.
Take Thurlestone turning from A379 Plymouth to Salcombe road. Club situated 4 miles S of Kingsbridge. Downland course.
18 holes, 6337 yards, S.S.S.70
Club founded 1897
Visitors: must produce a current handicap certificate from recognised club.
Green fees: £12 per day, any day.
Society meetings: not catered for.
Catering: available all day.
Hotels: Thurlestone.

A42 **Tiverton**
☎Tiverton (0884) 252187
Post Hill, Tiverton, Devon EX16 4NE.
5 miles from junction 27 on M5, towards Tiverton on A373. Take 1st exit left on dual carriageway through

Samford Peverell to Halberton. Parkland/meadowland course.
18 holes, 6263 yards, S.S.S.71
Course designed by James Braid.
Club founded in 1931.
Visitors: letter of introduction or handicap certificate.
Green fees: £9 weekdays; £12 weekends.
Catering: lunch, teas available.
Hotels: Tiverton, Green Headland; Hartnoll.

A43 **Torquay**
☎Torquay (0803) 37471
Petitor Rd, St Marychurch, Torquay TQ1 4QF.
N of Torquay on A379 Teignmouth road, on the outskirts of the town. Parkland course.
18 holes, 6192 yards, S.S.S.69
Club founded in 1910.
Visitors: handicap certificates required.
Green fees: £9 weekdays; £10 weekends and public holidays.
Society meetings: by arrangement.
Catering: except Mondays.
Hotels: numerous good hotels in area.

A44 **Trevose CC**
☎Padstow (0841) 520208
Constantine Bay, Padstow, Cornwall PL28 8JB.
4 miles W of Padstow off B3276.
Seaside links course.
18 holes, 6608 yards, S.S.S.72
9 holes, 1357 yards
Course designed by H S Colt.
Club founded in 1925.
Visitors: welcome anytime but 3 and 4 ball matches restricted. Telephone first.
Green fees: varies according to season.
Society meetings: any time except Jul/Aug.
Catering: all meals, good restaurant.

Hotels: Treglos (own self-catering accommodation available).

A45 **Truro**
☎Truro (0872) 72640
Treliske, Truro, Cornwall TR1 3LG.
1.5 miles W of Truro on A390.
Course signposted just off roundabout.
Undulating parkland course.
18 holes, 5347 yards, S.S.S.66
Course designed by Colt, Alison & Morrison.
Club founded in 1937.
Visitors: welcome.
Green fees: £9 weekdays; £12 weekends and Bank Holidays, (£4.50 with member).
Society meetings: catered for.
Catering: lunch, evening meals every day.
Hotels: Brookdale; Carlton; Alverton Manor.

A46 **Warren**
☎Dawlish (0626) 862255
Dawlish Warren, Dawlish, Devon EX7 0NF.
Take A379 from Exeter to Dawlish Warren.
Links course.
18 holes, 5968 yards, S.S.S.69
Club founded in 1892.
Visitors: welcome on weekdays.
Green fees: £8.50 weekdays; £10 weekends.
Society meetings: weekdays by arrangement with Sec.
Catering: bar snacks all week, meals served except Mon.
Hotels: Langstone Cliff; Dawlish Warren, Dawlish.

A47 **West Cornwall**
☎Penzance (0736) 753401 Sec, 753319 members.
Lelant, St Ives, Cornwall TR26 3DZ.
A30 to Hayle, then A3074 to St Ives.
Seaside course.

TREVOSE
GOLF AND COUNTRY CLUB
Constantine Bay, Padstow, Cornwall
Padstow 520208

- Championship Golf Course of 18 holes. S.S.S. 71. Fully automatic watering on all greens.
- 9 hole Short Course.
- Excellently appointed Club House with Restaurant providing full catering and air conditioning throughout the Club House.
- Accommodation in very superior chalets, bungalows, flats and dormy suites each having modern sanitation, baths, heating and cooking facilities. Midweek bookings are encouraged.

- 3 Hard Tennis Courts.
- Heated swimming pool open from mid May to mid September.
- In addition to membership for Golf and Tennis, social membership of the Club is also available with full use of the Club House, Putting Greens and Sports Room.
- Six glorious sandy bays within about a mile of the Club House, with pool, open sea and surf bathing, and an open coast line for walks.

18 holes, 5839 yards, S.S.S.69
Club founded in 1889.
Visitors: handicap certificate required.
Green fees: £7 per round; £8 per day; £30 per week; weekends £9 per round; £12 per day.
Catering: lunch and dinner except Mon.
Hotels: Badger; Lelant, St Ives.

A48 **Whitsand Bay Hotel GC**
☎St Germans (0503) 30276/30470.
Portwinkle, Crafthole, Torpoint, Cornwall.
On B3274 6 miles SW of Torpoint.
Clifftop course.
18 holes, 5367 yards, S.S.S.67
Course designed by William Fernie.
Club founded in 1905.
Visitors: welcome by arrangement.
Green fees: £6 weekdays; £8

weekends.
Society meetings: by arrangement with Sec or Manager of Whitsand Bay Hotel.
Catering: as and when required.
Hotels: Whitsand Bay.

A49 **Wrangaton**
☎South Brent (036 47) 3229
Wrangaton, South Brent, S Devon.
TQ10 9HJ.
Turn off A38 between South Brent and Bittaford at Wrangaton P.O.
Moorland course.
9 holes, 5790 yards, S.S.S.68
Club founded in 1895.
Visitors: welcome weekdays and Sat.
Green fees: on application.
Society meetings: weekdays only.
Catering: snacks at lunchtime.
Hotels: The Stagecoach, Wrangaton.

A50 **Yelverton**
☎Yelverton (0822) 852824
Golf Links Rd, Yelverton, Devon
PL20 6BN.
8 miles N of Plymouth and 5 miles S of Tavistock on A386.
Moorland course.
18 holes, 6288 yards, S.S.S.70
Course designed by Herbert Fowler.
Club founded in 1904.
Visitors: Accredited golfers welcome.
Green fees: £8 weekdays, (£5 with member); £10 weekends/Bank Holidays, (£6 with member).
Society meetings: catered for on weekdays.
Catering: daily, bar snacks only on Tues.
Hotels: Moorland Links, Yelverton.

B Somerset, Dorset, Wiltshire and Avon

When the question of golfing holidays is discussed, this is not a region to which everyone inclines. However the Bournemouth area alone is bristling with fine courses and those who aren't familiar with them should immediately mend their ways. Ferndown, Parkstone and Broadstone stand comparison with any of the sand and heather courses in Surrey and, if a shade less demanding, can be a shade more enjoyable for some as a result.

They are in easy reach of each other while Bournemouth can also boast one of the finest public courses in the world, Queen's Park (Boscombe), with a touch of switchback in its make-up. It has housed national professional events and nobody should be deterred from playing there on account of the 'public' label.

On the other side of Poole Harbour and commanding some of the best views anywhere is Isle of Purbeck, which should form part of any holiday itinerary; but a little further west and north the more pastoral

setting of Sherborne is a scenic match for it. Sherborne is a delightful place to play and is a convenient halfway house for travellers bound for Somerset where Burnham and Berrow is undoubtedly worth the trip.

Here you find a links of challenge and charm, a stage chosen for many a championship and equally popular with the women as well as the men. J.H.Taylor described it as one of the most sporting courses conceivable, with large sandhills and small greens, paying it the ultimate accolade of helping to hone the mashie play for which he was famous.

Weston-super-Mare is another pleasant course and whilst Bath and Bristol aren't exactly renowned for their golf, Mendip, Lansdown, Long Ashton and Bristol and Clifton shouldn't be overlooked. Wiltshire is one of the least endowed golfing counties but Tidworth Garrison, open to the winds blowing across Salisbury Plain, is a lovely spot with fairways that soak up the heaviest rain.

B1 **Ashley Woods**
☎Blandford (0258) 52253
Wimborne Rd, Blandford, Dorset DT11 9HN.
From Blandford 1 mile S along B3082 Wimborne Rd.
Undulating meadowland course.
9 holes, 6227 yards, S.S.S.70
Club founded in 1952.
Visitors: welcome.
Green Fees: £7 (Mon-Fri), (£4.50 with member); £10 weekends and Bank Holidays.
Society meetings: welcome by arrangement with Sec.
Catering: Stewardess welcomes applications.
Hotels: Museum, Farnham, (7 miles).

B2 **Bath**
☎Bath (0225) 25182
Sham Castle, North Rd, Bath BA2 6JG.
Take A36 Bath to Warminster road, turn up North Rd and club is about 800 yards on left. 1.5 miles SE of

Bath.
Downland course.
18 holes, 6369 yards, S.S.S.70
Club founded in 1880.
Visitors: must have handicap. Welcome weekdays and weekends, subject to course availability.
Green fees: £9 weekdays; £11 weekends; subject to review.
Society meetings: catered for Wed and Fri.
Catering: everyday, bar snacks on Thurs.
Hotels: Bath; Beaufort; Dukes.

B3 **Boscombe**
☎Bournemouth (0202) 36198
Queens Park, Bournemouth.
Proceed along Wessex Way and turn R at the Queens Park Club roundabout.
Undulating course.
18 holes, 6505 yards, S.S.S.72
Club founded in 1938.
Visitors: apply to Recreation Officer, Parks Dept, Town Hall, Bournemouth.

Green fees: as above.
Society meetings: as above.
Catering: full facilities - Fairways club.
Hotels: many in Bournemouth.

B4 **Brean**
☎Brean Down (027 875) 467 or 359
Coast Rd, Brean, Burnham-on-Sea, Somerset TA8 2RF.
4.5 miles off M5, junction 22 following signs for Brean, Leisure Centre on right.
Moorland/meadowland course.
18 holes, 5436 yards, S.S.S.66
Club founded in 1973.
Visitors: welcome all days except before 12 noon on Sun and open days.
Green fees: £4 weekdays, (£3 with member); £6 weekends, (£5 with member).
Society meetings: welcome with prior arrangement.
Catering: snacks in clubhouse, meals and entertainment in adjacent Leisure Centre.

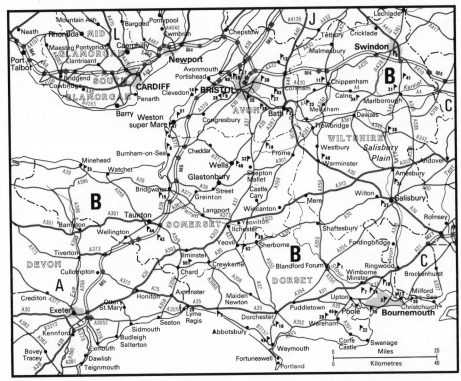

Hotels: Dunston House, Burnham-on-Sea.

B5 Bridport & W Dorset
☎Bridport (0308) 22597
East Cliff, West Bay, Bridport, Dorset DT6 4EP.
Off A35, 1.5 miles S of Bridport on B3157.
Seaside course.
18 holes, 5246 yards, S.S.S.66
Club founded in 1891.
Visitors: welcome.
Green fees: £8 weekdays; £10 weekends.
Society meetings: as arranged.
Catering: full plus licensed bar.
Hotels: Haddon House, West Bay.

B6 Bristol & Clifton
☎Bristol (0272) 393474
Failand, Bristol BS8 3TH.
Junction 19 off M5, 4 miles along A369 to Bristol turn R at traffic lights, then further 1.5 miles.
Parkland course.
18 holes, 6294 yards, S.S.S.70.
Club founded in 1891.
Visitors: welcome. Prior arrangement for weekends.
Green fees: £12 weekdays; £15

weekends.
Society meetings: by arrangement.
Catering: normal golf club catering available.
Hotels: Redwood Lodge; Beggar Bush Land; Failand.

B7 Broadstone
☎Broadstone (0202) 692595
Wentworth Drive, Off Station Approach, Broadstone, Dorset.
Off A349 halfway between Wimborne and Poole. Heathland course.
18 holes, 6151 yards, S.S.S.70
Course designed by George Dunn and H.S. Colt.
Club founded in 1898.
Visitors: weekdays after 9.30am; weekends and Bank Holidays after 10am.
Green fees: weekdays £14 per round, £16 per day; weekends £17 per round, £20 per day.
Society meetings: weekdays only by prior arrangement.
Catering: full facilities by prior arrangement.
Hotels: Kings Head; Fairlight.

B8 Broome Manor
☎ Swindon (0793) 32403

Pipers Way, Swindon, Wilts SN3 1RG.
2 miles from Junction 15 off M4 to Swindon.
Public parkland course.
18 holes, 6359 yards, S.S.S.70
9 holes, 2745 yards, S.S.S.67
Course designed by Hawtree & Son.
Club founded in 1976.
Visitors: welcome.
Green fees: 18 holes £4 weekdays; £4.50 weekends; 9 holes £2.40 weekdays; £2.70 weekends.
Society meetings: welcome Mon-Thurs.
Catering: full facilities all week.
Hotels: Goddard Arms.

B9 Burnham & Berrow
☎ Burnham-on-Sea (0278) 785760
Sec, 783137 Club.
St Christopher's Way, Burnham-on-Sea, Somerset TA8 2PE.
Junction 22 off M5, 1 mile N of Burnham-on-Sea.
Links course.
18 holes, 6327 yards, S.S.S.72
Club founded in 1890.
Visitors: welcome except Sat am, must be members of recognised club, book in advance.

Green fees: £13 weekdays; £16 Sat; £15 Sun and Bank Holidays.
Society meetings: catered for except Sat.
Catering: everyday 11am-6pm. Outside of hours must be booked in advance.
Hotels: Pine Grange; Battleborough Grange; Cloisters Guest House.

B10 Came Down
☎Upwey (030 581) 2531
Came Down, Dorchester, Dorset DT2 8NR.
2 miles S of Dorchester off A354.
Undulating downland course.
18 holes, 6224 yards, S.S.S.71
Course designed by J.H. Taylor.
Club founded in 1890.
Visitors: welcome; restricted Sun.
Green fees: £9 weekdays; £11 weekends and Bank Holidays.
Society meetings: catered for by appointment. Not weekends.
Catering: eating facilities - full service.
Hotels: Kings Arms; Wessex; Streamside.

B11 Chippenham
☎Chippenham (0249) 652040 Sec.
Malmesbury Rd, Chippenham, Wilts SN15 5LT.
Junction 17 off M4, 1 mile from town centre on A429.
Meadowland course.
18 holes, 5540 yards, S.S.S.67
Club founded 1896.
Visitors: welcome with restrictions (must have proof of handicap).
Green fees: £8 weekdays; £10 weekends.
Society meetings: weekdays only.
Catering: lunch (limited catering Mon.)
Hotels: Old Bell, Malmesbury.

B12 Chipping Sodbury
☎Chipping Sodbury (0454) 319042
Chipping Sodbury, Bristol BS17 6PU.
Leave M4 at Exit 18 and M5 at Exit 14; from Chipping Sodbury take Wickwar Rd, first turn on R.
Parkland course.
18 holes, 6912 yards, S.S.S.73
9 holes, 3076 yards.
Course designed by Fred Hawtree.
Visitors: welcome, but after 12 noon on Sun.
Green fees: £8 weekdays; £9 weekends and Bank Holidays (reduction with member).
Society meetings: welcome by arrangement on weekdays.
Catering: meals served.

Hotels: Moda; Cross Hands; The Poplars.

B13 Christchurch
☎Christchurch (0202) 473817
Iford Bridge Golf Course, Iford, Christchurch, Dorset.
Off A35, then signposted.
9 holes, 4824 yards.
Club founded in 1977.
Visitors: welcome.
Green fees: £3.00 weekdays; £3.50 weekends.
Society meetings: by arrangement with local Council.
Catering: bar facilities and snacks served.
Hotels: many good hotels in area.

B14 Clevedon
☎Clevedon (0272) 874057 Sec, 874704 Pro, 873140 Steward
Castle Rd, Clevedon, Avon BS21 7AA.
Leave M5 at Junction 19, follow signs to Clevedon, on outskirts of Clevedon turn R into Holly Lane, at top of hill turn R into private lane to golf club and castle.
Undulating parkland course.
18 holes, 5887 yards, S.S.S.69
Course designed by Sandy Herd.
Club founded in 1891.
Visitors: every day. Wed pm only must be playing members of a golf club.
Green fees: £10 weekday; £12 weekends and Bank Holidays.
Society meetings: Mon only, not Bank Holidays.
Catering: every day except Tues when only sandwiches available.
Hotels: Walton Park; Highcliffe.

B15 Enmore Park
☎Spaxton (027 867) 481
Enmore, Bridgwater, Somerset TA5 2AN.
3 miles W of Bridgwater on Spaxton Rd.
Undulating parkland course.
18 holes, 6443 yards, S.S.S.71
Course designed by A.R. Bradbeer.
Club founded in 1982.
Visitors: weekdays, check weekends.
Green fees: £10 per day.
Society meetings: welcome weekdays only.
Catering: yes, except Mon.
Hotels: Walnut Tree, North Petherton - 3 miles.

B16 Ferndown
☎Ferndown (0202) 874602

119 Golf Links Rd, Ferndown, Dorset BH22 8BU.
A31 to Tricketts Cross.
Heathland links course..
Old course 18 holes, 6442 yards, S.S.S.71.
New course 9 holes, 5604 yards, S.S.S.68
Old course designed by Harold Hilton.
Club founded in 1913.
Visitors: prior permission - handicap required.
Green fees: Old £17 weekday, £22 weekend; New £7 weekday, £12 weekend.
Society meetings: not at weekends.
Catering: full (except Mon but can be arranged for Societies).
Hotels: Coach House Motel.

B17 Filton
☎Bristol(0272) 694169
Golf Course Lane, Filton, Bristol BS12 7QS.
From Almondsbury Interchange (M4/5) take A38 towards Bristol, after 2 miles turn R at roundabout and R at traffic lights.
Parkland course.
18 holes, 6277 yards, S.S.S.70
Course designed by F. Hawtree & Son.
Club founded in 1909.
Visitors: welcome on weekdays.
Green fees: £9 weekdays, (£6 with member); weekends with members only.
Society meetings: catered for on weekdays.
Catering: by arrangement.
Hotels: Crest Hotel; Hambrook.

B18 Fosseway
☎Midsomer Norton (0761) 412214
Charlton Lane, Midsomer Norton, Bath, Somerset BA3 4BD.
Off A367 S of Bath, through Radstock and turn L at Charlton roundabout.
Parkland course.
9 holes, 4246 yards, S.S.S.61
Club founded in 1971.
Visitors: anytime except Sun mornings and Wed after 5pm.
Green fees: £4.50 per day; £5.50 weekends; including day membership.
Society meetings: None.
Catering: full facilities. A la carte restaurant/table d'hôte/Bar Meals.
Hotels: Centurion (own hotel).

B19 Henbury
☎Bristol (0272) 500044

Henbury Hill, Westbury-on-Trym, Bristol BS10 7QB.
Junction 17 off M5, 2 to 3 minutes to club.
Parkland course.
18 holes, 6039 yards, S.S.S.70
Club founded in 1891.
Visitors: welcome weekdays.
Green fees: on application.
Society meetings: catered for on Tues and Fri by arrangement.
Catering: full range available.
Hotels: Ship, Alveston, Bristol.

B20 **Highcliffe Castle**
☎Highcliffe (042 52) 72210
107 Lymington Rd, Highcliffe on Sea,
Dorset BH23 4LA.
A35 to Hinton Admiral, follow signpost to Highcliffe, approx 1 mile. On A337 3 miles E of Christchurch.
Seaside course.
18 holes, 4732 yards, S.S.S.63
Club founded in 1913.
Visitors: welcome if member of recognised Golf Club.
Green fees: £9 weekdays; £11 weekends.

Society meetings: catered for by arrangement.
Catering: bar and restaurant.
Hotels: Avonmouth; Waterford Lodge.

B21 **High Post**
☎Middle Woodford (072 273) 356
Great Durnford, Salisbury, Wilts.
Halfway between Salisbury and Amesbury on the A345.
Downland course.
18 holes, 6267 yards, S.S.S.70
Club founded in 1922.
Visitors: welcome weekdays.
Green fees: £10 weekdays.
Society meetings: catered for weekdays.
Catering: full catering facilities.
Hotels: The Inn; High Post.

B22 **Isle of Purbeck**
☎Studland (092 944) 361
Studland, Dorset BH19 3AB.
Between Studland and Swanage, on B3351, overlooking Poole Harbour and Bournemouth.
Undulating heathland course.
18 holes, 6248 yards, S.S.S.71
9 holes, 2022 yards, S.S.S.30
Course designed by H.S. Colt.

Club founded in 1892.
Visitors: welcome.
Green fees: 18 holes, £14 weekdays; £16 weekends and Bank Holidays; 9 holes, £7 per day.
Society meetings: welcome.
Catering: lunch and evening meals.
Hotels: Knoll House, Studland; Pines, Swanage; Studland.

B23 **Kingsdown**
☎Box (0225) 742530
Kingsdown, Corsham, Wilts SN14 9BS.
Turn off A4 onto A363, turn L at Crown Inn 250 yards, uphill for 2 miles.
Heathland course.
18 holes, 6265 yards, S.S.S.70
Club founded in 1880
Visitors: with handicaps are welcome except on competition days.
Green fees: £10 weekdays; £12.50 weekends.
Society meetings: by arrangement with Sec.
Catering: dining room meals or bar snacks.
Hotels: Beaufort, Bath; Conigre

Farm, Melksham; Park Lane Motel, Corsham.

B24 Knighton Heath
☎Bournemouth (0202) 572633
Francis Avenue, Bournemouth, Dorset B11 8NX.
On main A348 Poole to Ringwood road, 4 miles N of Bournemouth: signposted at Wallisdown roundabout.
Heathland course.
18 holes, 6206 yards, S.S.S.70
Club founded in 1976.
Visitors: after 9.30am weekdays, after 10.30am weekends.
Green fees: available on request.
Society meetings: weekdays by prior arrangement.
Catering: lunch daily except Mon.
Hotels: Bridge House, Longham.

B25 Knowle
☎Bristol (0272) 770660
Fairway, Brislington, Bristol BS4 5DF.
3 miles S of city centre on the A4 to junction with West Town Lane, entrance on left 800 yards along West Town Lane.
Parkland course.
18 holes, 6016 yards, S.S.S.69
Course designed by Hawtree & J.H. Taylor.
Club founded in 1905.
Visitors: welcome weekdays, weekends by special arrangement.
Green fees: £10 weekday, (£5 with member).
Society meetings: Thurs only.
Catering: lunch daily, evening meals by arrangement.
Hotels: Grange, Keynsham.

B26 Lakey Hill
☎Bere Regis (0929) 471776
Hyde, Wareham, Dorset BH20 7NT.
3 miles W of Wareham off Worgret Rd.
Meadowland course.
18 holes, 6146 yards, S.S.S.69
Course designed by Brian Bamford.
Club founded in 1978.
Visitors: welcome on weekdays.
Green fees: £8 weekdays; £12 weekends and Bank Holidays.
Society meetings: catered for on Wed.
Catering: club restaurant serving lunch, evening meals also Society menu. Club bar facility.

B27 Lansdown
☎Bath (0225) 22138, 20242 Pro
Lansdown, Bath BA1 9BT.

Junction 18 off M4, next to Bath Racecourse.
Parkland course.
18 holes, 6267 yards, S.S.S.70
Course designed by C.K. Cotton.
Club founded in 1895.
Visitors: welcome with handicap.
Green fees: £8 weekdays; £9 weekends and Bank Holidays.
Society meetings: welcome by arrangement.
Catering: available.
Hotels: Lansdown Grove; Francis; Beaufort.

B28 Long Ashton
☎Bristol (0272) 392316
Long Ashton, Bristol BS18 9DW.
Leave M5 at Junction 19, take A369 to Bristol, turn R into B3129 at traffic lights and then L onto B3128. Club is 0.5 mile on R.
Undulating, moorland/parkland course.
18 holes, 6051 yards, S.S.S.70
Course designed by Hawtree & Taylor.
Club founded in 1893.
Visitors: must have official club handicap.
Green fees: £13 weekdays; £16 weekends.
Society meetings: by arrangement.
Catering: full facilities daily until 6pm. Evening meal by arrangement.
Hotels: Redwood Lodge.

B29 Lyme Regis
☎Lyme Regis (029 74) 2963
Timber Hill, Lyme Regis, Dorset DT7 3HQ.
Off A3052 Charmouth road 1 mile E of town.
Undulating meadowland course.
18 holes, 6282 yards, S.S.S.70
Club founded in 1893.
Visitors: welcome all days subject to telephone confirmation.
Green fees: £12 summer, £8 after 2pm; £10 winter (7 days), £7 after 12am.
Society meetings: apply for booking. Exclusive Thurs and Sun.
Catering: lunch, tea, dinner every day. Not Mon during winter months.
Hotels: Fernhill; Devon; Mariners; Alexandra.

B30 Mangotsfield
☎Bristol (0272) 565501
Carsons Rd, Mangotsfield, Bristol.
M32 - leave junction Filton/Downend. Follow sign for Downend and Mangotsfield.
Hilly meadowland course.
18 holes, 5300 yards, S.S.S.66

Club founded in 1975.
Visitors: welcome
Green fees: £6 weekdays; £8 weekends.
Society meetings: by arrangement with Manager.
Catering: meals served.
Hotels: The Linden, Kingswood.

B31 Marlborough
☎Marlborough (0672) 52147
The Common, Marlborough, Wilts SN8 1DU.
0.75 mile from town centre on A345 to Swindon.
Downland course.
18 holes, 6440 yards, S.S.S.71
Club founded in 1888.
Visitors: welcome weekdays and weekends on non-competition days.
Green fees: £8.50 weekdays per round/day, (£5.50 with member); £9.50 weekends per round/day, (£7 with member).
Catering: full catering for whole week.
Hotels: Castle & Ball; Bear.

B32 Mendip
☎Oakhill (0749) 840570 Sec, 840793 Pro.
Gurney Slade, Bath, Avon BA3 4UT.
3 miles N of Shepton Mallet, just off A37
Undulating downland course.
18 holes, 5982 yards, S.S.S.69
Course designed by H.Vardon with an extension by F.Pennink.
Club founded in 1908.
Visitors: weekends when visitors are required to play with member unless visitor is member of affiliated club.
Green fees: £8 per day weekdays; £10 per day weekends.
Society meetings: welcome Mon-Fri after 9.30am.
Catering: full facilities every day.
Hotels: White Hart.

B33 Minehead & W Somerset
☎Minehead (0643) 2057
The Warren, Minehead, Somerset TA24 5SJ.
E end of sea front.
Links course.
18 holes, 6130 yards, S.S.S.69
Course designed by Johnny Alan.
Club founded in 1882.
Visitors: welcome.
Green fees: £11 weekdays; £13.50 weekends and public holidays.
Society meetings: welcome on written application.

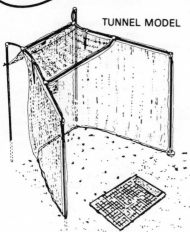

Catering: by prior arrangement with steward/stewardess. Snacks always available.
Hotels: Wyncott; York; Northfield; Marshfield.

B34 North Wilts
☎Cannings (038 086) 627
Bishops Cannings, Devizes, Wilts SN10 2LP.
1 mile from the A4 at Calne.
Downland course.
18 holes, 6450 yards, S.S.S.71
Club founded in 1890.
Visitors: welcome.
Green fees: on application.
Society meetings: welcome by prior arrangement.
Catering: full facilities available.
Hotels: Bear, Devizes; Lansdowne Strand, Calne.

B35 Parkstone
☎Parkstone (0202) 707138
Links Rd, Parkstone, Poole, Dorset BH14 9JU.
A35 Bournemouth to Poole road, turn S at St Osmonds Church.
Undulating heathland course.
18 holes, 6250 yards, S.S.S.70

Course designed by Willie Park and James Braid.
Club founded in 1910.
Visitors: welcome on weekdays (book in advance).
Green fees: £15 per round, £19 per day weekdays; £17 per round, £20 per day weekends and Bank Holidays.
Society meetings: catered for on weekdays.
Catering: lunch available every day.
Hotels: numerous hotels in area.

B36 RAF Upavon
☎Stonehenge (0980) 630787
Asst. Sec.
RAF Upavon, Pewsey, Wilts SN9 6BE.
2 miles SE of Upavon village on A342.
Undulating downland course.
9 holes, 5116 metres, S.S.S.67
Visitors: welcome on weekdays and with member at weekends.
Green fees: on application.
Society meetings: welcome on weekdays, maximum 32.
Catering: by special arrangement.
Hotels: Antelope, Upavon.

B37 Salisbury & S Wiltshire
☎Salisbury (0722) 742645 Sec.
Netherhampton, Salisbury, Wilts SP2 8PR.
On A3094 2 miles from Salisbury and from Wilton.
Parkland course.
18 holes, 6146 yards, S.S.S.70
9 holes, 2424 yards, S.S.S.32 .
Course designed by J.H. Taylor.
Club founded in 1888.
Visitors: welcome.
Green fees: £8.50 weekdays; £10 weekends.
Society meetings: welcome by arrangement.
Catering: full service except Tues.
Hotels: Pembroke Arms.

A38 Saltford
☎Saltford (022 17) 3220
Saltford, Bristol.
Off A4 between Bath and Bristol.
Meadowland course.
18 holes, 6081 yards, S.S.S.69
Visitors: welcome.
Green fees: £8.50 weekdays, (£5.50 with member); £10.50 weekends, (£6 with member). Juniors £3.50.
Society meetings: Thurs by

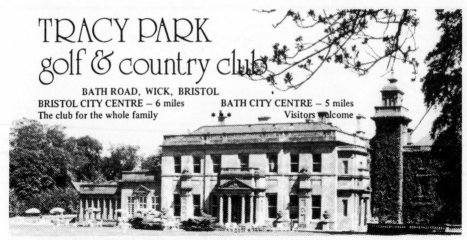

TRACY PARK
golf & country club

BATH ROAD, WICK, BRISTOL

BRISTOL CITY CENTRE – 6 miles   BATH CITY CENTRE – 5 miles

The club for the whole family   Visitors welcome

18 Hole Championship Golf Course (6,800 yards) plus new 9 Hole Course (3,200 yards) open June, 1986. Other facilities include.

* 3 Banbury Squash Courts
* 2 Outdoor Heated Swimming Pools
* 2 Full size Snooker Tables

* 2 All weather tennis courts
* 3 Croquet Lawns
* Restaurant, bars and dancing

Golf societies, conferences, meeting rooms & all forms of party catering are our speciality. For all inquiries and membership details, telephone: 027 582 2251

---

arrangement.

Catering: meals served daily.

Hotels: Grange, Keynsham; Crown, Saltford.

B39 Sherborne
☎Sherborne (0963) 814431.
Higher Clatcombe, Sherborne, Dorset DT9 4RN.
1 mile N of Sherborne off B3145 to Wincanton.
Parkland course.
18 holes, 5758 yards, S.S.S.68
Course designed by James Braid.
Club founded in 1894.
Visitors: weekdays after 10am, weekends dependant on Club Diary.
Green fees: £12 weekdays; £15 weekends.
Society meetings: Tues and Fri.
Catering: comprehensive.
Hotels: Post House; Half Moon.

B40 Shirehampton Park
☎Avonmouth (0272) 822083 Sec, 823059 Club.
Park Hill, Shirehampton, Bristol BS11 0UL.
1.5 miles from Junction 18 on M5, B4018 through village of Shirehampton.
Undulating parkland course.

18 holes, 5493 yards, S.S.S.67.
Club founded in 1908.
Visitors: weekdays welcome. Weekends - only with member.
Green fees: £9 per round/day, (£6 with member).
Society meetings: only Mon by arrangement.
Catering: snacks, lunch always available. Evening meals by arrangement with Stewardess 823059.
Hotels: numerous good hotels in area.

B41 Swindon
☎Ogbourne St George (067 284) 327
Ogbourne St George, Marlborough, Wilts SN18 1TB.
Junction 15 off M4, on A345 to Marlborough.
Undulating course.
18 holes, 6226 yards, S.S.S.70
Course designed by Taylor, Hawtree and Cotton.
Club founded in 1929.
Visitors: welcome on weekdays.
Green fees: £12 per day, £8.50 per round weekdays; £13 per day, £13 per round weekends.
Society meetings: weekdays.

Catering: restaurant, bar snacks available all week.

Hotels: Crest; Post House; Castle & Ball.

B42 Taunton & Pickeridge
☎Blagdon Hill (082 342) 240
Corfe, Taunton, Somerset TA3 7BY.
Take B3170, 4 miles S of Taunton, pass through Corfe village, then take first L.
Undulating course.
18 holes, 5927 yards, S.S.S.68
Club founded in 1892.
Visitors: welcome weekdays by arrangement, handicap certificate required.
Green fees: on application.
Society meetings: catered for by arrangement on weekdays except Tues.
Catering: lunch and evening meals available.
Hotels: County, Taunton; Castle, Taunton.

B43 Tracy Park G & CC
☎Abson (027 582) 2251
Bath Rd, Wick, Bristol BS15 5RN.
Junction 18 off M4, S on A46 for 4 miles, R A420 for 2 miles.
Parkland course.

Sherborne

Sherborne belongs to that category of courses that provides the right degree of testing quality without, in any way, impairing the enjoyment of a round in an incomparable setting - views, on a good day, spanning two or three counties. Taking the road up the hill out of a town famous for its abbey and its schools, you reach the club down a narrow country lane. Before the club's founding in 1894, the whole area was part of the fertile agricultural plain that surrounds it, but the second nine in particular covers some gently rolling land of which Harry Colt would undoubtedly have approved.

He believed that undulations and hummocks are of great value through the green as they provide difficult stances and lies, without which no golf course can be deemed to be perfect. There never will be the perfect course because it all depends, as Professor Joad used to say, on what you mean by perfect. However, there is a pleasant contrast at Sherborne between the first ten holes on one side of the road and the last eight on the other.

Judged from the first six holes, Sherborne suggests a non-stop assault with woods and long irons. The first nine is, in fact, more than 800 yards longer than the second although that does not necessarily mean that the second nine is any easier in relation to par. What it does mean is that the first six holes, which include three par 5s, hold the key to a good score, the 1st and 3rd being notably good par 4s.

It is easy enough though to have your card in tatters almost before you have started. There is plenty of scope for going out of bounds with an opening drive to a fairway which tapers cleverly to ensure that the further you hit the ball, the straighter you have to be. Control is essential, too, with the second shot to the 2nd, doglegging round the practice ground, while the 3rd and 4th, running up and back, are two of the best holes.

The 5th is the first of an excellent batch of short holes which vary in length and character, as all good short holes should, the 5th being perhaps the finest and the 7th the most daunting. In between, the par 5, 6th demands a well positioned drive to allow a flat stance for what is most likely to be a long second; and the second, too, requires both care and thought in order to leave the easiest pitch when the pin is tucked away at the back of the green.

Nothing less than the most truly-hit tee shot will suffice at the 7th but there is a little respite at the 8th and 9th which epitomises the compact nature of the layout on a limited acreage. It accommodates one more hole, the third par 3, before crossing back and passing the clubhouse and on down the excellent 459-yard 11th where the sloping terrain demands that, to hold both fairway and green, there is a very definite, if narrow, line to adopt.

It is from the tee that the full panorama of the view unfolds, an unmistakable slice of England at its greenest and best. There are other chances to stand and stare but not until the business in hand is complete and the ridge up the 18th fairway has been safely scaled.

In the meantime, the tiny 12th is not to be taken lightly. It is an admirable illustration that short holes don't have to be 200 yards to give a sense of achievement at hitting the green; and, though of modest length also, the 13th and 14th, one up and one back down again, permit little error in judging the pitches comprising the second shots.

The 15th has much in common with the 7th, a tee shot with the emphasis on carry, while the drive at the 16th must be well flighted to clear the trees guarding the wooded menace on the right. It may be wiser to take the safer line to the left and to rub shoulders with those turning back up the 17th with its hopes of a birdie. But, by now, thoughts are focused on negotiating the final slope to the 18th.

This is done preferably with a drive and crisp iron but, for those flagging physically and in spirit, the sight of the clubhouse has the same effect as an oasis in the desert and it's no mirage. It has splendid reviving powers and if, on reflection, your golf is best forgotten, look not on the dark side. A further glimpse at the scenic splendour will promptly persuade you that it has been amply worthwhile.

18 holes, 6800 yards, S.S.S.73
9 holes, 5200 yards.
Course designed by Grant Aitken.
Club founded in June 1975.
Visitors: welcome - telephone
ahead. Also squash, tennis,
swimming (o/d), croquet, snooker.
Green fees: weekdays £10 per
round, £12 per day; weekends £12
per round, £14 per day.
Society meetings: welcome 7 days
by arrangement.
Catering: lunch, dinner, bar snacks.
Hotels: Lansdown Grove; Linden;
Manor House.

B44 Vivary
☎Taunton (0823) 289274 or
333875.
Taunton, Somerset.
In centre of Taunton.
Parkland course.
18 holes, 4620 yards, S.S.S.63
Course designed by Herbert Fowler.
Club founded in 1930's.
Visitors: welcome municipal course.
Green fees: £4.50 peak; £3.50 off
peak.
Society meetings: welcome
weekdays only.
Hotels: County, Taunton; Castle,
Taunton.

B45 Wareham
☎Wareham (092 95) 54147 Sec,
54156 members.
Sandford Rd, Wareham, Dorset
BH20 4DH.
A351 from Poole, 8 miles from
Poole.
Undulating meadowland course.
9 holes, 2453 yards, S.S.S.64
18 hole course due by 1989.
Club founded in 1926.
Visitors: welcome most days with
some restrictions at weekends.
Green fees: £5 per player per day/
round.
Society meetings: none.
Catering: bar snacks available.
Hotels: numerous good hotels in
area.

B46 Wells (Somerset)
☎Wells (0749) 72868
East Horrington Rd, Wells, Somerset
BA5 3DS.
1.5 miles from city centre off B3139.
Meadowland/parkland course.
18 holes, 5354 yards, S.S.S.67
Club founded in 1895.
Visitors: welcome. Telephone
booking for starting times.
Green fees: £7 weekdays, (£5 with
member); £9 weekend (with current

handicap card) (£7 with member).
Society meetings: welcome on
advance booking, weekdays only.
Catering: bar/mid-day and evening
meals available 7 days. Caravan
facilities available adjacent to course.
Hotels: numerous in Wells.

B47 Weston-super-Mare
☎Weston-s-Mare (0934) 21360
Uphill Rd North, Weston-super-Mare
Avon BS23 4NQ.
M5 or A370 from Bristol.
Seaside course.
18 holes, 6225 yards, S.S.S.70
Course designed by T. Dunn.
Visitors: welcome.
Green fees: £9 weekdays; £12
weekends.
Society meetings: by arrangement.
Catering: snacks and meals daily.
Hotels: Royal Pier; Grand Atlantic;
Beachlands.

B48 West Wilts
☎Warminster (0985) 212702
Elm Hill, Warminster, Wilts
BA12 0AU
A350 towards Westbury, on edge of
town.
Downland course.
18 holes, 5701 yards, S.S.S.68
Course designed by J.H. Taylor.
Club founded in 1891.
Visitors: welcomed with handicap
certificate.
Green fees: £9.50 weekdays;
£12.50 weekends.
Society meetings: accepted Wed/
Thur/Fri.
Catering: available.
Hotels: The Bell.

B49 Weymouth
☎Weymouth (0305) 773981 Sec,
784994 Members.
Links Rd, Westham, Weymouth,
Dorset DT4 0PF.
Off main Dorchester Rd via Radipole
Lane.
Seaside course.
18 holes, 5979 yards, S.S.S.69
Course designed by J. Hamilton
Stutt.
Club founded in 1965.
Visitors: welcome with proof of
membership of club.
Green fees: £8 weekdays; £10 Sat/
Sun/Bank Holidays.
Society meetings: welcome Mon,
Tues and Fri.
Catering: full meals and snacks.
Hotels: Prince Regent; Kingswood;
Lupins; Compton Lodge.

B50 Windwhistle
☎Winsham (046 030) 231
Cricket St Thomas, Chard, Somerset
TA20 4DG.
On the A30 5 miles from Crewkerne,
3 miles from Chard, opposite wildlife
park.
Parkland course.
12 holes, 6055 yards, S.S.S.69
Course designed by James Braid
and J.H. Taylor.
Club founded in 1935.
Visitors: welcome but telephone
first.
Green fees: weekdays £6 per day;
weekends and holidays £8 per day.
Society meetings: by appointment
only.
Catering: Mon-Sat inclusive.
Hotels: The Shrubbery, Ilminster.

B51 Worlebury
☎Weston-super-Mare (0934) 23214
Clubhouse, 25789 Sec.
Worlebury Hill Rd, Weston-super-
Mare, Avon BS22 9SX.
Off A370 from Bristol 2.5 miles from
Weston-super-Mare.
Seaside meadowland course.
18 holes, 5945 yards, S.S.S.68
Course designed by Harry Vardon.
Club founded in 1909.
Visitors: welcome on weekdays.
Green fees: £7.50 weekdays (£4.50
with member); £12 weekends (£7
with member).
Society meetings: catered for on
weekdays.
Catering: snacks, lunch and evening
meals available.
Hotels: Grand Atlantic, Beachland.

B52 Yeovil
☎Yeovil (0935) 22965 Sec, 75949
Club.
Sherborne Rd, Yeovil, Somerset
BA21 5BW.
1 mile E of Yeovil on A30 Yeovil to
Sherborne road.
Undulating parkland course.
18 holes, 6139 yards, S.S.S.69
Course designed by Fowler & Alison.
Club founded in 1919.
Visitors: welcome weekdays.
Weekends, golfers with handicaps
only. Ring in advance at weekends,
advisable weekdays.
Green fees: £10 weekdays; £12
weekends.
Society meetings: by arrangement -
not weekends.
Catering: full except Mondays.
Hotels: Manor Crest; Mermaid;
Yeovil Court.

C Hampshire, Berkshire, Isle of Wight

For the purposes of competitive county golf, Hampshire includes the Isle of Wight and also the Channel Islands (see section A). It is a county of great significance and variety when considering its courses. It also claims Hayling Island to add to that variety and where better to start a brief summary of Hampshire's delights? The championship qualities of Hayling, on the edge of the Solent, have a nautical air, giving it undoubted distinction while its seaside character contrasts nicely with the mainland clubs.

My pick of these would be North Hants (Fleet), Blackmoor and Liphook, a noble trinity that exemplify the best of inland golf, a continuation of the rich seam of heather, sand, pine and silver birch running west-wards from Surrey and Berkshire. It is hard to know which to put first, all demanding close acquaintance and affection, but a word, too, for the Army GC (Aldershot), Stoneham and Brokenhurst Manor on the edge of the New Forest.

Brokenhurst is a real favourite of mine but, as this section takes in Berkshire as well, let us retrace our steps and pay our reverent respects to the Red and Blue courses at the Berkshire, East Berks, very much in the same mould, Swinley Forest, a hallowed retreat, and Sunningdale, although in terms of playing qualification Sunningdale is more in Surrey than Berkshire.

On the matter of golf in the Isle of Wight, I have to rely on favourable hearsay.

C1 **Alresford**
☎Winchester (0962) 733746
Cheriton Rd, Alresford, Hants
SO24 0PN.
1 mile S of Alresford town.
Undulating parkland course.
11 holes, 5986 yards, S.S.S.69
Course designed by Frank Pennink.
Club founded in 1890.
Visitors: welcome.
Green fees: £7 per round, £10 per day weekdays; £12 per round weekends and Bank Holidays (reductions for playing with member).
Society meetings: weekdays.
Catering: full except Mon.
Hotels: Swan; Bell, Alresford.

C2 **Alton**
☎Alton (0420) 82042
Old Odiham Rd, Alton, Hants
GU34 4BU.
On A32 out of Alton towards Odiham, after 2 miles turn R at Golden Pot Public House, take next R immediately and club is 0.5 mile on R.
Undulating meadowland course.
9 holes, 5699 yards, S.S.S.67

Club founded in 1908.
Visitors: welcome except on competition days when course is closed until 5.30pm.
Green fees: £6 weekdays; £9 weekends and Bank Holidays.
Society meetings: weekdays only by arrangement.
Catering: by arrangement.
Hotels: Alton House.

C3 **Ampfield Par 3**
☎Braishfield (0794) 68480, 68750 Pro.
Winchester Rd, Ampfield, Romsey, Hants SO5 9BQ.
On A31 2.5 miles W of Hursley village, next door to White Horse Public House.
Parkland course.
18 holes, 2478 yards, S.S.S.53
Course designed by Henry Cotton MBE.
Club founded in 1963.
Visitors: welcome but advisable to telephone first to avoid busy times.
Green fees: £4 per round, £5.50 per day weekdays; £6.60 per round, £9 per day weekends and Bank

Holidays.
Society meetings: small societies welcome weekdays by prior arrangement.
Catering: light lunch (not Tues), snacks and society dinners by prior arrangement,
Hotels: Pottersheron; White Horse.

C4 **Andover**
☎Andover (0264) 58040 Sec, 23980 Mem, 24151 Pro.
Winchester Rd, Andover, Hants
SP10 2EF
Just off A303 on Andover by-pass, entrance to club about 500 yards after leaving A303.
Undulating parkland course.
9 holes, 5933 yards, S.S.S.68
Club founded in 1907
Visitors: welcome on weekends.
Green fees: £6 (£4 with member) weekdays; £8 (£6 with member) weekends; full day £2 extra.
Society meetings: welcome weekdays.
Catering: snacks, lunch, evening meal except Tues.
Hotels: Danebury; White Hart, Andover.

C5 **Army**
☎Farnborough (0232) 540638 Sec, 541104 Club, 547232 Pro. Laffans Road, Aldershot, Hants GU11 2HF.
A325 to Queens Hotel, follow signs to club.
Heathland course.
18 holes, 6533 yards, S.S.S.71
Course designed by Frank Pennink.
Club founded in 1883.
Visitors: welcome on Mon, Thurs and Fri; at weekends as guest of

member only.
Green fees: on application.
Society meetings: welcome Mon, Thurs and Fri.
Catering: available 11am to 5pm.
Hotels: Queens.

C6 **Barton-on-Sea**
☎New Milton (0425) 615308
Marine Drive, Barton-on-Sea, New Milton. Hants BH25 7BY.
Off A337 at the extreme E end of Marine Drive at Barton.

Seaside course.
18 holes, 5565 yards, S.S.S.67
Course designed by H.S. Colt.
Club founded in 1898.
Visitors: welcome weekdays after 8.30am and weekends and Bank Holidays after 11.15am; advisable to ring to ascertain programme for day.
Green fees: £12 per round weekdays; £15 weekends and Bank Holidays.
Society meetings: societies 12 and over on Mon, Wed and Fri accepted.

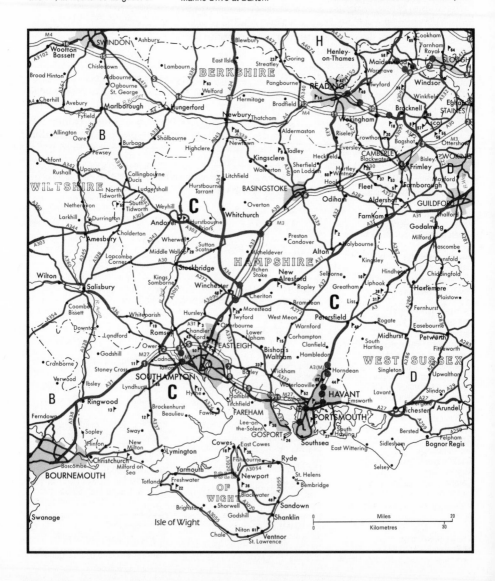

Catering: snacks and teas available, evening catering for societies by arrangement.
Hotels: Chewton Glen; Red House; Old Coastguard.

C7 Basingstoke
☎ Basingstoke (0256) 465990
Kempshott Park, Basingstoke, Hants RG23 7LL.
On A30 3 miles W of Basingstoke.
Parkland course.
18 holes, 6284 yards, S.S.S.70
Course designed by Harry Vardon.
Club founded in 1927.
Visitors: weekdays with handicap certificate weekends with member.
Green fees: £10.50 per round; £15 per day weekdays.
Society meetings: Wed and Thurs.
Catering: full every day except Mon.
Hotels: Tudor Lodge, Basingstoke.

C8 Berkshire
☎ Ascot (0990) 21495
Swinley Rd, Ascot, Berks SL5 8AY.
Situated on A332 between Ascot and Bagshot.
Heathland course.
18 holes, 6356 yards, S.S.S.70,
18 holes, 6258 yards, S.S.S.70.
Courses designed by Herbert Fowler.
Visitors: on request to Sec.
Green fees: £23 per day; £14 per round.
Society meetings: book with Sec.
Catering: lunch available.
Hotels: Berystede; Cricketers; Royal Foresters.

C9 Bishopswood
☎ Tadley (0756) 5213
Bishopswood Lane, Tadley, Basingstoke, Hants RG26 6AT.
6 miles N of Basingstoke, off A340 W of Tadley.
Parkland course.
9 holes, 6476 yards, S.S.S.71
Course designed by Blake and Phillips.
Club founded in 1976.
Visitors: welcome (prior booking)
Green fees: £2.50 per 9 holes; £4 per 18 holes.
Society meetings: weekdays by arrangement.
Catering: bar snacks, restaurant (not Mon).
Hotels: numerous good hotels in area.

C10 Blackmoor
☎ Bordon (042 03) 2775
Golf Lane, Whitehill, Bordon, Hants

GU35 9EH.
Off A325 between Farnham and Petersfield, turn into Firgrove Rd at Whitehall Crossroads.
Parkland/heathland course.
18 holes, 6213 yards, S.S.S.70
Course designed by H.S. Colt.
Club founded in 1913.
Visitors: welcome weekdays with handicap certificate.
Green fees: weekdays £16, (£8 with member); £10, (£5 with member) per round. No weekends.
Society meetings: Wed, Thurs and Fri.
Catering: full, available every day.
Hotels: Silver Birch, Greatham.

C11 Bramshaw
☎ Southampton (0703) 813433
Brook, Lyndhurst, Hants SO4 7HE.
Exit from M27 (Cadnam) and B3078 for 1 mile.
Manor course, parkland;
Forest course, undulating.
Manor 18 holes, 6233 yards, S.S.S.70
Forest 18 holes, 5774 yards, S.S.S.69
Club founded in 1880.
Visitors: not weekends unless playing with member.
Green fees: £10 per day.
Society meetings: any weekday.
Catering: full catering (except Mon). Facilities at Bell Inn on Mon.
Hotels: Bell (free golf when staying at hotel).

C12 Brokenhurst Manor
☎ Lymington (0590) 23332 Sec.
Sway Rd, Brokenhurst, Hants SO4 7SG.
1 mile outside Brokenhurst village on Sway Rd, 5 miles from Lymington.
Parkland course.
18 holes, 6216 yards, S.S.S.70
Course designed by H.S. Colt.
Club opened for play in 1917.
Visitors: welcome, advised to contact Sec, (during business hours).
Restricted play weekends.
Green fees: £15 per day; £20 weekends when available.
Society meetings: Thurs. Minimum 30.
Catering: daily, Mon and Tues no evening catering.
Hotels: Whitly Ridge; Carey's Manor; Southlawns.

C13 Burley
☎ Burley (042 53) 2431
Burley, Ringwood, Hants BH24 4BB.
A31 from Ringwood, turn R at Picket

Post, through Burley St and Burley; club on L at top of hill.
Undulating downland course.
9 holes, 6149 yards, S.S.S.69
Club founded in 1905.
Visitors: welcome weekdays and most Sundays. Wed after 1pm.
Green fees: £6 weekdays, (£3 with member); £8 weekends and Bank Holidays (£4 with member).
Society meetings: not catered for.
Catering: snacks lunchtime (not Tues), snacks Wed, Thur, Fri, Sat evenings 6-8pm.
Hotels: Moorhill House; Burley Manor; White Buck.

C14 Calcot Park
☎ Reading (0734) 27124
Bath Rd, Calcot, Reading RG3 5RN.
From junction 12 on M4 take A4 to Reading for 1 mile.
Parkland course.
18 holes, 6283 yards, S.S.S.70
Club founded in 1930.
Visitors: welcome weekdays only, except Bank Holidays.
Green fees: on application.
Society meetings: catered for on Tues, Thurs and Fri.
Catering: lunch served except Mon.
Hotels: Calcot, Bath Rd, Calcot; Gatehouse, Bath Rd, Reading.

C15 Corhampton
☎ Droxford (0489) 877279.
Sheeps Pond Lane, Droxford.
Southampton, Hants SO3 1QZ.
Right off A32 at Corhampton on B3057 for 1 mile.
Downland course.
18 holes, 6088 yards, S.S.S.69.
Club founded in 1891.
Visitors: welcome weekdays, with member at weekends.
Green fees: £10 per round; £15 per day, weekdays.
Society meetings: welcome Mon and Thurs.
Catering: lunch, tea, dinners except Tues.
Hotels: Little Uplands Country Guest House; Coach House Motel.

C16 Cowes
☎ Cowes (0983) 292303
Crossfield Ave, Cowes PO31 8HN.
Make for Cowes High School, the course is at the far end of the school playing field.
Parkland course.
9 holes, 2940 yards, S.S.S.68
Club founded in 1908.
Visitors: welcome by arrangement.

Green fees: on application.
Society meetings: none.
Catering: bar snacks on weekdays from 11.30am to 1pm except Sun.
Hotels: Fountain, High St, Cowes.

C17 **Dibden**
☎Southampton (0703) 845596.
Dibden, Southampton, Hants
SO4 5TB.
Follow Hythe sign at Dibden roundabout on A326, course entrance 0.5 mile at bottom of hill on right hand side.
18 holes, 6206 yards, S.S.S.70
Course designed by Hamilton Stutt.
Visitors: welcome.
Green fees: £3.60 weekdays; £5.30 weekends.
Society meetings: by arrangement with Pro.
Catering: full catering facilities available.
Hotels: numerous hotels in Southampton.

C18 **Downshire**
☎Bracknell (0344) 424066.
Easthampstead Park, Wokingham, Berks RG11 3DH.
M3 or M4 to Bracknell, then follow signs, 2 miles from Bracknell.
Parkland course.
18 holes, 6382 yards, S.S.S.70
Course designed by F. Hawtree.
Club founded in 1973.
Visitors: welcome every day.
Green fees: on application.
Society meetings: welcome by arrangement.
Catering: bar and cafeteria facilities available.
Hotels: Ladbroke Mercury, Bracknell; St Annes Manor, Wokingham.

C19 **Dunwood Manor**
☎Romsey (0794) 40549.
Shootash Hill, Romsey, Hants
SO5 0GF.
Off A27 Romsey to Salisbury road, after 2 miles turn right at Shootash crossroads into Danes Rd, club is on left.
Undulating parkland course.
18 holes, 6004 yards, S.S.S.69
Club founded in 1972.
Visitors: welcome weekdays by arrangement. Snooker room available.
Green fees: £8 per round; £12 per day; £12 per round weekends and Bank Holidays.
Society meetings: by arrangement.
Catering: bar meals 12-2pm and 7-

9.30pm or by arrangement.
Hotels: Moat House, Ower; White Horse, Romsey.

C20 **East Berkshire**
☎Crowthorne (0344) 772041
Ravenswood Ave, Crowthorne, Berks RG11 6BD.
SW of Bracknell on A3095 and B3348.
Heathland course.
18 holes, 6315 yards, S.S.S.70
Course designed by P. Paxton.
Club founded in 1903.
Visitors: welcome on weekdays.
Green fees: £18 weekdays, (£8 with member).
Society meetings: catered for on weekdays.
Catering: lunch and snacks every day.
Hotels: Waterloo.

C21 **Fleming Park**
☎Eastleigh (0703) 612797 Pro.
619692 Catering.
Magpie Lane, Eastleigh, Hants
SO5 PLH.
A27/M27, turn off at Eastleigh sign, 1 mile to course.
Parkland course.
18 holes, 4402 yards, S.S.S.62
Course designed by Charles Lawrie.
Club founded in 1973.
Visitors: welcome, useful to telephone in advance.
Green fees: on application.
Society meetings: by arrangement with David Miller, Pro.
Catering: bar snacks and meals available.
Hotels: Crest, Leigh Rd.

C22 **Freshwater Bay**
☎Freshwater (0983) 752955
Afton Down, Freshwater Bay, Isle of Wight PO40 9TZ.
2 miles from Yarmouth on A3055 overlooking Freshwater Bay.
Seaside, downland course.
18 holes, 5628 yards, S.S.S.68
Club founded in 1893.
Visitors: welcome at all times.
Green fees: £8 weekdays; £9 weekends and Bank Holidays.
Society meetings: catered for at reduced rates.
Catering: lunch and snacks.
Hotels: Albio; Country Garden; Farringford; Saunders.

C23 **Goring & Streatley**
☎Goring-on-Thames (0491) 873229.
Rectory Rd, Streatley-on-Thames,

Berks RG8 9QA.
On A329 10 miles NW of Reading.
Parkland course.
18 holes, 6255 yards, S.S.S.70
Club founded in 1893.
Visitors: welcome Mon-Fri.
Weekend with member only.
Green fees: £14 per day.
Society meetings: apply for details.
Catering: full à la carte and table d'hôte restaurant.
Hotels: Swan; Beetle & Wedge.

C24 **Gosport & Stokes Bay**
☎Gosport (0705) 527941 Sec, 581625 Club.
Military Rd, Haslar, Gosport.
On A32 6 miles S of Fareham.
Seaside course.
9 holes, 5806 yards, S.S.S.68
Club founded in 1885.
Visitors: welcome except Sun mornings.
Green fees: £6 per day.
Society meetings: welcome.
Catering: available.
Hotels: Anglesey Hotel, Gosport.

C25 **Hartley Wintney**
☎Hartley Wintney (025 126) 4211
Sec,H 3779 Pro, 2214 Club.
London Rd, Hartley Wintney, Hants
RG27 8PT.
On A30 8 miles NE of Basingstoke.
Parkland course.
9 holes, 6096 yards, S.S.S.69
Club founded in 1891.
Visitors: weekdays, Bank Holidays and weekends with member only.
Restrictions on Wed.
Green fees: £6 per round weekdays, (£3.50 with member). £9 per round weekends and Bank Hols. (£6 with member).
Society meetings: Tues and Thurs only.
Catering: snacks and full catering 7 days.
Hotels: Lismoyne; Lamb.

C26 **Hawthorn Hill**
☎Maidenhead (0628) 75588.
Drift Rd, Nr Maidenhead, Berks.
Leave M4 going W at exit 8/9. Take the A330 towards Bracknell for 2.5 miles. Course on right. Course 1 mile from ICI Research Centre at Jealotts Hill.
Undulating parkland course.
18 holes, 6212 yards, S.S.S.70
Course designed by Clive D. Smith.
Club founded in 1985.
Visitors: welcome.
Green fees: on application.
Society meetings: by arrangement.

Catering: bar snacks, lunch and dinners available.
Hotels: nearby in Maidenhead, Windsor, Bracknell, Reading and Ascot.

C27 Hayling
☎Hayling Island (0705) 464446 Sec, 464491 Pro, 463712 Steward.
Farry Rd, Hayling Island, Hants PO11 0BX.
5 miles S of Havant off M27 to A3023, situated at W end of the seafront.
Seaside course.
18 holes, 6489 yards, S.S.S.71
Course designed by Tom Simpson.
Club founded in 1883.
Visitors: private club handicap certificate required and letter of introduction from Home Club appreciated.
Green fees: £15 per day; £20 weekends approx.
Society meetings: Tues and Wed only by prior arrangement.
Catering: not Mon.
Hotels: Post House, Northey.

C28 Hockley
☎Twyford (0962) 713165
Twyford, Winchester, Hants SO21 1PL.
2 miles S of Winchester on A33.
Downland course.
18 holes, 6260 yards, S.S.S.70
Course designed by James Braid.
Club founded in 1915.
Visitors: welcome weekdays, and at weekends with member or by arrangement with Secretary.
Society meetings: not Mon, Tues or Fri.
Catering: lunch served.
Hotels: Wessex, Winchester.

C29 Leckford & Longstock
☎Andover (0264) 810710.
Leckford, Stockbridge, Hants.
2.5 miles N of Stockbridge on Andover road.
Downland course.
9 holes, 3251 yards, S.S.S.71
Course designed by John Morrison.
Visitors: invitation only.
Green fees: on application
Society meetings: none.
Catering: none.
Hotels: Grosvenor, Stockbridge.

C30 Lee-on-the-Solent
☎Lee-on-the-Solent (0705) 551170.
Brune Lane, Lee-on-the-Solent, Hants PO13 9HP.
3 miles S of Fareham.
Meadowland course.
18 holes, 6022 yards, S.S.S.69
Club founded in 1905.
Visitors: welcome on weekdays.
Green fees: £9 per round, £11 per day weekdays; (£4.50/£5.50 with member).
Society meetings: catered for on Thurs.
Catering: lunch and snacks served except Mon.
Hotels: Belle Vue, Marine Parade E, Lee-on-the-Solent.

C31 Liphook
☎Liphook (0482) 723271.
Wheatsheaf Enclosure, Liphook, Hants GU30 7EH.
1 mile S of Liphook on A3.
Heathland course.
18 holes, 6250 yards, S.S.S.70
Course designed by Arthur Croome.
Club founded in 1922.
Visitors: by prior arrangement with Sec.
Green fees: £11 per round, £18 per day weekdays; £16 per round, £20

per day weekends.
Society meetings: maximum 24 Wed, Thur, Fri occasionally Mon.
Catering: bar snacks every day. 3 course lunch available - should be ordered in advance.
Hotels: Links; Angel.

C32 Maidenhead
☎Maidenhead (0628) 24693 Sec, 20545 Club, 20467 Pro.
Shoppenhangers Rd, Maidenhead, Berks SL6 2PZ.
Off A308, adjacent to Maidenhead railway station.
Parkland course.
18 holes, 6360 yards, S.S.S.70
Club founded in 1896.
Visitors: weekdays before 4.30pm Tues-Thurs. Fri after 12 noon by request. After 4.30pm Mon.
Green fees: £15 per round/day.
Society meetings: welcome by arrangement.
Catering: light lunch, tea available except Mon. Full lunch, dinner by arrangement except Mon.
Hotels: Frederick's; Crest.

C33 Meon Valley G & CC
☎Wickham (0392) 833455
Sandy Lane, Shedfield, Southampton SO3 2HQ.
On A334 8 miles E of Southampton between Botley and Wickham.
Parkland course.
18 holes, 6519 yards, S.S.S.71
Course designed by Hamilton Stutt.
Club founded in 1978.
Visitors: welcome.
Green fees: £13 weekdays, 36 holes £17; £17 weekends and Bank Holidays.
Society meetings: by arrangement, residents only at weekends.
Catering: meals and snacks

HAWTHORN HILL

Liphook

For most golfers charm is a more important quality in a course than challenge. Liphook is the type which combines the two in equal measure. 6207 yards is not long these days but matching the par of 70 is another matter when the heather and trees, the hallmark of the best Surrey and Hampshire courses, place such a premium on controlled shot-making.

You can certainly appreciate the lovely setting rather more when you keep straight, the countryside possessing more normal contouring than the valleys, plateaux and gulleys that characterise the land surrounding the Devil's Punchbowl at Hindhead just up the Portsmouth Road. It is a road that, when the club was founded in 1922, was very much more peaceful than it is now. Crossing in order to get to the 15th tee is quite a task for weary limbs but, in terms of golf course architecture, Liphook has rightly been hailed as an example for the connoisseur.

My late senior partner, Ken Cotton, was always singing its praises but the remarkable part of the story is that its designer, A.C.M. Croome, was first and foremost a schoolmaster. Liphook was the only new course for which he was entirely responsible. Jack Neville keeps him notable company in this regard, Neville's lone masterpiece being Pebble Beach. However, it was ill health rather than lack of demand that prevented Croome pursuing the final chapter of a working life that had more variety than most.

In addition to being a housemaster at Radley College, he wrote about cricket and golf for several newspapers, both games at which he excelled himself. He was founder member of the Oxford and Cambridge Golfing Society, donating the Croome Shield for annual competition among College pairs at the President's Putter, and was a regular competitor in the Amateur and other championships.

It was while he was writing that he formed a lasting friendship with J.F. Abercromby, the designer of Addington, among others, who persuaded him to join forces in the firm of Fowler, Abercromby, Simpson and Croome - as elite a quartet as anyone could muster. At first, Croome's role was primarily on the administrative and publicity side, but inside every golfer is a golf course architect clamouring to get out. Croome did so and Liphook was the expression of his talents.

His creation obeys the dictum that there is a right and a wrong way to play every hole, a golfer having to plan his strategy and then supply the shots to match. The position of the clubhouse was changed after World War II, calling for a new first and last hole, the work of John Morrison whose plan was to provide a fine, long short hole to get players moving.

No clubhouse gets a better view of its 1st and 18th holes but, apart from the difficulty of the opening tee shot, Liphook is quick to let golfers know what is expected of them. There are three par 4s of well over 400 yards in the first six holes, the 4th, High View, being particularly demanding. It leads to the first crossing of the busy road and on to the first of three par 5s where some individual thorn trees are a feature of the drive.

The 6th, with its little grassy hollow behind the green, doubles back on the 5th, the attractive short 7th starting the section of ten holes on the other side of the railway. The railway is not the feature it is on some courses although the 7th and 8th run roughly parallel to it. The 9th, 438 yards, another demanding 4, prompts a long uphill second over a road and a heathery dell but the 10th offers a more inviting drive even if a ditch lurks on the approach to the green.

A large central bunker dominates the short 11th in a visual sense, the 12th, Forest Mere, completing the long par 4s and invariably not without a victim or two. A nice downhill drive and a slightly uphill second gives the longer hitters a chance of a birdie at the 13th, and, for those negotiating the dogleg successfully, a good pitch can do the same at the 14th.

Then it is a deep breath and a mad dash to the 15th where the drive takes us up over a steep ridge with the temptation to cut off more than is good for us. The 16th is the reverse of the 15th, a quarry and the corner of a wood awaiting any poorly struck or mis-directed second. The walk to the 17th is a last reminder of the Portsmouth Road which explains in part the club's traditionally strong links with the Navy; but the 17th's tee shot across a diagonal, corrugated bank of gorse and heather makes the fifth and last short hole difficult to judge, a further instance of Liphook's reputation that is it not just nautical men who are all at sea.

available.
Hotels: Meon Valley.

C34 Newbury & Crookham
☎Newbury (0635) 40035.
Bury's Bank Rd, Greenham,
Newbury Berks RG15 8BZ.
2 miles SE of Newbury off A34.
Parkland course.
18 holes, 5880 yards, S.S.S.68
Course designed by J.H. Turner.
Club founded in 1873.
Visitors: weekdays members of other clubs; weekends with members only.
Green fees: £11; (£5.50 with member).
Society meetings: Wed, Thurs and Fri.
Catering: lunch, snacks and evening meals.
Hotels: Bacon Arms; Chequers; Enborne Grange.

C35 New Forest
☎Lyndhurst (042 128) 2450 or 2752.
Lyndhurst, Hants SO4 7BU.
NE of Lyndhurst on the A35.
Heathland course.
18 holes, 5748 yards, S.S.S.68
Course designed by Peter Swann.
Club founded in 1888.
Visitors: welcome Mon to Sat, Sun after 1.30pm.
Green fees: £5 per round/day.
Society meetings: welcome Mon to Sat.
Catering: service available 11am to 5pm.
Hotels: Crown: Lyndhurst Park.

C36 Newport
☎Newport (0983) 525076.
St George's Down, Newport, Isle of Wight PO30 3BA.
A3056 Newport to Sandown road half mile from Newport.
Undulating parkland course.
9 holes, 5704 yards, S.S.S.68
Course designed by Guy Hunt.
Club founded in 1896.

Visitors: welcome all times except during major Club competitions.
Green fees: £7 per day, £5 per afternoon on Sun.
Society meetings: welcome. Bar catering available.
Catering: bar meals on request to Stewardess before round.
Hotels: numerous good hotels in area.

C37 North Hants
☎Fleet (0252) 6443
Minley Rd, Fleet, Hants GU13 8RE.
0.5 mile N of Fleet Station on B3013.
Heathland course.
18 holes, 6090 yards, S.S.S.70
Visitors: by prior application to Sec. Letter of introduction and handicap certificate required.
Green fees: on application.
Society meetings: Tues and Wed.
Catering: lunch, tea, dinner. Pre-booking required.
Hotels: Various in Fleet, Camberley and Farnborough.

C38 Old Thorns
☎Liphook (0428) 724555
London Kosaido G & CC, Longmoor Rd, Liphook, Hants GU30 7PE.
On A3 into Liphook, at mini-roundabout go down B2131 for about 1 mile until sign on left hand side saying London Kosaido G C; turn up this lane and go right to end.
18 holes, 5620 yards S.S.S.72
Course designed by Commander John Harris, adapted by Peter Alliss and Dave Thomas.
Club founded in 1982.
Visitors: welcome.
Green fees: £12 per round; £18 per day.
Society meetings: welcome.
Catering: full à la carte menu and Japanese restaurant.
Hotels: Old Thorns.

C39 Osborne
☎(0983) 295421

Osborne, East Cowes, Isle of Wight PO32 67X.
A3052 Newport to E Cowes Rd, situated in the grounds of Osborne House.
Parkland course.
9 holes, 6304 yards, S.S.S.70
Club founded in 1903.
Visitors: welcome except Sun before 12am; Tues between 11.30am and 2.30pm.
Green fees: £9 Bank Holidays; £7 Mon to Fri; £8 Sat and Sun.
Society meetings: by arrangement.
Catering: limited, by arrangement.
Hotels: Padmore House, Crossway; Clarence House.

C40 Petersfield
☎Petersfield (0730) 62386 Sec, 63725 Club, 67732 Pro.
The Heath, Petersfield, Hants GU31 4EJ.
A3 to town centre, then Heath Rd to course.
Heath and meadowland course.
18 holes, 5751 yards, S.S.S.68
Club founded in 1881.
Visitors: welcome daily but not before 10.30am weekends.
Green fees: £7 per round, £19 per day weekdays; £10.50 per round, £14 per day weekends.
Society meetings: not weekends or public holidays. Reduction £1 per member after reservation. Catering available, lunch and evening meal.
Catering: Lunch available Tues-Sat. inclusive. Evening meal for parties of more than 12.
Hotels: Concorde, Weston Rd, Petersfield.

C41 Portsmouth
☎Portsmouth (0705) 372210
Crookhorn Lane, Widley, Portsmouth, Hants PO7 5QL.
Located on the hills overlooking Portsmouth Harbour on the N of the city, within 1 mile of both the A3 and A3M.
Undulating parkland course.

18 holes, 6200 yards, S.S.S.70
Club founded in 1926.
Visitors: welcome.
Green fees: £4 weekdays; £5
weekends.
Society meetings: please arrange
weekdays.
Catering: full facilities available.
Hotels: Bear; Corner House.

C42 **Reading**
☎Reading (0734) 472909.
Kidmore End Rd, Emmer Green,
Reading, Berks RG4 8SG.
2 miles N of Reading off Peppard
Rd. (B481).
Parkland course.
18 holes, 6207 yards, S.S.S.70
Club founded in 1910.
Visitors: Mon to Fri (unless with
member).
Green fees: £13 per day/round.
Society meetings: Tues, Thurs
unlimited; Mon, Fri 25 maximum.
Catering: full facilities except Mon.
Hotels: Remada, Reading.

C43 **Romsey**
☎Southampton (0703) 734637.
Nursling, Southampton SO1 9XW.
Junction of M271 and A3057 N of
Southampton.
Undulating woodland course.
18 holes, 5759 yards, S.S.S.68
Course designed by Charles Lawrie.
Club founded in 1925.
Visitors: weekdays only.
Green fees: on application.
Society meetings: Mon to Fri - not
Thurs.
Catering: full facilities.
Hotels: White Hart, Romsey.

C44 **Rowlands Castle**
☎Rowlands Castle (0705) 412784.
Links Lane, Rowlands Castle, Hants
PO9 6AE.
3 miles N of Havant off B2149.
Parkland course.
18 holes, 6627 yards, S.S.S.72
18 holes, 6381 yards, S.S.S.70
Club founded in 1902.
Visitors: welcome weekdays and
weekends. Advisable to ring prior to
arriving at weekends during summer
season.
Green fees: £12 per round/day
weekdays; £15 per round/day
weekends and Bank Holidays.
Society meetings: catered for Tues,
Thurs, Fri: details on application.
Catering: service until 6pm except
Mon.
Hotels: Brookfield, Emsworth; Bear

Hotel, Havant; Fountain Inn,
Rowlands Castle.

C45 **Royal Ascot**
☎Ascot (0990) 25175.
Winkfield Rd, Ascot, Berks SL5 7LJ.
In centre of Royal Ascot racecourse.
Heathland/moorland course.
18 holes, 5653 yards, S.S.S.67
Course designed by J.H. Taylor
Club founded in 1887.
Visitors: welcome on weekdays.
Green fees: on application.
Society meetings: welcome.
Catering: available all week by
arrangement.
Hotels: Forresters; Berystede.

C46 **Royal Winchester**
☎Winchester (0962) 52462.
Sarum Rd, Winchester, Hants
SO22 5QE.
Leave Winchester on Romsey Rd.
Downland course.
18 holes, 6218 yards, S.S.S.70
Course designed by H.S. Colt and
A.P. Taylor.
Club founded in 1888.
Visitors: weekdays (handicap
certificate required).
Green fees: £15 per round/day.
Society meetings: Mon, Tues, Wed.
Catering: every day except Thurs.
Liaise with Steward.
Hotels: Royal; Wessex.

C47 **Ryde**
☎Ryde (0983) 614809.
Binstead Rd, Ryde, Isle of Wight
PO33 3NF.
Main Ryde to Newport road.
Parkland course.
9 holes, 5200 yards, S.S.S.66
Club founded in 1921.
Visitors: welcome except Wed
afternoons and Sun mornings.
Green fees: on application.
Catering: meals and snacks served.
Hotels: Yelfs.

C48 **Shanklin & Sandown**
☎Shanklin (0983) 403217.
The Fairway, Sandown, Isle of Wight
PO36 9PR.
On A3055 near Sandown station.
Seaside course.
18 holes, 5980 yards, S.S.S.69
Course designed by Dr. J. Cowper.
Club founded in 1900.
Visitors: welcome.
Green fees: £12 per round/day
weekdays; £14 per round/day
weekends. 5 day tickets £40; 7 day
tickets £55.

Society meetings: on request.
Catering: bar snacks available all
day. Restaurant for dining, lunch and
evening meals.
Hotels: various within 2 miles of
club.

C49 **Sonning**
☎Reading (0734) 69332.
Duffield Rd, Sonning-on-Thames,
Berks RG5 4RJ.
A4 Maidenhead/Reading road,
behind Readingensians Rugby
Ground.
Parkland course.
18 holes, 6310 yards, S.S.S.70
Club founded in 1914.
Visitors: welcome weekdays with
handicap certificate.
Green fees: on application.
Society meetings: welcome by prior
arrangement.
Catering: full service available.
Hotels: White Hart, Sonning-on-
Thames.

C50 **Southampton**
☎Southampton (0703) 760373.
Golf Course Rd, Bassett,
Southampton. Hants.
N end of city, off Bassett Ave,
halfway between Chilworth
roundabout and Winchester Rd
roundabout.
Parkland municipal course.
18 holes, 5683 metres, S.S.S.70
9 holes, 2185 metres.
Club founded in 1935.
Visitors: welcome.
Green fees: on application.
Society meetings: by arrangement
with Council Municipal Golf Course
Manager.
Catering: breakfast, lunch, bar
snacks available.
Hotels: Albany, The Ave,
Southampton; Bassett, Bassett.

C51 **Southsea**
☎Portsmouth (0705) 660945.
The Mansion, Great Salterns,
Eastern Rd, Portsmouth PO3 6QB.
2 miles off M27/A27/A3 on E road
into Portsmouth.
Meadowland municipal course.
18 holes, 5800 yards, S.S.S.68
Club founded in 1972.
Visitors: welcome.
Green fees: £3.50 weekdays; £4.20
weekends.
Society meetings: by arrangement
with Portsmouth City Council.
Catering: none available.
Hotels: numerous good hotels in
area.

Sunningdale (New)

When you talk of Fortnum and Mason, Morecambe and Wise, Darby and Joan or Brighton and Hove, there is no suggestion that one name is mightier than the other. With golf courses, mention of Old and New tends to imply the opposite. Old Prestwick, the Old courses at St Andrews, Sunningdale or Walton Heath possess a seniority and a hallowed ring that is impossible to deny.

As a rule, club golfers deplore change although they invariably express their dislike without even considering the implications. When a New or second course is added, blind loyalty allows it to be tolerated rather than cherished. Few go to St Andrews to play the New if they can play the Old. Much the same applies to Walton Heath and Sunningdale but, whilst believing firmly that a day's golf isn't complete without a round on each, my preference at Sunningdale is marginally for the New, chosen by the English Golf Union to house the 1986 Brabazon Trophy.

The most lamented New course was that at Addington which fell victim to a housing scheme after the last war. There were some who maintained that J.F. Abercromby only built it to prove that the land could be drained but it was laid out in the same bracken, heather and silver birch country that lends Sunningdale its glory.

When the Roberts brothers founded Sunningdale at the turn of the century, the whole area right out to Chobham Common and beyond was a barren, treeless wilderness. Whereas the Old has become more or less enclosed, the New has retained its original character. Its density of heather is decidedly thicker and envelops the ball with relish when a slightly stray shot drifts on the wind.

In the Youths championship of 1983, played in stiff winds over hard ground, the degree of control necessary was far greater than it would have been on its more celebrated neighbour. Out by the 4th, 6th and 8th, there is little protection or comfort. Just the forlorn feeling that only a succession of stoutly hit drives and second shots will keep a good score intact.

It was over the New course that Gary Player first came to the public eye in this country, his victory in the Dunlop tournament of 1956 climaxing a titanic struggle with Arthur Lees, the local professional who, for years, played both courses better and more consistently than anyone has ever done. The New, like the Old, demands that the drives are well positioned in order to achieve the best angle and line for the second shots, accuracy being the greater virtue than power.

The opening drive, for instance, has to be up the left in order not to sacrifice length by seeing it running sideways down the slope. The tee shot at the 2nd, the first of five short holes, has little margin for error when the pin is tucked on the top shelf of a tapering green. The penalties for missing many of the greens on the New can be quite alarming and this is undoubtedly one of its defences. The other is that on many of the holes, there is a temptation to bite off more than you can chew with drives involving longish carries on holes which curve rather than run straight.

The 3rd has caught countless in this manner, the 7th, 11th, 12th and 15th running it a close second. One of the hardest par 4s is the 4th with the last part of a long second uphill; but the most spectacular hole, both in appearance and in a playing sense, is the par 5 6th. It weaves a serpentine path through a minefield of heather, making it difficult to know whether to attack or play safe. Both approaches have their drawbacks.

An extension of the hole and a modified green are one of several changes made in the last twenty years or so, although the biggest improvement surrounds the 8th, a short second to an unusual green being replaced by a long iron that has to be inch perfect to hold a new green. The 9th, despite a blind drive over a ridge to a fairway that plunges as soon as the guide post is cleared, is a second shot hole and nothing but the best serves at the short 10th, very often a wood even for the strongest.

Wind direction dictates how hard the homeward holes play. The New has enormous variety in the shots it demands especially on the last eight. For those without yardage charts, which in any case can be a doubtful blessing, judgement of distance is a problem. On the 12th and 15th, this is largely because the greens are above the level of the fairway although on the short 14th, a classic hole, the angling of the green reduces the size of the landing area.

On the long 13th, the problem is more of getting approaches to stop on a green running away from you while on the 16th the threat of out of bounds lurks. It is an elegant hazard in the shape of landscaped gardens but out of bounds all the same. The 17th, the last of the par 3s, is another difficult green to hit, and, if the 18th offers the chance of a finishing birdie, the drive must be as truly hit as any.

C52 Southwick Park
☎Corsham (0705) 380131.
Pinsley Drive, Southwick, Fareham, Hants PO17 6EL.
A333 7 miles N of Portsmouth, follow signs to HMS Dryad.
Parkland course.
18 holes, 5855 yards, S.S.S.68
Course designed by Charles Lawrie.
Club founded in 1977.
Visitors: weekdays, weekends guest of member.
Green fees: £7.
Society meetings: welcome Tues.
Catering: available.
Hotels: Holiday Inn.

C53 Southwood
☎Farnborough (0252) 548700.
Ively Rd, Cove, Farnborough, Hants GU14 0LJ.
1 mile W of A325 Farnborough.
Parkland public course.
9 holes, 2263 yards, S.S.S.31
Course designed by John D. Harris.
Club founded in 1977.
Visitors: welcome, bookable at weekends.
Green fees: on application.
Society meetings: weekdays.
Catering: bar snacks, tea and lunch available.
Hotels: Queens, Lynchford Rd, Farnborough.

C54 Stoneham
☎Southampton (0703) 768151, 769272 Sec.
Bassett Green Rd, Bassett, Southampton, SO2 3NE.
From A33 turn left at Chilworth roundabout, 0.5 mile on left side of A27.
Heather, parkland course.
18 holes, 6310 yards, S.S.S.70
Course designed by Willie Park.

Club founded in 1908.
Visitors: welcome any time, advisable to telephone in advance.
Green fees: £12 per round/36 holes weekdays; £14 weekends. No fees competition days.
Society meetings: Mon, Thurs, Fri by appointment only.
Catering: full catering available.
Hotels: Wessex; Albany.

C55 Sunningdale
☎Ascot (0990) 21681.
Ridgemount Rd, Sunningdale, Ascot, Surrey SL5 9RW.
Ridgemount Rd is 50 yards W of Sunningdale Railway Station crossing on the A30.
Heathland course.
Old - 18 holes, 6341 yards, S.S.S.70
New - 18 holes, 6676 yards, S.S.S.72
Course designed by Willie Park.
Club founded in 1901.
Visitors: weekdays by prior arrangement.
Green fees: £35 per day.
Society meetings: Tue, Wed, Thur by arrangement.
Catering: full catering facilities.
Hotels: Berystede, Ascot; Runnymede, Egham.

C56 Sunningdale Ladies'
☎Ascot (0990) 20507.
Cross Rd, Sunningdale, Surrey SL5 9RX.
Second turning left on A30 going W from Sunningdale level crossing.
Heathland course.
18 holes, 3622 yards, S.S.S.60.
Course designed by Edward Villiers.
Club founded in 1902.
Visitors: welcome, telephone first.
Green fees: £9 ladies, £9 men weekdays; £11 ladies, £14 men

weekends and Bank Holidays.
Society meetings: catered for Ladies only.
Catering: lunch and tea except Sun.
Hotels: Berystede, Ascot.

C57 Swinley Forest
☎Ascot (0990) 20197.
Coronation Rd, South Ascot, Berks SL5 9LE.
1.5 miles from Ascot Station, through S Ascot village, right into Coronation Rd and fourth right to club.
Undulating course.
18 holes, 6011 yards, S.S.S.69
Course designed by H.S.Colt.
Club founded in 1909.
Visitors: welcome only by invitation of member.
Green fees: on application.
Society meetings: apply to Sec.
Catering: lunch served.
Hotels: Berystede, Ascot; Royal Foresters, Ascot.

C58 Temple
☎Littlewick Green (062 882) 4795 Sec, 4248 Steward, 4254 Pro.
Henley Rd, Hurley, Maidenhead, Berks SL6 5LH.
A423 Maidenhead to Henley from M4.
Undulating parkland course.
18 holes, 6206 yards, S.S.S.70
Course designed by Willie Park.
Club founded in 1909.
Visitors: welcome on weekdays.
Must have proof of handicap.
Green fees: £18.
Society meetings: catered for Tues, Wed, Fri. Maximum 40.
Catering: full catering except Mon.
Hotels: Eurocrest, Maidenhead; Compleat Angler, Marlow.

C59 Tidworth Garrison
☎Stonehenge (0980) 42301 Sec,

42321 Club, 42393 Pro.
Bulford Rd, Tidworth, Hants
SP9 7AF.
A388 to Tidworth, then 1 mile along
Bulford Rd from bus station.
Downland course.
18 holes, 5990 yards, S.S.S.69
Club founded in 1908.
Visitors: welcome by arrangement.
Green fees: £8 per day, (£5 with
member).
Society meetings: catered for Tues,
Thurs, Fri.
Catering: meals by prior arrange-
ment except Mon, bar snacks every
day.
Hotels: Antrobus Arms; George.

C60 **Tylney Park**
☎ Hook (025 672) 2079.
Rotherwick, Basingstoke, Hants.
Off A30 at Nately Scures, follow
signs for Rotherwick: approx 1.5
miles.
Parkland course.
18 holes, 6138 yards, S.S.S.70
Course designed by W. Wiltshire.
Visitors: welcome.
Green fees: £8.50 weekdays, (£5.50
with member); £11 weekends (with
certificate) (£6 with member).
Society meetings: welcome Mon to
Fri.
Catering: meals served.
Hotels: Raven Hook.

C61 **Ventnor**
☎ Ventnor (0983) 853326.
Steephill Down Rd, Ventnor, Isle of
Wight.
A3055 to Ventnor, course on downs
above
Undulating downland course.

9 holes, 5772 yards, S.S.S.68
Club founded 1892.
Visitors: welcome except Sun
morning.
Green fees: £6 weekdays; £7
weekends.
Society meetings: anytime except
Sun morning.
Catering: snacks at bar.
Hotels: Llynfi; Maracarpa.

C62 **Waterlooville**
☎ Portsmouth (0705) 263388.
Idsworth Rd, Cowplain, Portsmouth
PO8 8BD.
Off A3 in Cowplain, 5 miles N of
Portsmouth.
18 holes, 6647 yards, S.S.S.72.
Course designed by Henry Cotton.
Club founded in 1907.
Visitors: welcome Mon to Fri.
Green fees: £12 per round/day.
Society meetings: Thurs only.
Catering: 10am to 5pm daily.
Hotels: Post House, Northney,
Hayling Island; Bear, Havant.

C63 **West Berks**
☎ Chaddleworth (048 82) 574.
Chaddleworth, Newbury, Berks.
Off M4 at Junction 14, A338 towards
Wantage, first right turn for 1 mile,
follow signs to RAF Welford.
Downland course.
18 holes, 7053 yards, S.S.S.74
Club founded in 1978.
Visitors: welcome with reservation.
Green fees: £6 weekdays; £10
weekends.
Society meetings: catered for by
arrangement.
Catering: full service available.
Hotels: numerous good hotels in
area.

C64 **Wexham Park**
☎ Fulmer (028 16) 3271.
Wexham St, Wexham, Slough,
Bucks SL3 6ND.
2 miles from Slough towards
Gerrards Cross, follow signs to
Wexham Park Hospital and club is
0.5 mile further on.
Parkland course.
18 holes, 5424 yards, S.S.S.67
Course designed by Emil Lawrence
and David Morgan.
Club founded in 1976.
Visitors: welcome.
Green fees: weekdays, £4 (18
holes), £2.60 (9 holes); weekends,
£5.50 (18 holes), £3.30 (9 holes).
Society meetings: welcome.
Catering: full service available.
Hotels: Bull, Gerrards Cross.

C65 **Winter Hill**
☎ Bourne End (062 85) 27613.
Grange Lane, Cookham, Maiden-
head, Berks SL6 9RP.
4 miles from Maidenhead via M4; 6
miles from M40 via Marlow.
Parkland course.
18 holes, 6408 yards, S.S.S.71
Course designed by Charles Lawrie.
Club founded in 1976.
Visitors: welcome weekdays. After
12 noon weekends by prior
arrangement with Sec or Pro.
Green fees: £11 weekdays; £14
weekends.
Society meetings: welcome main
day Wed.
Catering: full service available.
Hotels: Eurocrest, Maidenhead.

D Surrey and West Sussex

Surrey is a county which is more richly endowed with fine golf courses than any other. Its richness is, in many ways, a freak of nature because the discovery in the early part of the century of what is generally called the sand and heather belt led to a rapid increase in the population of inland courses.

It was land, what is more, that had a poor agricultural value, although the building of golf courses soon led to an explosion of house building as everyone, not just golfers, found that the fashionable and desirable thing was to own a lovely garden running down to a green fairway. It has formed the basis of much fortune making in property development in all corners of the world but the pioneer was T.A. Roberts, founder of Sunningdale, who as agent of St John's College, Cambridge, more than earned his agent's fee by planning many of the houses that adorn part of both courses.

Sunningdale was open for play (the Old course, at any rate) in 1902 but the oldest of the heathery courses is Woking, still one of the best. It is not as formidable as Sunningdale, Walton Heath and, more recently Wentworth but it heads the list of those where interest and enjoyment are paramount. There are now so many of them that it is impossible to class them in any sort of order of precedence so I will list them alpha-

betically for the sheer pleasure of doing so: Addington, Burhill, Camberley Heath, Coombe Hill, Hankley Common, New Zealand, St George's Hill, Sunningdale and then the welter of Ws, Walton Heath, Wentworth, West Byfleet, West Hill, Woking and Worplesdon. Given nice weather and good condition of the courses, it would be impossible not to enjoy a day's golf on any of them; Surrey golf is full of variety and contrast.

For lovers of parkland golf, there is Royal Mid-Surrey, Roehampton, RAC and Tandridge, Effingham and Guildford proclaim the best of golf on chalky downland while Farnham and West Surrey have parts that are heathery and parts that are a mixture of parkland and downland.

I have led this section on Surrey but West Sussex has much to offer, not least West Sussex GC itself at Pulborough which is every bit as good as anything in Surrey and far more beautiful. In terms of setting, there is nothing much better than Goodwood while Cowdray Park at Midhurst has its admirers. For the rest, there is Selsey, Bognor, Littlehampton and Ham Manor, working east along the coast, while Worthing is another fine example of downland golf and Hill Barn, its neighbour, a splendid municipal course on which several fully-fledged professional tournaments have been held.

D1 **Addington**
☎01-777 6057
205 Shirley Church Rd, Croydon, Surrey CR0 5AB.
2.5 miles from E Croydon station.
Heathland course.
18 holes, 6243 yards, S.S.S.71
Course designed by J.F. Abercromby.
Club founded in 1914.
Visitors: welcome on weekdays only.
Green fees: on application.
Society meetings: only by advance booking.
Catering: meals served.
Hotels: numerous good hotels in

Croydon.

D2 **Addington Court**
☎01-657 0281/2/3
Featherbed Lane, Addington, Croydon, Surrey CR0 9AA.
Undulating public courses.
Championship 18 holes, 5577 yards, S.S.S.67
Falconwood 18 holes, 5513 yards, S.S.S.67
Course designed by F. Hawtree Snr.
Club founded in 1933.
Visitors: welcome.
Green fees: Championship £5.30,

Falconwood £3.10. Reduced winter rate Nov/Mar.
Society meetings: welcome weekdays.
Catering: full catering facilities.
Hotels: Holiday Inn; Selsdon Park.

D3 **Addington Palace**
☎01-654 3061
Gravel Hill, Addington Park, Croydon, Surrey CR0 5BB.
2 miles from E Croydon station.
Parkland course.
18 holes, 6262 yards, S.S.S.71
Club founded in 1923.

Visitors: welcome on weekdays and with member at weekends or Bank Holidays.
Green fees: £15 per round/day.
Society meetings: catered for on Tues, Wed, Fri and Thurs afternoons.
Catering: snacks and meals during day, except Mon.
Hotels: Holiday Inn; Selsdon Park.

D4 Banstead Downs
☎01-642 2284
Burdon Lane, Belmont, Sutton, Surrey SM2 7DD.
100 yards E of junction A216 and B2230.
Downland course.
18 holes, 6150 yards, S.S.S.69
Club founded in 1890.
Visitors: welcome with letter of introduction Mon-Sat; Bank Holidays and Sun mornings with member only.
Green fees: on application.
Society meetings: by arrangement.
Catering: 11am-6pm, dinner by arrangement.
Hotels: Thatched House, Cheam; Drift Bridge, Epsom.

D5 Betchworth Park
☎Dorking (0306) 882052 Sec, 884334 Pro.
Reigate Rd, Dorking, Surrey RH4 1NZ.
1 mile E of Dorking on A25 to Reigate entrance opposite horticultural gardens.
Parkland course.
18 holes, 6266 yards, S.S.S.70
Club founded in 1913.
Visitors: welcome weekdays except Tues and Wed am; restricted at weekends, subject to club events.
Green fees: £13 per day (arrange with Sec)
Society meetings: catered for all day Mon and Thurs and Tues and Wed pm.
Catering: lunch and tea served.
Hotels: Burford Bridge; White Horse; Punchbowl.

D6 Bognor Regis
☎Bognor Regis (0243) 821929
Downview Rd, Felpham, Bognor Regis, Sussex PO22 8JD.
A259 Littlehampton to Bognor Road, turn right at traffic lights at Felpham, 2 miles short of Bognor Regis.
Parkland course.
18 holes, 6238 yards, S.S.S.70
Club founded in 1892.
Visitors: welcome with handicap certificate, weekends from April - Oct

with member only.
Green fees: £12 weekdays; £16 weekends.
Society meetings: restricted, by arrangement only.
Catering: meals served by arrangement.
Hotels: Royal Norfolk; Beach.

D7 Bramley
☎Guildford (0483) 892696
Bramley, Guildford, Surrey GU5 0AL.
Situated 4 miles S of Guildford on A281 Guildford to Horsham road, between the villages of Shalford and Bramley.
Parkland course.
18 holes, 5910 yards, S.S.S.68
Course designed by Charles Mayo and redesigned by James Braid.
Club founded in 1913.
Visitors: welcome Mon - Fri.
Green fees: £11 per round; £13 per day; no fees at weekend unless guest of member.
Society meetings: Mon - Fri by prior arrangement with Sec.
Catering: bar snacks and grill menu daily.
Hotels: Bramley Grange, High St, Bramley.

D8 Burhill
☎Walton-on-Thames (0932) 227345.
Walton-on-Thames, Surrey KT12 4BL.
Off A3 on A425 towards Byfleet, right into Seven Hills Rd and again into Burwood Rd, entrance is second on right.
Parkland course.
18 holes, 6224 yards, S.S.S.70
Course designed by Willie Park.
Club founded in 1907.
Visitors: weekdays by arrangement; handicap certificate required.
Green fees: £20; £13 after 12 noon.
Society meetings: catered for weekdays.
Catering: lunch, snack bar facilities available except Mon.
Hotels: Oatlands Park, Weybridge.

D9 Camberley Heath
☎Camberley (0276) 23258
Golf Drive, Camberley, Surrey GU15 1JG.
On A325 to Camberley, near M3 Exit 4, follow signs to Frimley and Bagshot.
Undulating heathland course.
18 holes, 6402 yards, S.S.S.71
Course designed by H.S. Colt.
Club founded in 1913.

Visitors: welcome, but must have handicap certificate from recognised golf club and should telephone for tee reservation.
Green fees: on application.
Society meetings: by arrangement.
Catering: meals and snacks served.
Hotels: good hotels in area.

D10 Chessington
☎01-391 0948
Garrison Lane, Chessington, Surrey KT9 2LW.
Opposite Chessington South station, very near to Chessington Zoo.
Parkland course.
9 holes, 1655 yards, S.S.S.30
Course designed by Patrick Tallack PGA.
Club founded in 1983.
Visitors: welcome.
Green fees: £2 for 9 holes weekdays; £2.50 9 holes weekends; £1.50 OAP's and Juniors anytime.
Society meetings: welcome.
Catering: full catering facilities.
Hotels: Seven Hills; Oatlands Park.

D11 Chipstead
☎Downland (073 75) 55781
How Lane, Coulsdon, Surrey CR3 3PR.
Follow signs to Chipstead from A217.
Undulating parkland course.
18 holes, 5454 yards, S.S.S.67
Club founded in 1906.
Visitors: welcome weekdays.
Green fees: £12 per day; £8 after 2pm. (£5 with member).
Society meetings: catered for on weekdays.
Catering: lunch served except Mon. Prior booking required.
Hotels: numerous hotels in area.

D12 Coombe Hill
☎01-942 2284
Golf Club, Kingston Hill, Surrey KT2 7DG.
Quarter mile W of A3.
Parkland course.
18 holes, 6286 yards, S.S.S.71
Course designed by J.F.Abercromby.
Club founded in 1911.
Visitors: by appointment only.
Green fees: £30 weekdays; £35 weekends.
Society meetings: welcome weekdays.
Catering: lunches served every day.
Hotels: Seven Hills; Richmond Hill.

D13 Coombe Wood
☎01-942 0388

George Rd, Kingston Hill, Surrey KT2 7NS.
1 mile N of Kingston-on-Thames, off Kingston Hill.
Parkland course.
18 holes, 5210 yards, S.S.S.66
Course designed by T. Williamson.
Club founded in 1904.
Visitors: weekdays only.
Green fees: on application.
Society meetings: welcome Wed, Thurs.
Hotels: Antoinette, Beaufort Rd, Kingston-on-Thames.

D14 Copthorne
☎0342 712508
Bovers Arms Rd, Copthorne,

Crawley, West Sussex RH10 3LL.
On A264, 4 miles E of Crawley.
Heathland course.
18 holes, 6505 yards, S.S.S.71
Course designed by James Braid.
Club founded in 1892.
Visitors: welcome weekdays and afternoons at weekends.
Green fees: £12 per round; £15 per day weekdays; £18 afternoon at weekends.
Society meetings: Thurs and Fri.
Catering: lunch Mon-Fri and Sun.
Hotels: Copthorne, Copthorne.

D15 Cottesmore
☎Crawley (0293) 28256
Bucham Hill, Pease Pottage,

Crawley, Sussex RH11 9AT.
Last turn off M23 to Pease Pottage,
1 mile down Horsham road, from Pease Pottage on right hand side.
Undulating meadowland course.
Old - 18 holes, 6100 yards, S.S.S.70
New - 18 holes, 5400 yards, S.S.S.68
Course designed by M.D. Rogerson.
Club founded in 1974.
Visitors: welcome at weekends.
Green fees: old/new £10 weekdays; old £16, new £10 weekends.
Society meetings: catered for weekdays only. Weekend breaks at club accommodation.
Catering: restaurant and lounge bar, banquet room, hot and cold snacks.

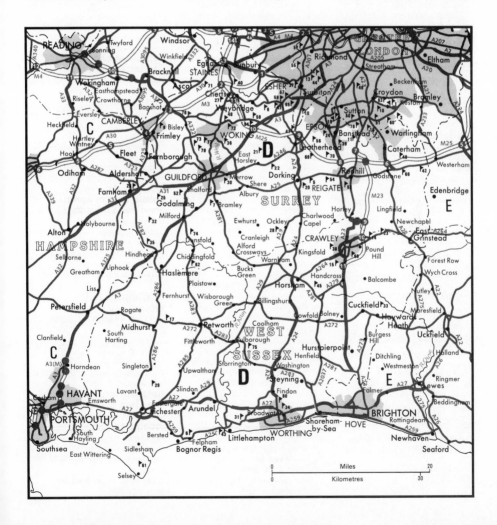

Hotels: 15 room accommodation at club.

D16 Coulsdon Court
☎01-668 0414
Coulsdon Rd, Coulsdon, Surrey CR3 2LL.
Just off A23, 2 miles S of Croydon, 2 miles N of M25 and M23.
Parkland course.
18 holes, 6030 yards, S.S.S.70
Course designed by H.S. Buck.
Club founded in 1926.
Visitors: welcome anytime, telephone confirmation.
Green fees: £5.50 weekdays; £7.75 weekends.
Society meetings: 36 holes with full catering.
Catering: snacks, banquets, lunch, barbecues, dinners, breakfasts.
Hotels: Croydon Court; Holiday Inn.

D17 Cowdray Park
☎Midhurst (073 081) 3599 Sec, 2091 Pro.
Midhurst, W. Sussex GU29 0BB.
Situated about 1 mile E of Midhurst on A272.
Parkland course.
18 holes, 5972 yards, S.S.S.70
Club founded in 1920.
Visitors: welcome.
Green fees: on application.
Society meetings: catered for on weekdays except Fri and Tues.
Catering: bar snacks daily, evening meals by arrangement.
Hotels: Angel, Midhurst; Spread Eagle, Midhurst.

D18 Croham Hurst
☎01-657 2075
Croham Rd, South Croydon, Surrey CR2 7HJ.
On A23 half mile from South Croydon station, on road to Selsdon, on right.
Parkland course.
18 holes, 6274 yards, S.S.S.70
Course designed by Hawtree and Sons.
Club founded in 1911.
Visitors: welcome weekdays, telephone Pro 01-657 7705.
Green fees: £14 per day.
Society meetings: welcome Wed, Thurs, Fri.
Catering: full catering except Mon.
Hotels: Selsdon Park; Aerodrome.

D19 Cuddington
☎01-393 0952

Banstead Rd, Banstead, Surrey SM7 1RD.
200 yards from Banstead station.
Parkland course.
18 holes, 6282 yards, S.S.S.70
Course designed by H.S. Colt.
Club founded in 1929.
Visitors: welcome by appointment.
Green fees: £18 per round/day after 12 noon; £14 weekdays.
Society meetings: Thurs only.
Catering: available weekdays by appointment.
Hotels: Driftbridge; Picard Motel.

D20 Dorking
☎Dorking (0306) 886917
Chart Park, Dorking, Surrey RH5 4BX.
A24, 1 mile S of Dorking.
Undulating parkland course.
9 holes, 5120 yards, S.S.S.65
Course designed by James Braid.
Club founded in 1897.
Visitors: welcome weekdays, members only weekends and Bank Holidays, Ladies Day Wed morning.
Green fees: £7.50 weekdays; £4.50 weekends, (visitors with member only); juniors £3.50 weekday, (£2 with member).
Society meetings: by arrangement.
Catering: snacks served weekdays, meals weekends only.
Hotels: Burford Bridge; White Horse; Punch Bowl.

D21 Drift
☎East Horsley (048 65) 4641
The Drift, East Horsley, Surrey KT24 5HD.
Turn off A3 onto B2039 signposted East Horsley, 2 miles.
Woodland course.
18 holes, 6404 yards, S.S.S.71
Club founded in 1975.
Visitors: welcome on weekdays.
Green fees: on application.
Society meetings: welcome week-days.
Catering: bar snacks available every day and evening meals except Mon; lunches available by arrangement.
Hotels: Thatchers, East Horsley.

D22 Effingham
☎Bookham (0372) 52203/4
Guildford Rd, Effingham, Surrey KT24 5PZ.
On A246 8 miles E of Guildford.
Downland course.
18 holes, 6488 yards, S.S.S.71
Course designed by H.S. Colt.
Club founded in 1927.

Visitors: Mon - Fri only by arrangement.
Green fees: £18 per day; £14 after 12 noon.
Society meetings: Wed, Thurs and Fri.
Catering: lunch, tea, evening meal, snacks etc.
Hotels: Thatchers, East Horsley; Preston Cross, Great Bookham.

D23 Effingham Park
☎Copthorne (0342) 716528
West Park Road, Copthorne, Sussex RH10 3EU.
Easy access from M23.
Parkland course.
9 holes, 1749 yards, S.S.S.30
Club founded in 1980.
Visitors: welcome except Sun morning.
Green fees: £4 weekdays; £6 weekends and Bank Holidays.
Society meetings: welcome.
Catering: lunch, snacks, supper.
Hotels: Effingham Park.

D24 Epsom
☎Epsom (037 27) 21666 Sec.
Longdown Lane, Epsom, Surrey KT17 4JR.
0.25 mile N of Epsom Downs station.
Downlands course.
18 holes, 5290 yards, S.S.S.66
Club founded in 1889.
Visitors: welcome on weekdays from 8am, except Tues from 12.30pm, weekends only after 11am.
Green fees: on application.
Society meetings: catered for on Wed and Fri, maximum 32.
Catering: sandwiches, sausage rolls, pasties etc.
Hotels: Drift Bridge.

D25 Farnham
☎Runfold (025 18) 2109
The Sands, Farnham, Surrey GU10 1PX.
1 mile E of Farnham on A31, turning to The Sands signposted.
Parkland/heathland course.
18 holes, 6313 yards, S.S.S.70
Club founded 1896.
Visitors: welcome weekdays with handicap certificate; guests of members only at weekends.
Green fees: £12 per round.
Society meetings: welcome by arrangement weekdays.
Catering: full catering available on request.
Hotels: Hogs Back; Bush; Mitre; Bishops Table.

AFTER THE GOLF YOU CAN STILL HAVE A BALL.

At Selsdon Park you can enjoy a round of golf on our Championship 5854 metre golf course and meet Bill Mitchell the Resident Professional. You can enjoy the free golf clinic every Saturday between 3 pm and 4 pm and find that life still goes with a swing long after you've left the 18th green.

Selsdon Park, just ½ hour from London, welcomes you to an active world of floodlit tennis, croquet, riding* and children's play area. The restaurant offers interesting menus, panoramic views and dancing every Saturday. The exclusive Tropical Leisure Complex features mini gym, sauna, jacuzzi, steam bath, solarium*, swimming and tropical cocktails.

Not to mention 175 rooms with private bathroom and colour TV. And an atmosphere of relaxation that is, at Selsdon Park, par for the course.

*Nominal extra charge

Weekend Demi Pension from £52 per person per day 2/3 nights or enjoy Full Board for a week from only £57 per person per day. (Reduced rates for children).

SELSDON PARK HOTEL

♛ ♛ ♛ ♛ ♛

Sanderstead
South Croydon
Surrey
Tel: 01-657 8811.
Telex: 945003.

The Ultimate Sports and Leisure Hotel.

Goodwood

From the top of Trundle Hill, an impregnable fortress in Roman times, the view takes the breath away. As well as picking out all the coastal landmarks from Worthing to Portsmouth, the inland splendour offers contrast at all points of the compass. It is no wonder that descriptions of the racecourse are always wrapped in superlatives. Although not enjoying quite such an elevated view of things, Goodwood's golfers are seldom unaware of the surroundings in which they play.

Unless the wind is blowing you off your feet or low cloud descends like a veil, Goodwood stimulates. It is true that the course needs a bit of wind to give it necessary bite (which does not?) but one of the game's most priceless assets is to get you away from the rigours of everday life. Goodwood does that in abundant measure.

Some of the holes would win no prizes in a design contest. I believe that applies to all downland courses, which vary alarmingly according to ground and air conditions. A hole that is a drive and pitch one day can be two woods the next, but a change in Goodwood's character is not entirely dependent on the elements. Four holes, the 3rd to the 6th, in the valley in the lee of Trundle Hill, offer a more sheltered interlude and there is some surprise when the visitor finds himself grappling with a treelined finish for the last two holes on the other side of the road.

Coming from Chichester, it is possible to drive past the clubhouse without knowing that it is a clubhouse and there is a longish walk to the first tee. Coming from the direction of Havant, on the other hand, bunkers and guide posts can be spotted a long way off. The 1st is a reasonably gentle opener, a par 5 within the scope of most, although to get home in two the drive has to be well placed and the second shot bold enough to skirt the corner of the wood which forms the dogleg. The 2nd offers an inviting drive but then comes the first variation. Downhill short holes are always appealing and the 3rd introduces us to a loop in which positional play is all important.

The left is the side to be on the 4th and 5th from the tee, the 6th offering a definite chance of a birdie. This is just as well because the climb up to the 7th reveals the hardest par 4 on the course at 470 yards with a wind against more often than not.

A pleasant second shot to a well guarded green at the 9th brings us back to the vicinity of the clubhouse and then it is about turn down the 10th where two large bunkers dominate the drive. There is a chance to survey the scene from the 11th tee but it is too exciting a hole to be distracted for long. A par 5 with a downhill drive and an uphill second is the herald to three holes round an attractive wood.

The wood flanks the second part of the 11th and the short 12th which provides a demanding target but it is even more a peril at the 319-yard 13th, the drive having to be threaded between the trees on the right and the threat of out of bounds on the left. There is a real pastoral flavour about this part of the course which continues with the stronger players flexing their muscles to get home in two at the par 5 14th — if wary of the dew pond awaiting a pushed second.

The 15th, a longish 4, follows the opposite direction to the 11th and is a splendid foil to the 16th, a short par 4 like the 6th. A small glade of pines on the left of the green is the main feature but there is nothing to suggest what follows on the other side of the road. There is a definite enclosed look about the 17th and several ways of straying from the straight and narrow. The rough is fiercer than anywhere else and the trees are old and well established.

Pheasant calls may soften the pain of failing to match par on the last of the 5s but Goodwood is one of those courses ending with a short hole and there is the added lure of the welcome of the clubhouse built in characteristic Sussex flint.

D26 **Farnham Park**
☎Farnham (0252) 715216
Folly Hill, Farnham, Surrey.
0.75 mile N of Farnham, next to
Castle in Farnham park.
Par 3 parkland course.
9 holes, 1161 yards, S.S.S.54
Course designed by Henry Cotton.
Club founded in 1963.
Visitors: welcome at all times.
Green fees: £1.65 adult weekdays;
£1.90 weekends; £1.20 junior
weekdays; £1.20 weekends.
Society meetings: none.
Catering: light snacks only.
Hotels: The Bush, Farnham.

D27 **Foxhills**
☎Ottershaw (093 287) 2050
Stonehill Rd, Ottershaw, Surrey
KT16 0EL.
Off A320 at Otter Public House, turn
right and right again into Foxhills Rd.
Heathland courses.
Chertsey 18 holes, 6658 yards,
S.S.S.71
Longcross 18 holes, 6406 yards,
S.S.S.71
Course designed by F. Hawtree.
Club founded in 1973.
Visitors: welcome with member
Monday to Friday.
Green fees: £16 per round; £23 per
day.
Society meetings: only by
appointment.
Catering: two restaurants plus bars.
Hotels: Seven Hills Motel; Great
Fosters.

D28 **Gatton Manor**
☎Oakwood Hill (030 679) 555
Ockley, Dorking, Surrey RH5 5PQ.
A29 1.5 miles SW of Ockley.
Undulating parkland course.
18 holes, 6145-6902 yards,
S.S.S.69-73.
Course designed by D.B. & D.G.

Heath.
Club founded in 1969.
Visitors: welcome except Sun
mornings.
Green fees: on application.
Society meetings: catered for on
weekdays.
Catering: meals and snacks served.
Hotels: Gatton Manor.

D29 **Goodwood**
☎Chichester (0243) 774968
Goodwood, Chichester, West
Sussex PO18 0PN.
On A286 5 miles N of Chichester.
Downland/parkland course.
18 holes, 6318 yards, S.S.S.70.
Course designed by James Braid.
Club founded in 1891.
Visitors: not before 10am weekends
and public holidays. Book in at Pro
shop.
Green fees: £12 weekdays; £15
weekends.
Society meetings: Wed, Thur, Fri.
Essential to book early.
Catering: full catering by booking,
except Mon.
Hotels: Goodwood Park; Chichester
Lodge Motel; Dolphin & Anchor.

D30 **Guildford**
☎Guildford (0483) 63941
High Path Rd, Merrow, Guildford,
Surrey GU1 2HI.
2 miles E of Guildford on A246.
Downland course.
18 holes, 6080 yards, S.S.S.70
Course designed by James Braid.
Club founded in 1886.
Visitors: welcome on weekdays;
weekends with member only.
Green fees: on application.
Society meetings: welcome by
arrangement.
Catering: bar snacks, restaurant by
arrangement.
Hotels: Angel; White Horse,

Guildford; Cleverdale, Epsom.

D31 **Ham Manor**
☎Rustington (0903) 783288
Angmering, W Sussex BN16 4JE.
3 miles E of Littlehampton.
Gently undulating parkland course.
18 holes, 6216 yards, S.S.S.70
Course designed by H.S. Colt.
Club founded in 1936.
Visitors: welcome after 8.45 am by
prior arrangement.
Green fees: £12 weekdays; £16
weekend.
Society meetings: by arrangement.
Catering: lunch except Mon.
Hotels: The Beach, Littlehampton.

D32 **Hankley Common**
☎Frensham (025 125) 2493
Tilford Rd, Tilford, Farnham, Surrey
GU10 2DD.
4 miles SE of Farnham, take road to
Hindhead over railway crossing, fork
right to Tilford.
Heathland course.
18 holes, 6403 yards, S.S.S.71
Course designed by James Braid.
Club founded in 1895.
Visitors: welcome on weekdays and
by arrangement with Sec at
weekends and Bank holidays; must
have a bona fide handicap and be
member of recognised golf club.
Green fees: £16 weekdays; £20
weekends and Bank Holidays;
reductions after 2pm.
Society meetings: on Tues and
Wed.
Catering: always available.
Hotels: Frensham Pond, Frensham;
Pride of the Valley, Churt; The Bush,
Farnham.

D33 **Haywards Heath**
☎Haywards Heath (0444) 414457
High Beech Lane, Haywards Heath,
W. Sussex RG16 1SL.

N of Haywards Heath, Nr Lindfield.
Parkland course.
18 holes, 6206 yards, S.S.S.70.
Club founded in 1922.
Visitors: welcome except
competition days subject to tee
reservations.
Green fees: £11 per day weekdays;
£15 per day weekends and Bank
Holidays; subject to review.
Society meetings: Wed and Thurs
only.
Catering: lunch available, evening
catering by arrangement.
Hotels: Hilton Park; Birch.

D34 Hill Barn
☎Worthing (0903) 37301
Hill Barn Lane, Worthing, Sussex
BN14 9QE.
N of Worthing off Upper Brighton
road to Excess roundabout.
Downland municipal course.
18 holes, 6224 yards, S.S.S.70
Course designed by Hawtree and
Son.
Club founded in 1935.
Visitors: welcome weekdays and
afternoons on weekends.
Green fees: £6 weekdays; £7
weekends.
Society meetings: bookings for 20
or more.
Catering: breakfasts, snacks, hot
meals available all day.
Hotels: Beach Wood; Ardington.

D35 Hindhead
☎Hindhead (042 873) 4614
Churt Rd, Hindhead, Surrey
GU26 6HX.
1.5 miles N of Hindhead on A287.
Heathland Course.
18 holes, 6349 yards, S.S.S.70
Club founded in 1904
Visitors: welcome weekdays,
weekends by appointment.
Green fees: £15 weekdays, (£7 with
member); £20 weekends, (£10 with
member).
Society meetings: Wed and Thurs
only.
Catering: lunch and teas daily.
Dinners for Societies only.
Hotels: Devil's Punch Bowl,
Hindhead; Pride of the Valley, Churt.

D36 Hoebridge
☎Woking (048 62) 22611
Old Woking Rd, Old Woking, Surrey
GU22 8JH.
On B382 Old Woking road between
Old Woking and West Byfleet.
Meadowland course.
Main-18 holes, 6587 yards, S.S.S.71

Par 3-18 holes, 2296 yards.
Course designed by John Jacobs.
Club founded in 1982.
Visitors: welcome any time. Must
book at weekends.
Green fees: £5.80 per round Main;
£3.45 per round Par 3.
Society meetings: not at weekends.
Catering: 8-10am breakfast; 12-
2.30pm lunch; 7-9.30pm dinner.
Hotels: Northfleet, Woking.

D37 Home Park
☎01-977 2423
Hampton Wick, Richmond-upon-
Thames, Surrey KT1 4AS.
From Kingston over Kingston Bridge,
at roundabout turn left, 50 yards on
left through iron gates at Old Kings
Heath Public House, straight road to
club.
Parkland course.
18 holes, 6519 yards, S.S.S.71
Club founded in 1895.
Visitors: welcome.
Green fees: £8/£12 weekdays, (£5/
£4 with member); £12/£22
weekends, (£4/£16 with member).
Society meetings: weekdays only.
Catering: lunch served.
Hotels: Lion Gate.

D38 Ifield G and CC
☎Crawley (0293) 20222 Sec,
23088 Pro.
Rusper Rd, Ifield, Crawley,
W. Sussex RH11 0LW.
M23, Crawley junction. Follow signs
to Brighton and A23. After 3 round-
abouts take R turning. L into Ifield
Drive, 2nd R after shops. 1st L into
Rusper Rd 0.5 mile then signposted.
Parkland course.
18 holes, 6289 yards, S.S.S. 70
Club founded in 1927.
Visitors: welcome weekdays only, or
with member at weekends.
Green fees: £12 per round, £15 per
day weekdays.
Society meetings: welcome
weekdays only,
by arrangement.
Catering: full facilities available all
week.
Hotels: numerous in area.

D39 Kingswood (Surrey)
☎Mogador (0737) 832188
Sandy Lane, Kingswood,
Surrey KT20 6NE.
4 miles S of Sutton on A217.
Parkland course.
18 holes, 6821 yards, S.S.S.73
Course designed by James Braid.
Club founded in 1928.

Visitors: welcome when space
available.
Green fees: £15 per day weekdays;
£25 per round weekends.
Society meetings: welcome
weekdays.
Catering: full restaurant facilities
including à la carte menu.
Hotels: Bridge, Reigate; Piccard
Motel, Banstead.

D40 Laleham
☎Chertsey (093 28) 64211
Laleham Reach, Chertsey, Surrey
KT16 8RP.
A320 between Staines and Chertsey,
opposite Thorpe Water Park.
Meadowland course.
18 holes, 6203 yards, S.S.S.70
Club founded in 1907.
Visitors: welcome weekdays only.
Green fees: £10.50 per day; £8.50
per round (to be revised).
Society meetings: Mon, Tues, Wed
only. To play in 3 or 4 balls.
Catering: full.
Hotels: Runnymede, Egham.

D41 Leatherhead
☎Oxshott (037 284) 3966
Kingston Rd, Leatherhead, Surrey
KT22 0DP.
Off M25 Leatherhead Interchange.
Parkland course.
18 holes, 6060 yards, S.S.S.69
Course designed by S McMillian
Club founded in 1901.
Visitors: welcome.
Green fees: £15.
Society meetings: welcome if
vacancy, not weekends.
Catering: full restaurant facilities.
Hotels: Proston Cross.

D42 Limpsfield Chart
☎Limpsfield Chart (088 388) 2106
Limpsfield, Oxted, Surrey RH8 0SL.
On A25 between Oxted and
Westerham. E of Oxted over traffic
lights 300 yards on right.
Parkland course.
9 holes, 5718 yards, S.S.S.68
Club founded in 1889.
Visitors: welcome Mon, Tues, Wed
and Fri.
Green fees: on application.
Society meetings: can be arranged.
Catering: meals served.
Hotels: Kings Arms, Westerham;
White Hart, Brasted.

D43 Littlehampton
☎Littlehampton (0903) 717170
170 Rope Walk, Riverside,
Littlehampton, W Sussex BN17 5DL.

From Littlehampton take the road to Bognor Regis. After crossing the bridge over the river take the first turn to the left, marked To Golf Club. Links and Meadowland course.
18 holes, 6244 yards, S.S.S.70.
Club founded in 1889.
Visitors: welcome 7 days.
Green fees: £12 weekdays; £15 weekends.
Society meeting: Tues and Wed.
Catering: full catering facilities daily.
Hotels: Beach, Littlehampton.

D44 Malden
☎01-942 0654
Traps Lane, New Malden, Surrey KT3 4RS.
0.5 mile from New Malden railway station, close to A3 between Wimbledon and Kingston.
Parkland course.
18 holes, 6201 yards, S.S.S.70
Club founded in 1926.
Visitors: weekdays - unrestricted; weekends - restricted.
Green fees: £15 weekdays; £19 weekends.
Society meetings: Wed, Thurs, Fri.
Catering: Wed, Thurs, Fri, Sat, Sun.
Hotels: numerous good hotels in area.

D45 Mannings Heath
☎Horsham (0403) 210228 Sec, 210168 Club.
Goldings Lane, Mannings Heath, W Sussex RH13 6JU.
3 miles SE of Horsham on A281. 4 miles from M25, exit at Pease Pottage or Handcross.
Undulating parkland course.
18 holes, 6404 yards, S.S.S.71
Club founded in 1908
Visitors: welcome weekdays with handicap certificate and preferably by prior arrangement.

Green fees: £12 weekdays.
Society meetings: catered for Tues, Wed, Fri.
Catering: lunch and dinner by prior arrangement, not Monday.

D46 Mitcham
☎01-648 1508
Carshalton Rd, Mitcham Junction, Surrey CR4 4HN
A237 off A23, by Mitcham Junction station.
Meadowland course.
18 holes, 5935 yards, S.S.S.68
Club founded in 1886.
Visitors: weekdays, restrictions on weekends.
Green fees: on application.
Society meetings: Tues and Thurs only.
Catering: full facilities.
Hotels: numerous hotels in area.

D47 Moore Place (Esher)
☎Esher (0372) 63533
Portsmouth Rd, Esher, Surrey KT10 9LN.
On A3 Portsmouth road, 0.5 mile from centre of Esher towards Cobham.
Undulating parkland public course.
9 holes, 3512 yards, S.S.S.58 (18 holes)
Course designed by H. Vardon.
Club reformed in 1977.
Visitors: welcome.
Green fees: £2.50 weekdays; £3.50 weekends.
Society meetings: telephone for information.
Catering: lunch and evening meals available.
Hotels: Ladbrokes Seven Hills.

D48 New Zealand G C
☎West Byfleet (09323) 45049, 42891 Sec, 49619 Pro.

Woodham Lane, Woodham, Weybridge, Surrey KT15 3QD.
A3, join A245 at Cobham and follow road past West Byfleet. Course on R. Parkland course.
18 holes, 6012 yards, S.S.S.69
Course designed by Muir-Fergusson.
Club founded in 1895.
Visitors: welcome, weekdays only. Please book.
Green fees: £19 per round, £23 per day, weekdays only.
Society meetings: weekdays only, by arrangement.
Catering: Restaurant or bar snacks by arrangement. 5-course lunch for societies available.
Hotels: numerous in area.

D49 North Downs
☎Woldingham (088 385) 2057/3298/3004
Northdown Rd, Woldingham, Caterham, Surrey CR3 7AA.
Woldingham road at roundabout on A22 at N end of Caterham by-pass.
Undulating course.
18 holes 5787 yards, S.S.S.68
Club founded in 1899.
Visitors: welcome weekdays.
Green fees: on application.
Society meetings: catered for weekdays.
Catering: bar lunch by arrangement except Mon.
Hotels: numerous hotels in area.

D50 Oaks Sport Centre
☎01-643 8363
Woodmansterne Rd, Carshalton, Surrey, SM5 4AN.
On the B2032 past Carshalton Beeches Station, Oak Sports Centre signposted N of A2022, halfway between A217 and A237.
Meadowland course.
18 holes, 5975 yards, S.S.S.68

9 holes, 1590 yards, S.S.S.29
Course designed by Alphagreen
Limited.
Club founded in 1972.
Visitors: welcome.
Green fees: £4.15 (18 holes) week-
days; £5.25 weekends; £1.75
(9 hole) weekdays; £2.30 weekends.
Society meetings: by arrangement.
Catering: refreshments all day,
public bar open normal pub hours.
Hotels: Greyhound; Carshalton.

D51 **Purley Downs**
☎01-657 8347 Sec, 657 1231
Steward.
106 Purley Downs Rd, Purley,
Surrey CR2 0RB.
Off A233 between Purley and
Croydon stations, past Volkswagen
Building and first left.
Downland course.
18 holes, 6243 yards, S.S.S.70
Club founded in 1894.
Visitors: Mon, Tues, Fri, must have
recognised handicap and be a
member of a golf club by arrange-
ment with Sec/Manager.
Green fees: £13.50.
Society meetings: Mon, Thurs, Fri
only.
Catering: bar snacks, lunch, tea,
evening 20 or more persons.
Hotels: numerous good hotels in
area.

D52 **Puttenham**
☎Guildford (0483) 8104898
Heath Rd, Puttenham, Guildford,
Surrey GU13 1AL.
Just off A31, Farnham to Guildford
road (Hogs Back), 4 miles W of
Guildford.
Heathland course.
18 holes, 5300 yards, S.S.S. 66
Club founded in 1894.
Visitors: welcome weekdays only;
accomplished players only.
Green fees: £15 per day.
Society meetings: Wed, Thurs only.
Catering: full facilities available.
Hotels: Hogs Back.

D53 **Redhill & Reigate**
☎Reigate (0737) 244626
Clarence Lodge, Pendleton Rd,
Redhill, Surrey RH1 6LB.
1 mile S of Reigate (A217), at traffic
lights turn left (A2044), after 0.25
mile, turn left into Pendleton Rd.
Moorland course.
18 holes, 5261 yards, S.S.S.66
Course designed by James Braid.
Club founded in 1887.

Visitors: welcome Mon-Fri; Sat after
11am; not Sun.
Green fees: £5 weekdays; £9
weekends.
Society meetings: Wed and Thurs
only.
Catering: only by advance booking.
Hotels: Mill House, Brighton Rd,
Salford.

D54 **Reigate Heath**
☎Reigate (0737) 242610
Reigate Heath, Reigate RH2 8QR.
0.5 mile S of A25 to W of Reigate.
Heathland course.
9 holes, 5554 yards, S.S.S.67
Club founded in 1895.
Visitors: welcome weekdays, but
telephone first.
Green fees: on application.
Society meetings: Wed and Thurs.
Catering: full catering facilities
except Mon.
Hotels: Reigate Manor; Cranleigh.

D55 **Richmond**
☎01-940 4351/940 1463
Sudbrook Park, Richmond, Surrey
TW10 7AS.
On A307 1 mile S of Richmond, look
for Sudbrook Lane on left.
Parkland course.
18 holes, 5965 yards, S.S.S.69
Club founded in 1891.
Visitors: welcome on weekdays and
at weekends by prior arrangement.
Green fees: on application.
Society meetings: welcome Tues
and Thurs from mid-March until late
Oct.
Catering: bar snacks available every
day; lunches must be ordered before
10am.
Hotels: Petersham; Richmond Gate.

D56 **RAC CC**
☎Ashted (037 22) 763111
Woodcote Park, Epsom, Surrey
KT18 7EW.
A24, 1.75 miles from Epsom.
Parkland courses.
Coronation-18 holes, 5520 yards,
S.S.S.67
Old-18 holes, 6672 yards, S.S.S.72
Club founded in 1913.
Visitors: no.
Green fees: on request.
Society meetings: on request.
Catering: full services available.
Hotels: Chalk Lane, Epsom, Surrey.

D57 **Royal Mid-Surrey**
☎01-940 1894
Old Deer Park, Richmond, Surrey

TW9 2SB.
250 yards from Richmond
roundabout on A316, entrance by
Richmond Athletic Ground.
Parkland courses.
Inner-18 holes, 5544 yards, S.S.S.67
Outer-18 holes, 6052 yards,
S.S.S.70
Course designed by J.H. Taylor.
Club founded in 1892.
Visitors: weekdays with letter of
introduction from own Club,
membership or handicap certificate,
or playing with member. Weekends
and Bank Holidays with prior
approval.
Green fees: £15 per round week-
days; £20 weekends.
Society meetings: recognised
societies welcome if previously
arranged with Sec.
Catering: lunch served except Mon,
snack lunch served every day.
Hotels: Richmond Hill; Richmond
Gate; Quinn's.

D58 **St George's Hill**
☎Weybridge (0932) 842406
St George's Hill, Weybridge, Surrey
KT13 0NL.
B374 from station towards Cobham,
0.5 mile on left.
Heathland course.
18 holes, 3305 yards, S.S.S.72
Course designed by H.S. Colt.
Club founded in 1913.
Visitors: welcome but must book tee
time in advance.
Green fees: on application.
Society meetings: catered for Wed-
Fri.
Catering: full restaurant lunch and
bar snacks served.
Hotels: numerous good hotels in
area.

D59 **Sandown Park**
☎Esher (0372) 65921 or 63340
Moor Lane, Esher, Surrey
KT10 8AN.
About 1 mile from Esher station, in
centre of Sandown Park racecourse,
off Portsmouth road.
Parkland course.
9 holes, 5656 yards, S.S.S.67
Course designed by John Jacobs
and Harold Bowpitt.
Club founded in 1972.
Visitors: welcome at any time.
Green fees: £3.30 weekends; £2.70
weekdays.
Society meetings: by arrangement
contact General Manager.
Catering: lunch daily, dinner by

arrangement.
Hotels: Seven Hills, Cobham.

D60 Selsdon Park Hotel
☎01-657 8811
Sanderstead, S Croydon, Surrey
CR2 8YA.
B275 from Croydon, B268 at
Selsdon.
Parkland course.
18 holes, 6402 yards, S.S.S.71
Course designed by J.H. Taylor.
Club founded in 1930.
Visitors: welcome, contact Pro at
first tee.
Green fees: £12.50 per round, £17
per day weekdays; £17.50 per round,
£12.50 after 4pm Sat; £20 per round,
£15 after 4pm Sun.
Society meetings: welcome by prior
arrangement.
Catering: full service available.
Hotels: Selsdon Park.

D61 Selsey
☎Selsey (0243) 602203
Golf Links Lane, Selsey, Chichester,
W Sussex PO20 9DR.
On B2145, 7 miles S of Chichester.
Seaside course.
9 holes, 5730 yards, S.S.S.67
Club founded in 1909.
Visitors: welcome if members of
recognised club.
Green fees: £6 per round weekdays;
£7.50 per round weekends, Bank
Holidays. No play Sun morning.
Society meetings: small societies
welcome.
Catering: lunch and snacks served.

D62 Shillinglee Park
☎Haslemere (0428) 53237
Chiddingfold, Goldalming, Surrey
GU8 4TA.
Off A283, 2 miles S of Chiddingfold.
Undulating parkland course.
9 holes, 2500 yards, S.S.S.63.
Course designed by Roger Mace.
Club founded in 1980.
Visitors: welcome, advisable to
book. Phone bookings accepted.
Green fees: Adults £3.75 (9 holes),
£6.50 per day; Juniors/O.A.P. £2.75
(9 holes), £4.50 per day.
Society meetings: welcome.
Catering: Sun breakfast, lunch.
Tues to Sat full à la carte or bar food,
lunch and dinner.
Hotels: Lythe Hill; Crown Inn.

D63 Shirley Park
☎01-654 1143
194 Addiscombe Rd, Croydon

CR0 7LB.
1 mile from E Croydon station.
Parkland course.
18 holes, 6210 yards, S.S.S.70
Club founded in 1914.
Visitors: welcome Mon-Fri without
reservation.
Green fees: £15 per day/round.
Society meetings: catered for daily
except Wed, weekends and public
holidays.
Catering: lunch and tea daily.
Hotels: Croydon Court; Holiday Inn.

D64 Silvermere
☎Cobham (0932) 67275
Redhill Rd, Cobham, Surrey,
KT11 1EF.
At Junction 10 of M25 and A3 take
B366 to Byfleet. Silvermere is 0.5
mile on right.
Woodland/parkland/meadowland
course.
18 holes, 633 yards, S.S.S.71
Club founded in 1976.
Visitors: welcome, book seven days
in advance. Members only am Sat
and Sun.
Green fees: £6 weekdays; £8.50
weekends.
Society meetings: weekdays only,
£21.95 full day including dinner.
Catering: full catering facilities
from 8am.
Hotels: Ladbrokes Seven Hill.

D65 Surbiton
☎01-398 3101
Woodstock Lane, Chessington,
Surrey KT9 1UG.
2 miles E of Esher, off A3 at Ace of
Spades roundabout.
Parkland course.
18 holes, 6211 yards, S.S.S.70
Club founded in 1896.
Visitors: welcome with reservation.
Green fees: £15 per person.
Society meetings: catered for.
Catering: full catering facilities.
Hotels: Haven, Portsmouth Rd,
Esher.

D66 Tandridge
☎Oxted (088 33) 2274
Oxted, Surrey RH8 9NQ.
Off A25 by Oxted, 2 miles E of
Godstone. Junction 6 from M25.
Parkland course.
18 holes, 6260 yards, S.S.S.70
Club founded in 1923.
Visitors: welcome on Mon, Wed and
Thurs only unless with member.
Green fees: on application.
Society meetings: catered for on

Mon, Wed and Thurs.
Catering: lunch every day except
Tues.
Hotels: Hoskins Arms, Oxted.

D67 Thames Ditton & Esher
☎01-398 1551
Scilly Isles, Portsmouth Rd, Esher,
Surrey.
Off A3 by Scilly Isles roundabout.
(0.25 mile from Sandown Park Race
Course).
Parkland course.
9 holes, 5606 yards, S.S.S:65
Club founded in 1892
Visitors: welcome 6 days; Sun after
1pm.
Green fees: £5.50 weekdays; £7
weekends and Bank Holidays.
Society meetings: maximum 32
booked with Sec.
Catering: cold lunch, hot snacks,
buffet for societies.
Hotels: Haven, Hinchley Wood.

D68 Tilgate Forest GC
☎Crawley (0293) 30103
Titmus Drive, Tilgate, Crawley
W Sussex.
M23, junction Pease Pottage, follow
main road to Crawley, at 1st
roundabout turn R, follow sign to
Club.
Parkland Course.
18 holes, 6359 yards, S.S.S.70
Course designed by Huggett and
Coles.
Club founded in 1983.
Visitors: welcome.
Green fees: £5.35 per round, £10.20
per day weekdays; £8 per round/day,
weekends.
Society meetings: welcome, not
weekends.
Catering: restaurant, bar and snacks
available.
Hotels: numerous in area.

D69 Tyrrells Wood
☎Leatherhead (0372) 376025
Tyrrells Wood, Leatherhead, Surrey
KT22 8QP.
Turn off Leatherhead by-pass at sign
to Tyrrells Wood, after 1.25 miles
turn right, Club house is 0.75 miles
on right.
Undulating parkland course.
18 holes, 6219 yards, S.S.S.70
Course designed by James Braid.
Club founded in 1922.
Visitors: welcome by appointment.
Green fees: £15 weekdays; £20
weekends limited.
Society meetings: limited Wed,

West Hill

For cricketers, mention of the three Ws conjures up memories of the great West Indians, Frank Worrell, Everton Weekes and Clyde Walcott. Down in Surrey, however, golfers recognise the three Ws as West Hill, Woking and Worplesdon.

They are an attractive trinity of courses where, if a few large houses and trees didn't block the way, it would be perfectly possible to play from one to the other two with a few stout strokes.

An enviable fixture list at Cambridge took me to all three in early spring for three years in a row and great fun it was. Later, there came participation in the mixed foursomes at Worplesdon and the Alba Trophy at Woking but I had known West Hill from the days when my brother and I took turns to partner my father in the Fathers and Sons, a tournament whose popularity is as strong as ever.

Coming from a course where there was a little more latitude from the tee, West Hill always seemed alarmingly narrow, particularly as, in common with most of Surrey's best courses, the fairways are lined with trees and heather. Young golfers have to learn the hard way that discretion is the better part of long hitting valour.

Control is the first requirement but the thing which has always impressed me about West Hill is the architectural balance it displays. You are as likely to use all fourteen clubs in your bag as anywhere; and there is a definite emphasis on positional play.

This may have something to do with the fact that the club was founded by a woman, Mrs Geoffrey Lubbock. Anyone bold enough to have done such a thing because they were unable to find anywhere to play on a Sunday around the turn of the century may well have insisted that the design bore the ladies primarily in mind. On the other hand, I would give credit to Willie Park, architect of Sunningdale's Old course a few years earlier, and Jack White, Sunningdale's first professional, for doing no more than good architects should.

Anyway, they certainly proved they meant business straightaway, a broad ditch adding devilment to the second shot to the 1st and running on to broaden out and do much the same at the par 5 3rd with its drive over a heathery ridge alongside the busy railway line to Bournemouth.

The 2nd, parallel to the 1st, is the first of many admirably testing par 4s and the 4th the first of five short holes which vary both in length and direction. The 5th and 6th involve drives up long slopes but two of my favourite holes are the 8th and 10th, the 8th with the ideal drive down the left and the 10th where the temptation to play away from the out of bounds on the left is easily and frequently overdone.

At the 11th, both drive and second shot have to carry thick belts of heather although the 12th, in spite of the tricky contouring of its green, offers the chance of a birdie. Contrast to the short 13th is found at the 15th, one of the best examples of long short holes, but it is all part of what amounts to a stern finish.

Ability to shape the drive is an advantage at the 14th; two good shots are needed at the 16th and there are all sorts of ways of turning a five into a six at the 17th. Then, finally, the 18th has out of bounds awaiting a hook, heather and scrub to the right and a large bunker to be surmounted before reaching the green in front of the clubhouse.

It is reached not without relief but with the feeling that all worthwhile achievement involves a mixture of risk and judgement plus the urge, for those whose achievement was modest or whose judgement was poor, to try again.

Thurs, Fri only.
Catering: for members and green fees.
Hotels: Burford Bridge, Dorking.

D70 **Walton Heath**
☎Tadworth (073 781) 2380
Tadworth, Surrey KT20 7TP.
Leave M25 at Exit 8, follow A217 towards London, turn left onto B2032, turning for golf club about 1 mile on right.
Heathland course.
Old-18 holes, 6813 yards, S.S.S.73
New-18 holes, 6659 yards, S.S.S.72
Course designed by Herbert Fowler.
Club founded in 1904.
Visitors: welcome weekday with letter of introduction. Weekends with members only.
Green fees: £22.50; £16.25 after 11.30am.
Society meetings: by arrangement.
Catering: full restaurant facilities.
Hotels: Copthorne; Burford Bridge.

D71 **Wentworth**
☎Wentworth (099 04) 2201
Virginia Water, Surrey GU25 4LS.
On the A30 between Egham and Sunningdale.
West 18 holes, 6945 yards, S.S.S.74
East 18 holes, 6176 yards, S.S.S.70
9 holes, 1731 yards, S.S.S.30
Course designed by H.S. Colt.
Club founded in 1924.
Visitors: weekdays only with prior booking.
Green fees: £37.
Society meetings: Tues-Thurs each week.
Catering: lunch only.
Hotels: Royal Berkshire, Runnymede.

D72 **West Byfleet**
☎Byfleet (093 23) 45230,

43433 Sec.
Sheerwater Rd, West Byfleet, Surrey KT14 6AA.
On A245 about 0.75 miles W of West Byfleet.
Heathland/parkland course.
18 holes, 6211 yards, S.S.S.70
Course designed by Cuthbert Butchart.
Club founded in 1904.
Visitors: welcome weekdays only.
Green fees: on application.
Society meetings: by arrangement on Tues and Wed only.
Catering: snacks, lunch and tea served. Evening meals by arrangement. Lunch only on Sun.
Hotels: Seven Hills; Wheatsheaf.

D73 **West Hill**
☎Brookwood (048 67) 4365
Bagshot Rd, Brookwood, Surrey GU22 0BH.
On A322 which connects Guildford to Bagshot, club entrance next to railway bridge at Brookwood.
Moorland course.
18 holes, 6353 yards, S.S.S.70
Course designed by Willie Park and Jack White.
Club founded in 1909.
Visitors: Mon-Fri only.
Green fees: £12.50 per round; £19 per day weekdays.
Society meetings: Mon-Fri by application to Sec.
Catering: full facilities available.
Hotels: Worplesdon Place, Worplesdon; Northfleet, Woking.

D74 **West Surrey**
☎Godalming (048 68) 21275
Enton Green, Godalming GU8 5AG.
1.5 miles from Milford traffic lights on A2, 0.5 mile from Milford station.
Parkland course.
18 holes, 6247 yards, S.S.S.70

Course designed by Herbert Fowler.
Club founded in 1909.
Visitors: welcome preferably by arrangement to avoid reservations or restrictions (including weekends).
Collar and tie in dining room.
Green fees: £16 all day (2 rounds) weekdays; £20 (1 or 2 rounds) weekends and Bank Holidays.
After 12am winter or 1pm summer (1 round) £11.
Society meetings: normally Wed (pm) Thurs and Fri by arrangement.
Catering: full restaurant facilities available by arrangement.
Hotels: Inn on the Lake; Pride of the Valley.

D75 **West Sussex**
☎Pulborough (079 82) 2563
Pulborough, W Sussex RH20 2EN.
1.5 miles E of Pulborough on A283.
Heathland course.
18 holes, 6156 yards, S.S.S.70
Course designed by Col. S.K.Hotchkin, Guy Campbell and Cecil Hutchison.
Club founded in 1931.
Visitors: welcome with letter of introduction and handicap certificate.
Tues members only.
Green fees: on application.
Society meetings: Wed and Thurs.
Catering: lunch and tea.
Hotels: Abingworth Hall; The Roundabout.

D76 **Windlemere**
☎Chobham (099 05) 8727
Windlesham Rd, West End, Woking, Surrey GU24 9QL.
Take A322 from Bagshot towards Guildford. Turn left on A319 towards Chobham. Course is on left opposite the Gordon Boys' School.
Gently undulating parkland course.
9 holes, 2673 yards, S.S.S.33.

Course designed by Clive D. Smith. Club founded in 1978.
Visitors: open to public upon payment of green fees.
Green fees: (18 holes) £5.30 weekdays; £6.50 weekends and Bank Holidays; (9 holes) £3 weekdays, £3.70 weekends.
Society meetings: as arranged with Pro at Club.
Catering: bar snacks always available.
Hotels: are to be found in the neighbouring towns of Woking (5 miles), Ascot (5 miles), Bracknell (8 miles), Camberley (4 miles).

D77 **Woking**
☎Woking (048 62) 60053
Pond Rd, Hook Heath, Woking, Surrey GU22 0JZ.
Just S of first road bridge over railway, W of Woking station (Woking-Brookwood line), take Hollybank Rd. Then immediately right into Golf Club Rd and right at end to clubhouse. Avoid Woking town centre.
Heathland course.
18 holes, 6322 yards, S.S.S.70.
Course designed by Tom Dunn.
Club founded in 1893.
Visitors: book in advance. Not weekends and public holidays.
Green fees: £12.50 per round; £20

per day weekdays.
Society meetings: booked in advance.
Catering: lunch available everyday if ordered in advance.
Hotels: Myford Manor; Glen House.

D78 **Woodcote Park**
☎01-668 2788
Meadow Hill, Bridle Way, Coulsdon, Surrey CR3 2QQ.
Situated at the far end of Meadow Hill, which is off Smitham Bottom Lane, Purley, main road from Wallington to Coulsdon. A23 (nearest A Road).
Slightly undulating parkland course.
18 holes, 6624 yards, S.S.S.71
Club founded in 1912.
Visitors: welcome on weekdays.
Green fees: £12.
Society meetings: Mon, Wed, Thurs.
Catering: bar snacks daily.
Hotels: The Aerodrome, Croydon.

D79 **Worplesdon**
☎Brookwood (048 67) 2277 Sec
Heath House Rd, Woking, Surrey GU22 0RA.
Leave Guildford on A322 to Bagshot, after 4 miles turn right into Heath House Rd.
Heathland course.
18 holes, 6422 yards, S.S.S.71

Course designed by J.F. Abercromby.
Club founded in 1908.
Visitors: welcome with introduction from Club Sec, weekdays only.
Green fees: £14 per round; £20 per day.
Society meetings: Mon, Wed, Thurs, Fri.
Catering: lunch served except Tues.
Hotels: Worplesdon Place.

D80 **Worthing**
☎Worthing (0903) 60801
Links Rd, Worthing, W Sussex BN14 9QZ.
At top of hill on A27 0.25 mile E of Offington roundabout at junction with A24 London road.
Downland course.
Lower-18 holes, 6477 yards, S.S.S.71
Upper-18 holes, 5243 yards, S.S.S.66.
Course designed by H.S. Colt.
Club founded in 1906.
Visitors: welcome on weekdays.
Green fees: on application.
Society meetings: catered for on weekdays except Tues.
Catering: lunch served except Mon when only snacks available.
Hotels: Chatsworth; Findon Manor.

E Kent and East Sussex

Kent and East Sussex combine just about the full range of courses to be found in this country. There are the seaside championship links of Rye, Littlestone, Deal, Sandwich and Princes. Fine examples of parkland golf are provided by Knole Park, Wildernesse and Sundridge Park. Crowborough Beacon and Seaford extol the virtues of golf on the Downs. Royal Ashdown is part moorland, part downland and part heathery heath while Pyecombe and Piltdown, also a bit of a mixture, epitomise the glories of the type of clubs and courses found only in Britain.

On the subject of Rye, my pen is always liable to run away with me and has done often enough in the past not to warrant a repeat. Maybe, at times, it has been at the expense of Littlestone which is good enough to test the best but better known as an ideal holiday course. The finish is particularly good and there is a joyous feeling of escape that so many golfers prize. This becomes increasingly apparent from whichever direction Littlestone is approached. It wouldn't be stretching a point too far, in fact, to say Littlestone is the type of course that makes it the town's main attraction.

Taking the winding coast road from Rye, the county boundary is crossed; but, before straying too far into Kent, a word for the Brighton courses, notably the Dyke, for Cooden Beach and Seaford from whose elevated perch it is possible to enjoy some glorious views. Beachy Head is one landmark although that is along the coast towards Eastbourne and Royal Eastbourne the course close to Henry Longhurst's prep school. Longhurst claims his eye was repeatedly attracted by the silhouette of golfers when he should have been getting on with his work.

Royal Ashdown Forest is another course with magnificent views but the surroundings in no way supersede the challenge of the golf which everyone admires. It is a course, Piltdown is another, where there are no sand bunkers. Its defences are sure enough without them, although the most famous course in Kent, Royal St George's, boasts some of the biggest bunkers to be seen in England.

There is little to mistake this stretch of coast for the Garden of England, North Foreland sharing a certain bleak beauty with its famous neighbours. You have to go west of Canterbury to see the hop gardens, the orchards and the green fields, but the best and most valuable regions for agriculture are rarely noted for golf and you have to head for London before the golfing instincts become more satisfied.

Sevenoaks has Knole Park and Wildernesse which are splendid, Rochester and Cobham is pleasant, while West Kent, Langley Park and Sundridge Park are well worth breaking a journey for 18 holes.

E1 **Ashdown Forest Hotel**
☎ Forest Row (034 282) 4866
Chapel Lane, Forest Row, E Sussex
RH18 5BB.
3 miles S of East Grinstead on A22 in village of Forest Row, left on B2110, Chapel Lane fourth on right. Heathland/woodland course.
Club founded in 1985.
18 holes, 5510 yards, S.S.S.67
Visitors: welcome any day but advisable to check, particularly at weekends.
Green fees: £7 per round, £10 per day weekdays; £8 per round, £12 per day weekends and Public Holidays.
Society meetings: catered for seven days.
Catering: full restaurant service and bar snacks seven days. Banqueting facilities up to 100.
Hotels: Ashdown Forest.

E2 **Ashford (Kent)**
☎ Ashford (0233) 22655
Sandyhurst Lane, Ashford, Kent
TN25 4NT.
Off A20, 1.5 miles N of Ashford.
Undulating heathland course.
18 holes, 6246 yards, S.S.S.70
Club founded in 1904.
Visitors: welcome any day except before 11am weekends and Bank Holidays.
Green fees: £9 per day, (£4 with member).
Society meetings: restricted to Tues and Thurs, (morning coffee, lunch and dinner).
Catering: full catering and bar facilities. (functions, banquets etc.)
Hotels: Eastwell Manor; The Croft.

E3 **Barnehurst**
☎Crayford (0322) 523746
Mayplace Rd East, Barnehurst, Kent
DA7 6JU.
To Bexleyheath Clock Tower then on
to Mayplace Rd East, golf club on
left.
Moorland course.
9 holes, 5320 yards, S.S.S.66
Club founded in 1903.
Visitors: welcome Mon, Wed and
Fri.
Green fees: on application.
Society meetings: none.
Catering: bar snacks served, lunch
can be arranged with Stewardess.
Hotels: Crest, Bexley.

E4 **Bearsted**
☎Maidstone (0622) 38198 Sec,
38389 Club.
Ware St, Bearsted, Kent
ME14 9PQ.
3 miles E of Maidstone on A2011,
near Bearsted station.
Undulating course.
18 holes, 6253 yards, S.S.S.70
Course designed by Golf Land-
scapes Ltd.
Club founded in 1895.
Visitors: must be member of bona
fide club with current handicap. Not
weekends.

Green fees: £15 per day; £10 per
round.
Society meetings: Tues-Fri by
arrangement with Sec.
Catering: cooked snack lunch,
business lunches by arrangement.
Hotels: Great Danes Motel,
Hollingbourne.

E5 **Beckenham Place Park**
☎01-650 2292
Beckenham Hill Rd, Beckenham,
Kent BR3 2BP.
1 mile from Catford going towards
Bromley, right at Homebase.
Parkland course.
18 holes, 5722 yards, S.S.S.68
Club founded in 1932.
Visitors: welcome.
Green fees: £2.50 (18 holes), £1.40
(9 holes) weekdays; O.A.P £2 (18
holes), £1 (9 holes) weekdays; £6
(18 holes), £3.30 (9 holes) weekends
and Bank Holidays.
Society meetings: none.
Catering: meals and snacks served.
Hotels: Bromley Court.

E6 **Bexleyheath**
☎01-303 6951
Mount Row, Mount Rd, Bexleyheath,
Kent DA6 8JS.
1 mile from Bexleyheath station, off

Upton Rd.
Undulating course.
9 holes, 5239 yards, S.S.S.66
Club founded in 1907.
Visitors: welcome 8am-4pm Mon-
Fri.
Green fees: £7, (£3 with member).
Society meetings: by arrangement.
Catering: lunch, snacks and evening
meals except Mon.
Hotels: Crest, Southwold Rd,
Bexley.

E7 **Brighton & Hove**
☎Brighton (0273) 556482
Dyke Rd, Brighton, E Sussex
BN1 8YJ.
N of Brighton Centre, 2.5 miles up
Dyke Rd on left side.
Downland course.
9 holes, 5722 yards, S.S.S.68
Club founded in 1887.
Visitors: welcome.
Green fees: £8 (18 holes); Sun £10;
£5 (9 holes); Sun £6.
Society meetings: catered for
weekdays.
Catering: full service available.
Hotels: Old Ship, Brighton.

E8 **Bromley**
☎01-462 7014
Magpie Hall Lane, Bromley, Kent

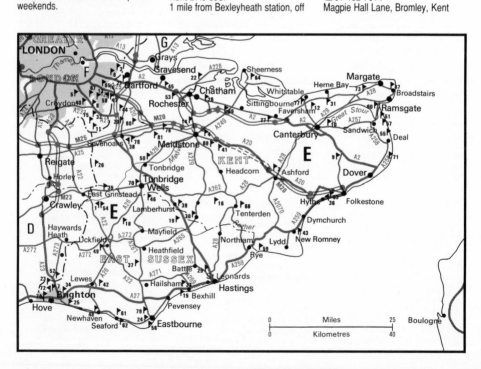

BR2 8JF.
A21, 2 miles S of Bromley.
Parkland course.
9 holes, 2507 yards, S.S.S.69.
Visitors: welcome.
Green fees: on application.
Society meetings: welcome.
Catering: snacks available.

E9 **Broome Park G & C C**
☎Canterbury (0227) 831701
Barham, Canterbury, Kent CT4 6QX.
Off M2 onto A2 then Folkestone Rd
A260, 700 yards on right hand side,
8 miles from Canterbury.
Parkland course.
18 holes, 6610 yards, S.S.S.72
Course designed by Donald Steel.
Club founded in 1979.
Visitors: must hold valid handicap
certificate to be presented on arrival.
Start times to be booked in advance.
Green fees: none on Sunday; £12
per round weekdays; £15 Saturday.
Society meetings: Tues-Fri; half
day and evening meal £17.50; full
day coffee, lunch, evening meal (36
holes) £26.
Catering: two bars, two restaurants
seven days.
Hotels: Woodpeckers Country.

E10 **Canterbury**
☎Canterbury (0227) 453532
Scotland Hills, Canterbury, Kent
CT1 1TW.
A257 1 mile from Canterbury.
Parkland course.
18 holes, 6249 yards, S.S.S.70
Course designed by H.S. Colt.
Club founded in 1927.
Visitors: welcome on weekdays.
Green fees: £10 per round; £15 per
day weekdays;
£13 per round; £17 per day Sat;
Sun (afternoons only) £16.
Society meetings: Tues and Thurs
only.
Catering: full menu Mon-Sat.
Hotels: Ebury; Canterbury; Abbots
Barton.

E11 **Cherry Lodge**
☎Biggins Hill (0959) 72550
Jail Lane, Biggins Hill, Kent
TN16 3AX.
Off A233 by RAF station.
Undulating downland course.
18 holes, 6908 yards, S.S.S.73
Course designed by John Day.
Club founded in 1969.
Visitors: welcome Mon-Fri only.
Green fees: £13.50 per day, £11 per
round; Guest £7.50 weekday, £8.50

weekend.
Society meetings: Mon-Fri.
minimum 20; all day £30.
Catering: lunchtime snacks, meals;
à la carte Tues-Sat.
Hotels: Bromley Court.

E12 **Chestfield (Whitstable)**
☎Chestfield (022 779) 2365 Sec,
2243 Club, 3563 Pro.
103, Chestfield Rd, Whitstable, Kent
CT5 3LU.
0.5 mile off Thanet Way (Chestfield
roundabout).
Parkland seaside course.
18 holes, 6080 yards, S.S.S.69.
Club founded in 1925.
Visitors: welcome weekdays,
subject to other tee reservations.
Green fees: £9 per round; £12 per
day.
Society meetings: by arrangement
on Tues, Wed and Fri.
Catering: casual meals available;
dinners by arrangement.
Hotels: Marine; Hotel St George.

E13 **Chislehurst**
☎01-467 2782
Camden Park Rd, Chislehurst, Kent
BR7 5HJ.
Half mile from Chislehurst station,
on A222 to Bromley.
Parkland course.
18 holes, 5128 yards, S.S.S.65
Club founded in 1894.
Visitors: welcome weekdays only.
Green fees: £12 weekdays, (£5 with
member).
Society meetings: by arrangement
with Sec.
Catering: lunch each day.
Hotels: Bromley Court.

E14 **Cobtree Manor**
☎Maidstone (0622) 53276
Maidstone, Kent.
M2 or M20 and then A229 turn off,
Club is on A229.
Parkland course.
18 holes, 5701 yards, S.S.S.68
Club founded in 1984.
Visitors: welcome (Municipal
course)
Green fees: on application.
Society meetings: none.
Catering: bar food available,
evening meals by arrangement.
Hotels: Great Danes; Crest.

E15 **Cooden Beach**
☎Cooden (042 43) 2040
Cooden Sea Rd, Cooden, E Sussex

TN39 4TR.
A259 Eastbourne to Hastings road,
follow Cooden Beach sign at Little
Common roundabout.
Seaside parkland course
18 holes, 6450 yards, S.S.S.71
Course designed by Herbert Fowler.
Club founded in 1913.
Visitors: welcome.
Green fees: £12 weekdays; £15
weekends public holidays.
Society meetings: Thurs, Fri.
Catering: full services available.
Hotels: Cooden Resort.

E16 **Cranbrook**
☎Cranbrook (0580) 712833 or
712934
Benenden Rd, Cranbrook, Kent
TN17 4AL.
14 miles S of Maidstone, A229 to
Sissinghurst, 1.25 miles from
Sissinghurst on Benenden Rd.
Parkland course.
18 holes, 6216 yards, S.S.S.70
Course designed by John D. Harris.
Club founded in 1969.
Visitors: welcome weekdays; not
before 10am weekends except with
member.
Green fees: £9 weekdays; £12
weekends.
Society meetings: Wed, Thurs, Fri
by prior appointment. All day,
including catering, £24.
Catering: full restaurant facilities
every day except Tues.
Hotels: Willesley; Kennel Holt.

E17 **Cray Valley**
☎Orpington (0689) 39677 Sec,
37909 Shop, 39127 Catering.
Sandy Lane, St Paul's Cray,
Orpington, Kent BR5 3HY.
A20 to Ruxley roundabout, junction
with A223.
Undulating meadowland course.
18 holes, 5624 yards, S.S.S.67.
9 hole Beginner's course.
Course designed by Golf Centres
Ltd.
Club founded in 1972.
Visitors: weekdays unlimited;
weekends restricted.
Green fees: £5 weekdays; £7
weekends.
Society meetings: Weekdays and
Sat & Sun afternoons only.
Catering: telephone above.
Hotels: numerous good hotels in
area.

E18 **Crowborough Beacon**
☎Crowborough (089 26) 61511

Beacon Rd, Crowborough, E Sussex
TN6 1UJ.
8 miles S of Tunbridge Wells on A26.
Heathland course.
18 holes, 6304 yards, S.S.S.70
Club founded in 1895.
Visitors: weekdays, weekends and
Bank Holidays after 3pm. Handicap
certificate or letter of introduction
required.
Green fees: £10 per round; £13 per
day weekdays; £11 per round weekends.
Society meetings: Mon, Tues, Wed
by prior arrangement with Sec.
Catering: for up to 60. Breakfast
available by prior arrangement.

E19 Dale Hill
☎Ticehurst (0580) 200112
Ticehurst, Wadhurst, E Sussex
TN5 7DQ.
Turn off A21 at Flimwell, on B2087
towards Ticehurst.
Parkland/meadowland course.
18 holes, 6055 yards, S.S.S.69
Club founded in 1972.
Visitors: welcome. Telephone pro
to obtain tee time.
Green fees: £10 per day weekdays.
Society meetings: booking form
obtained from Sec. Minimum number
sixteen.
Catering: full catering facilities all
week. Breakfast provided if ordered
in advance.
Hotels: Tudor Arms; Spindlewood.

E20 Darenth Valley
☎Otford (095 92) 2944 Steward,
2922 Pro
Station Rd, Shoreham, Kent TN15
7SA.
Along A225 Sevenoaks to Dartford
road, 4 miles N of Sevenoaks.
Meadowland course.
18 holes, 6356 yards, S.S.S.71
Course designed by R. Tempest.
Club founded in 1973.
Visitors: welcome. Bookings for
weekends and public holidays.
Green fees: (18 holes) £5.50; (9
holes) £3.25 weekdays.
Society meetings: welcome, prices
on application to the Steward.
Catering: bar meals and society
catering.
Hotels: Royal Oaks, Sevenoaks.

E21 Dartford
Dartford Heath, Dartford, Kent
DA1 2TN.
Situated on Dartford Heath, 2 miles
from Dartford town centre.

Heathland course.
18 holes, 5914 yards, S.S.S.68
Club founded in 1897.
Visitors: welcome weekdays if
member of recognised club or with
member and at weekends only with
member.
Green fees: £12 weekdays, (£6 with
member).
Society meetings: catered for on Fri
only; booking well in advance.
Catering: snacks available, lunch by
arrangement, evening meals on Wed
and Fri by arrangement.
Hotels: Royal Bull; Victoria.

E22 Deangate Ridge
☎Medway (0634) 251180
Hoo, Rochester, Kent ME3 8RZ.
A228 from Rochester to Isle of Grain,
then take road signed to Deangate
Ridge, 4 miles NE of Rochester.
Parkland municipal course.
18 holes, 6300 yards, S.S.S.70
Course designed by Hawtree &
Sons.
Club founded in 1972.
Visitors: welcome anytime,
bookings essential weekends.
Green fees: £4.20 weekends; £3.80
weekdays.
Society meetings: weekends and
weekdays.
Catering: lunch and dinner served,
bookings essential weekends.
Hotels: Inn on the Lake, Park Pale,
Rochester, on main A2 road.

E23 Dyke
☎Poynings (079 156) 296
Dyke Rd, Brighton, Sussex BN1 8YJ.
Situated on the Downs, 4.5 miles N
of Brighton, take Dyke road from
Brighton.
Downland course.
18 holes, 6212 yards, S.S.S.71
Club founded in 1910.
Visitors: welcome, telephone Sec
for availability.
Green fees: £10 per round, £12 per
day weekdays; £15 per round, £20
per day weekends.
Society meetings: welcome by
appointment only weekdays.
Catering: full catering facilities.
Hotels: Old Ship, Kings Rd,
Brighton.

E24 Eastbourne Downs
☎Eastbourne (0323) 20827
East Dean Rd, Eastbourne,
E Sussex BN20 8ES.
On A259 W of Eastbourne.
Downland course.

18 holes, 6635 yards, S.S.S.72
Course designed by J.H. Taylor.
Club founded in 1907.
Visitors: welcome.
Green fees: £7 (18 holes).
Society meetings: welcome.
Catering: Tues-Sun.
Hotels: Queens; Princes; Lans-
downe; Wish Tower.

E25 East Brighton
☎Brighton (0273) 604838
Roedean Rd, Brighton, E Sussex
BN2 5RA.
Follow A259 from Brighton town
centre and turn left opposite Brighton
Marina.
Downland course.
18 holes, 6304 yards, S.S.S.70
Club founded in 1893.
Visitors: welcome on weekdays,
weekends by appointment.
Green fees: £9 per day.
Society meetings: catered for on
weekdays.
Catering: lunch served except
Monday.
Hotels: Old Ship.

E26 Edenbridge G & CC
☎Edenbridge (0732) 865097
Crouch House Rd, Edenbridge, Kent
TN8 5LQ.
Travelling N through Edenbridge
High St turn left into Stangrove Rd
(30 yards before Edenbridge Town
railway station), at end of road turn
right, course will be found a short
distance on left.
Undulating meadowland course.
18 holes, 6635 yards, S.S.S.71
Club founded in 1975.
Visitors: welcome weekdays and
weekends.
Green fees: £5 weekdays; £7
weekends and Bank Holidays.
Society meetings: weekdays only.
Catering: lunch and bar snacks
served daily.
Hotels: Wonham.

E27 Faversham
☎Eastling (079 589) 561
Belmont Park, Faversham, Kent
ME13 0HB.
Leave M2 at Junction 6, take A251 to
Faversham, follow A2 to Sitting-
bourne for 0.5 mile, turn left at
Brogdale Rd, and follow golf club
signs.
Parkland course.
18 holes, 5979 yards, S.S.S.69
Club founded in 1902
Visitors: no green fees weekends or

public holidays.
Green fees: £10 per round; £15 per day weekdays; £12 per round; £16 per day (with member) weekends.
Society meetings: Wed and Fri only £11 per round; £16 per day.
Catering: by arrangement with Steward.
Hotels: Ship, Faversham.

E28 Gillingham
☎Medway (0634) 53017 Sec, 55862 Pro, 50999 Bar
Woodlands Rd, Gillingham, Kent ME7 2BX.
On A2 at Gillingham, about 2 miles from M2 turn off to Gillingham.
Meadowland course.
18 holes, 5863 yards, S.S.S.68
Course designed by James Braid.
Club founded in 1908.
Visitors: must be a member of another club when playing without a member or hold current handicap certificate.
Green fees: £5 per round, £7 per day weekday with member; £8 per round, £11 per day; weekends only with member £5 per round, £7 per day.
Society meetings: catered for any day except Thurs. Must be 24 or over Mon/Tues. Fee £12.65 including VAT.
Catering: Wed-Sun lunch and evening meals.
Hotels: Park Hotel.

E29 Hastings
☎Hastings (0424) 52981
Battle Rd, St Leonards-on-Sea, E Sussex TN37 7AB.
A2100 from Battle to Hastings, 3 miles NW of Hastings.
Undulating parkland course.
18 holes, 6248 yards, S.S.S.71
Course designed by Frank Pennink.
Club founded in 1973.
Visitors: Municipal golf course. Tee booking system.
Green fees: £5.50 weekdays; £6.50 weekends and Bank Holidays. Reductions for OAP, juniors, students.
Society meetings: welcome at all times if booked in advance.
Catering: full catering facilities at all times.
Hotels: Beauport Park.

E30 Hawkhurst
☎Hawkhurst (058 05) 2396
High St, Hawkhurst, Cranbrook, Kent TN18 4JS.
On A268, 2 miles from A21 at Flimwell, 0.5 mile from junction with A229.
Undulating parkland course.
9 holes, 5791 yards, S.S.S.68
Course designed by Rex Baldock.
Club founded in 1968.
Visitors: welcome
Green fees: £8 weekdays, £10 weekends.
Society meetings: on application.
Catering: by arrangement.
Hotels: Royal Oak, Hawkhurst.

E31 Herne Bay
☎Herne Bay (0227) 373964
Eddington, Herne Bay, Kent CT6 7PG.
Take Thanet Way to Herne Bay, near railway station.
Parkland course.
18 holes, 5403 yards, S.S.S.66
Club founded in 1920.
Visitors: welcome at all times, but some restrictions at weekends and Bank Holidays.
Green fees: on application.
Society meetings: welcome any time.
Catering: full facilities at club, prior notice required by Steward for full meals.
Hotels: numerous good hotels in area.

E32 High Elms
☎Farnborough (0689) 58175
High Elms Rd, Downe, Kent.
5 miles out of Bromley off the A21 to Sevenoaks.
Parkland course.
18 holes, 5626 yards, S.S.S.69
Course designed by Fred Hawtree.
Club founded in 1969.
Visitors: welcome.
Green fees: £4.50 weekdays, £6.50 weekends.
Society meetings: weekdays catered for.
Catering: full meals and snacks available.
Hotels: Bromley Court.

E33 Highwoods
☎Bexhill (0424) 212625
Ellerslie Lane, Bexhill-on-Sea, E Sussex TN39 4LJ.
Off A259 from Eastbourne or Hastings, 2 miles from Bexhill; from Battle A269 via Ninfield, turn right in Sidley.
18 holes, 6218 yards, S.S.S.70
Course designed by J.H. Taylor.
Club founded in 1925.

Visitors: welcome with handicap certificate Sun no visitors before 12 noon unless with member.
Green fees: £11 per round/day weekdays; £14 weekends and Bank Holidays.
Society meetings: by arrangement.
Catering: lunch by arrangement, snacks, tea.
Hotels: Cooden Resort; White Friars.

E34 Hollingbury Park
☎Brighton (0273) 552010
Ditchling Rd, Brighton, Sussex BN1 7HS.
1 mile from Brighton, A23 to Brighton town centre, turn L at one way, up hill to top, turn L, 200 yards on R.
Undulating downland course.
18 holes, 6502 yards, S.S.S.71
Course designed by J. Braid and J. Taylor.
Club founded in 1908.
Visitors: welcome anytime.
Green fees: £5.25 per round, £7.35 per day.
Society meetings: weekdays only.
Catering: full restaurant facilities open seven days.
Hotels: Old Ship, Brighton.

E35 Holtye
☎Cowden (034 286) 635/576
Holtye Common, Cowden, Edenbridge, Kent TN8 7ED.
On A264 between East Grinstead and Tunbridge Wells, 5 miles from East Grinstead.
Heathland course.
9 holes, 5300 yards, S.S.S.66
Club founded in 1893.
Visitors: welcome weekdays; restricted Thurs am and weekends am.
Green fees: £7 weekdays; £7.50 weekends.
Society meetings: weekdays by prior arrangement.
Catering: snacks available, meals by prior arrangement.
Hotels: Felbridge, East Grinstead.

E36 Hythe Imperial
☎Hythe (0303) 67554 Sec.
Princes Parade, Hythe, Kent CT21 6AE.
Turn off M20 to Hythe, to E end of seafront.
Seaside course.
2 x 9 holes, 5589 yards, S.S.S.67
Club refounded in 1950.
Visitors: welcome, handicap certificate desired.

Green fees: £8 weekdays, (£7 with member); £10 weekends, (£7 with member).
Society meetings: by arrangement.
Catering: hotel; clubhouse for light snacks.
Hotels: Hythe Imperial; Stade Court.

E37 Horam Park
☎Horam (043 53) 3477
Chiddingly Road, Horam, Nr Heathfield, E Sussex TN21 0JJ.
0.5 mile S of Horam on road to Chiddingly. Horam is 13 miles N of Eastbourne on A267.
Undulating parkland/woodland course.
18 holes, 5600 yards, S.S.S.66
Club founded in 1985.
Visitors: welcome except Sat mornings.
Green fees: (18 holes) £7 per day; (9 holes) £3.75.
Society meetings: welcome by arrangement.
Catering: carvery and bar meals except Mon.
Hotels: Boship Farm, Hailsham.

E38 Knole Park
☎Sevenoaks (0732) 452150
Seal Hollow Rd, Sevenoaks, Kent TN15 0HJ.
0.5 mile W of Seal is Seal Hollow Rd leading to Sevenoaks, approx 1 mile up Seal Hollow Rd.
Parkland course.
18 holes, 6249 yards, S.S.S.70
Course designed by Fowler, Abercrombie.
Club founded in 1924.
Visitors: weekdays by appointment only; must have authorised handicap.
Green fees: £14 per round; £20 per day.
Society meetings: by appointment.
Catering: lunch, tea, dinner.
Hotels: Sevenoaks Park; Royal Oak.

E39 Lamberhurst
☎Lamberhurst (0892) 890241
Church Rd, Lamberhurst, Kent TN3 8DT.
On A21 S from Tunbridge Wells, entrance to course immediately left on outskirts of Lamberhurst village.
Undulating parkland course.
18 holes, 6277 yards, S.S.S.70
Course designed by Frank Pennink.
Club founded in 1920.
Visitors: welcome any day after 12 noon at weekends and Bank Holidays unless accompanied by

member.
Green fees: £15 per round/day weekdays; £15 per round/day weekends.
Society meetings: catered for on Tues, Wed and Thurs only.
Catering: lunch, dinner and snacks served except Mon when sandwiches only available.
Hotels: Star and Eagle, Goudhurst.

E40 Langley Park
☎01-658 6849, 650 1663 Pro
Barnfield Wood Rd, Beckenham, Kent BR3 2SZ.
At lights near Bromley South station turn into Westmoreland Rd, clubhouse 1.75 miles on left.
Gently undulating parkland course.
18 holes, 6488 yards, S.S.S.71
Course designed by J.H. Taylor.
Club founded in 1910.
Visitors: not at weekends.
Telephone Pro for bookings.
Green fees: £15 per round; £20 per day.
Society meetings: Wed only.
Catering: full facilities every day.
Hotels: Bromley Court.

E41 Leeds Castle
☎Hollingbourne (0627) 80467
Maidstone, Kent.
M20 from Maidstone towards Ashford, onto A20 at Hollingbourne, after 1.5 miles turn right into Broomfield Rd, entrance 50 yards on the right.
Parkland course.
9 holes, 18 tees, 5936 yards, S.S.S.69
Course opened in 1924.
Visitors: welcome 7 days.
Green fees: £6.95 (18 holes); £4.95 (9 holes).
Society meetings: welcome Mon-Fri.
Catering: full facilities.
Hotels: Great Danes.

E42 Lewes
☎Lewes (0273) 473245
Chapel Hill, Lewes, Sussex.
On A27 Lewes to Eastbourne road opposite junction of Cliffe High St and South St.
Downland course.
18 holes, 5951 yards, S.S.S.69
Club founded in 1896.
Visitors: no restrictions on weekdays subject to Society meetings. Weekends after 10.30am. Sat restricted between 12 and 2pm.
Green fees: £8 weekdays; £10

weekends and Bank Holidays.
Society meetings: by arrangement.
Catering: full time Steward can provide bar snacks or full à la carte meals.
Hotels: White Hart; Shelleys.

E43 Littlestone
☎New Romney (0679) 63355
St Andrews Rd, Littlestone, New Romney, Kent TN28 8RB.
A20 to Ashford, B2070 to New Romney, 1 mile from New Romney.
Seaside links course.
18 holes, 6417 yards, S.S.S.71
9 holes, 1998 yards, S.S.S.32
Course designed by Laidlaw Purvis.
Club founded in 1888.
Visitors: welcome every day including weekends by arrangement with Sec.
Green fees: on application.
Society meetings: welcome every day including weekends by arrangement.
Catering: every day except Tues.
Hotels: Stade Court; Broadacre; Blue Dolphins.

E44 Lullingstone Park
☎Knockholt (0959) 34542 Pro, 34517 Restaurant.
Park Gate, Chelsfield, Orpington, Kent.
A20 to Swanley, then B258 Daltons Rd, to Park Gate.
Parkland municipal course.
18 holes, 6674 yards, S.S.S.72
9 holes, 2432 yards
Course designed by Fred Hawtree.
Club founded in 1923.
Visitors: welcome.
Green fees: on application.
Society meetings: by arrangement.
Catering: meals by arrangement.
Hotels: Bull, Swanley.

E45 Mid-Kent
☎Gravesend (0474) 68035
Singlewell Rd, Gravesend, Kent DA11 7RB.
A2 S of Gravesend, turn off at Tollgate Moathouse Hotel.
Parkland course.
18 holes, 6206 yards, S.S.S.70
Course designed by Frank Pennink.
Club founded in 1909.
Visitors: weekdays and weekends with member.
Green fees: on application.
Society meetings: Tues only.
Catering: lunch except Mon, dinner by arrangement.
Hotels: Inn on the Lake, Cobham.

Leeds Castle

There is something awe-inspiring about playing golf against a backcloth of castles. At Harlech, the castle is 'monarch of all she surveys'. It would be quite easy to follow those playing over Royal St David's from its ramparts with a keen eye or good telescope, and at Dunstanburgh, on the north-east coast, ancient walls are a dominant, if more derelict, feature of a charming course. Brancepeth Castle is another notable example, and air travellers on the approach to London's Heathrow may have noticed, with much less golfing envy, the few holes within the confines of Windsor Castle.

However there is nothing to compare with the delightful surroundings of Leeds Castle, which is in the green heartland of Kent and not West Yorkshire.

A more cryptic view is that it is all so beautiful, it is a pity to spoil things by playing golf, but if you hit lucky on a nice, quiet day, you can look upon it as all part of gracious living on your own private estate. There is a welcome peace and spaciousness about the park and its magnificent trees that calls to mind St Pierre, another historic setting where the old Manor House stored the crown jewels during the Battle of Agincourt.

A tour of Leeds Castle is a history lesson in itself but the nine holes make it difficult to concentrate on the task in hand. Nowhere else that I know does an elegant moat form such an appealing water hazard as black swans and other rare birds glide lazily over it dodging wayward balls. The one criticism I have, in fact, is that the best comes in the first two holes.

The 1st, between a large tree and the reeds bordering the moat, is a superb hole in any context. At 441 yards with a glorious drive and a long second to a green slightly above you, is as hard a four as you will find; but the 2nd provides definite options, a death or glory stroke across the clear waters of the moat or the dry land route in easy stages. A really long drive will get you home, or so you are inclined to think. The 300 yards may not have been measured as the crow flies or, in the environment of Leeds, some exotic goose, but whatever glory or disaster befalls you, the remaining seven holes are more pastoral.

After a long walk to the tee, the 3rd launches on the only par 5, the second part of the hole being nicer than the first. There is an invitation to open the shoulders as, indeed, there is at the 4th, a modest length dogleg to the right over a high bunker. The small greens have been thoughtfully constructed and add considerably to both the pleasure and the challenge. The 5th, the first short hole, is a case in point, the left and front guarded by a couple of bunkers, the right fringed by a sharp slope the bottom of which leaves an awkward pitch.

The 6th calls for a firm drive up over a brow and a well judged second to a green amid a stand of pines. The 7th, with a tee almost backing on to the busy A20, a mile or so from the southern end of the M20, is a right angle dogleg to the left with another excellent green, but after playing the short 8th along a ridge, the 9th, it must be said, is a rival to the 1st.

An invitingly downhill well hit drive leaves a second to be lined up on one of the towers of the castle, a subtle swale bordering the green making club selection awkward for the better players; but one beauty of a nine hole course is that there is always a second time around. You may not improve given another chance. Ignorance can be bliss where golf is concerned but you will never be disappointed. My guess is that Leeds Castle will feature large on your list of return fixtures.

E46 Nevill
☎Tunbridge Wells (0892) 25818
Benhall Mill Rd, Tunbridge Wells,
Kent TN2 5JW.
Turn into Forest Rd from A267 out of
Tunbridge Wells.
Parkland/heathland course.
18 holes, 6336 yards, S.S.S.70
Course designed by C.K. Cotton.
Club founded in 1914.
Visitors: accepted with handicap
certificate.
Green fees: £12 per day, (£5 with
member) weekdays; £16 per day,
(£6 with member) weekends.
Society meetings: welcome Mon,
Wed, Thurs, Fri.
Catering: seven days a week.
Hotels: Spa; Calverley, Tunbridge
Wells.

E47 North Foreland
☎Thanet (0843) 62140
Convent Rd, Broadstairs, Kent
CT10 3PU.
1.5 miles from Broadstairs station.
Seaside, downland course.
18 holes, 6382 yards, S.S.S.70
Course designed by Fowler and
Simpson.
Club founded in 1903.
Visitors: welcome except Sat, Sun,
Bank Holiday mornings. Handicap
certificate required.
Green fees: Summer £10 per round,
£12 per day; winter £8 per round,
£12 per day weekdays. Summer £12
per round, winter £10 per round
weekends.
Society meetings: Wed, Fri by
arrangement with Sec. (Society
members must hold handicap with
a golf club).
Catering: available during day.
Hotels: Royal Albion; The Oak; The
White Horse; Castle Keep.

E48 Peacehaven
☎Newhaven (0273) 514049
Brighton Rd, Newhaven, E Sussex
BN9 9UH.
On A259 1 mile W of Newhaven.
Undulating downland course.
9 holes, 5007 yards, S.S.S.65
Club founded in 1895.
Visitors: welcome weekdays, after
11.30am weekend and Bank
Holidays.
Green fees: weekdays (18 holes)
£5.50; all day £8; Sat, Sun, Bank
Holidays (18 holes) £7; weekdays (9
holes) £3; Sat, Sun, Bank Holidays
(9 holes) £4.
Society meetings: catered for Mon-

Fri.
Catering: lunch, bar snacks, except
Mon and Tues.
Hotels: Peacehaven; Old Ship,
Brighton.

E49 Piltdown
☎Newick (082 572) 2033
Piltdown, Uckfield, E Sussex
TN22 3XB.
2.5 miles W of Uckfield, between
A272 and B2102.
Undulating moorland course.
18 holes, 6059 yards, S.S.S.69
Course designed by J. Rowe,
G.M. Dodd, Frank Pennink.
Club founded in 1904.
Visitors: not before 9.30am; not am
Tues, Thurs, Sun unless with
member; introduction or
certificate of club.
Green fees: £13 per round/day
weekdays; £15 per round/day
weekends.
Society meetings: by arrangement
weekdays.
Catering: lunch by arrangement (not
Tues); bar snacks every day.
Hotels: Roebuck; Maidens Head;
Horsted Place.

E50 Poult Wood
☎Tonbridge (0732) 364039
Higham Lane, Tonbridge, Kent.
2 miles N of Tonbridge off A227.
Parkland course.
18 holes, 5569 yards, S.S.S.67
Course designed by Fred Hawtree.
Club founded in 1974.
Visitors: welcome, book in advance
if registered at golf shop.
Green fees: £4, Juniors/OAP £2.25
weekdays; £5.50 weekends.
Society meetings: weekdays (18
hole) £5; day tickets £9.
Catering: bar, restaurant with views
of course, small meeting room.
Hotels: Rose & Crown; Chequers;
Leavers Manor; Langley.

E51 Princes
☎Sandwich (0304) 611118
Sandwich Bay, Sandwich, Kent
CT13 9QB.
3 miles from Sandwich through town
centre.
Seaside links course.
9 holes, 6690 yards, S.S.S.70
Course designed by J.S.F. Morrison
and Sir Guy Campbell.
Club founded in 1904.
Visitors: welcome except Sun.
Green fees: £14 per round, £16 per
day weekdays; £16 per round, £19

per day weekends.
Society meetings: catered for
except Sun.
Catering: full à la carte.
Hotels: Bell, Sandwich.

E52 Pyecombe
☎Hassocks (079 18) 5372
Clayton Hill, Pyecombe, Sussex
BN4 7FF.
On A273, 0.5 mile from junction with
A23 at Pyecombe, 5 to 6 miles N of
Brighton.
Downland course.
18 holes, 6234 yards, S.S.S.70
Club founded in 1894.
Visitors: weekdays after 9.15am;
Sat 10.30-11.30 and after 2.30pm;
Sun after 3pm.
Green fees: £11 weekdays; £13
weekends.
Society meetings: catered for Mon,
Wed, Thurs, Fri.
Catering: full services available.
Hotels: wide range in Brighton - 5
miles.

E53 Rochester & Cobham Park
☎Shorne (0474 82) 3411
Park Pale by Rochester, Kent
ME2 3UI
Situated on A2, turn left on to B2009
and follow signs to clubhouse.
Undulating parkland course.
18 holes, 6467 yards, S.S.S.71
Club founded in 1891.
Visitors: weekdays (unaccompa-
nied) handicap certificate required;
weekends (with member before
5pm).
Green fees: £14 per round; £18 per
2 rounds.
Society meetings: Tues and Thurs.
Catering: details on request.
Hotels: Inn on the Lake; Tollgate
Motel.

E54 Royal Ashdown Forest
☎Forest Row (034 282) 2018
Chapel Lane, Forest Row, East
Grinstead, E Sussex RH18 5LR.
A22 E Grinstead to Eastbourne road,
4.5miles S of E Grinstead turn left in
Forest Row opposite church onto
B2110, after 0.5 mile turn R into
Chapel Lane, top of hill turn L, over
heath to clubhouse.
Undulating moorland course.
18 holes, 6439 yards, S.S.S.71
Club founded in 1888.
Visitors: welcome, restricted
weekends, Bank Holidays. Prior
arrangement preferred.

LEEDS CASTLE GOLF COURSE

Play a round of golf at Leeds Castle and you could end up facing the same hazard as a mediaeval army — the moat.

Open all year round, this challenging course is available for everyone to come along and enjoy the game as well as the splendid views of the Castle.

The 9-hole, 18-tee course has recently been extensively redesigned by Neil Coles, with some additional water hazards. A new Golf Centre provides improved changing and shower facilities, with a Golf Shop. Golfers can use the Green Room in the adjacent Park Gate Inn throughout the day.

Clubs and trolleys are available for hire. Coaching for individuals or groups. Golf Societies and groups are welcomed. Also residential Golfing Weekend packages and company Golf Days can be organised.

Green Fees

	9-hole round	18-hole round
Adults	£4.95	£6.95
Senior Citizens/ Juniors/Disabled	£2.75*	£3.75*

*(*rates apply up to 5 pm midweek and after 2 pm on weekends)*

For further information contact Chris Miller, Golf Professional

Leeds Castle, nr. Maidstone, Kent.   Tel (0622) 65400

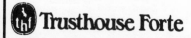

Green fees: £14.50 weekdays; £17.50 weekends.
Society meetings: Wed-Fri normal catering; Mon limited catering.
Catering: 4 course lunch for Social. Casual-golfers soup, sandwiches always available.
Hotels: Ashdown Forest; The Chequers.

E55 Royal Cinque Ports
☎Deal (0304) 374007
Golf Rd, Deal, Kent CT14 6RF.
Go to N of seafront at Deal.
Seaside links course.
Medal 18 holes, 6407 yards, S.S.S.71
Club founded in 1892.
Visitors: welcome weekdays.
Green fees: £16 per day, £12 per round.
Society meetings: welcome weekdays.
Catering: full by arrangement.
Hotels: Royal, Deal; The Bell, Sandwich.

E56 Royal Eastbourne
☎Eastbourne (0323) 29738
Steward & Members.
Paradise Drive, Eastbourne, Sussex BN20 8BP.
0.5 mile from Town Hall.
Undulating downland course.
18 holes, 6109 yards, S.S.S.69
Club founded in 1887.
Visitors: welcome.
Green fees: £10.50 weekdays, £12 weekends.
Society meetings: Wed, Thurs, Fri.
Catering: full facilities except Mon.
Hotels: Grand, Lansdowne.

E57 Royal St George's
☎Sandwich (0304) 613090
Sandwich, Kent CT13 9PB.
1 mile from Sandwich to Sandwich Bay, turn left at district sign of Worth for clubhouse.
Links course.
18 holes, 6857 yards, S.S.S.74
Course designed by Laidlaw Purvis.
Club founded in 1887.
Visitors: Mon-Fri only.
Green fees: £20 per round, £27 per day.
Society meetings: 1987 package £37 inclusive of coffee on arrival, lunch serving sandwiches.
Catering: dinners arranged.
Hotels: Bell, Sandwich.

E58 Ruxley
☎Orpington (0689) 71490

Sandy Lane, St Paul's Cray, Orpington, Kent.
A20 to Ruxley roundabout, into Sandy Lane.
Undulating parkland public course.
18 holes, 4964 yards, S.S.S.65
Club founded in 1973.
Visitors: welcome weekdays from 7am and weekends after 11.30am.
Green fees: £5 weekdays; £6.50 weekends.
Society meetings: welcome.
Catering: breakfasts and lunch served daily; evening meals Fri and Sat.
Hotels: Crest, Bexley, Kent.

E59 Rye
☎Camber (0797) 225241
Camber, Rye, E Sussex.
A259 from Rye, then Camber road to Lydd.
Links course.
18 holes, 6301 yards, S.S.S.72
Course designed by H.S. Colt.
Club founded in 1894.
Visitors: only on introduction by a member.
Green fees: £14 per round weekdays.
Society meetings: none.
Catering: lunch every day except Tues.
Hotels: George; Mermaid; Broomhill Lodge; Playden Cottage; Hope Anchor.

E60 St Augustine's
☎Thanet (0843) 590333 Sec, 590222 Pro.
Cottington Rd, Cliffsend, Ramsgate, Kent CT12 5JN.
B2048 Ramsgate to Sandwich road, turn right at Hoverport, left at Viking Caravan Club, right at Post Office, entrance at railway bridge.
Parkland course.
18 holes, 5138 yards, S.S.S.65
Course designed by Tom Vardon.
Club founded in 1907.
Visitors: welcome with handicap certificate weekdays and after 10.30am weekends.
Green fees: £10 weekdays; £12 weekends and Bank Holidays.
Society meetings: catered for weekdays except Mon. Prior bookings essential.
Catering: full catering except Mon. Sandwiches, snacks available daily.
Hotels: Oak; Sylvan; Bell.

E61 Seaford
☎Seaford (0323) 892442

East Blatchington, Seaford, E Sussex BN25 2JD.
Off A259 N of Seaford.
Downland course.
18 holes, 6241 yards, S.S.S.70
Course designed by J.H. Taylor.
Club founded in 1887.
Visitors: welcome weekdays after 9.30am and weekends after 1pm; telephone in advance.
Green fees: on application.
Society meetings: welcome after 9.30am by prior arrangement.
Catering: lunch, tea and dinner available.
Hotels: Dormy House on course.

E62 Seaford Head
☎Seaford (0323) 894843
Southdown Rd, Seaford, E Sussex BN25 4JS.
S of A259, 12 miles from Brighton, 8 miles from Eastbourne.
Seaside course.
18 holes, 5348 metres, S.S.S.68
Course designed by Thomsons of Felixstowe (1887).
Club founded in 1907.
Visitors: welcome.
Green fees: on application.
Society meetings: welcome.
Catering: light snacks and bar facilities.
Hotels: Seaford Head, Chyngton Rd, Seaford; Victoria Sea, Esplanade, Seaford.

E63 Sene Valley
☎Folkestone (0303) 68514
Sene, Folkestone, Kent.
A20 from Ashford or from Folkestone, club is signposted from A20 between Ashford and Folkestone.
Undulating downland course.
18 holes, 6320 yards, S.S.S.70
Course designed by Henry Cotton.
Club founded in 1888.
Visitors: welcome but advisable to telephone to check availability.
Green fees: on application.
Society meetings: welcome by arrangement with Manager.
Catering: available daily, except Mon.
Hotels: Imperial, Hythe; Burlington.

E64 Sheerness
☎Sheerness (0795) 662585
Power Station Rd, Sheerness, Kent ME12 3AE.
9 miles from Sittingbourne on A249.
Seaside course.
18 holes, 6500 yards, S.S.S.71

Royal Cinque Ports, Deal

Nowhere in Britain, indeed nowhere in the world, do three Open championship courses lie in such close proximity as Prince's, Sandwich and Deal. You can chip a ball from Prince's to Sandwich and you could almost drive a ball from Sandwich onto the furthest reaches of Deal if it were not for the line of buildings that once included the late lamented Guilford Hotel.

Nowadays, only Sandwich, re-instated in 1981, meets all the demands imposed by a modern Open, the old version of Prince's being largely demolished during the last war; but no course has remained more untouched by the years than Deal or, to give it its proper title, the Royal Cinque Ports GC.

The sea has done its best on three occasions to sweep it away, large areas being devastated by floods swept in on angry tides. The most recent invasion was 1978 but it resulted in a gigantic exercise to strengthen the sea wall which is now thought to be man enough to repulse everything the elements can throw at it.

Like many championship links, Deal was no doubt more formidable in the days of the gutty ball and hickory shafts, the hummocky nature of the ground on many fairways being considerably easier to negotiate with a steel shaft and modern ball.

Its last Open was in 1920 when George Duncan profited from Abe Mitchell's spectacular collapse on the final day, but the tournament that keeps Deal in the forefront of the public eye is the Haford Hewitt whose participating legions descend every April to put themselves through a process of friendly torture.

The drama invariably unfolds on the 18th and 19th and, for that reason, they are the best remembered holes. The 1st is innocent enough as a first hole in spite of the stream in front of the green, the chance of driving out of bounds or of burying a hook in the clumps of rushes. However, as the 19th, its cloak is far more sinister. The fairway seems to shrink in width and the stream casts some hypnotic power over those who seem to have all strength and co-ordination drained from their hands.

The 2nd, a stern two-shooter, is the sort of hole you could only find on a British seaside links, a label even more applicable to the 3rd. There are two or three enormous hollows between twin sandhills and the green.

The 4th, Sandy Parlour, is the first of three short holes which make as good a set as you will find, each calling for a different shot with a different club in a different direction. David Blair thought enormously highly of them and was very much what one might term a Deal man, as was Leonard Crawley. Their shotmaking powers were well suited to controlling the ball in moderate winds that for ordinary folk made the fives many and the fours few.

From the 2nd to the 7th, you get used to the wind from the same quarter except for the pitch to the 6th - a stroke that catches many by surprise. First time players on the course never expect to find the green where it is.

The 9th, 10th and 11th are excellent fours, running largely at right angles to the rest of the holes particularly the finish which is easy or difficult according to the wind. The 12th is another old-fashioned shaped green while the 16th and 17th also have their own distinctive contours. The 16th, in fact, is perched up like a gun turret, the steep, guardian bank frequently killing off a long second seeking a birdie four.

On the 17th, the problem for the second shot is finding a predictable landing area but at the 18th the only recommended way of hitting a flat, plateau green is carrying the shot all the way. Here again, the stream crossing the fairway claims its haul of balls although there is less excuse for causing a ripple than on the 1st. Bernard Darwin wrote many moons ago that Deal consists of plenty of 'fine, straight-ahead, long-hitting golf'. It still does.

Club founded in 1906.
Visitors: welcome weekdays; weekends with member.
Green fees: £8 weekdays; £12 weekends.
Society meetings: welcome Tues-Fri.
Catering: not Mon.
Hotels: Royal, Broadway, Sheerness; Abbey, Broadway, Minster.

E65 **Sidcup**
☎01-300 2150
7 Hurst Rd, Sidcup, Kent DA15 9AE.
A222 off A2, 400 yards N of Sidcup railway station.
Parkland course.
9 holes, 5692 yards, S.S.S.67.
Course designed by James Braid & H. Myrtle.
Club founded in 1891.
Visitors: welcome, handicap certificate required.
Green fees: £10 per round.
Society meetings: small societies welcome.
Catering: lunch, snacks available.
Hotels: numerous hotels in area.

E66 **Sittingbourne & Milton Regis**
☎Newington (0795) 842261
Wormdale, Newington, Sitting-bourne, Kent ME9 7PX.
1 mile N of Exit 5 off M2 on A249.
Undulating course.
18 holes, 6121 yards, S.S.S.69
Course designed by Harry Hunter.
Club founded in 1929.
Visitors: welcome weekdays.
Green fees: £9.50 weekdays; £12.50 weekends.
Society meetings: catered for Tues & Thurs.
Catering: Tues to Sat.
Hotels: Coliston, Sittingbourne.

E67 **Sundridge Park**
☎01-460 0278
Garden Rd, Bromley, Kent BR1 3LU.
5 minutes walk from Sundridge Park station.
Parkland courses.
East-18 holes, 6148 yards, S.S.S.70
West-18 holes, 6027 yards, S.S.S.68
Course designed by James Braid and Jack Randall.
Club founded in 1902.
Visitors: welcome weekdays only.
Official club handicap required.
Green fees: £15 per day.
Society meetings: on application.
Catering: full facilities daily.

Hotels: Bromley Court; Bromley Continental.

E68 **Tenterden**
☎Tenterden (058 06) 3987
Woodchurch Rd, Tenterden, Kent.
1 mile E of Tenterden on B2067.
Undulating parkland course.
9 holes, 5119 yards, S.S.S.65
Visitors: welcome except Sun mornings.
Green fees: £6 weekdays; £8 weekends and Bank Holidays.
Society meetings: by arrangement.
Catering: light meals served; other catering by arrangement.
Hotels: Vine Inn; White Lion.

E69 **Tudor Park G & CC**
☎(0622) 34334
Ashford Rd, Bearsted, Maidstone, Kent ME14 4NR.
Follow A20, Ashford Rd, on the right, 3 miles from Maidstone centre.
Complex: hotel, conference, golf and country club.
Parkland course.
Course designed by Donald Steel.
Club founded in 1988.
Visitors: welcome with handicap certificate.
Green fees: £12 weekdays; £16 weekends.
Society meetings: welcome weekdays with prior arrangement.
Catering: restaurant and leisure club restaurant.
Hotels: available at club, 120 beds, swimming pool, squash, snooker, 2 restaurants.

E70 **Tunbridge Wells**
☎Tunbridge Wells (0892) 23034
Langton Rd, Tunbridge Wells.
Adjacent to Spa Garage & Hotel.
Undulating course.
9 holes, 4684 yards, S.S.S.62
Club founded in 1889.
Visitors: welcome weekdays only.
Green fees: £7.50.
Society meetings: by arrangement.
Catering: Tues-Sun, lunch and dinners.
Hotels: Spa, Wellington; Royal Wells.

E71 **Walmer & Kingsdown**
☎Deal (0304) 373256
The Leas, Kingsdown, Deal, Kent CT14 8ER.
Off A258, 2.5 miles S of Deal.
Undulating meadowland course.
18 holes, 6451 yards, S.S.S.71
Course designed by James Braid.

Club founded in 1909.
Visitors: welcome on weekdays and after 11am at weekends.
Green fees: on application.
Society meetings: welcome, but must book in advance.
Catering: full catering available. For parties of societies book in advance.
Hotels: Royal; Clarendon; Guildford House; Dover Moat House.

E72 **Waterhall**
☎Brighton (0273) 508658
Mill Rd, Brighton, E Sussex BN1 8YN.
W of the town, 5 miles from centre, towards Devil's Dyke.
Hilly downland course.
18 holes, 5692 yards, S.S.S.68
Club founded in 1923.
Visitors: welcome.
Green fees: £5.50 per round, £8 per day weekdays; £7 per round weekends and Bank Holidays.
Society meetings: welcome by prior arrangement on weekdays.
Catering: available daily during summer; limited in winter.
Hotels: numerous good hotels in area.

E73 **Westgate & Birchington**
☎Thanet (0843) 31115
Domneva Rd, Westgate-on-Sea, Kent.
A27, 0.25 mile from Westgate station.
Seaside links course.
18 holes, 4926 yards, S.S.S.64
Club founded in 1923.
Visitors: welcome if members of recognised club.
Green fees: £6 weekdays; £7 weekends.
Society meetings: by arrangement.
Catering: by arrangement.
Hotels: Edgewater; Iveyside.

E74 **West Hove**
☎Brighton (0273) 419738
369 Old Shoreham Rd, Hove, Sussex.
N of Portslade Station, junction with A272.
Downland course.
18 holes, 6130 yards, S.S.S.69
Course designed by James Braid.
Club founded in 1910.
Visitors: welcome weekdays all day and weekends afternoons.
Green fees: £8 weekdays; £11 weekends.
Society meetings: catered for weekdays.

Catering: available daily except Mon.
Hotels: numerous good hotels in area.

E75 **West Kent**
☎Farnborough (0689) 51323
West Hill, Downe, Orpington, Kent BR6 7JJ.
A21 to Orpington, head for Downe village.
Undulating meadowland course.
18 holes, 6392 yards, S.S.S.70
Club founded in 1916.
Visitors: welcome weekdays with letter from Sec or handicap certificate.
Green fees: £14 per round, £17 per day.
Society meetings: by arrangement.
Catering: full facilities except Mon.
Hotels: Bromley Continental.

E76 **West Malling**
☎Maidstone (0732) 844785 Sec, 844795 Enquiries, 844022 Pro.
London Rd, Addington, Maidstone, Kent.
A20 from London, turn left at Greenaway Hotel, 8 miles NW of Maidstone.
Parkland course.
18 holes, 7029 yards, S.S.S.73
Club founded in 1974.
Visitors: welcome mid-week; after 12 noon, weekends.
Green fees: £10 per round.
Society meetings: welcome by prior arrangement.
Catering: full facilities.
Hotels: Larkfield; Trusthouse Forte.

E77 **Whitstable & Seasalter**
☎Whitstable (0227) 272020
Collingwood Rd, Whitstable, Kent CT51 1EB.
From A299 Thanet Way turn off at Long Reach roundabout and drive down Borstal Hill, pass under railway bridge, take second left into Nelson Rd and second left again along unmade road.
Seaside links course.
18 holes, 5276 yards, S.S.S.63
Club founded in 1910.
Visitors: welcome weekdays; weekends only with member.
Green fees: £7.50, (£3.50 with member).
Society meetings: weekdays by arrangement.
Catering: bar snacks.
Hotels: Marine, Marine Parade, Whitstable.

E78 **Wildernesse**
☎Sevenoaks (0732) 61199
Seal, Sevenoaks, Kent.
On A25 from Sevenoaks to Maidstone, turn right at sign in village of Seal.
Parkland course.
18 holes, 6478 yards, S.S.S.72
Club founded in 1890.
Visitors: weekdays by prior arrangement.
Green fees: on application.
Society meetings: on application.
Catering: lunch and tea daily.
Hotels: Post House; Royal Oak; Sevenoaks Park.

E79 **Willingdon**
☎Eastbourne (0323) 32383
Southdown Rd, Eastbourne, E Sussex BN20 9BU.
0.5 mile N of Eastbourne off A22.
Downland course.
Course designed by J.H. Taylor, modernised by Dr Mackenzie 1925.
Club founded in 1898.
Visitors: welcome weekdays.
Green fees: (18 holes) £9, (36 holes) £12 weekdays; (18 holes) £12, (36 holes) £15 weekends and Bank Holidays.
Society meetings: catered for weekdays except Mon.
Catering: by arrangement.
Hotels: Grand; Queens; Lansdown.

E80 **Woodlands Manor**
☎Otford (095 92) 3806
Tinkerpot Lane, Sevenoaks, Kent TN15 6AB.
Off A20 at Portobello Inn, West Kingsdown, or A225, 4 miles NE of Sevenoaks.
Undulating parkland course.
18 holes, 5858 yards, S.S.S.68 (summer)
Club founded in 1928.
Visitors: welcome weekdays; weekends after 1pm, with handicap certificate.
Green fees: on application.
Society meetings: welcome.
Catering: meals served.
Hotels: Brands Hatch Place, Fawkham.

E81 **Wrotham Heath**
☎Borough Green (0732) 884800
Seven Mile Lane, Comp, Sevenoaks, Kent TN15 8QZ.
Off A20 1 mile S of Wrotham Heath.
Undulating parkland course.
9 holes, 5823 yards, S.S.S.68
Club founded in 1906.
Visitors: welcome weekdays only; weekends if playing with member.
Green fees: (18 holes) £8.50 per round; £11.50 per day; (with member £4).
Society meetings: Fri only. Maximum number of players 20.
Catering: light lunch, tea, dinner by arrangement.
Hotels: Post House, Wrotham Heath.

F Greater London

Anyone writing about London courses in the early part of this century would have found a very different picture from that existing today. Almost thirty have fallen victim to the city's spread including Hanger Hill, West Drayton, Neasden, Acton, Harrow, Northwick Park, Clapham Common, Ranelagh (Barnes), Tooting Bec and Streatham. But there has been the odd addition in recent years. One on the site of the old Heston Aerodrome is a case in point while another is planned not far away on reclaimed land.

With so many suburban settings, Greater London, and Middlesex in particular, can hardly be classed as a centre for holiday golf. Soil foundations, which nobody can do anything about, tend to be on the heavy side but there is much for which to be thankful and, if you live in London, it is far easier to regard golf courses as havens of retreat than if you live surrounded by green fields.

Hampstead, Hendon, Highgate, much of it laid out on top of a reservoir, and Mill Hill are as close an any to the centre of the capital but there are courses further out which, when they were designed, were very much on the edge of the country. Ashford Manor and Northwood are good examples, Northwood earning two pages in Bernard Darwin's "The Golf Courses of Great Britain", a rare compliment.

By way of introduction, he remarked that 'Northwood is the best course on which to be taken ill, if you must be ill, since it is there that half the doctors in London play. But there is nothing in the golf to make you feel ill, especially in dry weather, it is very attractive'. Having lived in the neighbourhood for years and played against Middlesex there, I can vouch that its attraction lives on, but I remember other county battles at West Middlesex, Ashford Manor, Hendon and Fulwell.

Enfield, Crews Hill and Bush Hill Park are situated a mile or two apart in North Middlesex and, if I mention Hillingdon and Harefield Place, it is on the understandable grounds of sentiment that they were the first golf courses I ever saw. I used to cycle for piano lessons down Vine Lane in Hillingdon, stopping to look over the fence at golfers putting on the green nearest to the road, but Greater London (why can't it still be Middlesex?) takes in many famous names, notably Royal Blackheath, Royal Wimbledon, Royal Epping Forest and Wimbledon Common. I am also reminded that it includes Sandy Lodge and South Herts but, having played against Hertfordshire on both, no amount of so called boundary reorganisation can convince me that they are in anything other than Hertfordshire.

F1 **Airlinks**
☎01-561 1418
Southall Lane, Hounslow, Middx TW5 9PE.
Off M4 at Junction 3 onto A312 and A4020.
Meadowland/parkland course.
18 holes, 5883 yards, S.S.S.69
Course designed by P. Alliss & D. Thomas.
Club founded in Jan 1984.
Visitors: welcome.
Green fees: £4.50 per round weekdays; £6 weekends.
Society meetings: welcome Mon-

Fri, fees by negotiation.
Catering: hot and cold snacks, licensed bar.
Hotels: all London Airport hotels in vicinity.

F2 **Aquarius**
☎01-693 1626
Marmora Rd, Honor Oak, London SE22.
Off Forest Hill Rd.
9 holes, 5034 yards, S.S.S.65
Club founded in 1912.
Visitors: welcome with member only.
Society meetings: none.

Catering: limited service available.
Hotels: numerous good hotels in London.

F3 **Ashford Manor**
☎Ashford (0784) 257687
Fordbridge Rd, Ashford, Middx TW15 3RT.
Staines by-pass A308, 2 miles E of Staines.
Parkland course.
18 holes, 6343 yards, S.S.S.70
Club founded in 1898.
Visitors: welcome on weekdays but must be member of recognised golf

club; at weekends only by prior arrangement.
Green fees: £12 weekdays.
Society meetings: catered for on weekdays.
Catering: lunch daily except Mon, high tea daily.
Hotels: many hotels in area.

F4 Brent Valley
☎01-567 1287
Church Rd, Cuckoo Lane, Hanwell, London W5.
A4020 Uxbridge Rd, Hanwell, on to Church Rd by Brent Lodge Animal Centre.
Meadowland course.
18 holes, 5440 yards, S.S.S.66
Course designed by P. Alliss and Dave Thomas.
Club founded in 1938.

Visitors: welcome 7 days.
Green fees: £3 weekdays; £4 weekends; reductions for OAP and unemployed.
Society meetings: organised via the Pro.
Catering: restaurant open from 8am.
Hotels: numerous in Ealing/Chiswick.

F5 Bush Hill Park
☎01-360 5738
Bush Hill Rd, Winchmore Hill, London N21 2BU.
0.5 mile S of Enfield town.
Parkland course.
18 holes, 5809 yards, S.S.S.67
Club founded in 1894.
Visitors: welcome weekdays.
Green fees: £12 (per 18 holes); £15 (per 36 holes).

Society meetings: Tues, Thurs and Fri only.
Catering: bar snacks, lunch.
Hotels: Royal Chase, The Ridgeway, Enfield.

F6 Crews Hill
☎01-363 6674
Cattlegate Rd, Crews Hill, Enfield, Middx EN2 8AZ.
Off A1005 Enfield to Potters Bar road into East Lodge Lane, turn right into Cattlegate Rd.
Parkland course.
18 holes, 6230 yards, S.S.S.70
Club founded in 1921.
Visitors: weekends and Bank Holidays, only with member; members of recognised golf clubs welcome on weekdays.
Green fees: information on request.

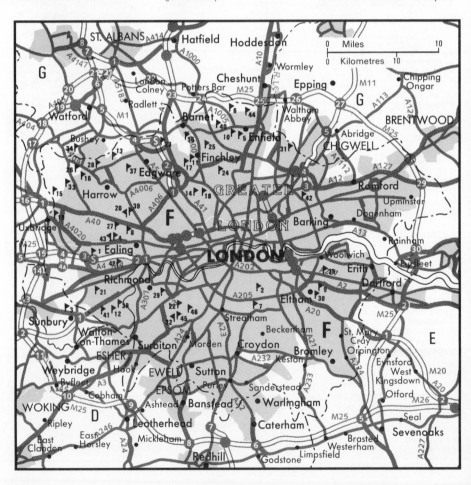

Society meetings: catered for by advance booking.
Catering: lunch served except Mon.
Hotels: Royal Chase Hotel, The Ridgeway, Enfield.

F7 **Dulwich & Sydenham Hill**
☎01-693 3961
Grange Lane, College Rd, London SE21 7LH.
Off S Circular road at Dulwich College and College Rd.
Parkland course.
18 holes, 6051 yards, S.S.S.69
Club founded in 1893.
Visitors: welcome weekdays only.
Green fees: £15 per round.
Society meetings: weekdays by arrangement.
Catering: lunch daily, dinner by arrangement.
Hotels: Queens, Crystal Palace.

F8 **Ealing**
☎01-997 0937/997 2595
Perivale Lane, Greenford, Middx UB6 8SS.
Off A40 W opposite Hoover factory.
Parkland course.
18 holes, 6216 yards, S.S.S.77
Club founded in 1923.
Visitors: welcome weekdays only.
Green fees: £14, (£6.50 with member).
Society meetings: Mon-Thurs only; evening meals by arrangement.
Catering: bar snacks, lunches every day; evening meal by arrangement only.
Hotels: Master Brewer; Caernarvon.

F9 **Eltham Warren**
☎01-850 1166
Bexley Rd, Eltham, London SE9 2PE.
Continuation of Eltham High St, half mile E.
Parkland course.
9 holes, 5840 yards, S.S.S.68
Club founded in 1890.
Visitors: weekdays only and must be member of recognised club.
Green fees: £10.
Society meetings: welcome weekdays.
Catering: not Mon or Fri, otherwise full catering by arrangement; bar snacks.
Hotels: in London.

F10 **Enfield**
☎01-363 3970
Old Park Rd S, Enfield, Middx

EN2 7DA.
1 mile NE of Enfield, near Enfield Chase railway station.
Parkland course.
18 holes, 6137 yards, S.S.S.70
Course designed by James Braid.
Club founded in 1984.
Visitors: welcome on weekdays, 24 hours notice, with handicap and if member of another club.
Green fees: on application.
Society meetings: weekdays only.
Catering: meals available every day.
Hotels: Royal Chase, The Ridgeway; Enfield, Bycullah Rd.

F11 **Finchley**
☎01-346 2436
Nether Court, Erith Lane, Mill Hill, London NW7 1PU.
Nearest main junction is A1 and A41, Mill Hill East underground station five minutes walk.
Parkland course.
18 holes, 6411 yards, S.S.S.71
Course designed by James Braid.
Club founded in 1929.
Visitors: welcome weekdays, pm weekends.
Green fees: £12 per round weekdays; £18 per round weekends.
Society meetings: Wed and Fri.
Catering: every day except Mon.
Hotels: Hendon Hall, Ashley Lane NW4.

F12 **Fulwell**
☎01-977 2733
Wellington Rd, Hampton Hill, Middx TW12 1JY
2 miles S of Twickenham on A311, opposite Fulwell station.
Meadowland course.
18 holes, 6490 yards, S.S.S.70
Course designed by D. Morrison.
Club founded in 1904.
Visitors: welcome weekdays.
Green fees: £15 per day; £13 after 1.30pm.
Society meetings: occasionally Wed, Thurs, Fri.
Catering: full service available for societies but advisable to phone.
Hotels: Cardinal Wolsey, Hampton Court.

F13 **Grimsdyke**
☎01-428 4539
Oxhey Lane, Hatch End, Pinner, Middx HA5 4AL.
2 miles W of Harrow, A4008.
Parkland course.
18 holes, 5598 yards, S.S.S.67
Course designed by James Braid.

Club founded in 1910.
Visitors: welcome weekdays.
Green fees: £13 weekdays.
Society meetings: Tues-Fri.
Catering: lunch served except Mon, dinner by arrangement.
Hotels: Grimsdyke, Old Reading, Hatch End.

F14 **Hampstead**
☎01-455 7089, 455 7421
Stewardess.
Winnington Rd, Hampstead, London N2 0TU.
A41 from Highgate village, 1 mile down Hampstead Lane, course adjacent to Spaniards Inn.
Undulating parkland course.
9 holes, 5812 (18 holes) yards, S.S.S.68
Club founded in 1893.
Visitors: welcome on weekdays, prior booking with Pro requested. Restricted times at weekends.
Green fees: £10 per round (18 holes) weekdays, £12.50 per day; Weekends and Bank Holidays; £15 per round (18 holes), £20 per day.
Society meetings: none.
Catering: lunch by prior booking; snacks always available.
Hotels: La Gaffe, Heath St, Hampstead; Central, Golders Green.

F15 **Harefield Place**
☎Uxbridge (0895) 31169
The Drive, Harefield Place, Uxbridge, Middx UB10 9PA.
2 miles N of Uxbridge.
Public parkland course.
18 holes, 5711 yards, S.S.S.68
Visitors: by arrangement with London Borough of Hillingdon.
Green fees: £3.30 weekdays; £5 weekends.
Society meetings: by arrangement with London Borough of Hillingdon.
Catering: full catering facilities.
Hotels: Master Brewer, Hillingdon.

F16 **Haste Hill**
☎Northwood (092 74) 26485
The Drive, Northwood, Middx HA6 1HN.
On A404.
Parkland course.
18 holes, 5787 yards, S.S.S.68
Club founded in 1930.
Visitors: welcome.
Green fees: £3.30 weekdays; £5 weekends.
Society meetings: welcome by arrangement.

Catering: meals served daily.

F17 Hendon

☎01-346 6023
Off Sanders Lane, Mill Hill, London
NW7 1DG.
To Hendon Central take Queens Rd
through Brent St, continue to round-
about, take first exit on left, club is
0.5 mile on left in Devonshire Rd.
Parkland course.
18 holes, 6241 yards, S.S.S.70
Course designed by H.S.Colt.
Club founded in 1901.
Visitors: Sat, Sun, Mon limited;
Tues-Fri all day.
Green fees: £12 per round, £16 per
day weekdays; £18 weekends and
Bank Holidays.
Society meetings: Tues-Fri by
arrangement.
Catering: snacks only Mon; all other
days lunch, snacks, high tea to 6pm.
Hotels: Hendon Hall.

F18 Highgate

☎01-340 1906
Denewood Rd, London N6 4AH.
Off Hampstead Lane near Renwood
House, turn into Sheldon Ave then
first left into Denewood Rd.
Parkland course.
18 holes, 5982 yards, S.S.S.69
Club founded in 1904.
Visitors: weekdays excluding Wed
morning; no visitors weekends.
Green fees: £12 per round; £19 per
day.
Society meetings: during week by
arrangement.
Catering: 12.00am-2.30pm; 4.30-
6.30pm.
Hotels: numerous hotels in London.

F19 Hillingdon

☎Uxbridge (0895) 33956 Sec,
51980 Pro, 39810 Members.
18 Dorset Way, Hillingdon, Middx
UB10 0JR.
Turn off A40 to Uxbridge, past RAF
Station, up Hillingdon Hill to left turn
at Vine Public House into Vine Lane,
club gates 0.75 mile on left.
Undulating parkland course.
9 holes, 5459 yards, S.S.S.67
Course designed by Harry Woods &
Chas. E Stevens.
Club founded in 1892.
Visitors: welcome Mon, Tues, Wed,
Fri. Not Sat, Sun, Bank Holidays
unless with full member after
12.30 pm. Must be members of golf
club with handicap certificate.
Green fees: £9 per (18 holes).

Society meetings: any weekday
except Thurs.
Catering: sandwiches lunchtime;
other meals on request of members
and societies.
Hotels: Master Brewer Motel; The
Old Cottage.

F20 Horsenden Hill

☎01-902 4555
Woodland Rise, Greenford, Middx
UB6 0RD.
Signposted off Whitton Ave E.
Undulating parkland course.
9 holes, 3236 yards, S.S.S.56
Club founded in 1935.
Visitors: welcome.
Green fees: £1.75, Juniors/OAP 85p
weekdays; £2.45, Juniors/OAP £1.15
weekends.
Society meetings: none.
Catering: snacks available,
restaurant meals by arrangement.
Hotels: numerous in area.

F21 Hounslow Heath

☎01-570 5721
Staines Rd, Hounslow, Middx.
On main road from Hounslow town to
Bedfont, on left hand side.
Parkland course.
18 holes, 5820 yards, S.S.S.68
Course designed by Fraser
Middleton.
Club founded in 1979.
Visitors: welcome.
Green fees: £3.50 per round
weekdays; £4.50 weekends.
Society meetings: by arrangement.
Catering: snacks, hot drinks
available, no drinks licence.
Hotels: Hounslow.

F22 London Scottish

☎01-788 0135
Windmill Enclosure, Wimbledon
Common, London SW19 5NQ.
2 miles from Wimbledon railway
station.
Parkland course.
18 holes, 5436 yards, S.S.S.67
Club founded in 1865.
Visitors: welcome on weekdays,
except Bank Holidays.
Green fees: £6 per round.
Society meetings: none.
Catering: lunch served and evening
meals if ordered, except Mon.
Hotels: numerous in London.

F23 Mill Hill

☎01-959 2339
100 Barnet Way, Mill Hill, London
NW7 3AL.

On A1, 0.5 mile N of Apex Corner,
1 mile S of Stirling Corner.
Parkland course.
18 holes, 6286 yards, S.S.S.70
Club founded in 1925.
Visitors: welcome weekdays.
Green fees: £12 per round; £15 per
day.
Society meetings: arranged on
Mon, Wed and Fri.
Catering: lunch served daily.
Hotels: numerous hotels in London.

F24 Muswell Hill

☎01-888 1764 Sec, 888 8046 Pro.
Rhodes Ave, Wood Green, London
N22 4UT.
1 mile from Bounds Green tube
station, 1.5 miles from N Circular
Road.
Undulating course.
18 holes, 6474 yards, S.S.S.71
Club founded in 1893.
Visitors: weekdays unrestricted;
weekend and Bank Holiday limited
bookings through Pro.
Green fees: £13.50 per round, £13
per day weekdays; £19 weekend,
Bank Holiday; (£5 members guests
anytime).
Society meetings: Mon and Wed-
Fri inclusive booked through Sec.
Catering: meals and snacks
available, bar facilities.
Hotels: numerous hotels in London.

F25 North Middlesex

☎01-445 1604
Friern Barnet Lane, Whetstone,
London N20.
A1000 5 miles N of Finchley.
Undulating parkland course.
18 holes, 5611 yards, S.S.S.67
Club founded in 1928.
Visitors: welcome if members of
recognised club.
Green fees: on application.
Society meetings: welcome except
Mon.
Catering: lunch served except Mon.

F26 Northwood

☎Northwood (092 74) 25329
Rickmansworth Rd, Northwood
HA6 2QW.
On main road between Northwood
Hills and Rickmansworth A404.
Parkland course.
18 holes, 6493 yards, S.S.S.71
Course designed by James Braid.
Club founded in 1608.
Visitors: welcome weekdays only.
Green fees: £11.50 per round; £17
per day.

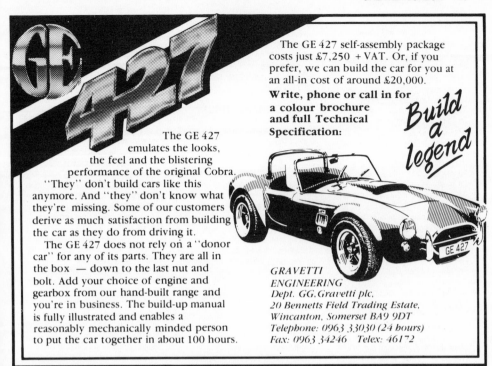
Society meetings: Mon, Thurs and Fri.
Catering: full lunchtime catering daily.
Hotels: Tudor Lodge, Eastcote; Long Island, Rickmansworth.

F27 **Perivale Park**
☎01-578 1693
Ruislip Rd East, Greenford, Middx.
On Ruislip Rd East between Greenford and Perivale.
Parkland course.
9 holes, 2667 yards, S.S.S.65 (men) 67 (women).
Visitors: welcome.
Green fees: £1.95 weekdays; £2.75 weekends.
Society meetings: welcome.
Catering: snacks served.
Hotels: Kenton, Hanger Hill.

F28 **Pinner Hill**
☎01-866 0963
South View Rd, Pinner Hill, Middx HA5 3YA.
Off A404 at Northwood Hills roundabout.
Parkland course.
18 holes, 6260 yards, S.S.S.70

Course designed by J.H. Taylor.
Club founded in 1928.
Visitors: welcome weekdays or by previous arrangement Sat pm.
Green fees: Mon, Tues, Fri £10 per round, £15 per day; Sat £14 per round. Wed, Thurs open to public £5 per round, £7 per day.
Society meetings: weekdays only £10 per round; £15 per day. Full catering available.
Catering: full catering by arrangement, (24 hours notice).

F29 **Roehampton**
☎01-876 5505
Roehampton Lane, London SW15 5LR.
Off A306 bottom of Roehampton Lane.
Parkland course.
18 holes, 6011 yards, S.S.S.69
Club founded in 1901.
Visitors: welcome with member only.
Green fees: £8 weekdays; £10 weekends.
Society meetings: limited 32 players, must be introduced by a member.

Catering: full 7 day service.
Hotels: numerous hotels in area.

F30 **Royal Blackheath**
☎01-850 1795
Court Rd, Eltham, London SE9 5AF.
5 minutes walk from Mottingham station.
Parkland course.
18 holes, 6214 yards, S.S.S.70
Course designed by James Braid.
Club founded in 1608.
Visitors: welcome with handicap certificate.
Green fees: £25 per day.
Society meetings: Wed and Thurs.
Catering: dining room, bar.
Hotels: Yardley Court, Eltham; Clarendon, Blackheath.

F31 **Royal Epping Forest**
☎01-529 2195 Sec.
Forest Approach, Chingford, London E4 7AZ.
300 yards S of Chingford railway station.
Parkland course.
18 holes, 6220 yards, S.S.S.70
Club founded in 1888.
Visitors: red coats or red trousers

compulsory.
Green fees: £3.45 weekdays.
Society meetings: limited.
Catering: by arrangement.
Hotels: Moat House, Woodford Green, Essex.

F32 **Royal Wimbledon**
☎01-946 2125
29 Camp Rd, Wimbledon
SW19 4UW.
0.75 mile W of War Memorial in Wimbledon village.
Parkland course.
18 holes, 6300 yards, S.S.S.70
Club founded in 1865.
Visitors: by prior arrangement with Sec.
Green fees: on application.
Society meetings: weekdays only.
Catering: snacks and lunch available on certain days.
Hotels: numerous good hotels in area.

F33 **Ruislip**
☎Ruislip (0895) 638835/632004
Ickenham Rd, Ruislip, Middx.
1 mile N of A40, Hillingdon.
Parkland course.
18 holes, 5500 yards, S.S.S.68
Course designed by Sandy Herd.
Club founded in 1936.
Visitors: welcome, telephoned tee bookings can be made.
Green fees: £3.30 weekdays; £5 weekend.
Society meetings: catered for every day; booking essential.
Catering: breakfast, lunch, snacks, à la carte menu daily until 10pm.
Hotels: Barn, Ruislip; Master Brewer Motel, Hillingdon.

F34 **Sandy Lodge**
☎Northwood (092 74) 25429
Sandy Lodge Lane, Northwood, Middx HA6 2JD.
2 miles S of Watford and 2 miles N of Northwood, immediately adjoining Moor Park station, Metropolitan line. Take A4125 from Northwood to Watford, left into Sandy Lodge Lane.
Links course.
18 holes, 6340 yards, S.S.S.70
Course designed by Harry Vardon.
Club founded in 1910.
Visitors: welcome weekdays; weekends and Bank Holiday with member.
Green fees: £17 per day, £12 per round.
Society meetings: Mon, Thurs, Fri.
Catering: full facilities.

Hotels: Dean Park, St Albans Rd.

F35 **Shooters Hill**
☎01-854 6368
'Lowood', Eaglesfield Rd, London SE18 3DA.
Off Shooters Hill.
Parkland course.
18 holes, 5718 yards, S.S.S.68
Club founded in 1903.
Visitors: weekdays only.
Green fees: £14
Society meetings: Tues and Thurs only.
Catering: available.
Hotels: Clarendon, Blackheath.

F36 **South Herts**
☎01-445 2035
Links Drive, Totteridge, London N20 8QU.
400 yards from A1000 at Whetstone to Totteridge Lane then 400 yards to Links Drive.
Parkland course.
18 holes, 6432 yards, S.S.S.71
Course designed by Harry Vardon.
Club founded in 1899.
Visitors: weekdays only (Tues Ladies Day).
Green fees: on application.
Society meetings: catered for on Wed, Thurs and Fri.
Catering: lunch, snacks, tea served, except Mon when only snacks.
Hotels: Crest, South Mimms.

F37 **Stanmore**
☎01-954 2599
Gordon Ave, Stanmore, Middx HA7 2RL.
Entrance off Gordon Ave, via Old Church Lane.
Undulating parkland course.
18 holes, 5815 yards, S.S.S.68
Club founded in 1893.
Visitors: welcome Tues, Wed and Thurs. Public days Mon and Fri.
Green fees: public days £5 per round; weekdays £10 per round.
Society meetings: Wed and Thurs.
Catering: full facilities except Mon and Fri.
Hotels: Grim's Dyke.

F38 **Strawberry Hill**
☎01-894 0165
Wellesley Rd, Twickenham, Middx.
Adjacent to Strawberry Hill station.
Parkland course.
9 holes, 2381 yards, S.S.S.62
Course designed by J.H. Taylor.
Club founded in 1900.
Visitors: welcome weekdays only.

Green fees: £8.
Society meetings: 24 maximum number considered on application.
Catering: bar snacks except Mon.

F39 **Sudbury**
☎01-902 3713
Bridgewater Rd, Wembley, Middx HA0 1AL.
Junction of A4005 and A4090, Sudbury Town Station (Piccadilly Line) 5 minutes walk.
Undulating parkland course.
18 holes, 6282 yards, S.S.S.70
Course designed by Holt.
Club founded in 1920.
Visitors: welcome weekdays; weekends with member.
Green fees: £13.50 weekdays; £18 weekends.
Society meetings: Wed and Thurs.
Catering: full not Mon.
Hotels: Carnarvon, Ealing Common; Cumberland, Harrow; Kenton, Ealing.

F40 **Trent Park**
☎01-366 7432
Bramley Rd, Southgate, London N14
Opposite Oakwood tube station (Piccadilly Line).
Parkland course.
18 holes, 6008 yards, S.S.S.69
Club founded in 1973.
Visitors: welcome anytime; booking required weekends and Bank Holidays.
Green fees: £3.40 weekdays; £4.60 weekends and Bank Holidays (18 holes).
Society meetings: weekdays or after 11am weekends.
Catering: snacks, meals by arrangement.
Hotels: Royal Chase, Enfield.

F41 **Twickenham**
☎01-892 5579 Sec, 979 0032 Pro.
Staines Rd, Twickenham, Middx.
On A305 near Hope and Anchor roundabout.
Municipal commonland course.
9 holes, 6014 yards, S.S.S.69
Course designed by Charles Lawrie.
Club founded in 1977.
Visitors: welcome.
Green fees: £3.50 weekdays; £5.30 weekends.
Society meetings: welcome by arrangement with Pro.
Catering: full licensed bar; snacks and cooked meals to order.
Hotels: Richmond Gate, Richmond.

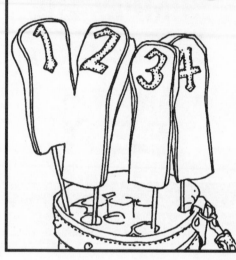
F42 **Wanstead**
☎01-989 3938
Overton Drive, Wanstead, London
E11 2LW.
Off A12 at Wanstead station, right
into 'The Green' into St Mary's Ave,
left at T-junction at St Mary's Church.
Parkland course.
18 holes, 6211 yards, S.S.S.70
Club founded in 1893.
Visitors: welcome on weekdays with
prior arrangement.
Green fees: £15 per round/day.
Society meetings: welcome by
arrangement weekdays only.
Catering: meals served.
Hotels: Sir Alfred Hitchcock, 147
Whipps Cross Road, Leytonstone;
Prince Regent, Woodford Bridge.

F43 **West Middlesex**
☎01-574 3450 Sec, 574 1800 Pro.
Greenford Rd, Southall, Middx
UB1 3EE.
A40 from Central London to
Greenford, take left exit off
roundabout, 2 miles straight down
road.

Undulating parkland course.
18 holes, 6242 yards, S.S.S.70
Course designed by James Braid.
Club founded in 1890.
Visitors: welcome on weekdays,
Mon and Wed are Public days.
Green fees: Mon and Wed £5; Tues,
Thurs, Fri £8.
Society meetings: can be booked
only on Tues, Thurs and Fri.
Catering: hot and cold snacks
available all week. 3 course meals
should be booked in advance.
Hotels: Carnarvan, Ealing Common.

F44 **Whitewebbs**
☎01-363 4458
Beggars Hollow, Clay Hill, Enfield,
Middx.
1 mile N of Enfield.
Parkland course.
18 holes, 5881 yards, S.S.S.68
Club founded in 1932.
Visitors: welcome.
Green fees: on application.
Society meetings: by arrangement.
Catering: meals served.
Hotels: West Lodge, Royal Chace.

F45 **Wimbledon Common**
☎01-946 7571 Sec, 946 0294 Pro.
Camp Rd, Wimbledon Common
SW19 4UW.
1 mile NW of War Memorial, past
Fox and Grapes on right in Camp
Rd.
Moorland course.
18 holes, 5486 yards, S.S.S.67
Course designed by Tom and Willie
Dunn.
Club founded in 1908.
Visitors: welcome weekdays.
Green fees: on application.
Society meetings: accepted if spon-
sored by club members only.
Catering: light meals available.
Hotels: numerous hotels in Wimble-
don.

F46 **Wimbledon Park**
☎01-946 1002
Home Park Rd, Wimbledon Park,
London SW19 7HR.
250 yards from Wimbledon Park station (District Line).
Parkland course.
18 holes, 5465 yards, S.S.S.67

Club founded in 1899.
Visitors: weekdays with handicap certificate or letter of introduction from club. Weekends as above but after 3pm.
Green fees: £15 per day weekdays; £18 per round weekends.
Society meetings: usually Tues and Thurs.
Catering: full facilities available excluding Monday.

Hotels: Canizaro Park.

F47 **Wyke Green**
☎01-560 8777
Syon Lane, Osterley, Isleworth, Middx TW7 5PT.
Golf club located in Syon Lane, off the A4 N of Gillette Corner.
Parkland course.
18 holes, 6242 yards, S.S.S.70
Course designed by W.H. Tate.

Club founded in 1928.
Visitors: welcome by arrangement.
Green fees: £14 weekdays; £17 weekends after 3pm.
Society meetings: £25 (36 holes) including morning coffee, lunch and evening meal.
Catering: bar snacks, light lunch, table d'hôte, 3 - course meals. Sunday lunch.
Hotels: Osterley Motel; Master Robert.

G Essex and Hertfordshire

Michael Bonallack was raised on the courses of Essex which is recommendation enough for any county. Thorpe Hall was his home club although he is an honourary member of many more, all inclined to regard him as one of their own. Thorndon Park, Chelmsford and Orsett are perhaps the pick of the courses in Essex with Frinton lending a touch of the seaside to emphasise how far its limits extend from the chimes of Bow Bells. However, the majority serve some of the most densely populated areas around the capital.

Romford, Ilford, Chingford, Chigwell, Wanstead and West Essex are the best examples, Romford once being the club of James Braid. Essex is liberally served with public courses, Epping Forest even having the prefix 'Royal'. There are nine in all making Essex fourth in the league table behind Lancashire, Yorkshire and Middlesex in the provision made to municipal golfers. The two courses at Hainault Forest are as busy as any and there are others at Basildon, Belhus Park, Southend and Thurrock.

For a relatively small county, Hertford-

shire can boast more than forty courses, most of them of the parkland variety although Berkhamsted, one of the best known, certainly cannot be so categorised. On a ridge of the Chilterns, it is a natural, old-fashioned common ideal for golf and testing enough to have no need for sand bunkers. Ashridge, a near neighbour, is defined as a parkland course but it is not so obvious a candidate as Moor Park, Porters Park or West Herts which is situated in Cassiobury Park, Watford.

Professional tournaments and a much photographed clubhouse account for Moor Park's reputation, handsome trees and undulating ground making the High an acknowledged test, while Sandy Lodge, on the other side of the Metropolitan Line, is very much on a par. There is a West Herts, South Herts, East Herts and Mid-Herts, making it something of a puzzle why there is no North Herts to complete the set; but the county can claim eight or nine new courses in the last twenty years or so, including a new Home for East Herts. Three of the best courses are Hadley Wood, Harpenden and Brookmans Park.

G1 **Abridge G & CC**
☎Stapleford (040 28) 396
Epping Lane, Stapelford Tawney,
Abridge, Essex RM4 1ST.
M11 from London Exit 5 via Abridge,
from the north, M11 exit 7 via
Epping.
Parkland course.
18 holes, 6703 yards, S.S.S.72
Course designed by Henry Cotton.
Club founded in 1964.
Visitors: weekdays by arrangement.
Green fees: £15.
Society meetings: Mon and Wed.
Catering: every day except Fri.
Hotels: Post House, Epping.

G2 **Aldenham G & CC**
☎Radlett (092 76) 3929
Radlett Rd, Aldenham, Watford,
Herts.

Junction 5 on M1, follow A41 toward
London, turn off at Ladbroke Hotel
towards Radlett, 30 minutes by car
from Marble Arch.
Undulating course.
18 holes, 6445 yards, S.S.S.71
Club founded in 1975.
Visitors: welcome weekdays, after
1pm Sat, Sun.
Green fees: £10 weekdays; £17.50
weekends.
Society meetings: Mon-Fri by
arrangement.
Catering: snack bar, full à la carte
restaurant.
Hotels: Ladbroke; Spiders Web.

G3 **Arkley**
☎01-449 0394
Rowley Green Rd, Barnet, Herts
EN5 3HL.

Off A1 at Stirling Corner to A411.
Signposted at Rowley Lane on left.
Parkland course.
2 x 9 holes, 6045 yards, S.S.S.69
Course designed by James Braid.
Club founded in 1909.
Visitors: weekdays unrestricted;
weekends with member; (Tues
Ladies day).
Green fees: £8 per round; £11 per
day.
Society meetings: Wed, Thurs
maximum 40.
Catering: snacks daily except Mon
by arrangement with Steward.
Hotels: Thatched Barn (now Moat
House).

G4 **Ashridge**
☎Little Gaddesden (044 284) 2244
Little Gaddesden, Berkhamsted,

Herts HP4 1LY.
A41 to Berkhamsted, turn right at
Northchurch on B4506.
Parkland course.
18 holes, 6508 yards, S.S.S.71
Course designed by Sir Guy
Campbell, Colonel Hotchkin and
Cecil Hutchison.
Club founded in 1932.
Visitors: telephone Sec for booking.
Green fees: £14 per round; £20 per
day.
Society meetings: telephone Sec
for booking.
Catering: morning coffee, lunch,
afternoon tea, sandwiches always.
Hotels: Bell Inn.

G5 Basildon
☎Basildon (0268) 3849
Clay Hill Lane, Basildon, Essex.
From A127 through Basildon to
Kingswood roundabout; from A13
turn left at Five Bells roundabout to
Kingswood roundabout.
Undulating parkland course.
18 holes, 6122 yards, S.S.S.69
Course designed by Frank Pennink.
Club founded in 1967.
Visitors: welcome at all times.
Green fees: on application.
Society meetings: catered for
weekdays.
Catering: except Tues lunch.
Hotels: Crest, Basildon.

G6 Batchwood Hall
☎St Albans (0727) 52101
Batchwood Drive, St Albans.
NW corner of town.
Parkland course.
18 holes, 6463 yards, S.S.S.71
Club founded in 1935.
Visitors: welcome without
reservation.
Green fees: £4 weekdays; £5.25
weekends.
Society meetings: not catered for.
Catering: none.
Hotels: numerous in area.

G7 Belfairs Park
☎Southend on Sea (0702) 525345
or 520322
Eastwood Rd North, Leigh-on-Sea,
Essex SS9 4LR.
Please note that the club is private
but plays on the undernoted public
course.
Parkland public course.
18 holes, 5871 yards, S.S.S.68
Club founded in 1926.
Visitors: unrestricted but bookings
Thurs am, weekends and public

holidays.
Green fees: £5.20 weekdays; £8
weekends and public holidays.
Society meetings: no facilities.
Catering: public restaurant.
Hotels: wide selection in Southend.

G8 Belhus Park
☎South Ockendon (0708) 854260
Belhus Park, South Ockendon, Essex
RM15 4QR.
A13 to Aveley, Essex.
Parkland course.
18 holes, 5900 yards, S.S.S.68
Course designed by Frank Pennink.
Visitors: welcome.
Green fees: £2.30 weekdays; £5.30
weekends.
Society meetings: by arrangement.
Catering: bar and restaurant.
Hotels: Royal, Purfleet; Europa,
North Stifford; Old Plough House,
Bulphan.

G9 Bentley
☎Brentwood (0277) 73179
Ongar Rd, Brentwood, Essex CM15
9SS.
4 miles from Brentwood on A128 to
Ongar.
Parkland course.
18 holes, 6709 yards, S.S.S.72
Course designed by Alec Swann.
Club founded in 1972.
Visitors: welcome Mon-Fri with letter
of introduction or handicap certificate.
Green fees: £9 per round; £12 per
day.
Society meetings: welcome
weekdays with prior arrangement.
Catering: snacks all day, hot food
lunchtimes, evening meals by
arrangement.
Hotels: Post House.

G10 Berkhamsted
☎Berkhamsted (044 27) 5832
The Common, Berkhamsted, Herts
HP4 2QB.
Take Junction 8 off M1 into Hemel
Hempstead, at roundabout take
Leighton Buzzard road. After about 3
miles take Potten End turn and follow
road to club.
Heathland course.
18 holes, 6568 yards, S.S.S.72.
Course designed by G.H. Gowring
(1890/2. Founder), 1912 C.J. Gilbert
with advice from Harry Colt, 1927
course extension with advice from
James Braid.
Club founded in 1890.
Visitors: welcome, must be member
of a golf club with handicap. Tues not

before 12.30. Sun and Bank Holiday
not before 11.30.
Green fees: £19 per round/day
weekdays; £11 per round weekends;
£16 per day Bank Holidays.
Society meetings: Wed and Fri.
Catering: full facilities daily, except
Mon when limited catering.
Hotels: Swan; Post House.

G11 Birch Grove
☎Layer de la Haye (0206) 34276
Layer Rd, Colchester CO2 0HS.
2 miles S of town.
Meadowland course.
9 holes, 4076 yards, S.S.S.62.
Club founded in 1970.
Visitors: welcome except Sun am.
Green fees: £5 (18 holes)
weekdays, (£4.50 with member); £6
(18 holes) weekends, Bank Holidays.
Society meetings: weekdays
catering for 60.
Catering: meals available during
opening hours; parties catered for by
prior arrangement.
Hotels: many in area.

G12 Bishop's Stortford
☎Bishop's Stortford (0279) 54715
Dunmow Rd, Bishop's Stortford,
Herts CM23 5HP.
Exit 8 from M11, follow signs to town
centre/hospital, golf course is on left
next to Nags Head on E edge of
town.
Parkland course.
18 holes, 6440 yards, S.S.S.71
Club founded in 1912.
Visitors: weekdays only; weekends
with member.
Green fees: £10 per round; £12 per
day.
Society meetings: by appointment
weekdays only.
Catering: lunch and dinner by
appointment. Bar meals available
until 9.30 pm.
Hotels: Foxley; Post House.

G13 Boxmoor
☎Hemel Hempstead (0442) 42434
18 Box Lane, Hemel Hempstead,
Herts.
0.75 mile from Hemel Hempstead
station on A41.
Undulating parkland course.
9 holes, 4854 yards, S.S.S.64
Club founded in 1890.
Visitors: welcome weekdays; not
Sun.
Green fees: £5 weekdays; £6 Sat.
Society meetings: welcome with
four weeks notice.

Catering: limited service available.
Hotels: numerous in area.

G14 Boyce Hill
☎South Benfleet (0268) 793625
Vicarage Hill, South Benfleet, Essex
SS7 1PD.
7 miles W of Southend-on-Sea, A127
to Rayleigh Weir (3 miles from
course), A13 to Victoria House
Corner (1 mile from course).
Undulating parkland course.
18 holes, 5882 yards, S.S.S.68
Course designed by J. Braid.
Club founded in 1922.
Visitors: welcome weekdays,
weekends with members.
Green fees: £12 per round/day.
Society meetings: Thurs only.
Catering: service throughout day.
Hotels: Crest; Airport.

G15 Braintree
☎Braintree (0376) 24117
Kings Lane, Stisted, Braintree, Essex
CM7 8DA.
1.5 miles NE of Braintree on A120.
Parkland course.
18 holes, 6026 yards, S.S.S.69
Course designed by Hawtree and
Son.
Visitors: welcome except Sun; Sat
with handicap certificate.
Green fees: £9 per round, £12 per
day weekdays, (£5.50 per round or
£8.50 per day with member)
weekends and Bank Holiday
handicap certificate required; £11 per
round; £21 per day;

(£6.50 per round or £12.50 per day
with member).
Society meetings: welcome by
arrangement on Mon, Wed and
Thurs (Tues Ladies Day).
Catering: meals served.
Hotels: White Hart, Braintree.

G16 Brickendon Grange
☎Bayford (099 286) 258
Brickendon, Nr.Hertford, Herts
SG13 8PD.
3 miles S of Hertford near Bayford
station.
Undulating parkland course.
18 holes, 6315 yards, S.S.S.70
Course designed by C.K. Cotton.
Club founded in 1968.
Visitors: welcome weekdays.
Green fees: on application.
Society meetings: welcome
weekdays.
Catering: snack lunch served.
Hotels: numerous good hotels in
area.

G17 Brookmans Park
☎Potters Bar (0707) 52487
Golf Club Rd, Hatfield, Herts
AL9 7AT.
On Hatfield Rd, A1000 1 mile N of
Potters Bar, 3 miles S of Hatfield.
Parkland course.
18 holes, 6438 yards, S.S.S.70
Club founded in 1930.
Visitors: welcome weekdays and at
weekends with member and
handicap certificate.
Green fees: on application.

Society meetings: accepted on
Wed, Thurs and Fri.
Catering: snacks served at
lunchtime; evening meals available
only for societies.
Hotels: Royal Chase, Enfield; West
Lodge Park, Barnet; Ponsbourne,
Hertford.

G18 Bunsay Downs
☎Danbury (024 541) 2648 or 2369
Members.
Little Baddow Rd, Woodham Walter,
Nr Maldon, Essex.
Leave A414 at Danbury (signposted
Woodham Walter), course 0.5 mile to
W of village.
Gently undulating meadowland
course.
9 holes, 2913 yards, S.S.S.68
Club founded in 1982.
Visitors: welcome.
Green fees: weekdays £3.50 (9
holes), £4.50 (18 holes); weekends
£4 (9 holes), £5 (18 holes).
Society meetings: welcome.
Catering: breakfast, lunch, evening
meals available from 10am (8am
weekends) to 10pm.
Hotels: many good hotels in
Chelmsford and Maldon.

G19 Burnham-on-Crouch
☎Maldon (0621) 782282
Ferry Rd, Creeksea, Burnham-on-
Crouch, Essex CM0 8PQ.
1.25 miles W of Creeksea.
Undulating meadowland course.
9 holes, 5350 yards, S.S.S.68

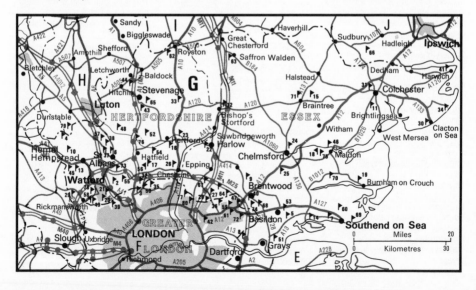

Club founded in 1918.
Visitors: welcome but not on weekend mornings.
Green fees: £7 weekdays; £9 weekends.
Society meetings: catered for mainly Wed (Ladies day Thurs).
Catering: bar snacks available except Mon, evening meals by arrangement.
Hotels: White Hart; The Quay, Burnham-on-Crouch.

G20 Bushey G & CC
☎01-950 2283
High St, Bushey, Herts.
On A411 1.5 miles from M1/A411 junction.
Private parkland course.
9 holes, 3000 yards, S.S.S.69
Course designed by Donald Steel.
Club founded in 1980.
Visitors: weekday before 6pm; weekend and Bank Holiday after 2pm; no visitors Wed.
Green fees: £5 weekdays; £9 weekends.
Society meetings: by arrangement. Limited numbers only. Not Wed.
Catering: meals served.
Hotels: Ladbrokes, Spiders Web.

G21 Bushey Hall
☎Watford (0923) 25802
Bushey Hall Drive, Bushey, Herts WD2 2EP.
1 mile SE of Watford.
Undulating parkland course.
18 holes, 6071 yards, S.S.S.69
Club founded in 1886.
Visitors: welcome on weekdays.
Green fees: on application.
Society meetings: catered for on weekdays, except Wed.
Catering: full service available.
Hotels: numerous hotels in London area.

G22 Canons Brook
☎Harlow (0279) 30976
Elizabeth Way, Harlow, Essex CM19 5BE.
M11 to Harlow, Edinburgh Way then Elizabeth Way.
Parkland course.
18 holes, 6462 yards, S.S.S.72
Course designed by Henry Cotton.
Club founded in 1963.
Visitors: welcome weekdays.
Green fees: £12 per day.
Society meetings: welcome weekdays.
Catering: lunch, dinners except Sun, Mon.
Hotels: Churchgate; Moat House.

G23 Chadwell Springs
☎Ware (0920) 3647
Hertford Rd, Ware, Herts SG12 9LE.
On A119 halfway between Hertford and Ware.
Parkland course.
9 holes, 3209 yards, S.S.S.71
Course designed by J.H. Taylor.
Club founded in 1975.
Visitors: welcome weekdays, weekends afternoons (subject to competition times).
Green fees: weekdays £4 (9 holes); £6 (18 holes); £9 day ticket.
Society meetings: welcome on weekdays.
Catering: meals served.
Hotels: Salisbury Arms, Hertford; Cannons, Ware.

G24 Channels
☎Chelmsford (0254) 440005
Belsteads Farm Lane, Little Waltham, Chelmsford, Essex CM3 3PT.
Undulating course.
18 holes, 6100 yards, S.S.S.69
Course designed by Cotton, Pennink, Lawrie and Partners.

Club founded in 1974.
Visitors: welcome weekdays without member.
Green fees: £10.50 (£6 with member).
Society meetings: weekdays only.
Catering: excellent table d'hôte, à la carte.
Hotels: County, Chelmsford.

G25 Chelmsford
☎Chelmsford (0245) 256483
Widford Rd, Chelmsford, Essex CM2 9AP.
A12 to Wood St roundabout, Chelmsford, turn right (from London) and right again.
Undulating parkland course.
18 holes, 5912 yards, S.S.S.68
Club founded in 1892.
Visitors: welcome weekdays if members of recognised club; weekends with member only.
Green fees: £15 per round/day.
Society meetings: limited number by arrangement. Wed and Thurs only.
Catering: lunch served except Mon, dinners Fri and Sat only, bar snacks every day.
Hotels: South Lodge, Miami, Chelmsford.

G26 Cheshunt
☎Waltham Cross (0992) 24009
Park Lane, Cheshunt, Herts EN7 6QD.
A10 to Cheshunt, then signposted.
Parkland course.
18 holes, 6608 yards, S.S.S.71
Club founded in 1976.
Visitors: welcome weekdays and by arrangement at weekends.
Green fees: £3.50 weekdays; £5 weekends.
Society meetings: catered for any time by arrangement.

Catering: cafeteria service all day.

G27 Chigwell
☎01-500 2059
High Rd, Chigwell, Essex IG7 5DH.
On A113, 13.5 miles NE of London.
Parkland course.
18 holes, 6279 yards, S.S.S.71
Club founded in 1925.
Visitors: welcome weekdays only.
Green fees: £11 per round; £15 per day.
Society meetings: welcome weekdays only.
Catering: Mon-Sat lunch; dinner by arrangement.
Hotels: Prince Regent; Roebuck.

G28 Chingford
☎01-529 5708
Bury Rd, Chingford, London E4.
Off Station Rd.
Parkland course.
18 holes, 6309 yards, S.S.S.69
Course designed by James Braid.
Club founded in 1888.
Visitors: welcome, red outer garment must be worn.
Green fees: £3.45 weekdays; £5.15 weekends; £1.55 OAP (10am-3pm)
Society meetings: by appointment.
Catering: snacks, no bar.

G29 Chorleywood
☎Chorleywood (092 78) 2009
Common Rd, Chorleywood.
Clubhouse close to Chorleywood station and Sportsman Hotel.
Parkland course.
9 holes, 5676 yards, S.S.S.67
Club founded in 1890.
Visitors: welcome weekdays except Tues and Thurs mornings.
Green fees: £6 weekdays.
Society meetings: by arrangement.
Catering: snacks available except Wed.
Hotels: The Sportsman, Chorleywood.

G30 Clacton-on-Sea
☎Clacton-on-Sea (0255)421919
West Rd, Clacton-on-Sea, Essex CO15 1AJ.
On A133 16 miles from Colchester, 1 mile W of pier next to old Butlins Holiday Camp.
Undulating seaside course.
18 holes, 6217 yards, S.S.S.70
Course designed by Jack White.
Club founded in 1892.
Visitors: midweek subject to availability; weekends and Bank Holidays handicap certificate only.

Green fees: £5 per round, £10 per day weekdays; £12 weekends and Bank Holidays.
Society meetings: by prior arrangement with Sec.
Catering: full except Mon.
Hotels: Royal; Glengarry.

G31 Colchester
☎Colchester (0206) 853396
Braiswick, Colchester, Essex CO4 5AU
0.75 mile up Bergholt Rd from Colchester North station.
Parkland course.
18 holes, 6319 yards, S.S.S.70
Course designed by James Braid.
Club founded in 1907.
Visitors: welcome weekdays; weekends with member.
Green fees: £12 per day, £8 per round.
Society meetings: weekdays by arrangement.
Catering: available.
Hotels: Marks Tey Motel; George.

G32 Dyrham Park
☎01-440 3361
Galley Lane, Barnet, Herts.
2 miles outside Barnet near Arkley, off A1
Parkland course.
18 holes, 6369 yards S.S.S.70
Course designed by C.K.Cotton.
Club founded in 1963.
Visitors: only as guest of member or member of Golf Society.
Green fees: £7 weekdays; £10 weekends.
Society meetings: Wed only; two rounds golf light lunch; dinner or lunch and afternoon tea.
Catering: full restaurant facilities.
Hotels: Crest, Bignalls Corner.

G33 East Herts
☎Ware (0920) 821978 Sec
Hamels Park, Buntingford, Herts SG9 9NA.
A10 between Buntingford and Ware, 0.25 mile N of Puckeridge roundabout.
Parkland course.
18 holes, 6449 yards, S.S.S.71
Club founded in 1898.
Visitors: Mon-Fri only.
Green fees: £12 per round, £15 per day.
Society meetings: larger Mon and Fri; restricted to 20 members other times.
Catering: facilities available.
Hotels: Ware Moat House on A10.

G34 Frinton
☎Frinton (025 56) 4618
Esplanade, Frinton-on-Sea, Essex CO13 9EP.
A133 Colchester to Weeley village, B1033 to Frinton and turn right at seafront.
Seaside course.
18 holes, 6259 yards, S.S.S.70
Course designed by Tom Dunn.
Club founded in 1896.
Visitors: welcome weekdays.
Green fees: £11 per round weekdays; £12 per round weekends after 11.30am.
Society meetings: catered for weekdays.
Catering: meals available except Mon.
Hotels: Maplin; Rock; Glencoe.

G35 Hadley Wood
☎01-499 4328
Beech Hill, Barnet, Herts EN4 0JJ.
From junction 24, M25 take A111 towards Cockfosters, third turning right into Beech Hill, entrance 400 yards on left.
Parkland course.
18 holes, 6473 yards, S.S.S.71
Course designed by Alister Mackenzie.
Club founded in 1921.
Visitors: weekday - require handicap certificate or identification of club membership. At weekends only if playing with member.
Green fees: £12 per round; £18 per day.
Society meetings: by arrangement.
Catering: morning coffee, lunch, dinner,
for functions and societies.
Hotels: West Park Lodge; Hadley.

G36 Hainault Forest
☎01-500 2097
Chigwell Row, Hainault, Essex.
On A217 12 miles from Central London.
Parkland course.
18 holes, 5754 yards, S.S.S.67
18 holes, 6445 yards, S.S.S.71
Club founded in 1912.
Visitors: public course.
Green fees: on application.
Catering: meals served.
Hotels: Valentine, Gants Hill.

G37 Harpenden
☎Harpenden (058 27) 2580
Hammonds End, Redbourn Lane, Harpenden, Herts AL5 2AX.
Off A1081 4 miles N of St Albans on

B487
Parkland course.
18 holes, 6363 yards, S.S.S.70
Visitors: welcome on weekdays only.
Green fees: on application.
Society meetings: catered for on weekdays except Thurs.
Catering: by arrangement.
Hotels: Moathouse; Gleneagles.

G38 Harpenden Common
☎Harpenden (058 27) 2856
East Common, Harpenden, Herts AL5 1BL.
Off A5183, 4 miles from St Albans on B487.
Commonland course.
18 holes, 5613 yards, S.S.S.67
Club founded in 1931.
Visitors: welcome Mon, Wed, Thurs, Fri.
Green fees: £10 per day; £7.50 per round.
Society meetings: Thurs and Fri.
Catering: lunch served except Mon.
Hotels: Gleneagles, Harpenden; Aubrey Park, Redbourne.

G39 Hartsbourne G & CC
☎01-950 1133
Hartsbourne Ave, Bushey Heath, Herts WD2 1JW.
Turn S of A411 at entrance to Bushey Heath village 5 miles SE of Watford.
Parkland course.
18 holes, 6305 yards, S.S.S.70
9 holes, 5432 yards, S.S.S.70
Club founded in 1946.
Visitors: accompanied by member only.
Green fees: not applicable.
Society meetings: welcome Wed and Fri.
Catering: lunch except Mon and Fri.
Hotels: Spiders Web; Ladbroke Mercury; both on A41.

G40 Hartswood
☎Brentwood (0277) 21850 Sec.
King Georges Playing Fields, Ingrave Rd, Brentwood Essex.
1 mile S of Brentwood on A128.
Municipal parkland course.
18 holes, 6160 yards, S.S.S.69
Club founded in 1964.
Visitors: welcome.
Green fees: £5 weekend; £3 weekdays.
Society meetings: not weekends.
Catering: lunch, bar snacks except Sun.
Hotels: Post House, Brentwood;

Ye Olde Plough House Motel, Bulphan.

G41 Harwich & Dovercourt
☎Harwich (0255) 503616
Station Rd, Parkeston, Harwich, Essex CO12 4NZ.
A120 towards Parkeston Quay, after last roundabout 200 yards on left.
Meadowland course.
9 holes, 5692 yards, S.S.S.68
Club founded in 1903.
Visitors: welcome
Green fees: on application.
Society meetings: welcome by arrangement.
Catering: bar snacks or full catering as required.
Hotels: Cliff, Dovercourt; Towers, Dovercourt.

G42 Ilford
☎01-554 2930
291 Wanstead Park Rd, Ilford, Essex IG1 3TR.
0.5 mile from Ilford railway station.
Parkland course.
18 holes, 5414 yards, S.S.S.68
Club founded in 1906.
Visitors: welcome Sat, Sun and Bank Holidays. Limited to member and guests.
Green fees: £6.50 per round (18 holes).
Society meetings: catered for weekdays.
Catering: restaurant most days.

G43 Knebworth
☎Stevenage (0438) 812752
Deards End Lane, Knebworth, Herts SG3 6NL.
1 mile S of Stevenage on B197.
Parkland course.
18 holes, 6428 yards, S.S.S.71
Club founded in 1908.
Visitors: weekdays unaccompanied; weekends, Bank Holidays with member only.
Green fees: £13 per day; £10 per round.
Society meetings: Mon-Fri (some restrictions on Fri); £24 all day.
Catering: facilities daily.
Hotels: Roebuck Inn, London Rd; Heath Lodge, Danesbury Park Rd.

G44 Letchworth
☎Letchworth (0462) 683203
Letchworth Lane, Letchworth, Herts SG6 3NQ.
2 miles from A1(M), near village of Willian, adjacent to Letchworth Hall Hotel.

Parkland course.
18 holes, 6082 yards, S.S.S.69
Course re-designed by Harry Vardon.
Club founded in 1905.
Visitors: weekdays with members only; weekends unaccompanied.
Green fees: £12.50 per day.
Society meetings: Wed, Thurs, Fri.
Catering: except Monday.
Hotels: Letchworth Hall.

G45 Little Hay
☎Hemel Hempstead (0442) 833783
Hemel Hempstead, Herts.
Off A41 at Box Lane traffic lights.
Meadowland course.
18 holes, 6610 yards, S.S.S.72
Course designed by Hawtree and Son.
Club founded in 1977.
Visitors: welcome.
Green fees: on application.
Society meetings: by arrangement.
Catering: full meal facilities.
Hotels: Bobsleigh.

G46 Maldon
☎Maldon (0621) 53212
Beeleigh, Langford, Maldon, Essex CM9 7SS.
2 miles NW of Maldon on B1019, turn off at the Essex Waterworks in Langford.
Meadowland course.
9 holes, 6197 yards, S.S.S.69
Club founded in 1891.
Visitors: welcome weekdays only.
Green fees: £7 per round; £9 per day.
Society meetings: weekdays by arrangement.
Catering: by arrangement.
Hotels: Blue Boar; Kings Head, High St, Maldon.

G47 Maylands G & CC
☎Ingrebourne (040 23) 73080
Colchester Rd, Harold Park, Romford, Essex RM3 0AZ.
On A12 between Romford and Brentwood.
Undulating parkland course.
18 holes, 6182 yards, S.S.S.69 (Ladies S.S.S.72)
Course designed by Colt, Alison and Morrison
Club founded in 1936.
Visitors: welcome if playing with member or if member of other club weekdays only.
Green fees: £10 weekdays.
Society meetings: Mon, Wed, Fri minimum numbers 20, maximum 40.

Price includes meal and 36 holes.
Catering: meals available, bar lunch.
Hotels: Post House; Ladbrokes.

G48 **Mid-Herts**
☎Wheathampstead (058 283) 2242
Gustard Wood, Wheathampstead, St
Albans, Herts AL4 8RS.
On B651 6 miles N of St Albans
Heathland/parkland course.
18 holes, 6094 yards, S.S.S.69
Club founded in 1893.
Visitors: Tues not before 1pm; Wed
not after 1pm. Weekends, Bank
Holidays only with a member.
Green fees: £14 per round/day.
Society meetings: Thurs - Fri only.
Catering: every day except Sun.
Hotels: St Michael's Manor, St
Albans.

G49 **Moor Park**
☎Rickmansworth (0923) 773146
Moor Park Mansion, Moor Park,
Rickmansworth, WD3 1QN.
Situated on A404 between
Rickmansworth and Northwood,
0.75 mile from Moor Park station.
Parkland course.
High-18 holes, 6713 yards, S.S.S.72
West-18 holes, 5815 yards, S.S.S.68
High championship tees 6903 yards,
S.S.S.73
Course designed by H.S. Colt.
Club founded in 1923.
Visitors: welcome with 24 hours
notice.
Green fees: on request.
Society meetings: accepted on
Mon, Tues, Wed and Fri.
Catering: snacks and meals served.
Hotels: Grimsdyke; Sportsman;
Belhouse.

G50 **Old Fold Manor**
☎01-440 9185
Hadley Green, Barnet, Herts.
On Potters Bar road, 0.25 mile from
Barnet.
Parkland course.
18 holes, 6449 yards, S.S.S.71
Club founded in 1910.
Visitors: welcome on weekdays,
with member only at weekends.
Green fees: £13 per day.
Society meetings: welcome Thurs
only.
Catering: meals served except Mon
and Wed.

G51 **Orsett**
☎(0375) 891352
Brentwood Rd, Orsett, Essex
RM16 3DS.
On A128 400 yds from A13.

Heathland course.
18 holes, 6622 yards, S.S.S.72
Course designed by James Braid.
Club founded in 1898.
Visitors: welcome by arrangement
weekdays.
Green fees: £12 per round, £15 per
day.
Society meetings: Mon, Tues, Wed
by arrangement.
Catering: restaurant seven days
8.30am-8.30pm.
Hotels: Orsett Hall; Plough Motel.

G52 **Panshanger**
☎Welwyn Garden City (0707)
333350
Herns Lane, Welwyn Garden City,
Herts.
Off B1000 close to A1, 1 mile NE of
town.
Undulating parkland course.
18 holes, 6538 yards, S.S.S.70
Club founded in 1976.
Visitors: unrestricted.
Green fees: £4 weekdays; £4.50
weekends and Bank Holidays.
Society meetings: welcome.
Catering: lunch every day.

G53 **Pipps Hill**
☎Basildon (0268) 23456
Aquatels Recreation Centre, Cranes
Farm Rd, Basildon, Essex.
Off A127 or A13.
Meadowland course.
9 holes, 2829 yards, S.S.S.67
Visitors: welcome.
Green fees: £4 weekdays; £5
weekends.
Society meetings: welcome
weekdays.
Catering: meals served.
Hotels: Essex Centre.

G54 **London CC**
☎Potters Bar (0707) 42624/42626
Bedwell Park, Essendon, Hatfield,
Herts AL9 6JA.
A1000 from Potters Bar, B158
towards Essendon.
Undulating parkland course.
18 holes, 6878 yards, S.S.S.73
Course designed by Fred Hawtree.
Club founded in 1976.
Visitors: welcome.
Green fees: £6 weekdays; £10.50
Sat, £11.50 Sun and Bank Holidays.
Society meetings: welcome.
Catering: bar snacks at lunchtime.
Hotels: numerous hotels in area.

G55 **Porters Park**
☎Radlett (092 76) 4127 Sec.
Shenley Hill, Radlett, Herts

WD7 7AZ.
Turn off A5183 to Shenley road at
railway station, 0.5 mile to top of hill,
club on bend of road.
Undulating parkland course.
18 holes, 6313 yards, S.S.S.70
Club founded in early 1890s-1899 at
present site.
Visitors: welcome weekdays.
Green fees: £15 per round, £20 per
day.
Society meetings: Wed, Thurs only
(Mar-Oct) 30-40 strong preferred.
Catering: own chef, full catering for
societies. Bar snacks other days
unless specially ordered.
Hotels: Red Lion, Radlett.

G56 **Potters Bar**
☎Potters Bar (0707) 52020
Darkes Lane, Potters Bar, Herts
EN6 1DE.
A1000 N of Barnet, Tesco opposite
entrance to club.
Undulating parkland course.
18 holes, 6273 yards, S.S.S.70
Course designed by James Braid.
Club founded in 1923.
Visitors: welcome weekdays.
Green fees: on application.
Society meetings: Mon, Tues, Fri.
Catering: lunch served daily.
Hotels: Brookmans Park.

G57 **Redbourn**
☎Redbourn (058 285) 3493
Kingsbourne Green Lane, Redbourn,
Herts AL3 7AQ.
S of M1 at junction 9 on to A5, turn
left, 1 mile down Luton Lane.
Parkland course.
18 holes, 6407 yards, S.S.S.71
9 holes, 1361 yards, Par 27 (public
course).
Course designed by H. Stovin.
Visitors: welcome weekdays.
Green fees: £6.50 weekdays, (£5
with member); weekends and Bank
Holidays £7 with member before
3pm.
Society meetings: Mon, Tues and
Thurs.
Catering: fully licensed bar, bar
snacks; restaurant meals daily by
arrangement; functions catered for.
Hotels: Aubrey Park.

G58 **Rickmansworth**
☎Rickmansworth (0923) 775278
Moor Lane, Rickmansworth, Herts
WD3 1QL.
A4145, 2 miles S of town.
Undulating municipal parkland
course.
18 holes, 4551 yards, S.S.S.62

Club founded in 1944/5
Visitors: welcome.
Green fees: £4.30 weekdays; £5 weekends, Bank Holidays.
Society meetings: catered for weekdays.
Catering: meals served all day.
Hotels: numerous hotels in area.

G59 **Risebridge**
☎Romford (0708) 41429
Risebridge Chase, Lower Bedfords Rd, Romford, Essex.
2 miles from Gallows Corner and Romford station.
Parkland course (also pitch & putt).
18 holes, 5237 yards, S.S.S.70
Visitors: welcome - bookings for weekends.
Green fees: £3.10 weekdays; £4.75 weekends.
Society meetings: by arrangement.
Catering: snacks daily.
Hotels: Brentwood Post House.

G60 **Rochford Hundred**
☎Southend (0702) 544302
Rochford Hall, Hall Rd, Rochford, Essex SS4 1NW.
Off Rochford to Southend road adjacent to airport. 4 miles N of Southend.
Parkland course.
18 holes, 6255 yards, S.S.S.69
Course designed by James Braid.
Club founded in 1893.
Visitors: welcome weekdays and with member only at weekends.
Green fees: £12 per round, £15 per day.
Society meetings: by arrangement on Wed or Thurs.
Catering: lunch only Mon-Fri.
Hotels: Airport, Aviation Way.

G61 **Romford**
☎Romford (0277) 40986
Heath Drive, Gidea Park, Romford, Essex RM2 5QB.
1.5 miles from Romford town centre, off A12.
Parkland course.
18 holes, 6365 yards, S.S.S.70
Course designed by James Braid.
Club founded in 1894.
Visitors: welcome weekdays only if member of golf club.
Green fees: £10 per round, £14 per day (not weekends).
Society meetings: available.
Catering: available.
Hotels: The Moat House, Brentwood.

G62 **Royston**
☎Royston (0763) 42696
Baldock Rd, Royston, Herts SG8 5BG.
Situated on the A505 on outskirts of town to E, actual golf course on Therfield Heath.
Undulating heathland course.
18 holes, 6032 yards, S.S.S.69
Club founded in 1892.
Visitors: welcome.
Green fees: £7 weekdays; £9 weekends.
Society meetings: by arrangement with Sec.
Catering: full facilities available.
Hotels: Old Bull Inn; The Banyers.

G63 **Saffron Walden**
☎Saffron Walden (0799) 22786
Windmill Hill, Saffron Walden, Essex CB10 1BX.
Take B184 from Stumps Cross roundabout on M11 (Junction 9), entrance just before entering town.
Parkland course.
18 holes, 6608 yards, S.S.S.72
Club founded in 1919.
Visitors: welcome weekdays but only with member at weekends and Bank Holidays.
Green fees: £14 per round, (£7 with member).
Society meetings: Mon, Wed, Thurs, occasional Fri.
Catering: lunch available every weekday; evening meals for societies.
Hotels: Saffron.

G64 **Skips**
☎Ingrebourne (040 23) 48234
Horsemanside, Tysea Hill, Stapleford Abbotts, Essex RM4 1JU.
B175 to Stapleford Abbotts, left up Tysea Hill.
Meadowland course.
18 holes, 6146 yards, S.S.S.71
Course designed by Cotton, Pennink, Lawrie and Partners.
Club founded in 1972.
Visitors: welcome at all times.
Green fees: £2 per 9 holes, £3 per 18 holes weekdays; £3 per 9 holes, £4 per 18 holes weekends.
Society meetings: none.
Catering: no catering.
Hotels: Post House, Brentwood.

G65 **Stevenage**
☎Shephall (043 888) 424
Aston Lane, Aston, Stevenage, Herts SG2 7EL.

On to A602 to Hertford from A1, course signposted about 1.5 miles.
Parkland/meadowland course.
18 holes, 6451 yards, S.S.S.71
Course designed by John Jacobs.
Club founded in 1972.
Visitors: welcome every day, but necessary to book at weekends.
Green fees: £3.25 weekdays; £4.70 weekends.
Society meetings: welcome weekdays.
Catering: full meals and bar snacks.
Hotels: Roebuck.

G66 **Stoke-by-Nayland**
☎Nayland (0206) 262836
Keepers Lane, Leavenheath, Colchester, Essex CO6 4PZ.
A134 from Colchester for 7 miles, turn off onto B1068 to Stoke-by-Nayland.
Undulating meadowland course.
18 holes, 6471 yards, S.S.S.71
18 holes, 6498 yards, S.S.S.71
Club founded in 1972.
Visitors: unrestricted during week; after 10.30am weekends - must have handicap certificate and club membership.
Green fees: £9 per round, £12 per day weekdays; £11 per round, £14 per day weekends.
Society meetings: weekdays only by arrangement.
Catering: full facilities available.
Hotels: The Mill; The Bull; The Swan.

G67 **Theydon Bois**
☎Theydon Bois (0378) 3054
Theydon Rd, Epping, Essex CM16 4EH.
Off B172 1 mile S of Epping.
Undulating woodland course.
18 holes, 5472 yards, S.S.S.68
Course designed by James Braid.
Club founded in 1891.
Visitors: must be members of a club, must have proof of membership.
Green fees: £12 Mon, Tues, Fri; £12 Wed, Thurs pm; £18 Sat, Sun pm.
Society meetings: Mon Tues only £12.50 per day.
Catering: full facilities available.
Hotels: The Bell; Trust House Forte.

G68 **Thorndon Park**
☎Brentwood (0277) 811666
Ingrave, Brentwood, Essex CM13 3RH.
2 miles SE of Brentwood on A128.
Parkland course.

18 holes, 6455 yards, S.S.S.71
Club founded in 1920.
Visitors: welcome weekdays and
with member weekends.
Green fees: £12 per round; £18 per
day.
Society meetings: catered for Tues
and Fri.
Catering: meals served weekdays
except Mon.
Hotels: Post House, Brentwood.

G69 **Thorpe Hall**
☎Southend-on-Sea (0702) 582205
Thorpe Hall Ave, Thorpe Bay, Essex
SS1 3AT.
Thorpe Hall Ave joins the seafront,
about 2 miles E of Southend Pier.
Parkland/meadowland course.
18 holes, 6259 yards, S.S.S.71
Club founded in 1907.
Visitors: welcome weekdays.
Green fees: £15 per day/round.
Society meetings: catered for Wed
and Fri only.
Catering: lunch served except Mon.
Hotels: Roslin; Ilfracombe; West
Park.

G70 **Three Rivers G & CC**
☎Maldon (0621) 828631
Stow Rd, Purleigh, Nr Chelmsford,
Essex CM3 6RR.
From London A127 to A130 to A132,
on B1012 from Chelmsford (10
miles), A12 to A130 to A132.
Parkland course.
Kings course 18 holes, 6609 yards,
S.S.S.72
Queens course 9 holes x 2, 2142
yards, Par 54.
Course designed by Fred Hawtree.
Club founded in 1973.
Visitors: weekdays and pm
weekends with member only,
restricted according to
competitions.
Green fees: £12, (£7.50 with
member) weekdays; £12, (£10 with
member) weekends.
Society meetings: Tues and Thurs
preferred other days by arrange-
ment.
Catering: at all times.
Hotels: Three Rivers G & CC

G71 **Towerlands**
☎Braintree (0376) 26802
Panfield Rd, Braintree, Essex
CM7 5BJ.
Course on B1053 out of Braintree.
Undulating meadowland course.
9 holes, 2698 yards S.S.S.66
18 holes, 5406 yards, S.S.S.66

Course designed by G.R. Shiels.
Club founded in 1985.
Visitors: welcome anytime not
before 12.30 Sun.
Green fees: £3 per (9 holes), £5 per
(18 holes) weekdays; £7 per (18
holes) weekends and Bank Holidays.
Society meetings: welcome
anytime by arrangement.
Catering: full bar and restaurant
facilities.
Hotels: various in Braintree.

G72 **Upminster**
☎Upminster (040 22) 22788
114 Hall Lane, Upminster, Essex.
A127 towards Southend.
Parkland course.
18 holes, 5926 yards, S.S.S.68
Club founded in 1927.
Visitors: welcome weekdays if
members of a recognised club.
Green fees: £9 per round, £15 per
day.
Society meetings: by arrangement.
Catering: meals served except Mon.
Hotels: Ladbroke; Post House.

G73 **Verulam**
☎St Albans (0727) 53327.
London Rd, St Albans, Herts AL1
1TG.
A1081 to St Albans.
Parkland course.
18 holes, 6836 yards, S.S.S.71
Visitors: welcome weekdays.
Green fees: £6 per round, £9 per
day Mon; £10 per round, £12 per day
Tues-Fri.
Society meetings: Tues, Thurs, Fri.
Catering: full facilities except Mon,
bar snacks only.
Hotels: Sopwell House; St Michaels
Manor.

G74 **Warley Park**
☎Brentwood (0277) 224891
Magpie Lane, Little Warley,
Brentwood, CM13 3DX.
Off M25 junction 29, A127 Southend
immediately left Gt Warley, left, first
right, left into Magpie Lane (6 mins
from M25).
Undulating parkland course.
27 holes, (3x9) played 1-2,1-3,2-3.
Course designed by R. Plumbridge.
Club founded in 1975.
Visitors: welcome with handicap
certificate.
Green fees: on application.
Society meetings: welcome by
arrangement.
Catering: first class restaurant.
Hotels: New World; Post House.

G75 **Warren**
☎Danbury (024 541) 3258
Woodham Walter, Maldon, Essex
CM9 6RW.
A414 6 miles E of Chelmsford
towards Maldon.
Undulating parkland course.
18 holes, 6211 yards, S.S.S.70
Club founded in 1934.
Visitors: welcome weekdays.
Green fees: £12.
Society meetings: Mon, Tues,
Thurs, Fri.
Catering: 7 day full facilities.
Hotels: Pontlands Park, Great
Baddow; Blue Boar, Maldon.

G76 **Welwyn Garden City**
☎Welwyn Garden City (0707)
325243
Mannicotts, High Oaks Rd, Welwyn
Garden City, Herts AL8 7BP.
Off A1 at Stanborough, follow B197
to town centre.
Undulating parkland course.
18 holes, 6200 yards, S.S.S.69
Course designed by Hawtree and
Son.
Club founded in 1922.
Visitors: welcome weekdays.
Green fees: £15 per day, £12.50 per
round.
Society meetings: Wed and Thurs
only.
Catering: bar snacks, lunch,
dinners.
Hotels: Clock; Heath Lodge Motel;
Crest, Welwyn Garden City.

G77 **West Essex**
☎01-529 4367 Pro, 529 7558
Bury Rd, Sewardstunkbury,
Chingford London E4 7QL.
Off A11, 0.75 mile from Chingford
station.
Parkland course.
18 holes, 6342 yards, S.S.S.70
Course designed by James Braid.
Club founded in 1900.
Visitors: welcome weekdays.
Green fees: £12 per round, £15 per
day, (£7 with member). No fees
unless with member Thurs
afternoons and weekends.
Society meetings: Mon, Wed, Fri.
Catering: lunch by arrangement
except Thurs.
Hotels: Royal Chase; Roebuck;
Woodford Moat.

G78 **West Herts**
☎Watford (0860) 513417 (Cellnet)
Cassiobury Park, Watford, Herts
WD1 7SL.

2 miles from Watford on A412.
Parkland course.
18 holes, 6488 yards, S.S.S.71
Course designed by Tom Morris &
Harry Vardon.
Visitors: welcome weekdays;
weekends with member only.
Green fees: on application.
Society meetings: welcome Wed
and Fri.
Catering: lunch and tea served
except Mon.
Hotels: Caledonian; Southern Cross.

G79 **Whipsnade Park**
☎Little Gaddesden (044 284) 2330
Studham Lane, Dagnall, Herts
HP4 1RH.

Off M1 at Junction 9 between
villages of Dagnall and Studham.
Parkland course.
18 holes, 6800 yards, S.S.S.72
Club founded in 1974.
Visitors: welcome mid-week.
Green fees: £8.50 per round, £12
per day.
Society meetings: welcome except
Mon and weekends.
Catering: restaurant and bar snacks,
except Mon.
Hotels: Post House, Hemel
Hempstead.

G80 **Woodford**
☎01-504 0553
2 Sunset Ave, Woodford Green,

Essex IG8 0ST.
A11 to Woodford Green, near Castle
Public House.
Parkland course.
9 holes, 5806 yards, S.S.S.68
Club founded in 1890.
Visitors: welcome weekdays, except
Tues and Thurs mornings and with
member only at weekends.
Green fees: £5 per round, £6 per
day.
Society meetings: by arrangement.
Catering: snacks served and meals
by arrangement.
Hotels: Castle; Packfords.

H Buckinghamshire, Bedfordshire, Oxfordshire and Northamptonshire

From Stoke Poges and Denham in the south to Woburn in the north, Buckinghamshire is full of good and enjoyable places to play. Beaconsfield, Burnham Beeches, Ellesborough, Harewood Downs and Gerrards Cross are further examples, although it is impossible for me not to link Berkshire and Oxfordshire with Buckinghamshire, as the men's county team does.

Huntercombe, Frilford Heath, Burford and Tadmarton Heath are obvious favourites in Oxfordshire but, for the geographical purposes of this Guide, Buckinghamshire and Oxfordshire are grouped with Northamptonshire and Bedfordshire, the latter with only about a dozen courses from which to draw their county teams.

Dunstable Downs and John O'Gaunt are two I can strongly recommend and, when crossing into Northamptonshire, the same goes for the Northamptonshire County Club at Church Brampton with its collection of excellent par 4s. Delapre Golf Complex has an assortment of attractions including a driving range, par 3 and pitch and putt courses to supplement a full 18 holes.

However, a word for the public courses in the area covered. Farnham Park near Slough, Abbey Hill at Milton Keynes, Windmill Hill at Bletchley, Mowsbury at Bedford and Stockwood Park at Luton are way above average.

H1 Abbey Hill
☎ Milton Keynes (0908) 562408
Monks Way, Two Mile Ash, Stony Stratford, Milton Keynes MK8 8AA.
2 miles S of Stony Stratford.
Meadowland course.
18 holes, 6193 yards, S.S.S.69
Course designed by Charles Lawrie.
Club founded in 1975.
Visitors: unrestricted.
Green fees: on application.
Society meetings: on application.
Catering: meals and snack bars.

H2 Aspley Guise & Woburn Sands
☎ Milton Keynes (0908) 583596
West Hill, Aspley Guise, Milton Keynes MK17 8DX.
2 miles S of M1 Junction 13, halfway between Aspley Guise and Woburn Sands.
Parkland course.
18 holes, 6115 yards, S.S.S.70
Course designed by Sandy Herd.
Club founded in 1914.
Visitors: welcome weekdays; with members weekends.
Green fees: £9 after 1pm; £12 before 1pm.
Society meetings: Wed and Fri.
Catering: full facilities except Mon.
Hotels: Bedford Arms, Woburn.

H3 Badgemore Park
☎ Henley-on-Thames (0491) 572206 Sec, 574175 Pro.
Badgemore Park, Henley-on-Thames, Oxon RG9 4NR.
Leave the M4 at Junction 8/9 on Henley and Oxford Spur, over the river into Henley, straight through the town (leaving the Town Hall on right), after 0.75 mile on right hand side.
Parkland course.
18 holes, 6112 yards, S.S.S.69
Course designed by Bob Sandow.
Club founded in July 1972.
Visitors: welcome weekdays; weekends by arrangement.
Green fees: £10 per round, £14 per day.
Society meetings: weekdays only, by arrangement.
Catering: full facilities available.
Hotels: Red Lion; Royal; Little White Hart.

H4 Beaconsfield
☎ Beaconsfield (049 46) 6545
Seer Green, Beaconsfield, Bucks HP9 2UR.
Off M40 onto A355 Amersham Rd, right at Jordans sign, adjacent to Seer Green/Jordans railway halt.
Parkland course.
18 holes, 6469 yards, S.S.S.71
Course designed by H.S. Colt.
Club founded in 1914.
Visitors: welcome weekdays.
Green fees: £15.
Society meetings: catered for Tues and Wed.
Catering: full facilities.
Hotels: The Bellhouse.

H5 Beadlow Manor
☎ Silsoe (0525) 60800
Beadlow, Shefford, Beds.
On A507 between Silsoe and Shefford, 1.5 miles W of Shefford.
Parkland course.
18 holes, 3021 yards, S.S.S.35
18 holes, 6238 yards, S.S.S.70
Club founded in 1973.
Visitors: welcome weekdays, weekends with handicap certificate.
Green fees: £12 per round, £17 per day weekdays; £15 per round, £20 per day weekends.
Society meetings: welcome anytime.
Catering: facilities in golf bar from 7am to 6pm. Restaurant on site after 6pm.
Hotels: on site.

H6 Bedford & County
☎ Bedford (0234) 52617
Green Lane, Clapham, Beds

MK41 6ET.
Off A6 N of Bedford before Clapham village.
Parkland course.
18 holes, 6347 yards, S.S.S.70
Club founded 1912.
Visitors: welcome weekdays, booking advisable. With member only at weekends.
Green fees: £9 per round, £11 per day.
Society meetings: restricted to Tues, Thurs and Fri.
Catering: available at all times for all parties. Please telephone.
Hotels: Shakespeare; Woodlands Manor.

H7 Bedfordshire
☎Bedford (0234) 61669
Bromham Rd, Biddenham, Bedford MK40 4AF.
1.5 miles from town centre on A428, NW of town boundary.
Parkland course.
18 holes, 6172 yards, S.S.S.69
Club founded in 1891.
Visitors: welcome weekdays and by appointment weekends.
Green fees: £10 per round, £12 per day.
Society meetings: catered for on weekdays.
Catering: lunch served every day.
Hotels: Moat House; Woodlands; De Parys Guest House.

H8 Bremhill Park
☎Shrivenham (0793) 782946
Shrivenham, Swindon, Wilts SN6 8HH.
A420 Swindon to Oxford road 6 miles from Swindon, leave by-pass for Shrivenham, club on E boundary of village.
Parkland course.
18 holes, 6040 yards, S.S.S.71
Course designed by D. Wright.
Club founded in 1968.
Visitors: welcome anytime, advance booking Sunday.
Green fees: £7 per day, (£4 with member); £9 weekends, (£6 with member).
Society meetings: catered for.
Catering: light snacks and meals served.
Hotels: Crest; South Marston and C.C, Swindon.

H9 Buckingham
☎Buckingham (0280) 815566
Tingewick Rd, Buckingham MK18 4AE.

2 miles from Buckingham on A421 towards Oxford.
Undulating parkland course.
18 holes, 6082 yards, S.S.S.69
Club founded in 1914.
Visitors: weekdays; members guests only at weekend.
Green fees: £12.
Society meetings: pre booking with Sec Tues to Fri only.
Catering: 7 days lunch, dinner.
Hotels: White Hart, Buckingham.

H10 Burford
☎Burford (099 382) 2583
Burford, Oxon OX8 4JG.
19 miles W of Oxford at junction of A40 and A361, at Burford round-about.
Parkland course.
18 holes, 6405 yards, S.S.S.71
Club founded in 1936.
Visitors: by arrangement.
Green fees: £13 per day.
Society meetings: limited.
Catering: full facilities available.
Hotels: over 12 hotels within 1 mile of course.

H11 Burnham Beeches
☎Burnham (062 86) 61448 Sec.
Green Lane, Burnham, Bucks SL1 8EG.
Take M40 to Beaconsfield turn off, follow signs to Slough, turn right and follow Burnham signs (not Burnham Beeches) to Green Lane.
Parkland course.
18 holes, 6415 yards, S.S.S.71
Club founded in 1891.
Visitors: Mon-Fri. Weekends guest of member.
Green fees: £13.50 per round, £16.50 per day.
Society meetings: Wed, Thurs, Fri.
Catering: full facilities except Mon.
Hotels: Burnham Beeches; Holiday Inn.

H12 Cherwell Edge
☎Banbury (0295) 711591
Chacombe, Banbury, Oxon.
3 miles E of Banbury, A442 to Northampton.
Public parkland course.
18 holes, 5322 metres, S.S.S.68
Course designed by Richard Davies.
Club founded in 1983.
Visitors: welcome 7 days.
Green fees:£3.20 weekdays; £4.20 weekends; £5.60 day ticket mid-week.
Society meetings: catered for Mon-Sat.

Catering: lunch, bar snacks, evening meals.
Hotels: Whatley Arms; Thatched House.

H13 Chesham & Ley Hill
☎Chesham (0494) 784541
Ley Hill, Chesham, Bucks HP5 1UZ.
A41, left at Boxmoor, to Bovingdon and follow signs.
Heathland course.
9 holes, 5147 yards, S.S.S.65
Club founded in 1919.
Visitors: welcome weekdays except Tues and Fri after 1pm; weekends with member only.
Green fees: on application.
Society meetings: by arrangement with committee.
Catering: light meals and snacks except Mon.
Hotels: at Chesham.

H14 Chesterton
☎Bicester (0869) 241204
Chesterton, Bicester, Oxon OX6 8TE.
From Oxford take Northampton road, then Chesterton sign at Weston-on-the-Green for 1 mile.
Meadowland course.
18 holes, 6520 yards, S.S.S.71
Course designed by R.R. Stagg.
Club founded in 1973/74.
Visitors: no restrictions.
Green fees: on application.
Society meetings: midweek, not Tues, by arrangement.
Catering: daily, bar food 12am-3pm (last orders 2.30pm), full group catering by arrangement 20-170 people.
Hotels: Weston Manor; Littlebury; Kings Arms; Jersey Arms.

H15 Chipping Norton
☎Chipping Norton (0608) 2383
Southcombe, Chipping Norton, Oxon.
0.5 mile S of town centre on London road or junction of A34/A44 on left driving north.
Parkland course.
9 holes, 6142 yards, S.S.S.69
Visitors: welcome weekdays only, unless with member.
Green fees: £10.
Society meetings: welcome weekdays.
Catering: full facilities.
Hotels: Crown & Cushion; White Hart.

H16 **City of Coventry (Brandon Wood)**
☎Coventry (0203) 543141
Brandon Lane, Brandon, Coventry.
On A45 6 miles S of Coventry, 120 yards S of London Rd roundabout.
Parkland course.
18 holes, 6530 yards, S.S.S.71
Course designed by Frank Pennink
Visitors: welcome.

Green fees: on application.
Society meetings: welcome but must book.
Catering: meals served every day.
Hotels: Brandon Hall.

H17 **Cold Ashby**
☎Northampton (0604) 740548, or 740099 Pro.
Cold Ashby, Northampton NN6 7EP.

5 miles E of Junction 18 (M1), just off A50 Northampton to Leicester road.
Undulating meadowland course.
18 holes, 5898 yards, S.S.S.69
Club founded in 1973.
Visitors: welcome weekdays and after 10.30am weekends.
Green fees: £6 per round, £7.50 per day weekdays; £7.50 per round, £9 per day weekends.

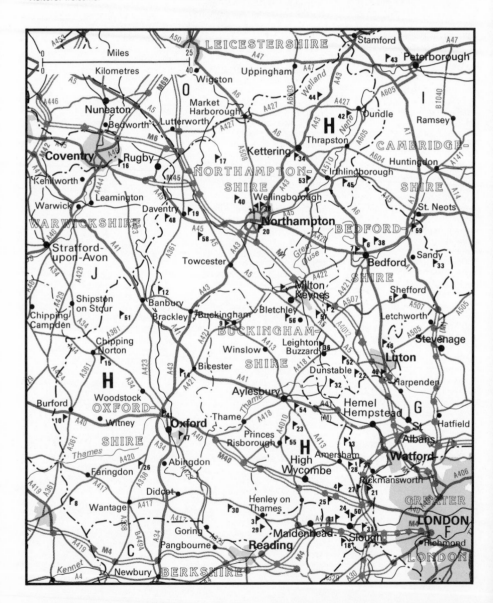

Society meetings: welcome weekdays, selected Sat and Suns after 10.30am.
Catering: full range of bar snacks, restaurant meals.
Hotels: Post House; Pytchley.

H18 Datchet
☎Slough (0753) 43887
Buccleuch Rd, Datchet, Slough, Berks SL3 5BP.
2 miles from Slough and Windsor, easy access from M4.
Parkland course.
9 holes, 5978 yards, S.S.S.69
Club founded in 1890.
Visitors: welcome weekdays before 3pm.
Green fees: £8 per round, £11 per day.
Society meetings: small societies welcome on Tues only.
Catering: bar snacks available.
Hotels: The Manor, Datchet.

H19 Daventry & District
☎Daventry (0327) 702829
Norton Rd, Daventry, Northants NN11 4AA.
1 mile NE of town, course next to BBC Station.
Undulating meadowland course.
9 holes, 5582 yards, S.S.S.67
Club founded in early 1920.
Visitors: welcome, except before 11am on Sun.
Green fees: on application.
Society meetings: for details contact Pro.
Catering: arranged for societies only.
Hotels: John-O'Gaunt, Daventry.

H20 Delapre Park
☎Northampton (0604) 763957/764036
Eagle Drive, Nene Valley Way.
Northampton NN4 0DU.
3 miles from Junction 15 (M1) on A508.
Parkland public course.
18 holes, 6293 yards, S.S.S.70
Course designed by J. Jacobs and J. Corby.
Club founded in 1976.
Visitors: welcome.
Green fees: £3.90 weekdays; £4.90 weekends.
Society meetings: welcome on most days, applications in writing.
Catering: catering daily 9am to 9.30pm.
Hotels: New Swallow; Westone Moathouse.

H21 Denham
☎Uxbridge (0895) 832022
Tilehouse Lane, Denham, Bucks UB9 5DE.
Leave M40 at Uxbridge/Gerrards Cross turn off, take A40 towards Gerrards Cross, turn right onto A412 towards Watford and take second turning left to club.
Parkland course.
18 holes, 6439 yards, S.S.S.71
Course designed by H.S. Colt.
Club founded in 1910.
Visitors: welcome Mon to Thurs.
Green fees: £18 per (36 holes); £11 per(18 holes).
Society meetings: catered for Tues, Wed and Thurs.
Catering: lunch served daily.
Hotels: The Bull, Gerrards Cross.

H22 Dunstable Downs
☎Dunstable (0582) 604472
Whipsnade Rd, Dunstable, Beds LU6 2WB.
2 miles from Dunstable on Whipsnade road, left at third mini-roundabout.
Downland course.
18 holes, 6184 yards, S.S.S.70
Club founded in 1907.
Visitors: welcome weekdays if member of recognised club.
Green fees: £15 per day, £11 per round weekdays.
Society meetings: Tues and Thurs.
Catering: full facilities except Mon.
Hotels: Old Palace Lodge; Kitts Inn, Dunstable.

H23 Ellesborough
☎Wendover (0296) 622114
Butlers Cross, Aylesbury, Bucks HP17 0TZ.
1 mile W of Wendover on B4010.
Undulating downland course.
18 holes, 6203 yards, S.S.S.70
Course designed by James Braid.
Club founded in 1906.
Visitors: weekdays only, handicap certificate required.
Green fees: on application.
Society meetings: welcome Wed & Thurs only £30 per day.
Catering: lunch served except Mon.
Hotels: The Red Lion, Wendover.

H24 Farnham Park
☎Farnham Common (028 14) 143332/Burnham (0628) 61521
Park Rd, Stoke Poges, Bucks SL2 4EP.
Turn off A4 at Slough, take Farnham road at Farnham Royal roundabout,

proceed about 0.5 mile, turn right and the course is on your left.
Parkland municipal course.
18 holes, 4864 yards, S.S.S.68
Visitors: municipal course.
Green fees: weekdays £3.40, £2.20 OAP, £2.20 juniors; weekends £4.70, £3.40 Juniors.
Society meetings: catered for.
Catering: grill etc.
Hotels: Burnham Beeches.

H25 Flackwell Heath
☎Bourne End (062 85) 20929
Treadaway Rd, Flackwell Heath, High Wycombe, Bucks HP10 9PE.
Off A40 High Wycombe to Beaconsfield road at Loudwater roundabout, up Treadaway Hill, on left before apex of hill into Treadaway Rd.
Undulating course.
18 holes, 6150 yards, S.S.S.69
Club founded in 1905.
Visitors: welcome weekdays.
Green fees: £14 per day.
Society meetings: Wed, Thurs and Fri.
Catering: limited Mon and Tues.
Hotels: Crest, High Wycombe.

H26 Frilford Heath
☎Frilford Heath (0865) 390428
Frilford Heath, Abingdon, Oxon OX13 5NW.
A338 Oxford to Wantage road, 3 miles W of Abingdon.
Wooded heathland course.
18 holes, 6768 yards, S.S.S.73
18 holes, 6006 yards, S.S.S.69
Course designed by J.H. Taylor and C.K. Cotton.
Club founded in 1908.
Visitors: welcome but must have handicap certificate.
Green fees: £16, (£10 with member) weekdays; £25, (£12 with member) weekends.
Society meetings: catered for by previous arrangement only.
Catering: cooked meals by prior arrangement, snacks at any time.
Hotels: Dog House; Crown & Thistle.

H27 Gerrards Cross
☎Gerrards Cross (0753) 885300
Chalfont Park, Gerrards Cross, Bucks SL9 0QA.
Leave A40 by A413, continue to first roundabout (approx 1 mile) and leave by third exit onto private road.
Parkland course.
18 holes, 6031 yards, S.S.S.69

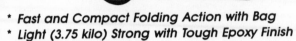
Course designed by Len Holland.
Club founded in 1922.
Visitors: welcome weekdays and after 3pm weekends and Bank Holidays. Please book in advance and bring handicap certificate.
Green fees: on application.
Society meetings: welcome Wed pm and all day Thurs and Fri.
Catering: bar snacks and lunch available by arrangement.
Hotels: Bull; Greyhound; Bellhouse.

H28 Harewood Downs
☎Little Chalfont (024 04) 2184
Cokes Lane, Chalfont St Giles, Bucks HP8 4TA.
Off A413 3 miles short of Amersham.
Parkland course.
18 holes, 5448 yards, S.S.S.69
Club founded in 1907.
Visitors: welcome weekdays.
Green fees: £14, (£6.50 with member) weekdays; £16, (£7 with member) by prior arrangement Sat, Sun and Bank Holidays.
Society meetings: weekdays only.
Catering: daily.
Hotels: Crown; Greyhound.

H29 Henley
☎Henley (0491) 575742
Harpsden, Henley-on-Thames, Oxon RG9 4HG.
M4 to Reading, follow A4155 to Caversham/Henley, turn left to Harpsden village 1 mile before reaching Henley, clubhouse on left.
Parkland course.
18 holes, 6130 yards, S.S.S.69
Course designed by James Braid.
Club founded in 1908.
Visitors: welcome weekdays, weekends with member.
Green fees: £15 per round/day.

Society meetings: catered for Wed and Thurs.
Catering: arrangements to be made with Steward.
Hotels: Red Lion; Elizabethan.

H30 Huntercombe
☎Nettlebed (0491) 641207
Nuffield, Henley-on-Thames, Oxon RG9 5SL.
A423, 6 miles from Henley towards Oxford.
Woodland/heathland course.
18 holes, 6108 yards, S.S.S.70
Course designed by Willie Park Junior.
Club founded in 1902.
Visitors: neckwear and jacket required in clubhouse. No 4 balls at all.
Green fees: £15 weekdays; £20 weekends after 10.30am. No 3 balls.
Society meetings: £17.50 Tues and Thurs only.
Catering: full meals for societies, bar snacks.
Hotels: White Hart, Nettlebed.

H31 Iver
☎Slough (0753) 655615
Hollow Hill Lane, Langley Park Rd, Iver, Bucks SL0 0JJ.
Nr Langley Station, Slough.
Parkland course.
9 holes, 6214 yards, S.S.S.70
Course designed by David Morgan.
Club founded in 1984.
Visitors: always welcome.
Green fees: £2.60 per (9 holes), £4 per (18 holes) weekdays; £3.30 per (9 holes), £5.50 per (18 holes) weekends.
Society meetings: welcome.
Catering: meals always available.
Hotels: Holiday Inn, Langley.

H32 Ivinghoe
☎Cheddington (0296) 668696
Wellcroft, Ivinghoe, Leighton Buzzard, Beds LU7 9EP.
In Ivinghoe village, 4 miles from Tring and 6 miles from Dunstable.
Meadowland course.
9 holes, 6203 yards, S.S.S.62
Course designed by R. Garrad & Sons.
Club founded in 1967.
Visitors: after 9am weekdays; after 8am weekends.
Green fees: £4 per (18 holes) weekdays; £4.50 (18 holes) weekends.
Society meetings: catered for weekdays.
Catering: lunch served except Mon.
Hotels: Rose & Crown, Tring.

H33 John O'Gaunt
☎Potton (0767) 260360
Sutton Park, Sandy, Beds SG19 2LY.
On B1040, 2.5 miles along Biggleswade to Potton road.
Undulating parkland courses.
John O'Gaunt-18 holes, 6513 yards, S.S.S.71
Carthagena-18 holes, 5869 yards, S.S.S.68
Visitors: welcome - advisable to contact club.
Green fees: £14 per day, (£7.50 with member) weekdays; £20 per day, (£10 with member) weekends.
Society meetings: weekdays only.
Catering: all meals available.
Hotels: Stratton House, Biggleswade.

H34 Kettering
☎Kettering (0536) 512074
Headlands, Kettering, Northants NN15 6XA.

Headlands joins Bowling Green Rd, past the Council Offices, continue along Headlands for about 0.5 mile, past the Fire Station on the left, and golf club is over railway bridge on the right.
Meadowland course.
18 holes, 6036 yards, S.S.S.69
Course designed by Tom Morris.
Club founded in 1891.
Visitors: welcome weekdays; weekends, Bank Holidays with member.
Green fees: £9, (£4.50 with member).
Society meetings: Wed and Fri.
Catering: lunch and evening meal except Mon.
Hotels: George Hotel; Royal Hotel.

H35 Kingsthorpe
☎Northampton (0604) 710610 Sec, 711173 Clubhouse.
Kingsley Rd, Northampton NN2 3BU.
2 miles from town centre, off A508.
Parkland course.
18 holes, 6006 yards, S.S.S.69
Visitors: welcome weekdays by arrangement, not weekends.
Green fees: £10 per round/day; (£5 per round/day with member).
Society meetings: welcome by arrangement, green fees £8 per day/round.
Catering: lunch, dinners served except Mon.
Hotels: Moat House.

H36 Leighton Buzzard
☎Leighton Buzzard (0525) 373811/2
Plantation Rd, Leighton Buzzard, Beds LU7 7JF.
1 mile N of Leighton Buzzard off A418, take left fork at Stag Inn.
Parkland course.
18 holes, 5454 yards, S.S.S.68
Club founded in 1925.
Visitors: welcome weekdays except Tues.
Green fees: £12 per round, £15 per day, (£7 with member).
Society meetings: welcome except Tues and weekends.
Catering: available except Mon.
Hotels: Swan.

H37 Little Chalfont
☎Little Chalfont (024 04) 4877
Lodge Lane, Little Chalfont, Bucks.
200 yards from A404 at Little Chalfont.
Undulating parkland course.
Course re-designed by James Dunne.
Club founded in 1980.
Visitors: welcome.

Green fees: £5 midweek; £7 weekends.
Society meetings: welcome midweek.
Catering: full facilities.
Hotels Sportsman, Chorley Wood.

H38 Mowsbury
☎Bedford (0234) 771041 or 771042
Cleat Hill, Kimbolton Rd, Bedford MK41 8DQ.
On Kimbolton road from Bedford, 2 miles N of city centre.
Parkland municipal course.
18 holes, 6514 yards, S.S.S.71
Club founded in 1965.
Visitors: welcome.
Green fees: on application.
Society meetings: on application to Amenities Dept, Bedford Town Hall.
Catering: snacks and meals available.
Hotels: numerous good hotels in area.

H39 Northampton
☎Northampton (0604) 711054
Kettering Rd, Northampton NN3 1AA.
NE of town centre on A43.
Meadowland course.
18 holes, 6002 yards, S.S.S.69
Club founded in 1893.
Visitors: welcome weekdays and with member only weekends.
Green fees: £9 per day.
Society meetings: catered for Mon, Thurs and Fri.
Catering: full facilities available.
Hotels: Northampton Moat House; Westone Moat House, Northampton.

H40 Northamptonshire County
☎Northampton (0604) 843025
Sandy Lane, Church Brampton, Northampton NN6 8AZ.
Off A50 Northampton to Leicester road, 4.5 miles from Northampton.
Undulating heathland/parkland course.
18 holes, 6503 yards, S.S.S.71
Course designed by H.S. Colt.
Club founded in 1909.
Visitors: with handicap by arrangement. Ladies Sat after 3.30pm. Sun after 11.15am.
Green fees: £13 per round, £15 per day weekdays; £15 per round/day weekends, (with member £4)
Society meetings: Wed, some Thurs and Mon.
Catering: snack menu 11am-6pm otherwise by arrangement.

Hotels: Moat House; Red Lion Inn; Post House.

H41 North Oxford
☎Oxford (0865) 54924
Banbury Rd, Oxford.
Situated between Summertown and Kidlington, 2.5 miles N of city centre.
Parkland course.
18 holes, 5485 yards, S.S.S.67
Club founded in 1921.
Visitors: welcome.
Green fees: £11 weekdays; £20 weekends.
Society meetings: facilities, book with Sec.
Catering: facilities available.
Hotels: Moat House, Oxford; Randolf.

H42 Oundle
☎Oundle (0832) 73267
Benefield Rd, Oundle, Peterborough, Cambs PE8 4EZ.
On A427 Oundle to Corby road, 1 mile from Oundle.
Undulating course.
18 holes, 5507 yards, S.S.S.67
Club founded in 1893.
Visitors: welcome weekdays.
Green fees: on application.
Society meetings: welcome except at weekends.
Catering: full service available.
Hotels: Talbot; Bridge, Thrapston.

H43 Peterborough Milton
☎Castor (0733) 380489
Milton Ferry, Peterborough PE6 7AG.
On A47 4 miles W of Peterborough.
Parkland course.
18 holes, 6431 yards, S.S.S.71
Course designed by James Braid.
Club founded in June 1938.
Visitors: weekdays only, by prior arrangement with Sec.
Green fees: on application.
Society meetings: weekdays only, by prior arrangement with Sec.
Catering: full facilities except Mon.
Hotels: Haycock Inn; Moat House.

H44 Priors Hall
☎Corby (0536) 60756
Stamford Rd, Weldon, Northants.
A43 Corby to Stamford Rd, 2 miles E of Weldon.
Parkland course.
18 holes, 6677 yards, S.S.S.72
Club founded in 1965.
Visitors: unlimited.
Green fees: £2.50 weekdays; £3.60 weekends.
Society meetings: welcome

Tadmarton, a testing time in the gorse

It is natural, I suppose, that golf clubs should develop a stronger individual character than clubs of other kinds, and in this country where there is such a variety of courses it is not surprising that this impression is more marked than anywhere else in the world.

At the older championship links - St Andrews, Prestwick, Royal St George's, Westward Ho! and so on - there is an atmosphere that is at once distinguishable from all the others, but the same applies to many less celebrated clubs upon which the public gaze is seldom directed. When I was invited to play at Tadmarton Heath in North Oxfordshire, this fact was quickly confirmed.

Perhaps my feelings were influenced by having achieved the perfect escape from the general confusion of Christmas week; or maybe the drive from Banbury Cross through the neighbouring countryside formed an unusually romantic introduction to the golf, but much respected opinion had told me that Tadmarton Heath - one of only seven clubs in the county - had many fine qualities. If it is a course that Roger Wethered saw fit to play as often as he could, it is surely one that is good enough for most of us.

In an age when there is so much emphasis on power and stretching holes to limits for which they were not designed, it was encouraging to see from a glance at the card that Tadmarton measured below 6,000 yards, but in this case bare details were deceptive. In winds that never miss those exposed parts it must frequently seem to play about twice its normal length.

As a course it has what may conveniently be described as a split personality; the first nine holes are open and the second nine possess a characteristic commonly associated with heathland golf - a profusion of gorse which makes some of the fairways alarmingly narrow.

As this tests a player's nerve at a critical point in the round, it is as well that there should have been temptation earlier to open the shoulders, but for all the latitude that may be allowed, there are many splendidly demanding second shots - particularly those at the 1st, 2nd, 4th, 6th and 9th - which can only be negotiated successfully from drives that have been strategically placed.

The first seven holes do not stray far from the clubhouse, the short 7th - with its attractive shot over the waters of the Holy Well which are said to provide a cure for rheumatism - bringing some danger to its walls and windows. But the fun really begins when the 9th turns away alongside the road by the gate and the short 10th (114 yards) induces a tremble or two at the prospect of seeing more of the prominent bunker and the intervening gorse than of the freely undulating green.

Gorse again dominates the drive over the distant ridge at the 11th and the cleverly angled second at the 14th, where a slice off the tee is not to be recommended, but the 15th (288 yards) and the 17th (365 yards), despite their innocent length, are the two holes where the slightest deviation from the fairway inevitably decrees a prickly fate.

Although the 18th immediately provides relief on the right, the staunchest of hopes may already have been destroyed, though even that need be no cause for discontent.

All around the scene is one of simple beauty and tranquility. The whirl of traffic is far away, and ahead, in the warmth of the old Cotswold stone clubhouse that was converted from a farmhouse, lies the assurance that all thoughts of golf can, if necessary, be dulled - though not, let me hasten to add, the urge to try again.

weekdays.
Catering: snacks and meals.
Hotels: Grosvenor, George St.

H45 **Rushden & District**

☎Rushden (0933) 312581
Kimbolton Rd, Chelveston.
Wellingborough, Northants
NN9 6AN.
On A45 2 miles E of Higham Ferrers.
Undulating meadowland course.
9 holes, 6381 yards, S.S.S.70
Club founded in 1921.
Visitors: welcome weekdays except
Wed pm. Weekends with member
only.
Green fees: £8, (£5 with member).
Society meetings: bookable in
advance.
Catering: any time.
Hotels: Tudor Gate, Finedon;
Westwood, Rushden.

H46 **South Bedfordshire**

☎Luton (0582) 591500
Warden Hill Rd, Luton, Beds
Take A6 N from Luton, course 2.5
miles from centre of Luton.
Undulating course.
18 holes, 6342 yards, S.S.S.70
9 holes, 2490 yards, S.S.S.64
Club founded in 1892.
Visitors: welcome weekdays;
telephone enquiry advisable.
Green fees: £8 per round, (£4 with
member); £12 per day, (£7 with
member); Sat, Sun £12.50
per round.
Society meetings: welcome by
arrangement, not Mon, Tues.
Catering: snacks available daily;
lunch, dinner, à la carte - by
arrangement.
Hotels: Culverdene; Chiltern;
Strathmore.

H47 **Southfield**

☎Oxford (0865) 242158
Hill Top Rd, Oxford OX4 1PF.
Cowley Rd, Southfield Rd, then right
into Hill Top Rd. Situated between
Headington and Cowley.
Undulating parkland course.
18 holes, 6230 yards, S.S.S.70
Course designed by James Braid.
Club founded in 1920.
Visitors: welcome weekdays, except
Bank Holidays.
Green fees: on application.
Society meetings: welcome
weekdays.
Catering: available daily except
Mon.
Hotels: Randolph; Moat House.

H48 **Staverton Park**

☎Daventry (0327) 705911/705506
Staverton, Daventry, Northants
NN11 6JT.
On A425 Daventry - Leamington
road, 1 mile S of Daventry.
Undulating meadowland course.
18 holes, 6204 yards, S.S.S.70
Course designed by Comm John
Harris.
Club founded in 1978.
Visitors: welcome.
Green fees: £12 per day, £8 per
round; £15 weekends.
Society meetings: welcome
(telephone Manager).
Catering: full facilities.
Hotels: John O'Gaunt, Daventry;
Wheatsheaf, Daventry.

H49 **Stockwood Park**

☎Luton (0582) 23612 Sec, 413704
Pro.
Stockwood Park, London Rd, Luton,
Beds.
Junction 10 off the M1, turn left
towards town centre, then left at first
set of traffic lights into Stockwood
Park.
Meadowland course.
18 holes, 5964 yards, S.S.S.69
Course designed by Charles Lawrie.
Club founded in 1973.
Visitors: welcome at all times.
Green fees: £3.10 weekdays; £4.60
weekends.
Society meetings: welcome
weekdays, contact Pro.
Catering: lunch served.
Hotels: Strathmore.

H50 **Stoke Poges**

☎Slough (0753) 26385
Stoke Park, Park Rd, Stoke Poges,
Slough, Bucks SL2 4PG.
Off A4 at Slough into Stoke Poges
Lane then 1.5 miles on left.
Parkland course.
18 holes, 6654 yards, S.S.S.72
Course designed by H.S. Colt.
Club founded in 1908.
Visitors: weekdays by arrangement,
weekends and Bank Holidays with
member only.
Green fees: £20 per day, £15 per
round. Letter of introduction/
handicap certificate required.
Society meetings: Mon, Wed,
Thurs, Fri.
Catering: full service available.
Hotels: Holiday Inn; Bull.

H51 **Tadmarton Heath**

☎Hook Norton (0608) 737278

Wiggington, Banbury, Oxon
OX15 5HL.
5 miles W of Banbury off B4035
Shipston on Stour road.
Heathland course.
18 holes, 5917 yards, S.S.S.69
Course designed by Major C.K.
Hutchison.
Club founded in 1922.
Visitors: weekdays only.
Green fees: on application.
Society meetings: Tues, Wed, Fri.
Catering: full facilities.
Hotels: Banbury Moat House; Old
School, Banbury.

H52 **Tilsworth**

☎Leighton Buzzard (0525) 210721
Dunstable Rd, Tilsworth, Leighton
Buzzard, Bedfordshire.
On A5, N of Dunstable.
Parkland course.
9 holes, 5443 yards, S.S.S.67
Club founded in 1972.
Visitors: welcome all times except
Sun 7.30am-11.30am.
Green fees: £3 per 18 holes
weekdays; £4 per 18 holes weekends.
Society meetings: welcome all times
except Sun am.
Catering: Hot and cold home cooked
food served every lunch and evening.
Hotels: Swan; Crest Luton.

H53 **Wellingborough**

☎Wellingborough (0933) 677324
Sec, 678752 Pro.
Harrowden Hall, Great Harrowden,
Wellingborough, Northants NN9 5AD.
2 miles N of Wellingborough on A509
to Kettering turn right (signposted to
Finedon) at church.
Parkland course.
18 holes, 6604 yards, S.S.S.72
Course designed by Hawtree & Sons.
Club founded in 1893.
Visitors: welcome weekdays, must
have handicap.
Green fees: £12 per day; £9 per
round.
Society meetings: welcome by
appointment.
Catering: up to 85; bar snacks or full
service; lunch and dinner.
Hotels: Hind; Oak House.

H54 **Weston Turville**

☎Aylesbury (0296) 24084
New Rd, Weston Turville, Aylesbury,
Bucks HP22 5QT.
A41 or A312, situated 2 miles from
Aylesbury town centre between Aston
Clinton and Wendover.
Parkland course.

The Duchess Takes Her Bow

When the idea of golf at Woburn was first conceived, the Dukes and Duchess courses were planned and cleared together. As events turned out, the Duchess was delayed while the Dukes earned immediate praise, but now the Duchess forms a twin attraction that has few equals.

In terms of character, the two courses have much in common, arising from the same dense forest in which it was virtually impossible seven or eight years ago to see more than ten yards ahead. The massive tree felling operation was the biggest ever undertaken on a new course in Britain but from the moment in the summer of 1979 when 18 holes on the Duchess were open for play, a remarkable story was complete.

Work only began on its construction in the summer of 1978, and in May 1979, after the severest winter for many years, half of it was not yet sown. Yet by October of that year all 18 holes were being played. Adjustments to the shape and levels of greens were made to mould with the natural contours, thus avoiding regular, artificial patterns. This was achieved by the club's own greenkeeping staff who wrought wonders. They were not alone in believing that it would have been impossible to have found a finer piece of land for an inland course in Britain; or that you could not improve upon the arrangement whereby a course is built by those who subsequently have to look after it.

Having seen the development of both Dukes and Duchess from the start, my main concern is that it might have blurred my judgment. However, that is a risk I have to take when describing a course which forms a nice contrast to its neighbour. Now the course has seen several professional tournaments and filmed matches as well as the English Amateur strokeplay championship for the Brabazon Trophy.

The Duchess is not as long, nor does it have the spectacular rises and falls that mark the beginning of the Dukes, but it is a supreme test of the art of control, manoeuvrability and varied shotmaking.

The enjoyment of the Duchess lies in an ideal balance of its holes. There is contrast in the par fives; the short holes vary nicely in length and there is a good mixture of par fours from a drive and pitch to two full shots. The 1st gives a good first impression, the distant green on an elusive plateau being reached only with a well struck second from a tumbling fairway.

In four holes, in fact, there is all the variation you can have. The 2nd, a par 3 needs a shot through the eye of a needle; the 3rd calls for a straight drive and well judged pitch over a belt of heather and the 4th, a left hand dogleg, is a par 5 where there are plenty of ways of taking six.

The 5th green in its alcove of giant beech is the first on the other side of the lane leading down to Bow Brickhill Church while the 6th, changing direction yet again, rewards positional play more than most par fives.

It is a rare feature that no two consecutive holes follow the same direction and the short 7th twists back over the ancient earth-works that make an excellent golfing landmark. Next comes the 8th, a classic dogleg to a three level green, and then the turn is reached by way of the 9th green which, like the 10th tee, needed enormous build-up.

Over the brow at the 10th, the chief hazard is the angled green, but the 11th, 12th and 13th all have distinctive markings, the 13th occupying a natural little punchbowl. From there it is over the road again with two spanking two shot holes for the experts and two three shot holes for the rest.

There is no doubt that the finish is demanding but the 16th and 17th offer scenic relief, if nothing else; and by then the 18th is the only obstacle, though a tough one, between you and the non-golfing delights which Woburn has to offer. Swimming, tennis and squash await those with the fitness and energy to tackle them but a relaxing drink will be the comfort that most seek. In which case, you can look out on a sylvan setting of peace and tranquillity; and ponder whether golf has anything better to offer.

THE BEDFORD ARMS HOTEL

GEORGE STREET, WOBURN
MILTON KEYNES MK17 9PX
Tel: Woburn (0525) 290441 Telex: 825205

Two miles from Woburn Golf Course and its neighbour the Abbey ground, the BEDFORD ARMS is cosily situated at the end of Woburn village. Historically an old coaching inn, the BEDFORD ARMS has developed into a high quality 4-star hotel. You'll find no better bedroom accommodation around.

The management know that as a serious golfer you require a comfortable bed, adequate room to spread out, and peaceful undisturbed rest. All these qualities are awaiting you at the BEDFORD ARMS and when you have finished for the day and you require to freshen, relax and eat, we are also the provider of good food, choice wines and comfortable surroundings. Here you can relax, plan tomorrow's action, enjoy pleasant company — or you can go off to bed with a good book (golf, of course).

---

13 holes, 6782 yards, S.S.S.72 Club founded in 1975.
Visitors: welcome except Sun morning.
Green fees: £5.50 weekdays; £7.50 weekends and Bank Holidays.
Society meetings: catered for weekdays, occasionally weekend.
Catering: cooked lunch, evening snacks.
Hotels: Five Bells; The Bell.

H55 Whiteleaf
☎Princes Risborough (084 44) 3097
The Clubhouse, Whiteleaf, Aylesbury, Bucks
1.5 miles from Princes Risborough on Aylesbury Rd, turn right for Whiteleaf.
Undulating course.
9 holes, 5391 yards, S.S.S.66
Club founded in 1904.
Visitors: welcome weekdays.
Green fees: £8 per 18 holes weekdays; £10 per 36 holes.
Society meetings: catered for weekdays.
Catering: lunch served except Mon.

Hotels: Bernard Arms; Thatchers.

H56 Windmill Hill
☎Milton Keynes (0908) 648149
The New Clubhouse, Tattenhoe Lane, Bletchley, Milton Keynes, Bucks MK3 7RB.
M1 exit 13 A421 turn off at sign for Windmill Hill golf course.
Meadowland course.
18 holes, 6773 yards, S.S.S.72
Course designed by Henry Cotton.
Club founded in 1972.
Visitors: welcome all times.
Green fees: £3.25 weekdays; £4.50 weekends, (subject to increases).
Society meetings: catered for Mon-Fri.
Catering: available by prior arrangement.
Hotels: Post House, central Milton Keynes.

H57 Woburn G & CC
☎Milton Keynes (0908) 70756/7/8
Bow Brickhill, Milton Keynes MK17 9LJ.
Junction 13 off M1, into Woburn

Sands, turn left for Woburn, after 0.5 mile turn right at sign.
Dukes-18 holes, 6913 yards, S.S.S.74
Duchess-18 holes, 6641 yards, S.S.S.72
Course designed by Charles Lawrie.
Club founded in 1976.
Visitors: midweek only by arrangement.
Green fees: on application.
Society meetings: by prior arrangement.
Catering: snacks and meals served.
Hotels: Bedford Arms; numerous in area.

H58 Woodlands
☎Preston Capes (032 736) 291
Woodlands Vale, Farthingstone, Towcester, Northants NN12 8MA.
Junction 16 off M1, W off A5 between Weedon and Towcester, 3 miles from Weedon.
Undulating parkland course.
18 holes, 6330 yards, S.S.S.71
Course designed by M. Gallagher.
Club founded in 1974.

Visitors: welcome at all times.
Green fees: £8 weekdays; £10 weekends.
Society meetings: welcome at all times.
Catering: full facilities at all times.
Hotels: Crossroads; Globe, Weedon.

H59 **Wyboston Lakes**
☎Huntingdon (0480) 212501
Wyboston Lakes, Wyboston, Beds.
Off A1 and A45, 1 mile S of St Neots.
Parkland course.
18 holes, 5310 yards, S.S.S.69
Course designed by Neil Oackden.
Club founded in 1980/81.

Visitors: welcome every day.
Green fees: £5 per 18 holes, £2.50 per 9 holes weekdays; £6.50 per 18 holes, £3.25 per 9 holes weekends.
Society meetings: welcome Mon-Fri.
Catering: full facilities available.
Hotels: motel on site.

I Suffolk, Norfolk and Cambridgeshire

In a book published in 1910, Bernard Darwin devoted as big a chapter to East Anglian courses as to almost any. He wrote with obvious warmth about them, hardly surprising since he first began to play the game at Felixstowe. One of the charms of reading his descriptions of clubs in Norfolk and Suffolk is that time seems to have brought little change. Nearly all are still recognisable.

Without becoming out-dated, they have retained their charm and natural features. In still conditions, few could examine fully the skills of modern professionals, but in the winds that so often plague balance and nerve, they are a formidable challenge, exemplifying the best traditions of British golf.

Where else in the world is there a course comparable to Brancaster? Here is the very essence of a seaside links; a long, narrow strip of land with the holes going out hugging the huge salt marsh and those coming home flirting with the dunes guarding the shore. The ground plays fast enough to make old men rub their hands, the greens hold only the truest of pitches and there are good, old-fashioned sleeper bunkers.

There are six courses in Norfolk and Suffolk which naturally divide themselves into three groups of near neighbours: Brancaster (Royal West Norfolk) and Hunstanton, Royal Cromer and Sheringham, Aldeburgh and Thorpeness.

Having dealt with Brancaster, we must pay our respects to Hunstanton, the only modern day championship course in the area. I take no part in the arguments about the respective merits of the two. It is a good thing that they are different and I enjoy a day's golf at one as much as the other.

My memories of Cromer and Sheringham are largely boyhood ones and I cannot now remember the individual holes too clearly except for the 18th at Sheringham

which is by the railway or, at least, was before the days of Dr Beeching. Golfers find it particularly hard to forgive him this particular closure since it was the source of Joyce Wethered's oft-quoted remark, "What train?".

Although both are hard by the sea, the turf is not like that at Brancaster; it is more downland in character. The names of Aldeburgh and Thorpeness are usually linked because of their proximity on the Suffolk coast although they are, in fact, surprisingly different: Thorpeness, with a good deal of heather, reminds one more of the Surrey heathland while Aldeburgh, a mile or so inland, is set on nice, light soil amid a thickish network of gorse. Whether there is too much gorse will depend on the accuracy of your driving. Not far from Aldeburgh is Woodbridge, a club which, like Yarmouth and Felixstowe, has celebrated its centenary and offers excellent golf.

For the connoisseur, Royal Worlington and Newmarket, the little nine hole course on which generations of Cambridge golfers have sharpened up their skills, is an absolute must.

It is hard when courses have sentimental attachments to view them critically but Worlington is an architectural masterpiece, laid out on the smallest of acreages yet supplying an expansive challenge of which nobody ever tires.

On account of Worlington's fame, some of the other courses in the neighbourhood are frequently overlooked; but Thetford, a few miles up the road to Norwich, is always worth a visit while in Norwich itself lies Royal Norwich and the modern complex of Barnham Broom, the handiwork of Frank Pennink.

Gog Magog is the best in Cambridgeshire but I can recommend St Neots, Ely and Cambridgeshire Hotel from first hand.

I1 Abbotsley

☎Huntingdon (0480) 215153
Eynesbury Hardwicke, St Neots,
Cambridgeshire PE19 4XN.
3 miles E of A1 through St Neots.
Undulating meadowland course.
18 holes, 6150 yards, S.S.S.71
Club founded in 1986.
Visitors: welcome every day.
Green fees: £7, (£4 with member);
Juniors £3.50, (£1.50 with member)
weekdays; £12, (£7 with member);
Juniors £6, (£3 with member) week-
ends.
Society meetings: weekdays and
off peak weekends am.
Catering: snacks, meals served 7
days; restaurant and bar facilities.
Hotels: available in 12th century
farmhouse on course, chalets;
Wyboston Lakes Motel.

I2 Aldeburgh

☎Aldeburgh (072 885) 2890
Saxmundham Rd, Aldeburgh, Suffolk
IP15 5PE.
6 miles E of A12 midway between
Ipswich and Lowestoft.
Heathland course.
18 holes, 6330 yards, S.S.S.71
9 holes, 4228 yards, S.S.S.64
Club founded in 1884.
Visitors: welcome weekdays;
weekends by arrangement with Sec.
Green fees: on application.
Society meetings: welcome by
arrangement with Sec.
Catering: lunch served.
Hotels: Wentworth; White Lion;
Brudenell; Uplands, all in Aldeburgh.

I3 Barnham Broom G & CC

☎Norwich (065 45) 393
Norwich, Norfolk NR9 4DD.
Off A47 8 miles W of Norwich.
Meadowland course.
18 holes, 6603 yards, S.S.S.72
Course designed by Frank Pennink.
Club founded in 1977.
Visitors: welcome midweek,
residents 7 days.
Green fees: £14, (£7 with member);
residents £12.
Society meetings: welcome, rates
on application.
Catering: all day snack bar, full
restaurant facilities.
Hotels: Barnham Broom.

I4 Beccles

☎Beccles (0502) 712244
The Common, Beccles, Suffolk.
1 mile off A146, 9 miles W of
Lowestoft.

Heathland course.
9 holes, 2781 yards, S.S.S.67
Club founded in 1899.
Visitors: weekdays unrestricted, but
Sat, Sun, Bank Holidays with
member.
Green fees: £5 weekdays; £6
weekends.
Society meetings: welcome, not
Sunday.
Catering: meals to order, light
refreshments, licensed bar.

I5 Bungay & Waveney Valley

☎Bungay (0986) 2337
Outney Common, Bungay, Suffolk
NR35 1DS.
A143 Bury St Edmunds to Great
Yarmouth road, about 0.5 mile from
town centre.
Moorland course.
18 holes, 6000 yards, S.S.S.68
Course designed by James Braid.
Club founded in 1889.
Visitors: welcome weekdays only or
with member at weekends.
Green fees: £9 per day/round.
Society meetings: arranged by
writing to club - midweek only.
Catering: full coverage (snacks
Mon).
Hotels: The Swan; King's Head.

I6 Bury St Edmunds

☎Bury St Edmunds (0284) 5979
Sec, 5978 Pro.
Tuthill, Bury St Edmunds, Suffolk
IP28 6LG.
Off A45 2 miles W of Bury St
Edmunds onto B1106.
Undulating parkland course.
18 holes, 6615 yards, S.S.S.72
Course designed by Ted Ray.
Club founded in 1924.
Visitors: welcome. Weekends not
before 10am unless playing with
member. Handicap certificates
required.
Green fees: £10 per day weekdays;
£16 per day weekends.
Society meetings: welcome by prior
arrangement any weekday. Not
weekends.
Catering: full service available.
Hotels: Angel.

I7 Cambridgeshire Moat House Hotel

☎Crafts Hill (0954) 80555
Bar Hill, Cambs CB3 8EU.
Adjacent to A604, 4 miles NW of
Cambridge.
Undulating parkland course.

18 holes, 6734 yards, S.S.S.72
Club founded in 1974.
Visitors: must be members of a golf
club with letter of introduction or
membership card. This rule waived
for hotel residents. Telephone to
check course availability.
Green fees: £12 weekdays; £19
weekends and Bank Holidays.
Society meetings: welcome. Only
resident societies may play at
weekends.
Catering: full facilities.
Hotels: Cambridgeshire Moat
House.

I8 Cretingham

☎Earl Soham (072 882) 275
Cretingham, Woodbridge, Suffolk
IP13 7BA.
2 miles from A1120 at Earl Soham.
Meadowland course.
9 holes, 1955 yards, S.S.S.30
Club founded in 1984.
Visitors: welcome every day from
8am until dusk.
Green fees: £4 weekday; £5
weekends and Bank Holidays.
Society meetings: by prior
arrangement.
Catering: lunch every day, dinner by
prior arrangement.
Hotels: accommodation arranged
locally.

I9 Dereham

☎Dereham (0362) 693122
Quebec Rd, East Dereham, Norfolk
NR19 2DS.
Take B1110 from East Dereham.
Parkland course.
9 holes, 6225 yards, S.S.S.70
Club founded in 1934.
Visitors: welcome with handicap
certificate.
Green fees: £7.50 weekdays; £9
weekends.
Society meetings: by arrangement.
Catering: by arrangement.
Hotels: Phoenix; George; Kings
Head.

I10 Diss

☎Diss (0379) 2847
Halfway between Norwich and
Ipswich, 2 miles W of A140 (turn at
Scole).
Commonland course.
9 holes, 5900 yards, S.S.S.68
Club founded in 1903.
Visitors: welcome weekdays before
4pm and weekends after 4pm in
summer; no restrictions between Oct
and March.

Green fees: £6 weekdays; £8 weekends; (half price with member).
Society meetings: welcome weekdays.
Catering: full facilities.
Hotels: Brome Grange; Park; Scole Inn.

111 Eaton

☎Norwich (0603) 51686
Newmarket Rd, Norwich NR4 6SF.
Take right exit off A11 into Sunningdale, signposted.
Undulating course.
18 holes, 6125 yards, S.S.S.69
Club founded in 1908.
Visitors: welcome all week.
Green fees: £12 weekdays; £15 weekends.
Society meetings: limited.
Catering: lunch served weekdays, teas all week.
Hotels: Post House; Hotel Norwich.

112 Ely City

☎Ely (0353) 2751
Cambridge Rd, Ely, Cambs CB7 4HX.
On A10, outskirts of Ely going towards Cambridge.

Parkland course.
18 holes, 6686 yards, S.S.S.72
Course designed by Henry Cotton.
Club founded in 1962.
Visitors: unlimited weekdays, handicap certificate required weekends unless playing with member.
Green fees: £10 weekdays; £14 weekends and Bank Holidays.
Society meetings: welcome Tues-Fri inclusive.
Catering: full facilities. Restaurant, bar snacks.
Hotels: Fenland Lodge; Nyton House; Lamb; Highways.

113 Fakenham

☎Fakenham (0328) 2867
Sports Centre, The Race Course, Fakenham, Norfolk.
B1146 from Dereham or A1067 from Norwich.
Parkland course.
9 holes, 5879 yards, S.S.S.68
Course designed by Charles Lawrie.
Club founded in 1981.
Visitors: welcome.
Green fees: £6 weekdays; £7.50 weekends.

Society meetings: by arrangement.
Catering: pending.
Hotels: Crown; Limes.

114 Felixstowe Ferry

☎Felixstowe (0394) 286834
Ferry Road, Felixstowe, Suffolk IP11 9RY.
A45 to Felixstowe, avoid turning right off A45. Follow signs to Yachting Centre.
Links course.
18 holes, 6042 yards, S.S.S.70
Course designed by Henry Cotton & Sir Guy Campbell.
Club founded in 1880.
Visitors: welcome weekdays and after 10.30am weekends and Bank Holidays
Green fees: weekdays £10 per day; £12 weekends and Bank Holidays (half price with member)
Society meetings: catered for on weekdays.
Catering: lunch available 7 days a week, evening meals by arrangement.
Hotels: Orwell Moat House; Marlborough.

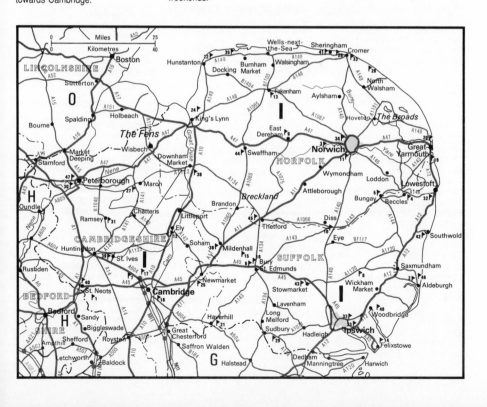

Aldeburgh

Whether Aldeburgh is more famous for its golf or its music depends where your interests lie. For some, there are presumably divided loyalties but golf unquestionably was there first and in 1984 Aldeburgh became the fourth club in East Anglia to celebrate its centenary.

In many little towns in Britain made famous by their courses, there are constant reminders of the modern world. Prestwick, the home of championship golf, and Troon resound to giant airliners; Sandwich has its distant cooling towers and the sight and noise of hovercraft. Golfers at St Andrews are faced by a skyline increasingly dotted with buildings neither royal nor ancient and even the Honourable Company of Edinburgh Golfers now have their first fairway overlooked by houses. Aldeburgh is one notable exception. All is recognisable as it was when six good men and true first realised the potential of some attractive heathland for golf.

Like most heathland, it is liberally sprinkled with gorse which, if lending an undeniably natural look, highlights the course's demands. In expressing his fondness for Aldeburgh, Bernard Darwin qualified his remarks: 'though now and again when I am sore and spiky from sitting in gorse bushes, and hot and tired from searching for my ball, I could wish there was just a little less gorse'. I rather fancy there is more gorse now than there was then but it remains a neat way of saying that you must keep straight.

Although everyone likes to see the ball hit long distances, and envies those who can, control is the most prized of Aldeburgh's golfing virtues. 6,330 yards is a relatively modest length by today's standards but, measured against a par of 68 which contains not a single five, good scoring is a tall order. Nine par fours over 400 yards put the problem in a nutshell.

Its championship qualities have been more freely acknowledged by the ladies than the men. The English Ladies' championship has been staged there on four occasions although this may be explained by the fact that the club has always given the ladies equal rights and that lady golfers, generally speaking, cope better with tight courses.

Aldeburgh does not extend her favours lightly but there is nothing misleading or unfair either. A glance around from the first tee shows exactly what is in store both in terms of golfing requirements and in the gentle rise and fall of the land that adds such a pleasant feature. Those well familiar with the surroundings can picture at will the view from the 5th or 6th with the waters of the River Alde shining behind a little row of fir trees. Known as Little Japan because of resemblance to a Japanese landscape, it typifies a tranquil scene which, despite the nearness of the sea, oozes pastoral delights.

After the first two holes have broken the golfer in as sympathetically as Aldeburgh can, the 3rd, slightly uphill before turning nicely left, raises the pitch an octave with the first of the outstanding two-shotters. You will travel a long way and not find four better short holes, the first of which, the 4th, is the next obstacle. Encircled by a large, horseshoe-shaped sleepered bunker, it is within the compass of all although, when the hole is cut at the back on the right, it is a brave player who attacks the flag.

The 5th takes you away with a fine sweep to the westernmost point; the 6th, a sharp dogleg round some mighty trees, does an about-turn while the 7th, where you have to dice with a central fairway bunker, is another excellent four with a downhill approach to the green.

In keeping with all good 9ths, Aldeburgh's returns to the clubhouse, a hole given extra renown by having been the scene of Bernard Darwin's final shot in a notable playing career. On the other hand, not recorded is his accompanying

ℭ𝔥𝔢 Links
Country Park Hotel & Golf Club

Luxurious accommodation.

Superb a la carte menus.

Friendly bars full of character.

New heated indoor swimming pool.

Luxury sauna and solarium.

Our own nine-hole golf course.

All facilities FREE to our residents.

Open to non-residents.

Famous for its superb golf and food, the Links offers the ideal meeting place to enjoy fabulous food, or to drink in our cocktail or real ale bars.

In spacious and elegant surroundings our restaurant provides superb English and Continental cuisine. A full a la carte or table d'hote menu is available with many speciality dishes.

For a lighter meal the Fairways Grill Room offers a varied menu at very reasonable prices, children are always welcome, with special half-price meals available.

**West Runton Cromer
Norfolk NR27 9QH
Tel (026 375) 691**

A short drive to the sea and a long list of pros—

What's the link?
The link is Hunstanton Golf Club, the BEST championship course in Norfolk and some of the finest seaside golf you'll find in Britain. At Hunstanton you'll follow in the footsteps of leading professionals and amateurs. The immaculate greens and wide, sweeping fairways offer an exciting challenge to low and high handicaps alike.

Enjoy the views over the Wash. The sea air keeps us frost-free and the sandy soil allows play in the wettest weather.

No wonder that Hunstanton was voted one of the top courses in Britain.

Pay us a visit soon. You'll be sure of a warm welcome.

Hunstanton Golf Club
Old Hunstanton, Norfolk PE36 6JQ
Tel: Hunstanton (04853) 2811

Recommended Hotels

Congham Hall Country House Hotel Tel: Hillington 600250
Le Strange Arms Hotel Tel: Hunstanton 34411
Linksway Country House Hotel Tel: Hunstanton 2209
Lodge Hotel Tel: Hunstanton 2896

remark which all who knew him will readily understand,'now I can retire gracefully from this unspeakable game'.

However, the temptation to go on is great — the lure of the 10th and 11th with more than their share of bunkers, the cracking short par four 12th and two contrasting fours to follow. The 15th and 17th, particularly the latter, are further examples of beautiful short holes but the 17th is preceded and followed by two more stouter than stout fours. Few will be able to boast a total of eight strokes or better for them even under favourable conditions but Aldeburgh does not have to be conquered to be enjoyed. It is reward enough to have come and seen.

---

115 **Flempton**
☎Culford (028 484) 291
Flempton, Bury St Edmunds, Suffolk.
4 miles NE of Bury St Edmunds on A1101 to Mildenhall.
Breckland course.
9 holes, 6074 yards, S.S.S.69
Course designed by J. H. Taylor.
Club founded in 1895.
Visitors: With members only on weekends and Bank Holidays.
Green fees: £12 per 18 holes; £15 per day.
Society meetings: Very limited.
Catering: by arrangement.
Hotels: Angel Hotel, Bury St Edmunds; Bell Hotel, Mildenhall.

116 **Fornham Park**
☎Bury St Edmunds (0284) 63426
Fornham St Martin, Bury St Edmunds, Suffolk
Off A45 to Bury St Edmunds or off A134 Bury to Thetford at Culford Rd, Fornham St Martin
18 holes, 6079 yards, S.S.S.69
Club founded in 1976.
Visitors: welcome
Green fees: £7 on weekdays; £11 at weekends
Society meetings: welcome
Catering: lunch and dinner served Tues-Sat.
Hotels: The Butterfly; The Suffolk; The Angel, Bury St Edmunds.

117 **Girton**
☎Cambridge (0223) 276169
Dodford Lane, Girton, Cambs CB3 0QE.
3 miles N of Cambridge A604
Flat open course.
18 holes, 5927 yards, S.S.S.68
Club founded in 1936.
Visitors: welcome weekdays.
Green fees: £10 per day weekdays.
Society meetings: catered for weekdays.
Catering: lunch, dinners served except Mon.

Hotels: Post House, Impington.

118 **Gog Magog**
☎Cambridge (0223) 247626
Shelford Bottom, Cambridge CB2 4AB
2 miles S of Cambridge on A1307 Colchester Road
Undulating course.
18 holes, 6386 yards, S.S.S.70
9 holes, 5532 yards, S.S.S.68
Club founded in 1901.
Visitors: welcome weekdays with introduction by member or handicap certificate.
Green fees: on application.
Society meetings: welcome on Tues and Thurs only.
Catering: lunch served daily.
Hotels: University Arms; Garden House; Gonville.

119 **Gorleston**
☎Great Yarmouth (0493) 661911
Warren Rd, Gorleston, Great Yarmouth, Norfolk NR31 6JT
Off A12 Yarmouth to Lowestoft road, Yarmouth end of dual carriageway, follow signs down Links Rd to Squash Club, club entrance 200 yards on left, Warren Rd.
Seaside course.
18 holes, 6279 yards, S.S.S.70
Club founded in 1906.
Visitors: welcome all times, but telephone call advisable.
Green fees: Weekdays £7.50 (£5 with member); Weekends/Bank Holidays £9 (£6 with member).
Society meetings: welcome weekdays, by prior arrangement.
Catering: available except Wednesday
Hotels: Cliff Hotel, Sliff Hill, Gorleston. St Edmunds Hotel, Marine Parade, Gorleston.

120 **Great Yarmouth & Caister**

☎Great Yarmouth (0493) 728699
Beach House, Caister-on-Sea, Great Yarmouth, Norfolk NR31 6JT
About 1 mile N of Great Yarmouth on A149 take right turn at roundabout, turn right into signposted lane almost immediately after roundabout.
Seaside links course.
18 holes, 6235 yards, S.S.S.70
Club founded in 1882.
Visitors: welcome, advisable to telephone in advance.
Green fees: on application.
Society meetings: welcome by arrangement.
Catering: coffee, lunch and evening meals always available.
Hotels: Carlton; Cavendish; Hamilton; Ocean Edge; Sandringham; Windyshore; all in Great Yarmouth.

121 **Haverhill**
☎Haverhill (0440) 61951
Coupals Rd, Haverhill, Suffolk GB9 7UR.
A604 from Cambridge, 0.5 mile SE of Haverhill, turn right in Coupals Rd after passing Snooker Club.
Parkland course.
9 holes, 5680 yards, S.S.S.68
Course designed by Charles Lawrie.
Visitors: welcome
Green fees: Weekdays £7.50, (£5 with member); weekends/Bank Holidays £10, (£5 with member).
Society meetings: By arrangement
Catering: No catering facilities.
Hotels: Woodlands Hotel

122 **Hunstanton**
☎Hunstanton (048 53) 2811
Golf Course Rd, Old Hunstanton, Norfolk PE36 6JQ.
Off A149 in Old Hunstanton (signposted to club), 1 mile NE of Hunstanton.
Link course.
18 holes, 6670 yards, S.S.S.72
Club founded in 1891.

The Lodge Hotel

AA**   RAC**

Old Hunstanton Norfolk
Telephone: Hunstanton (04853) 2896

Formerly a 17th century Dower House. This comfortable family run hotel offers good service & excellent food. The Hotel has an intimate fully licensed restaurant, well stocked bar and snooker room. The bedrooms have bath/showers, colour TV & tea/coffee making facilities.
Bargain golf breaks, with championship course within 300 yds of hotel. Centre of wild life area & beautiful sandy beaches.
Recommended by Ashley Courtenay and Les Routiers.

Visitors: welcome. Booking advisable. 3/4 ball play restricted.
Green fees: Weekdays £13 (£6.50 with member); weekends/Bank Holidays £18 (£9 with member).
Society meetings: welcome.
Catering: Available except Mondays.
Hotels: Le Strange Arms; Lodge; Linksway.

122 **Ipswich**
☎Ipswich (0473) 78941
Purdis Heath, Bucklesham Rd, Ipswich, Suffolk IP3 8QU.
3 miles E of Ipswich off A45, at roundabout by St Augustine's Church turn into Bucklesham Rd.
Heathland course.
18 holes, 6405 yards, S.S.S.71
9 holes, 3860 yards, S.S.S.59
Course designed by James Braid with Hawtree & Taylor.
Club founded in 1895.
Visitors: weekdays only by advance agreement.
Green fees: (18 holes) £12 per day/round weekdays; £14 per day/round weekends; (9 holes) £5 weekdays; £6 weekends.
Society meetings: weekdays by advance booking.
Catering: full facilities available.
Hotels: numerous hotels in area.

124 **King's Lynn**
☎Castle Rising (0533) 987654 Sec, 987656 Steward,
Castle Rising, King's Lynn, Norfolk PE31 6BD.
On A149 from King's Lynn to Hunstanton, at Castle Rising sign turn left, about 0.75 mile on left hand side.
Parkland course.
18 holes, 6552 yards, S.S.S.71
Course designed by Alliss &

Thomas.
Club founded in 1923.
Visitors: welcome weekdays.
Green fees: £12.50 weekdays (£6 with member); £17.50 weekends (£9 with member).
Society meetings: catered for weekdays only.
Catering: lunch daily weekdays, evening meals by arrangement.
Hotels: Red Cat; Dukes Head; Knights Hill.

125 **Links**
☎Newmarket (0638) 662708
Cambridge Rd, Newmarket, Suffolk.
1 mile S of Newmarket High St.
Undulating parkland course.
18 holes, 6162 yards, S.S.S.71
Club founded in 1902
Visitors: not before 11.30am Sun unless with member - no other restrictions.
Green fees: £12 weekdays; £16 weekends.
Society meetings: by arrangement.
Catering: full service available except Mon.
Hotels: White Hart.

126 **Links Country Park**
☎West Runton (026 375) 691
West Runton, Norfolk NR27 9QH.
In West Runton village 2 miles from Sheringham, turn for railway station, over the bridge 100 yards on left.
Undulating downland course.
9 holes, 2407 yards, S.S.S.32
Club founded in 1978.
Visitors: welcome.
Green fees: £9 weekends/Bank Holidays; £8 weekdays.
Society meetings: by arrangement.
Catering: clubhouse with grill room, hotel with full restaurant.
Hotels: Links Country Park, Cromer.

127 **March**
☎March (0353) 52364
Frogs Abbey, Grange Rd, March, Cambs.
A141, W off March by-pass, signposted.
Parkland course.
9 holes, 6200 yards, S.S.S.70
Club founded in 1920.
Visitors: welcome weekdays only.
Green fees: £7.
Society meetings: no facilities.
Hotels: Griffin, March.

128 **Mundesley**
☎Mundesley (0263) 720095 Sec, 720279 Club.
Links Rd, Mundesley, Norwich, Norfolk NR11 8ES.
Turn off the Mundesley to Cromer road by Mundesley Church, signposted as you enter the village.
Undulating course.
9 holes, 5410 yards, S.S.S.66
Course designed in part by Harry Vardon.
Club founded in 1903.
Visitors: welcome except 12.30 - 3.30pm Wed (Ladies); until 12 am Sun (Men).
Green fees: £7 per day weekdays; £10 per day weekends and Bank Holidays.
Society meetings: by arrangement.
Catering: available except Thurs.
Hotels: Royal; Sea View.

129 **Newton Green**
☎Sudbury (0787) 77501
Newton Green, Sudbury, Suffolk.
On A134, 3 miles E of Sudbury.
Moorland course.
9 holes, 5488 yards, S.S.S.67
Club founded in 1907.
Visitors: welcome weekdays; no visitors weekends, Bank Holidays.
Green fees: £7 per round/day.

Society meetings: none.
Catering: hot and cold snacks served. Holidays excluded.
Hotels: The Mill; The Four Swans, Sudbury.

130 **Orton Meadows**
☎Peterborough (0733) 237478
Ham Lane, Peterborough PE2 0UU.
On A605 Peterborough - Oundle road, 2 miles W of Peterborough at entrance to Ferry Meadows Country Park.
18 holes, 5800 yards, S.S.S.68
Course designed by Dennis & Roger Fitton.
Club founded in April 1987.
Visitors: welcome, municipal course.
Green fees: £3.40 weekdays; £5 weekends. OAP, Juniors, unemployed £2.10; U16 £1.60.
Society meetings: welcome except before 11am Sun.
Catering: adjoining steakhouse 'The Granary'
Hotels: Moat House, Peterborough.

131 **Ramsey**
☎Ramsey (0478) 812600
4 Abbey Terrace, Ramsey, Huntingdon, Cambs PE17 1DD.
12 miles SE of Peterborough, off B1040.
Parkland course.
18 holes, 6136 yards, S.S.S.70
Club founded in 1965.
Visitors: welcome anytime.
Green fees: £10, (£5 with member) weekdays; £15, (£8 with member) weekends/Bank Holidays.
Society meetings: welcome weekdays.
Catering: full catering facilities.
Hotels: St Ives, Huntingdon.

132 **Rookery Park**
☎Lowestoft (0502) 60380 Sec, 4009 Steward.
Beccles Rd, Carlton Colville, Lowestoft NR33 8HJ.
On A146 2 miles W of Lowestoft.
Parkland course.
18 holes, 6650 yards, S.S.S.72
Course designed by Charles Lawrie.
Club founded in 1975.
Visitors: welcome all year.
Green fees: £8.50 per day weekdays; £10 weekends.
Society meetings: any weekday except Tues.
Catering: full catering facilities.
Hotels: Victoria; Oulton; Wherry; Royal St George; Hedley House.

133 **Royal Cromer**
☎Cromer (0263) 512884
145 Overstrand Rd, Cromer, Norfolk NR27 0JH.
1 mile E of Cromer on B1159, main coast road adjoins Cromer lighthouse.
Undulating seaside course.
18 holes, 6508 yards, S.S.S.71
Course designed by James Braid.
Club founded in 1888.
Visitors: accepted weekdays and after 11am most weekends.
Green fees: on application.
Society meetings: accepted weekdays.
Catering: daily, but limited on Tues.
Hotels: Cliftonville; Cliff House.

134 **Royal Norwich**
☎Norwich (0603) 49928
Drayton High Rd, Hellesdon, Norwich NR6 5AH.
500 yards down A1067 Fakenham road from ring road.
Parkland/heathland course.
18 holes, 6603 yards, S.S.S.72
Club founded in 1893.
Visitors: must have handicap.
Green fees: £13 per round/day; £18 weekends, only with a member.
Society meetings: must book in advance.
Catering: restaurant facilities.
Hotels: Hotel Norwich; Elm Farm Chalet, Guest House.

135 **Royal West Norfolk**
☎Brancaster (0485) 2110223
Brancaster, King's Lynn, Norfolk PE31 8AX.
7 miles E of Hunstanton on A149, take Beach Rd, from Brancaster village to club.
Seaside links course.
Course designed by Holcombe Ingleby.
Club founded in 1892.
Visitors: welcome, except at weekends in Jul, Aug and Sept when must play with member.
Green fees: on application.
Society meetings: small societies by arrangement.
Catering: snacks daily, lunch by arrangement.
Hotels: The Manor; The Lodge; Tolcarne; Le Strange Arms; Caley Hall.

136 **Royal Worlington & Newmarket**
☎Mildenhall (0638) 712216
Worlington, Bury St Edmunds,

Suffolk IP28 8SD.
7 miles NE of Newmarket, A45 then A11 to Freckenham, turn left to Worlington.
Links course.
9 holes, 3105 yards, S.S.S.70
Course designed by H.S. Colt.
Club founded in 1893.
Visitors: weekdays only, telephone first.
Green fees: £15, (£7 with member).
Society meetings: weekdays by appointment, limited 24 players.
Catering: lunch and tea only.
Hotels: Bull; Bell; Worlington Hall.

137 **Rushmere**
☎Ipswich (0473) 75648
Rushmere Heath, Ipswich, IP4 5QQ.
Off A12 just E of Ipswich, at junction of A12 and A45 turn into Glenavon Rd and follow signs.
Undulating heathland course.
18 holes, 6287 yards, S.S.S.70
Club founded in 1896.
Visitors: handicap certificates requested.
Green fees: £9 per round. £12 per day; £12 weekends; no visitors before 2.30pm weekends/Bank Holidays.
Society meetings: welcome up to 75.
Catering: full services available.
Hotels: Meiton Grange; Post House.

138 **Ryston Park**
☎Downham Market (0366) 383834/ 382133
Denver, Downham Market, Norfolk PE38 0HH.
On A10 just before turning to village of Denver, 1 mile S of Downham Market.
Parkland course.
9 holes, 6292 yards, S.S.S.70
Club founded in 1933.
Visitors: welcome weekdays.
Green fees: £8, (£4 with member). One visitor per member weekends.
Society meetings: catered for weekdays.
Catering: full facilities except Monday.
Hotels: Castle; Crown, Downham Market.

139 **St Ives**
☎St Ives (0480) 68392
Westwood Rd, St Ives, Cambs PE17 4RS.
B1040 off A45.
Parkland course.
9 holes, 6100 yards, S.S.S.69

Club founded in 1923.
Visitors: welcome.
Green fees: £8 weekdays; £12 weekends, not before 11am.
Society meetings: welcome.
Catering: not Mon.
Hotels: Slepe Hall.

140 St Neots
☎Huntingdon (0480) 72363 Sec, 74311 Club.
Crosshall Rd, St Neots, Huntingdon, Cambs PE19 4AE.
On A45 1.5 miles W of St Neots off A1.
Parkland/meadowland course.
18 holes, 6027 yards, S.S.S.69
Course designed by Harry Vardon.
Club founded in 1890.
Visitors: welcome any day, Sun before 11am with member only.
Green fees: on application.
Society meetings: welcome except Sat, Sun and Mon. No start before 9am.
Catering: full service in clubhouse.
Hotels: Stephensons Rocket; Kings Head, St Neots.

141 Sheringham
☎Sheringham (0263) 823488
Weybourne Rd, Sheringham, Norfolk NR26 8HG.
0.5 mile from Sheringham on A149.
Seaside course.
18 holes, 6430 yards, S.S.S.71
Club founded in 1891.
Visitors: welcome with handicap.
Telephone first.
Green fees: £13 weekdays; £17 weekends and Bank Holidays.
Society meetings: by arrangement with Sec weekdays.
Catering: available all week.
Hotels: Beaumars; The Links, Westrunton; Burlington, Sheringham.

142 Southwold
☎Southwold (0502) 723234/723248
The Common, Southwold, Suffolk IP18 6TB.
From A12 follow A1095 signposted Southwold, turn right at Kings Head Hotel, proceed across Common, golf club about 0.5 mile on right hand side.
9 holes, 6001 yards, S.S.S.69
Club founded in 1884.
Visitors: welcome except on competition days.
Green fees: £7 weekdays; £9

weekends/Bank Holidays.
Subject to review.
Society meetings: by arrangement.
Catering: by arrangement with Steward.
Hotels: several in the district.

143 Stowmarket
☎Rattlesden (044 93) 473
Lower Rd, Onehouse, Stowmarket, Suffolk IP14 3DA.
2.5 miles SW of Stowmarket, off B115.
Parkland course.
18 holes, 6101 yards, S.S.S.69
Club reformed in 1962.
Visitors: welcome weekdays; weekends must have handicap certificate.
Green fees: £8, (£5 with member) weekdays; £12, (£6.50 with member) weekends.
Society meetings: Thurs and Fri.
Catering: meals usually available at all times.
Hotels: Cedars, Stowmarket.

144 Swaffham
☎Swaffham (0760) 21611/22487
Cley Rd, Swaffham, Norfolk PE37 8AE.
1 mile out of town on Cockley Cley road, signposted in town market place.
Moorland course.
9 holes, 6252 yards, S.S.S.70
Club founded in 1922.
Visitors: weekdays except with member.
Green fees: £8.
Society meetings: welcome by arrangement.
Catering: snacks always available, meals by arrangement.
Hotels: George, Swaffham.

145 Thetford
☎Thetford (0842) 2169
Brandon Rd, Thetford, Norfolk IP24 3NE.
1.25 miles NW of A11 on B1107 to Brandon.
Heathland course.
18 holes, 6499 yards, S.S.S.71
Course designed by C.H. Mayo.
Club founded in 1912.
Visitors: welcome weekdays and some weekends.
Green fees: £12.50 weekdays; £15 weekends.
Society meetings: catered for

weekdays.
Catering: lunch available every day except Tues; dinners available every day except Mon and Tues.
Hotels: Bell; Thomas Paine, Thetford.

146 Thorpeness
☎Aldeburgh (072 885) 2176
Thorpeness, Suffolk IP16 4NH.
Leave A12 at Saxmundham, on to B119, then B1353.
Moorland course.
18 holes, 6241 yards, S.S.S.71
Course designed by James Braid.
Club founded in 1923.
Visitors: welcome weekdays.
Green fees: £10 per round weekdays; £12 per round weekends.
Society meetings: catered for weekdays only.
Catering: full catering service.
Hotels: Thorpeness Golf Club.

147 Thorpe Wood
☎Peterborough (0733) 267701
Nene Parkway, Peterborough PE3 6SE.
On A47 to Leicester 2 miles W of Peterborough, next to Moat House Hotel.
Parkland course.
18 holes, 6595 yards, S.S.S.74
Course designed by Peter Alliss & Dave Thomas.
Club founded in 1976.
Visitors: unrestricted.
Green fees: £3.40 weekdays; £5 weekends and Bank Holidays.
Society meetings: by arrangement up to a year in advance.
Catering: at Greenkeeper.
Hotels: The Moat House.

148 Woodbridge
☎Woodbridge (039 43) 2038
Bromeswell Heath, Woodbridge, Suffolk IP12 2PF.
2 miles E of Woodbridge through village of Melton onto B1084.
Heathland course.
18 holes, 6314 yards, S.S.S.70
Club founded in 1893.
Visitors: weekdays only.
Green fees: £11 per round; £15 per day.
Society meetings: welcome by arrangement with Sec.
Catering: all meals, with notice.
Hotels: Melton Grange; Seckford Hall, Woodbridge.

J Warwickshire, Herefordshire, Worcestershire and Gloucestershire

Although the four counties cover considerable acreage, they are not heavily populated with golf courses. However, Worcestershire, Herefordshire and Gloucestershire can claim many courses with commanding views; Kington on Bradnor Hill in Herefordshire is the highest course in England.

Broadway, Cotswold Hills and Gloucester Golf and Country Club are other examples but Blackwell is a course of definite charm and challenge; the Worcestershire club, over a hundred years old, is in the heart of Elgar country; Tewkesbury is part of the St Pierre/Telford/Meon Valley stable and the Welcombe Hotel at Stratford-upon-Avon is another to combine good golf with a first rate hotel.

Closer to Birmingham, Copt Heath, Olton, Forest of Arden, Edgbaston, Moor Hall and Moseley offer a nice way to escape from the city. Then, of course, there's the Belfry, scene of the heartwarming European victory in the 1985 Ryder Cup.

J1 **Abbey Park**
☎(0527) 63918
Abbey Park, Dagnell End Rd, Redditch, Worcs B98 7BD.
A441 Redditch-Birmingham Road.
Parkland course.
18 holes, 5857 metres, S.S.S.71
Course designed by Donald Steel.
Club founded in 1985.
Visitors: welcome.
Green fees: (18 holes) £4 weekdays; £4.50 weekends.
(9 holes) £2.50 weekdays; £2.75 weekends.
Society Meetings: welcome special room.
Catering: 5 bars, 3 restaurants.
Hotels: Abbey Park.

J2 **Atherstone**
☎Atherstone (0827) 73110
The Outwoods, Atherstone, Warwicks HR2 9SA
Coleshill Rd out of Atherstone, 0.5 mile on left approached by private road.
Undulating parkland course.
11 holes, 6239 yards, S.S.S.70
Club founded in 1894.
Visitors: welcome weekdays.
Green fees: £8, (£4 with member); Bank Holidays £10.
Society meetings: catered for weekdays by prior arrangement.
Catering: full facilities except Tues.
Hotels: Old Red Lion; Three Tuns

J3 **Belmont**
☎Belmont (0432) 277445
Belmont House, Belmont, Hereford HR2 9SA
2 miles S of Hereford on Abergavenny Rd, A465.
Undulating meadowland course.
18 holes, 6448 yards, S.S.S.71
Course designed by R. Sandow.
Club founded in 1983.
Visitors: welcome.
Green fees: on application.
Society meetings: welcome.
Catering: restaurant and bar snacks (closed Sun evening and Mon).
Hotels: accommodation available at course from Summer '88.

J4 **Blackwell**
☎021-445 1994
Blackwell, Bromsgrove, Worcs B60 1PY.
3 miles E of Bromsgrove, from Blackwell village centre, along Station Rd and under railway bridge, club entrance on left after 40 yards.
Parkland course.
18 holes, 6202 yards, S.S.S.71
Club founded in 1893.
Visitors: unrestricted weekdays; playing with member only weekends and Bank Holidays.
Green fees: £14.
Society meetings: by arrangement with Sec.
Catering: full facilities by prior arrangement.
Hotels: numerous in area.

J5 **Broadway**
☎Broadway (0386) 853683
Willersey Hill, Broadway, Worcs WR12 7LG.
1.25 miles E of Broadway off A44.
Undulating course.
18 holes, 6122 yards, S.S.S.70
Course designed by James Braid.
Club founded in 1896.
Visitors: welcome. Handicap certificate required, prior notification advised.
Green fees: £10 weekdays; £12 weekends and Bank Holidays.
Society meetings: Wed, Thurs, Fri; limited to 24 in the year.
Catering: lunch, evening meals except Mon.
Hotels: Dormy House, Broadway; Noel Arms, Chipping Campden.

J6 **Churchill & Blackdown**
☎Kidderminster (0562) 700200
Churchill Lane, Blakedown, Kidderminster, Worcs DY10 3NB.
Off A456 3 miles NE of Kidderminster, turn under railway viaduct in the village of Blakedown.
Hilly, meadowland course.
9 holes, 5399 yards, S.S.S.67
Club founded in 1926.
Visitors: welcome. Weekends and Bank Holidays with member only.

Green fees: £7.50 per day, (£3 with member).
Society meetings: by arrangement with Sec.
Catering: lunch and evening meals served except Mon.
Hotels: Gainsborough, Kidderminster; Talbot, Stourbridge.

J7 Cirencester
☎Cirencester (0285) 2465
Cheltenham Rd, Bagendon, Cirencester, Glos GL7 7BH.
Adjoins A435 Cirencester to Cheltenham road, 1.5 miles from Cirencester.
Undulating course.
18 holes, 6100 yards, S.S.S.69
Course designed by James Braid.
Club founded in 1893.
Visitors: welcome at all times.
Green fees: £10, (£5 with member) weekdays;
£12, (£6 with member) weekends and Bank Holidays.
Society meetings: Tues, Wed and Fri.
Catering: lunch and evening meals.
Hotels: Kings Head; Stratton House; Fleece, Cirencester.

J8 Cleeve Hill Municipal
☎Bishop Cleeve (024 267) 2592
Cheltenham, Clos GL52 3PW.
Approx 6 miles N from M5, 4 miles N of Cheltenham off A46.
Undulating heathland course.
18 holes, 6217 yards, S.S.S.70
Visitors: welcome.
Green fees: £4.50 weekdays; £5 weekends; £2 OAP's.
Society meetings: welcome by arrangement.
Catering: restaurant facilities.
Hotels: Malvern View; De La Bere; Cleeve Hill.

J9 Cotswold Hills
☎Cheltenham (0242) 515264 Sec, 515263 Pro.
Ullenwood, Cheltenham, Glos GL53 9QT.
3 miles S of Cheltenham, between A436 and B4070.
Undulating course.
18 holes, 6716 yards, S.S.S.72
Course designed by M.D. Little.
Club founded in 1902.
Visitors: members of recognised clubs welcome.
Green fees: on application.
Society meetings: welcome Wed, Thurs and Fri.
Catering: bar snacks, lunch and

dinners except Mon when sandwiches available.
Hotels: Crest.

J10 Droitwich G & CC
☎Droitwich (0905) 774344
Westford House, Ford Lane, Droitwich WR9 0BQ.
Junction 5 off M5, A38 to Droitwich, take first right, 1 mile N of town.
Undulating meadowlane course.
18 holes, 6036 yards, S.S.S.69
Club founded in 1897.
Visitors: welcome Mon-Fri; weekends with member only.
Green fees: £10.
Society meetings: Wed and Fri; bookings must be confirmed with Sec.
Catering: restaurant, bar meals and snacks.
Hotels: Raven; St Andrews.

J11 Evesham
☎Evesham (0386) 860395/860822
Evesham Rd, Fladbury Cross, Pershore, Worcs WR10 2QS.
On B4084 3 miles from Evesham.
Parkland course.
9 holes, 6418 yards, S.S.S.71
Club founded in 1894.
Visitors: £8, (£3 with member); Sat, Sun only with member. Not competition days.
Green fees: as above.
Society meetings: only by arrangement with Sec.
Catering: bar snacks always available; special meals by arrangement with Steward.
Hotels: Northwick, Evesham; Star, Pershore.

J12 Gloucester G & CC
☎Gloucester (0452) 411331
Robinswood Hill, Gloucester GL4 9EA.
2 miles S of Gloucester city centre on B4073 to Painswick.
Parkland course.
18 holes, 6100 yards, S.S.S.69
Club founded in 1976.
Visitors: welcome anytime, telephone for reservation.
Green fees: £10 weekends; £8 weekdays.
Society meetings: Mon-Fri £19 per person, includes 36 holes, lunch, evening dinner.
Catering: full facilities available.
Hotels: at course.

J13 Habberley
☎Kidderminster (0562) 745756

Habberley, Kidderminster, Worcs DY11 5RG.
3 miles N of Kidderminster on Trimpley Rd.
Hilly parkland course.
9 holes, 5104 yards, S.S.S.69
Club founded in 1924.
Visitors: welcome weekdays if member of recognised club.
Green fees: £6.
Society meetings: by arrangement.
Catering: by prior notice.
Hotels: Gainsborough, Kidderminster; Swan, Stourport.

J14 Herefordshire
☎Hereford (0432) 71219
Ravens Causeway, Wormsley, Hereford HR4 8LY.
Turn left off A4110 at Three Elms Inn, 6 miles NW of Hereford on road to Weobley.
Undulating parkland course.
18 holes, 6200 yards, S.S.S.69
Course designed by Major C.K.Hutchison.
Club founded in 1898.
Visitors: welcome weekdays, limited at weekends.
Green fees: £7 weekdays; £9 weekends; reduced by £2 if playing with member.
Society meetings: by arrangement.
Catering: daily except Mon.
Hotels: Red Lion; Pilgrim; The Priory, Hereford.

J15 Kenilworth
☎Kenilworth (0926) 58517, 512732 Pro, 54038 Stewardess.
Crew Lane, Kenilworth, Warwickshire CV8 2EA.
A429 Kenilworth Rd, then via Common Lane, Knowle Hill and Crew Lane to clubhouse.
Undulating course.
18 holes, 6408 yards, S.S.S.71
Club founded in 1887.
Visitors: welcome daily; advisable to ring Pro beforehand.
Green fees: on application.
Society meetings: apply in writing, bookings preferred on Wed but other days accepted.
Catering: full facilities daily, advisable to contact Stewardess.
Hotels: De Montford; Avonside; Chesford Grange.

J16 Kidderminster
☎Kidderminster (0562) 822303
Russell Rd, Kidderminster, Worcs.
The course is signposted off A449 and is within 1 mile of town centre.

Parkland course.
18 holes, 5659 yards, S.S.S.70
Club founded in 1909.
Visitors: welcome weekdays only.
Green fees: £11.50.
Society meetings: welcome by prior
arrangement usually Thurs.
Catering: full facilities except Mon.
Hotels: several in town and nearby.

J17 Kington Herefordshire
☎Kington (0544) 230340
Bradnor, Kington, Herefordshire.
On B4355, 1 mile N of Kington.
Moorland course, it is the highest 18
hole course in England and Wales.
18 holes, 5820 yards, S.S.S.68
Course designed by
C.K. Hutchinson.
Club founded in 1925.
Visitors: welcome at all times.
Green fees: £5.50 weekdays; £7
weekends.

Society meetings: welcome
especially weekdays.
Catering: lunch and dinners; snacks
only Mon.
Hotels: Burton, Kington; Oxford
Arms, Kington.

J18 Leamington & County
☎Leamington Spa (0926) 25961
Golf Lane, Whitnash, Leamington
Spa, Warwickshire CV31 2QA.
2 miles S of town centre, off A452.
Undulating parkland course.
18 holes, 6425 yards, S.S.S.71
Course designed by H.S. Colt.
Club founded in 1909.
Visitors: welcome.
Green fees: on application.
Society meetings: welcome Wed,
Thurs, Fri.
Catering: lunch and evening meal
served except Mon.
Hotels: Regent; Ladbroke Mercury.

J19 Leominster
☎Leominster (0568) 2863
Ford Bridge, Leominster, Herefordshire HR6 0LE.
On A49, 4 miles S of Leominster.
Undulating meadowland course.
9 holes, 5250 yards, S.S.S.66
Club founded in 1967.
Visitors: welcome weekdays;
weekends by prior arrangement.
Green fees: on application.
Society meetings: catered for
weekdays; except Mon.
Catering: full facilities daily except
Mon.
Hotels: Talbot; Royal Oak,
Leominster.

J20 Lilley Brook
☎Cheltenham (0242) 526785
Cirencester Rd, Charlton Kings,
Cheltenham Glos GL53 8EG.
3 miles from centre of Cheltenham

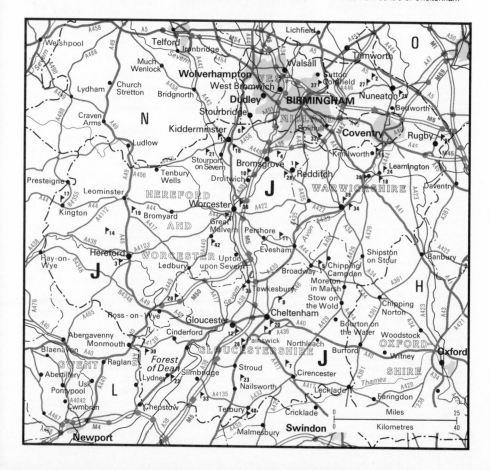

on the Cheltenham to Cirencester road, A435.
Parkland course.
18 holes, 6226 yards, S.S.S.70
Club founded in 1922.
Visitors: bona fide members of golf club with official handicap.
Green fees: £8 per round, £10 per day, (£6 with member) weekdays; £12 per round, £15 per day, (£6 with member) weekends.
Society meetings: welcome Mon-Fri.
Catering: lunch, dinners served except Mon.
Hotels: Queens; Carlton, Cheltenham.

J21 Little Lakes
☎Rock (0299) 266385
Lye Head, Rock, Bewdley, Worcs DY12 2UU.
A456 2 miles W of Bewdley, turn left at Greenhouse and Garden Centre, proceed for 0.5 mile.
Undulating parkland course.
9 holes, 6247 yards, S.S.S.72
Course designed by Michael Cooksey.
Club founded in 1975.
Visitors: welcome weekdays; weekends telephone.
Green fees: £4 weekdays; £5.50 weekends.
Society meetings: weekdays by arrangement.
Catering: lunch served.
Hotels: George; Black Boy, Worcester.

J22 Lydney
☎Dean (0594) 42614
Off Lakeside Ave, Lydney, Glos.
Entering Lydney on A48 from Gloucester, turn left at bottom of Highfield Hill and look for Lakeside Ave, 7th turning on left.
Parkland course.
9 holes, 5382 yards, S.S.S.66
Club founded in 1909.
Visitors: welcome weekends with member only, unless specially arranged.
Green fees: £6 per day.
Society meetings: small societies welcome, full facilities available, lunch, dinner but not morning coffee.
Catering: light snacks only.
Hotels: Feathers, Lydney.

J23 Minchinhampton
☎Nailsworth (045 383) 3866
New Course, Minchinhampton, Stroud, Glos GL6 9BE.

Leave M5 at Junction 13, 5 miles E of Stroud on Minchinhampton-Avening road.
Meadowland course.
18 holes, 6675 yards, S.S.S.72
New course designed by F.W. Hawtree.
Club founded in 1889.
Visitors: welcome at all times subject to availability of course.
Green fees: £10 weekdays; £12 weekends; (with member £6).
Society meetings: welcome subject to bona fide handicap and availability of course.
Catering: available at all times.
Hotels: Bear of Rodborough, Rodborough Common; Burleigh Court; Amberley Inn, Stroud; Hare and Hounds, Tetbury.

J24 Newbold Comyn
☎Leamington Spa (0926) 21157
Newbold Terrace East, Leamington Spa, Warwicks.
Off B4099 Willes Rd, centrally located.
Parkland course.
18 holes, 6259 yards, S.S.S.70
Club formed in 1972.
Visitors: welcome.
Green fees: £2.90 weekdays; £3.90 weekends and Bank Holidays.
Society meetings: by arrangement with Don Knight club Pro.
Catering: bar and restaurant.
Hotels: Manor; Regent, Leamington Spa.

J25 Nuneaton
☎Nuneaton (0203) 347810
Golf Drive, Whitestone, Nuneaton, Warwicks CV11 6QF.
Leave M6 at Junction 3 on A444, 2 miles S of Nuneaton, on B4114 to E of town.
Undulating meadowland course.
18 holes, 6412 yards, S.S.S.71
Club founded in 1906.
Visitors: welcome weekdays, but with member only weekends.
Green fees: £8, (£3.45 with member).
Society meetings: on Wednesday only.
Catering: full facilities except Mon.
Hotels: Long Shoot; Chase, Nuneaton.

J26 Painswick
☎Painswick (0452) 812180
Painswick Beacon, Painswick, Stroud, Glos.
1 mile N of Painswick village on A46.
Commonland course.

18 holes, 4780 yards, S.S.S.64
Club founded in 1891.
Visitors: welcome weekdays, Sat, Sun with member only.
Green fees: £5, (£4 with member) weekdays; £7, (£6 with member) weekends.
Society meetings: by prior arrangement with Sec.
Catering: by arrangement with Steward; snacks normally available.
Hotels: Hatton Court, Painswick.

J27 Purley Chase
☎Chapel End (0203) 395348
Ridge Lane, Atherstone, Nuneaton, Warwicks CV10 0RB.
4 miles from Nuneaton off B4114 Nuneaton to Birmingham road (turn right at Pipers Lane).
Meadowland course.
18 holes, 6604 yards, S.S.S.71
Course designed by B. Tomlinson
Club formed in 1980.
Visitors: welcome weekdays; weekends afternoons only.
Green fees: on application.
Society meetings: welcome weekdays and some weekends afternoons.
Catering: full facilities available daily.
Hotels: Chase; Longshoot, Nuneaton.

J28 Redditch
☎Redditch (0527) 43309
Lower Grinsty, Green Lane, Callow Hill, Redditch, Worcs B97 5JP.
Off A441 3 miles SW of town centre.
Undulating parkland/wooded course.
18 holes, 6671 yards, S.S.S.72
Course designed by Frank Pennink.
Club formed in 1913.
Visitors: members of recognised golf club welcome weekdays; with member weekends.
Green fees: £12 without membership.
Society meetings: accepted, fees on application.
Catering: full service except Mon.
Hotels: Southcrest, Mount Pleasant.

J29 Ross-on-Wye
☎Gorsley (098 982) 267 office
Two Park, Gorsley, Ross-on-Wye, Hereford HR9 7UT.
On B4421, 100 yards from Junction 3 off M50.
Parkland course.
18 holes, 6500 yards, S.S.S.73
New course designed by C.K.Cotton.
Club founded in 1903.

Visitors: have to be members of golf club. (Tues Ladies Day).
Green fees: £10.50 weekday; £14 weekends, subject to review.
Society meetings: 2 per week, 20 or over.
Catering: full facilities; limited on Mon to bar snacks.
Hotels: Chase; Royal, Ross-on-Wye.

J30 Royal Forest of Dean
☎Dean (0594) 32583
Lords Hill, Coleford, Glos GL16 8BD.
M5, M50 4 miles Monmouth, 8 miles Ross, M4 8 miles Chepstow.
Parkland course.
18 holes, 5519 yards, S.S.S.69
Course designed by John Day.
Club founded in 1972.
Visitors: welcome; car hire £8 per round; £12 per day.
Green fees: £7 per round, £9 per day weekdays; £8 per round, £10 per day weekends.
Society meetings: bargain daily break: lunch, three course evening meal, green fees, £16 per person.
Catering: restaurant serving table d'hôte, à la carte dinners and snacks all year round.
Hotels: own 32 bedroom on site.

J31 Rugby
☎Rugby (0788) 2306
Clifton Rd, Rugby CV21 3RD.
On Rugby to Market Harborough road, on right just past railway bridge as leaving town.
Parkland course.
18 holes, 5457 yards, S.S.S.67
Club formed in 1891.
Visitors: welcome weekdays; weekends and Bank Holidays with member.
Green fees: £8 per day/round.
Society meetings: by arrangement, weekdays only.
Catering: lunch and dinner, except Tues.
Hotels: Three Horse Shoes; Moathouse.

J32 Shirley
☎021-744 6001
Stratford Rd, Solihull, W Midlands.
On A34, 7 miles S of Birmingham, N from junction 4 off M42.
Parkland course.
18 holes, 6445 yards, S.S.S.71
Visitors: welcome, not weekends.
Green fees: £12 weekdays including VAT.
Society meetings: by arrangement.

Catering: meals served except Mon.
Hotels: St John's; George, Solihull.

J33 Stinchcombe Hill
☎Dursley (0453) 2015
Stinchcombe Hill, Dursley, Glos GL11 6AQ.
1 mile along narrow lane (signposted) off A4135 Tetbury to Dursley road or approach direct from Dursley town centre 0.5 mile up hill past bus station.
Meadowland, downland course.
18 holes, 5710 yards, S.S.S.68
Club founded in 1889.
Visitors: welcome any day, restricted weekends and Bank Holidays except with member.
Green fees: £8 weekdays; £9 weekends; (£6 with member).
Society meetings: weekdays by arrangement preferred Wed.
Catering: full facilities available.
Hotels: Hare and Hounds; Prince of Wales.

J34 Stratford-upon-Avon
☎Stratford-upon-Avon (0789) 205749
Tiddington Rd, Stratford-upon-Avon, Warwicks CV37 7BA.
0.5 mile from river bridge on B4089.
Parkland course.
18 holes, 6309 yards, S.S.S.70
Club formed in 1894 (1928 on present site).
Visitors: welcome weekdays by arrangement.
Green fees: £12.
Society meetings: Tues and Thurs by arrangement.
Catering: snacks and meals available.
Hotels: in area.

J35 Tewkesbury Park Hotel
☎Tewkesbury (0684) 295405
Lincoln Green Lane, Tewkesbury GL20 7DN.
Junction 9 off M5
Parkland course.
18 holes, 6533/6197 yards, S.S.S.71/69
Course designed by Frank Pennink.
Club formed in 1976.
Visitors: welcome with handicap certificate.
Green fees: £11 weekdays; £13 weekends.
Society meetings: welcome.
Catering: snacks and meals available.
Hotels: Tewkesbury Park.

J36 Tolladine
☎Worcester (0905) 21074
Tolladine Rd, Worcester WR4 9BA.
Leave M5 at Junction 6. Warndon about 1 mile from city centre.
Meadowland course.
9 holes, 5134 yards, S.S.S.67
Club founded in 1898.
Visitors: welcome weekdays.
Green fees: £6, (£3 with member) weekdays; £3.70 weekends and Bank Holidays with member only.
Society meetings: by appointment weekdays.
Catering: snacks available except Mon.
Hotels: Fownes; The Star; Gifford.

J37 Walmley
☎021-373 0029
Brooks Rd, Wylde Green, Sutton Coldfield, W Midlands B72 1HR.
6 miles N of Birmingham, turn off Birmingham to Sutton Coldfield road 0.25 mile N of Chester Road (Yenton Pub), right into Greenhill Rd, Brooks Rd continues from this.
Parkland course.
18 holes, 6277 yards, S.S.S.70
Club founded in 1902.
Visitors: welcome weekdays.
Green fees: £11 per round/day, (£3.50 with member).
Society meetings: catered for weekdays.
Catering: not Mondays.
Hotels: Penns Hall, Wylde Green.

J38 Warwick
☎Warwick (0926) 494316
The Racecourse, Warwick CV34 6HW.
Centre of Warwick Racecourse.
Meadowland course.
9 holes, 2682 yards, S.S.S.66
Course designed by D.G. Dunkley.
Club founded in 1886.
Visitors: welcome, not Sun mornings.
Green fees: £1.60 (9 holes) weekdays; £1.90 (9 holes) weekends.
Society meetings: by arrangement.
Catering: bar only.
Hotels: Tudor House; Warwick Arms;
Ladbroke Mercury; Woolpack.

J39 Welcombe Hotel
☎Stratford-upon-Avon (0789) 295252 Warwick Rd, Stratford-upon-Avon, Warwicks CV37 0NR.
1.5 miles from Stratford on A34 to Warwick.

Parkland course.
18 holes, 6202 yards, S.S.S.70
Course designed by T.J. McAuley.
Club founded in 1980.
Visitors: telephone booking
essential, not Sat, Sun mornings.
Green fees: £12 weekdays; £15
weekends/ Bank Holidays.
Society meetings: catered for
weekends.
Catering: everyday golfers bar; hotel
restaurant.
Hotels: Welcombe on site.

J40 **Westonbirt**
☎Tetbury (0666) 242
Tetbury, Glos GL8 8QP.
Turn off A433 3 miles SW of Tetbury,
through Westonbirt village, take
turning opposite Westonbirt
Arboretum entrance.
Parkland course.
9 holes, 4504 yards, S.S.S.62
Course designed by Monty Hearn.
Visitors: welcome.

Green fees: on application.
Society meetings: by arrangement.
Catering: available at Holford Arms.
Hotels: Hare and Hounds, Weston-
birt.

J41 **Worcester G & CC**
☎Worcester (0905) 422555
Boughton Park, Worcester WR2 4EZ.
1.5 miles from town centre on
Bransford road, a few yards from the
Portobello Inn, follow signs for
Hereford.
Parkland course.
18 holes, 5919 yards, S.S.S.68
Course designed by Dr. A. Mackenzie.
Club founded in 1898.
Visitors: welcome with handicap
certificate, with member only at
weekends.
Green fees: £11.
Society meetings: by arrangement.
Catering: every day except Mon.
Hotels: see AA and RAC handbooks.

J42 **Worcestershire**
☎Malvern (068 45) 5992/3905
Wood Farm, Malvern Wells, Worcs
WR14 4PP.
2 miles S of Great Malvern, turn off
A449 onto B4209, follow signs.
Meadowland/parkland course.
18 holes, 6449 yards, S.S.S.71
Course designed by Colt, Macken-
zie, Braid and later Jiggins and
Hawtree.
Club founded in 1879/1880.
Visitors: members of recognised
club, no play before 10am
weekends.
Green fees: £10 weekdays; £12
weekends.
Society meetings: Thurs and Fri.
Catering: maximum 70 seating, full
facilities except Mon.
Hotels: Abbey; Foley Arms; Cottage
in the Wood;
Mount Pleasant; Royal Malvern.

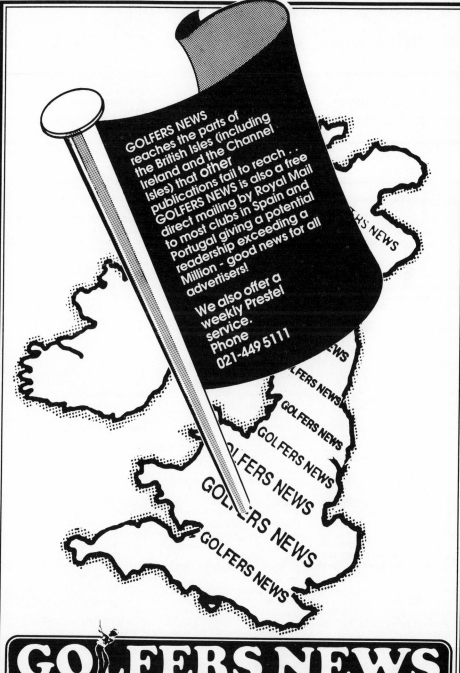

K Birmingham, West Midlands

K1 Belfry
☎Curdworth (0675) 70301
Lichfield Rd, Wishaw, N Warwicks
B76 9PR.
M6 Junction 4, follow signs to
Lichfield along A446, sited at the
apex of A4091 toTamworth and
A446 to Lichfield.
Parkland course, Championship
courses.
Brabazon-18 holes, 6975 yards,
S.S.S.72
Derby-18 holes, 6077 yards,
S.S.S.70
Course designed by Peter Alliss &
DaveThomas.
Club founded in 1977.
Visitors: welcome at all times.
Green fees: Brabazon - £16
weekdays, £18 weekends; Derby -
£8.50 weekdays, £10.50
weekends.
Society meetings: welcome at all
times.
Catering: full facilities within Hotel.
Hotels: own hotel.

K2 Bloxwich
☎Bloxwich (0922) 405724
Stafford Rd, Bloxwich, Walsall,
W Midlands WS3 3PQ.
A34, 4 miles N of Walsall centre.
Parkland course.
18 holes, 6286 yards, S.S.S.70
Course designed by J. Sixsmith.
Club founded in 1924.
Visitors: welcome weekdays, with
member at weekends.
Green fees: £10, (£4 with member);
members only weekends.
Society meetings: weekdays by
arrangement.
Catering: bar lunch, tea, evening
meals by arrangement except Mon.
Hotels: Barons Court; Crest; County;
Royal.

K3 Boldmere
☎021-354 3379
Monmouth Drive, Sutton Coldfield,
W Midlands.
A452 Chester Road, 6 miles NE of
Birmingham City Centre.
Parkland course.
Club founded in 1936.
Visitors: welcome anytime.
Green fees: £3.40 weekdays; £4
weekends.
Society meetings: not applicable.

Catering: lunchtimes only.
Hotels: Penns Hall; Parson and
Clarke.

K4 Calderfields
☎Walsall (0922) 640540/32243
Aldridge Rd, Walsall, W Midlands
WS4 2JS.
Take Junction 7 (M6), entrance next
to Duke Arms on Aldridge road A454.
Parkland course.
18 holes, 6700 yards, S.S.S.72
Course designed by Roy Winter.
Club founded in 1983.
Visitors: welcome anytime.
Green fees: £6 weekdays; £8
weekends.
Society meetings: welcome with
bookings.
Catering: restaurant 7 days; bar
snacks.
Hotels: Crest; Post House.

K5 Cocks Moor Woods
☎021-444 3584
Alcester Rd South, Kings Heath,
Birmingham B14 6ER.
On A435, near city boundary.
Parkland course.
18 holes, 5888 yards, S.S.S.68
Club founded in 1924.
Visitors: welcome.
Green fees: £3.40 per (18 holes),
£2.40 per (9 holes) weekdays, £4 per
(18 holes), £2.70 per (9 holes)
weekends.
Society meetings: by arrangement.
Catering: snacks served.
Hotels: in Birmingham.

K6 Copt Heath
☎Knowle (056 45) 2650
Warwick Rd, Knowle, Solihull, W
Midlands B93 9LN.
On A41 quarter mile S of Junction 5
with M42.
Parkland course.
18 holes, 6504 yards, S.S.S.71
Course designed by H. Vardon.
Club founded in 1910.
Visitors: members of recognised club
with official club handicap are
welcome.
Green fees: £17 per round; £17.50
per day.
Society meetings: welcome Wed
and Thurs only by arrangement with
Sec.
Catering: full facilities except Mon.

Hotels: Greswolde.

K7 Coventry
☎Coventry (0203) 414152
Finham Park, Coventry CV3 6PJ.
2 miles S of Coventry on A444
Stoneleigh to Leamington Spa road.
Parkland course.
18 holes, 6613 yards, S.S.S.72
Club founded in 1887.
Visitors: welcome weekdays only.
Green fees: £12.
Society meetings: Wed and Thurs.
Catering: full facilities.
Hotels: Leofric; Trust House Forte.

K8 Dartmouth
☎021-588 2131
Vale St, West Bromwich, W Midlands
B71 4DW.
West Bromwich to Walsall road, right
at Churchfield, behind Churchfield
HighSchool.
Undulating meadowland course.
9 holes, 6060 yards, S.S.S.69
Club founded in 1910.
Visitors: welcome weekdays and
weekends except Medal Days.
Green fees: £7.50, (£3 with
member) weekdays; £7.50
weekends with member.
Society meetings: welcome given
prior notice.
Catering: full menu with prior notice.
Hotels: Post House; The Moat.

K9 Druids Heath
☎Aldridge (0922) 55595
Stonnall Rd, Aldridge, W Midlands
W59 8JZ.
Off A452 6 miles NW of Sutton
Coldfield.
Undulating course.
18 holes, 6914 yards, S.S.S.73
Club founded in 1973.
Visitors: welcome weekdays.
Green fees: £8, (£5 with member)
weekdays; £15, (£10 with member)
weekends.
Society meetings: catered for
weekdays.
Catering: facilities all day.
Hotels: Barons Court; Fairlawns.

K10 Dudley
☎Dudley (0384) 53719
Turners Hill, Rowley Regis, Warley,
W Midlands B65 9DP.
1 mile S of town centre.

Play and stay at the Belfry.
The Ryder Cup Venue.

You don't need to be reminded that the Brabazon Course at The Belfry was the scene of that fantastic 1985 Ryder Cup victory and has been chosen again for the 1989 matches.

So, where better for you and your members to follow in the footsteps of the champions?

But The Belfry is so much more than just a world famous golf course; it's a unique country manor style hotel set in 370 acres of beautiful parkland. A hotel where your every comfort is assured – 168 bedrooms, all with private bath/shower, colour TV, direct dial telephone, radio and tea/coffee making facilities.

Then there's the award winning restaurant, superb carvery and all day service of light meals/snacks.

Aprés Golf is superbly catered for in our magnificent Leisure Club, with squash courts, saunas, solariums, spa-pool, swimming pool, turkish baths and trimnasium. Or you can dance

the night away in our fabulous Bel Air Nightclub.

The Belfry – it's a golfers dream, and so easy to find, just 1 minute from exit 9 of the M42 via M6.

NOW LOOK AT THESE UNBEATABLE BELFRY RATES

SPECIAL DAY PACKAGE
Monday – Friday, a meal at The Belfry plus one round of golf.
Derby Course £19.50
Brabazon Course £25.50

SPECIAL RESIDENTIAL PACKAGE
Any two nights – all year round – inclusive of twin room with private bath, three course dinner, full English Breakfast and all green fees (playing each course, Derby and Brabazon) £140.00 per person. Single room supplement £10 per person, per night.

—— MORE THAN JUST A HOTEL ——
WISHAW, NORTH WARWICKSHIRE. B76 9PR.
CONTACT SANDRA BUTLER FOR FULL DETAILS NOW ON 0675 70301. FAX: 0675 70178

—— DE VERE ⚜ HOTELS ——

Undulating course.
18 holes, 5715 yards, S.S.S.67
Club founded in 1966.
Visitors: weekdays only.
Green fees: £7.50; after 4pm £5
weekdays; (£4 with member).
Society meetings: by arrangement.
Catering: meals served.
Hotels: Station, Dudley.

K11 Edgbaston
☎021-454 1736
Church Rd, Edgbaston, Birmingham
B15 3TB.
A38 1 mile from Five Ways in
Birmingham city centre, entrance to
clubhouse is next door to Edgbaston
Old Church.
Parkland course.
18 holes, 6118 yards, S.S.S.69
Course designed by H.S. Colt.
Club founded in 1896.
Visitors: welcome at all times.
Green fees: £13 weekdays; £17
weekends and Bank Holidays.
Society meetings: weekdays only
by prior arrangement.
Catering: lunch daily, other meals
by arrangement.
Hotels: numerous in Birmingham.

K12 Forest of Arden G & CC
☎Meriden (0676) 22118
Maxstoke Lane, Meriden, Coventry,
Warwickshire CV7 7HR.
10 miles NW of Coventry off A45. 2.5
miles E of Birmingham International
Airport.
Parkland course.
18 holes, 6962 yards, S.S.S.72
Club founded in 1970.
Visitors: welcome with handicap
certificate.
Green fees: £12 weekdays; £15
weekends.
Society meetings: welcome
weekdays by prior arrangement.
Catering: restaurant and snacks.
Hotels: Manor; Haigs.

K13 Fulford Heath
☎Wythall (0564) 822806/824758
Tanners Green Lane, Wythall,
Birmingham B47 6BH.
1 mile from main Alcester Road,
signposted to Tanners Green.
Meadowland course.
18 holes, 6216 yards, S.S.S.70
Club founded in 1934.
Visitors: welcome weekdays.
Green fees: £9-£12 weekdays.

Society meetings: Tues or Thurs.
Catering: lunch and evening meals
served except Mon.
Hotels: George; Regency.

K14 Gay Hill
☎021-430 6523/430 8544/430
7077/474 6001
Alcester Rd, Hollywood, Birmingham
B47 5PP.
On A435, 7 miles from city centre.
Meadowland course.
18 holes, 6500 yards,, S.S.S.71
Club founded in 1921.
Visitors: unaccompanied weekdays;
with member only weekends and not
before 12.30pm Sunday.
Green fees: £10 per day.
Society meetings: Thurs only.
Catering: meals available.
Hotels: in Birmingham and Solihull.

K15 Grange
☎Coventry (0203) 451465
Copsewood, Coventry, W Midlands
CV3 1HS.
2.5 miles from Coventry Centre on
Binley Rd, A428.
Meadowland course.
9 holes, 3001 yards, S.S.S.69

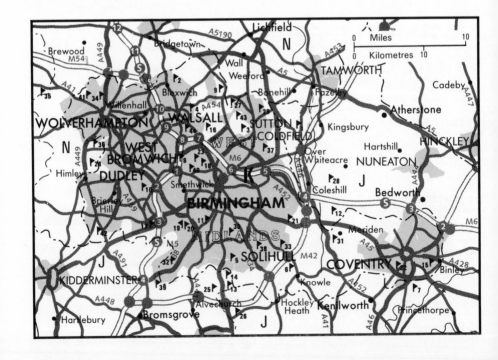

Course re-designed by T.J. McAuley.
Club founded in 1924.
Visitors: welcome weekdays before 2pm; Sunday after 11am. Not Sat.
Green fees: £5 per round, £7.50 per day.
Society meetings: by arrangement with Sec.
Catering: none; may arrange for Societies.
Hotels: numerous in area.

K16 Great Barr
☎021-357 1232
Chapel Lane, Great Barr, Birmingham B43 7BA.
Adjacent to Exit 7, off M6, 6 miles NW of Birmingham.
Meadowland course.
18 holes, 6545 yards, S.S.S.72
Club founded in 1961.
Visitors: weekdays.
Green fees: £9 weekdays.
Society meetings: small societies Tues, Thurs.
Catering: by arrangement.
Hotels: Post House, Great Barr.

K17 Halesowen
☎021-501 3606
The Leasowes, Halesowen, W Midlands B62 8QF.
Exit Junction 3 off M5, to Kidderminster, then to Halesowen.
Parkland course.
18 holes, 5646 yards, S.S.S.68
Club founded in 1902.
Visitors: not weekends. Bank Holidays by arrangement.
Green fees: £8.
Society meetings: by arrangement.
Catering: not Mon.
Hotels: numerous in Birmingham.

K18 Handsworth
☎021-554 0599
11 Sunningdale Close, Handsworth Wood, Handsworth, Birmingham B20 1NP.
3 miles NW of city centre off A41, 1 mile from M6.
Parkland course.
18 holes, 6312 yards, S.S.S.70
Club founded in 1895.
Visitors: welcome weekdays.
Green fees: £10, (£3 with member).
Society meetings: weekdays by arrangement.
Catering: lunch and dinner except Mon.
Hotels: Post House, Great Barr; Moat House, West Bromwich.

K19 Harborne
☎021-427 1728

40 Tennal Rd, Birmingham B32 2JE.
Via Harborne village and War Lane, SW of Birmingham.
Undulating parkland/moorland course.
18 holes, 6240 yards, S.S.S.70
Course designed by H.S. Colt.
Club founded in 1893.
Visitors: welcome weekdays only. Bank Holidays and weekends with member.
Green fees: £10, (£3 with member).
Society meetings: Wed, Thurs, Fri.
Catering: available except Mon.
Hotels: Claremont; Apollo.

K20 Harborne Church Farm
☎021-427 1204
Vicarage Rd, Harborne, Birmingham B17 0SN.
From Birmingham, via Broad St, Harborne Rd and War Lane to Vicarage Rd.
Parkland municipal course.
9 holes, 4514 yards, S.S.S.62
Club founded in 1926.
Visitors: welcome.
Green fees: on application.
Society meetings: none.
Catering: snacks and meals in cafe
Hotels: numerous in Birmingham.

K21 Hatchford Brook
☎021-743 9821
Coventry Rd, Sheldon, Birmingham B26 3PY.
Almost on city boundary adjacent to Airport, on main A45 Coventry Rd.
Parkland course.
18 holes, 6164 yards, S.S.S.69
Club founded in 1969.
Visitors: all welcome.
Green fees: on application.
Society meetings: not catered for.
Catering: canteen facilities while course open.
Hotels: numerous in NEC and Airport complex.

K22 Hearsall
☎Coventry (0203) 713470/713156
Beechwood Ave, Coventry CV5 6DF.
Just off A45.
Parkland course.
18 holes, 5951 yards, S.S.S.69
Club founded in 1894.
Visitors: welcome weekdays.
Green fees: £10 weekdays; £12 Sat.
Society meetings: Mon or Thurs by prior arrangement.
Catering: lunch, sandwiches available lunchtime, evening meals by prior arrangement.
Hotels: Leofric; De-Vere.

K23 Hill Top
☎021-554 4463
Park Lane, Handsworth Wood, Birmingham B21 8JP.
Parkland course.
18 holes, 6200 yards, S.S.S.69
Club founded in 1980.
Visitors: welcome.
Green fees: £4 weekends; £3.40 weekdays.
Society meetings: welcome.
Catering: hot or cold meals while course open.
Hotels: Europa.

K24 Himley Hall
☎Wombourne (0902) 895207
Log Cabin, Himley Hall Park, Dudley, W Midlands DY3 4DF.
From A449 Wolverhampton to Kidderminster road turn at traffic lights signposted Dudley onto B4176, then turn into Himley Hall Park on left.
Parkland course.
18 holes, 6107 yards, S.S.S.69
9 holes, 3090 yards.
Course designed by W.G. Cox and D.A. Baker.
Club founded in 1980.
Visitors: public course.
Green fees: £2 per (9 holes), £3 per (18 holes) weekdays; £2.50 per (9 holes), £3.60 per (18 holes) weekends.
Society meetings: by prior arrangement.
Catering: cafe and snack facilities only.
Hotels: Himley House, Park Hall.

K25 Kings Norton
☎Wythall (0564) 826789
Brockhill Lane, Weatheroak, Alvechurch, Birmingham B48 7ED.
8 miles from centre of Birmingham between A435 and A441.
Parkland course (3 loops of 9) 27 holes.
Blue-9 holes, 3567 yards,
Red-9 holes, 3294 yards, S.S.S.72
Also 12 hole Par 3 course.
Course designed by F Hawtree & Son.
Club founded in 1892.
Visitors: weekdays only, with member only at weekends.
Green fees: £10 all day (under revision).
Society meetings: weekdays only.
Catering: full facilities.
Hotels: St Johns, Solihull.

K26 Ladbrook Park
☎Tanworth-in-Arden (056 44) 2265

Poolhead Lane, Tanworth-in-Arden,
Solihull B94 5ED.
A4023 4 miles from Hockley Heath.
Undulating parkland course.
18 holes, 6407 yards, S.S.S.71
Course designed by H.S. Colt.
Club founded in 1908.
Visitors: welcome by prior
arrangement.
Green fees: £10.50 inclusive of
VAT.
Society meetings: by prior
arrangement.
Catering: daily except Mon by prior
arrangement.
Hotels: George, Solihull; Yew Trees,
Henley-in-Arden.

K27 **Little Aston**
☎021-353 2066
Streetly, Sutton Coldfield B74 3AN.
3 miles N of Sutton Coldfield in Little
Aston Park.
Parkland course.
18 holes, 6724 yards, S.S.S.73
Course designed by Harry Vardon.
Club founded in 1908.
Visitors: welcome weekdays.
Green fees: £16.
Society meetings: weekdays only.
Catering: lunch served to order
except Mon.
Hotels: Fairlawns.

K28 **Maxstoke Park**
☎Coleshill (0203) 64915
Castle Lane, Coleshill, Birmingham
B46 2RD.
Junction 4 off M6, A446 to Coleshill,
take B4114-6 to Atherstone for 2
miles, right turn into Castle Lane,
course in Maxstoke Castle grounds.
Parkland course.
18 holes, 6437 yards, S.S.S.71
Course designed by Ortree.
Club founded in 1896.
Visitors: welcome weekdays, Sat,
Sun with member.
Green fees: £12.
Society meetings: Mon, Tues and
Thurs.
Catering: lunch served daily.
Hotels: The Swan, Coleshill.

K29 **Moor Hall**
☎021-308 6130
Moor Hall Park, Sutton Coldfield,
W Midlands B75 6LN.
2 miles from Sutton Coldfield on
Tamworth road A453.
Parkland course.
18 holes, 6249 yards, S.S.S.70
Club founded in 1932.

Visitors: welcome weekdays only.
Green fees: £14, (£3 with member).
Society meetings: catered for Tues
and Wed only.
Catering: full service except Mon.
Hotels: Moor Hall; Penns Hall.

K30 **Moseley**
☎021-444 4957
Springfield Rd, Kings Heath,
Birmingham B14 7DX.
On Birmingham ring road, 0.5 mile E
of Alcester Rd.
Parkland course.
18 holes, 6227 yards, S.S.S.70
Club founded in 1892.
Visitors: welcome weekdays by
letter of introduction.
Green fees: £12.50, (£4 with
member).
Society meetings: catered for
Thurs.
Catering: by arrangement with
Stewardess.
Hotels: numerous in Birmingham.

K31 **North Warwickshire**
☎Meriden (0676) 22259
Hampton Lane, Meriden, W Midlands
CV7 7LL.
6 miles N of Coventry on A45.
Parkland course.
9 holes, 3181 yards, S.S.S.70
Club founded in 1894.
Visitors: weekdays except Thurs
(Ladies Day); weekends with
member only.
Green fees: £8 weekdays.
Society meetings: by arrangement.
Catering: bar snacks.
Hotels: Manor Hotel, Meriden; Post
House, Coventry.

K32 **North Worcestershire**
☎021-475 1047
Frankley Beeches Rd, Northfield,
Birmingham B31 5LP.
Main A38 road to Northfield, turn up
Frankley Beeches Rd, then 3rd road
on left brings you straight to club.
Meadowland course.
18 holes, 5919 yards, S.S.S.69
Course designed by James Braid.
Club founded in 1907.
Visitors: welcome weekdays, with
members weekends and Bank
Holidays.
Green fees: £10 plus VAT.
Society meetings: welcome any
day except Fri.
Catering: full facilities at club.
Hotels: Alexander; Bunbury,
Northfield.

K33 **Olton**
☎021-705 1083
Mirfield Rd, Solihull, W Midlands B91
1JH.
7 miles S of Birmingham off A41
Parkland course.
18 holes, 6229 yards, S.S.S.71
Visitors: welcome weekdays except
Wed.
Green fees: £11, (£3.50 with
member) weekdays; £4.50
weekends and Bank Holidays with
member.
Society meetings: by arrangement
weekdays except Wed.
Catering: by arrangement.
Hotels: St Johns Swallow; George.

K34 **Oxley Park**
☎Wolverhampton (0902) 25445
Bushbury, Wolverhampton
WV10 6DE.
Off A449, 1 mile N of
Wolverhampton.
Parkland course.
18 holes, 6153 yards, S.S.S.69
Visitors: welcome, booking
advisable at weekends.
Green fees: £9 weekdays; £12
weekends.
Society meetings: Wed by
arrangement.
Catering: bar lunch available, meals
on request.
Hotels: Mount; Ravensholt; Park
Hall.

K35 **Patshull Park**
☎Pattingham (0902) 700100
Burnhill Green, Wolverhampton,
W Midlands WV6 7HR.
Exit 3 from M54 to Albrighton then
signposted Patshull.
Parkland course.
18 holes, 6460 yards, S.S.S.71
Course designed by J. Jacobs.
Club founded in 1979.
Visitors: welcome, telephone for tee
reservation.
Green fees: £9 weekdays; £12
weekends and Bank Holidays.
Society meetings: full range of
packages available.
Catering: hotel on site with full
facilities.
Hotels: Own Hotel.

K36 **Penn**
☎Wolverhampton (0902) 341142
Penn Common, Penn, Wolverhamp-
ton, W Midlands WV4 5JN.
2 miles SW of Wolverhampton off
A449.

Heathland course.
18 holes, 6449 yards, S.S.S.71
Club founded in 1908.
Visitors: welcome weekdays.
Green fees: £7.
Society meetings: catered for weekdays.
Catering: lunch weekdays except Mon; dinner weekdays except Mon and Wed.
Hotels: Goldthorne; Park Hall.

K37 **Pype Hayes**
☎021-351 1014
Eachelhurst Rd, Walmley, Sutton Coldfield, W Midlands B76 8EP.
Off M6 at Spaghetti Junction, onto Tyburn Rd, 1 mile to Eaglehurst Rd.
Parkland course.
18 holes, 5811 yards, S.S.S.68
Club founded in 1932.
Visitors: welcome.
Green fees: £4.
Society meetings: welcome.
Catering: full facilities available.
Hotels: Sutton Court.

K38 **Robin Hood**
☎021-706 0061
St Bernards Rd, Solihull, W Midlands B92 7DJ.
From Olton station (6 miles S of

Birmingham on A41) travel NE up St Bernards Rd for 1 mile, clubhouse on right hand side.
Parkland course.
18 holes, 6609 yards, S.S.S.72
Course designed by H.S. Colt.
Club founded in 1893.
Visitors: welcome weekdays except Tues mornings and official hols.
Green fees: £11.50, (£4 with member).
Society meetings: Tues pm, Thurs and Fri.
Catering: bar snacks Tues-Fri.
Evening meal by arrangement.
Hotels: St Johns Swallow; George; Flemings, Solihull.

K39 **Rose Hill**
☎021-453 3159
Lickey Hills, Rednal, Birmingham.
M5, exit 4, on city boundary.
Parkland course.
18 holes, 6010 yards, S.S.S.69
Course designed by Carl Bretherton.
Club founded in 1927.
Visitors: welcome.
Green fees: £3.40 per (18 holes), £2.40 per (9 holes) weekdays; £4 per (18 holes), £2.70 per (9 holes) weekends.
Society meetings: by arrangement.

Catering: snacks served.
Hotels: Rose and Crown.

K40 **Sandwell Park**
☎021-553 4637
Birmingham Rd, West Bromwich, W Midlands B71 4JJ.
Junction 1 off M5, 0.25 mile from West Bromwich Albion Football Ground.
Parkland, links course.
18 holes, 6422 yards, S.S.S.72
Club founded in 1897.
Visitors: weekdays unlimited; weekends with member.
Green fees: £10 weekdays; £12 weekends.
Society meetings: Mon and Thur.
Catering: full facilities.
Hotels: Moat House.

K41 **South Staffordshire**
☎Wolverhampton (0902) 751065
Danescourt Rd, Tettenhall, Wolverhampton WV6 9BQ.
3 miles W of Wolverhampton town centre, on A41 to Telford.
Parkland course.
18 holes, 6621 yards, S.S.S.72
Course designed by H.S. Colt.
Club founded in 1893.
Visitors: weekdays except Tues am

(Ladies day); weekend only with member.
Green fees: £10 per round; £12 per day.
Society meetings: welcome except Tues am and weekends.
Catering: snacks, lunch, dinners.
Hotels: Mount; Connaught.

K42 **Stourbridge**
☎Stourbridge (0384) 395566
Worcester Lane, Pedmore, Stourbridge DY8 2RB.
2 miles from Stourbridge town centre on Worcester road.
Parkland course.
18 holes, 6178 yards, S.S.S.69
Club founded in 1892.
Visitors: welcome weekdays; with member only weekends.
Green fees: £9.50.
Society meetings: restricted to Tues and Fri.
Catering: available except Mon.
Hotels: Pedmore House.

K43 **Sutton Coldfield**
☎021-353 9633

110 Thornhill Rd, Streetly, Sutton Coldfield B74 3ER.
Located 9 miles NE of Birmingham on B4138 road, nearest motorway access is Junction 6 of M6.
Heathland course.
18 holes, 6248 yards, S.S.S.71
Course re-designed by Dr Mackenzie.
Club founded in 1889.
Visitors: welcome weekdays except Tues am.
Green fees: £10 per day, (£3.50 with member) weekdays; £12.50 per day, (£3.50 with member) weekends and Bank Holidays.
Society meetings: not accepted on Tues or weekends, Bank Holidays. Written applications required.
Catering: lunch and snacks available daily.
Hotels: Parson & Clarke; Fairlawns.

K44 **Walsall**
☎Walsall (0922) 613512
The Broadway, Walsall, W Midlands WS1 3EY.
1 mile S of Walsall centre, 400 yards

from the Crest Motel.
Parkland/meadowland course.
18 holes, 6232 yards, S.S.S.70
Club founded in 1907.
Visitors: welcome weekdays, must be with member at weekends.
Green fees: £12.50 per (18 holes); £15 per (27 holes); £18 per (36 holes), (£5 with member).
Society meetings: welcome.
Catering: full service at all times.
Hotels: Crest; Post House; County.

K45 **Warley**
☎021-429 2440
Lightwoods Hill, Warley, W Midlands.
Off A456 4.5 miles W of centre of Birmingham, behind Dog Public House.
Municipal parkland course.
9 holes, 2606 yards, S.S.S.64
Visitors: welcome all times.
Green fees: £2.80 per (18 holes) weekdays; £3.50 per (18 holes) weekends.
Society meetings: not catered for.
Catering: available.
Hotels: many on the main Hagley Rd.

L South Wales

Twenty years or so ago, golfers bound for Porthcawl and Southerndown took a rather more circuitous route than they do today although there was little except the lovely countryside to make them tarry. In a golfing sense, this was remote territory and even now Herefordshire has fewer courses than almost any other county in Britain; but in the building explosion of the sixties, Ken Cotton created St Pierre in an old deer park outside Chepstow. At the same time Ross-on-Wye forsook its original nine hole home, and its sheep, for something quite exceptional.

Both clubs always strike a chord with me because they were the first new courses I ever saw built and there could not have been a better or more contrasting initiation. Ross-on-Wye, carved out of the rough woodland, still stands as one of the major constructional feats in Britain in modern times. St Pierre is a fine example of a country club, nestling as it does almost within the shadow of the Severn Bridge in the neighbouring county of Monmouthshire.

For around £9,000, the old park at St Pierre, with its many huge trees which have stood for hundreds of years, was converted into a course which its architect modestly maintained made itself. Golfers quickly got to hear of its reputation and its owner and founder, Bill Graham, a man of energy and vision, established one of the most thriving clubs within the historic walls of the old manor house.

The facilities on offer, which include a splendid second course, squash and badminton, are a great tribute to Graham and it was no time at all before St Pierre, so accessible from all parts, was in demand for professional tournaments, notably the old Dunlop Masters; in 1980 it was honoured by the staging of the Curtis Cup.

From the Severn Bridge, it is possible to be teeing-off at Royal Porthcawl within the hour or sampling the delights of Southerndown on its more lofty perch overlooking acres of undeveloped dune land.

Porthcawl and Southerndown are well enough known not to need anything in the way of recommendation; they are as delightful in their separate ways as is the Newport Club at Rogerstone. The city of Cardiff has a number of clubs and there have been two recent additions at Monmouth and Belmont, Hereford.

L1 **Aberdare**
☎Aberdare (0685) 871188
Abernant, Aberdare, Mid Glam
CF44 0RY.
Through town centre of Aberdare past the General Hospital, 0.5 mile from town centre.
Meadowland course.
18 holes, 5845 yards, S.S.S.69
Club founded in 1921.
Visitors: welcome weekdays.
Green fees: £6 per day weekdays.
Society meetings: catered for weekdays.
Catering: full a la carte meals or bar snacks except Mon.
Hotels: Baverstocks.

L2 **Aberystwyth**
☎Aberystwyth (0970) 615104
Brynymor, Aberystwyth, Dyfed

N end of promenade immediately behind sea fron hotels, access road adjacent to Cliff Railway, 1 mile from town centre.
Undulating meadowland course.
18 holes, 5735 yards, S.S.S.68
Course designed by Harry Vardon.
Club founded in 1911.
Visitors: unrestricted.
Green fees: £5-£7 daily; £7-£8.50 weekends; £25 weekly.
Society meetings: by appointment.
Catering: full facilities available.
Hotels: Belle Vue Royal; Sea Bank; Court Royale.

L3 **Ashburnham**
☎Burry Port (055 46) 2269 Sec.
Cliffe Terrace, Burry Port, Dyfed
SA16 0HN.
9 miles from Llanelli exit on M4, 4

miles from Llanelli on A484.
Championship links course.
18 holes, 7016 yards, S.S.S.74
18 holes, 6646 yards, S.S.S.73/74
Club founded in 1894.
Visitors: weekdays; some weekends.
Green fees: £10 per round (£8 with member), £12 per day (£10 with member) weekdays; £12 per round (£10 with member), £14 per day (£12 with member) weekends.
Society meetings: welcome weekdays.
Catering: full facilities available.
Hotels: Stradey Park; Thomas Arms; Stepney, Llanelli; Ash Burnham, Burry Port.

L4 **Bargoed**
☎Bargoed (0443) 830143

Heolddu, Bargoed, Mid Glam.
15 miles from Cardiff on A469. Turn
left opposite Gwerthonor Hotel; 2nd
left at Heolddu Leisure centre.
Undulating parkland course.
18 holes, 6012 yards, S.S.S.70
Visitors: welcome weekdays;
weekend with member only.
Green fees: £6 weekdays, (£5 with
member); parties of ten or over £5;
weekends with member only.
Society meetings: weekdays by
arrangement.
Catering: snacks and meals served.
Hotels: Maes Manor, Blackwood.

L5 **Blackwood**
☎Blackwood (0495) 223152
Cwmgelli, Blackwood, Gwent.
0.75 mile N of Blackwood on A4048,
Tredegar road.
Meadowland course.
9 holes, 5304 yards, S.S.S.66
Club founded in 1914.
Visitors: welcome at all times.
Green fees: on application.
Society meetings: catered for on
weekdays by arrangement.
Catering: golf societies only by
arrangement.
Hotels: Maes Manor; Plas Inn,
Blackwood.

L6 **Borth & Ynyslas**
☎Borth (097 081) 202
Borth, Dyfed AY24 5JS.
7 miles N of Aberystwyth.
Seaside links course.
Club founded in 1885.
Visitors: welcome except when
major events are being held.
Green fees: £8 weekdays; £10
weekends and Bank Holidays.
Society meetings: welcome
weekdays by prior arrangement.
Catering: snacks and sandwiches;
lunch and dinner except on Stewards
day off.
Hotels: Cliff Haven; Golf Hotel;
Grand; Glanhor, Borth; Ynyshir
Country House, Eglwysfach.

L7 **Brecon**
☎Brecon (0874) 2004
Newton Park, Llanfaes, Brecon,
Powys LD3 8PA.
300 yards from roundabout on by
pass S of town.
Meadowland course.
9 holes, 5218 yards, S.S.S.66
Club founded in 1902.
Visitors: welcome.
Green fees: £4 weekdays; £5
weekends.

Society meetings: by arrangement.
Catering: none.
Hotels: Castle of Brecon; Bishops
Meadow; plus several guest houses.

L8 **Brynhill**
☎Barry (0446) 720277 Sec, 735061
Clubhouse
Port Rd, Barry, S Glam.
A48 to Culverhouse Cross from
Cardiff, then road to Barry, golf club
on Port Rd near Colcot Arms Hotel.
Undulating meadowland course.
18 holes, 5511 metres, S.S.S.69
Course designed by C.K. Cotton.
Club founded in 1921.
Visitors: welcome weekdays,
weekends with member.
Green fees: £7.50, (£5 with
member) weekdays; £10, (£7.50 with
member) Sat; Sunday with member
only.
Society meetings: catered for
weekdays.
Catering: lunch, dinners served
except Mon.
Hotels: Mount Sorrel; International.

L9 **Bryn Meadows G & CC
Hotel**
☎Blackwood (0495) 225590/227276
The Bryn, Hengoed, Mid Glam
CF8 7SM
A469 15 miles from Cardiff, turn up
lane opposite filling station near
Crown Hotel.
Parkland course.
18 holes, 5963 yards, S.S.S.69
Course designed by E. Jefferies &
B. Mayo.
Club founded in 1973.
Visitors: welcome weekdays.
Green fees: £6.50, (£5.50 with
member) weekdays; £7.50, (£6.50
with member) weekends.
Society meetings: welcome
weekdays.
Catering: full facilities except Sun.
Hotels: Bryn Meadows, 20 de luxe
double rooms.

L10 **Builth Wells**
☎Builth Wells (0982) 553296
Builth Wells, Powys LD2 3NF.
A483 immediately W of Builth Wells.
Parkland course.
18 holes, 5760 yards, S.S.S.67
Club founded in 1923.
Visitors: welcome anytime.
Green fees: £7 weekdays; £9
weekends and Bank Holidays.
Society meetings: catered for any
time.
Catering: available on request.

Hotels: Lake; Caeberis; Llanfair
Guest House.

L11 **Caerphilly**
☎Caerphilly (0222) 883481
Pencapel, Mountain Rd, Caerphilly,
Mid Glam CF8 1HJ.
10 minutes from Caerphilly railway
and bus stations, 7 miles from Cardiff
on A469.
Undulating course.
14 holes, 5819 yards, S.S.S.71
Club founded in 1905.
Visitors: welcome weekdays.
Green fees: only with member at
weekends and Bank Holidays. £7.50
per round; £8.50 per day.
Society meetings: catered for
weekdays.
Catering: except Wed.
Hotels: Mount; Greenhill, Caerphilly.

L12 **Cardiff**
☎Cardiff (0222) 753320 Sec,
753067 Club, 754772 Pro.
Sherborne Ave, Cyncoed, Cardiff, S
Glam CF2 6SJ.
Take A48M off the M4, 3 miles to
Pentwyn exit, take industrial road for
2 miles to village, turn left at
roundabout and again left at Spar
Shop, club 150 yards.
Undulating parkland course.
18 holes, 6016 yards, S.S.S.70
Club founded in 1921.
Visitors: welcome weekdays
arrange in advance, with member
only at weekends.
Green fees: on application.
Society meetings: Thurs by
advance booking.
Catering: full facilities available.
Hotels: The Post House; The Stakis
Inn, Eastern Avenue.

L13 **Cardigan**
☎Cardigan (0293) 612035
Gwbert-on-Sea, Cardigan, Dyfed
SA43 1PR.
3 miles NW of Cardigan, take left
fork at Cardigan Cenotaph at N end
of town.
Seaside meadowland course.
18 holes, 6207 yards, S.S.S.70
Club founded in 1928.
Visitors: unrestricted.
Green fees: £8 per day; £19 week-
ends and Bank Holidays.
Society meetings: welcome any
day with previous arrangement.
Catering: bar snacks, lunch and
evening meal available.
Hotels: Cliff-Gwbert; Castell
Malgwyn, Llechryd, Cardigan.

L14 Carmarthen
☎Conwyl Elfed (0267) 214
Blaenycoed Rd, Carmarthen, Dyfed
SA33 6EH.
4 miles NW of Carmarthen.
Undulating course.
18 holes, 6212 yards, S.S.S.71
Visitors: welcome.
Green fees: on application.
Society meetings: welcome by arrangement.
Catering: facilities available except Wed.
Hotels: numerous in Carmarthen.

L15 Cilgwyn
☎Llangybi (0570) 45286
Llangybi, Lampeter, Dyfed
SA48 8NN.
4 miles NE of Lampeter on A485 in village of Llangybi.

Parkland course.
9 holes, 5318 yards, S.S.S.67
Course designed by Robert Sandow.
Club founded in 1905.
Visitors: welcome.
Green fees: on application.
Society meetings: catered for throughout year.
Catering: restaurant and bar meals available Tues-Sun.
Hotels: Black Lion; Falcondale, Lampeter.

L16 Clyne
☎Swansea (0792) 401989
120 Owls Lodge Lane, Mayals, Black Pill, Swansea SA3 3DR.
Coast road from Swansea to Black Pill (3 miles), then turn right into Mayals Rd.
Moorland course.

18 holes, 6312 yards, S.S.S.71
Course designed by H.S. Colt.
Club founded in 1921.
Visitors: welcome weekdays only.
Green fees: £8 per day weekdays; £10 per day weekends.
Society meetings: £8 per head 1-20; £6 per head 21 and over.
Catering: full facilities except Mon.
Hotels: Dragon; Osborne.

L17 Cradoc
☎Brecon (0874) 3658
Penoyre Park, Cradoc, Brecon,
Powys LD3 9LP.
2 miles N of Brecon on B4520
Parkland course.
18 holes, 6318 yards, S.S.S.71
Course designed by C.K. Cotton.
Club founded in 1974.
Visitors: welcome any time.

Green fees: £6 weekdays; £9 weekends and Bank Holidays; reduction of £1 with member.
Society meetings: welcome anytime.
Catering: full facilities daily except Mon by special arrangement.
Hotels: Wellington; Castle of Brecon; George; Bishops Meadow, Brecon; Lake, Llangammarch Wells.

L18 **Creigiau**
☎Pentyrch (0222) 890263
Creigiau, Cardiff, S Glam CF4 8NN.
4 miles NW of Cardiff towards Llantrisant.
Parkland course.
18 holes, 5715 yards, S.S.S.68
Club founded in 1926.
Visitors: welcome weekdays; (Ladies day Tues).
Green fees: £8.
Society meetings: welcome weekdays by arrangement.
Catering: lunch and dinner except Mon.
Hotels: Miskin Manor; Park; Royal; Angel.

L19 **Dinas Powis**
☎Dinas Powis (0222) 512727
Old Highwalls, Dinas Powis, S Glam CF6 4AJ.
On A4055 Cardiff to Barry Road.
Parkland course.
18 holes, 5151 yards, S.S.S.66
Club founded in 1914.
Visitors: welcome.
Green fees: £7, (£4 with member) weekdays; £9, (£6 with member) weekends.
Society meetings: welcome.
Catering: full facilities available.
Hotels: Star, Station Rd.

L20 **Glamorganshire**
☎Penarth (0222) 701185
Lavernock Rd, Penarth, S Glam CF6 2UP.
Take junction 33 off M4, take A4232 then A4231 and then B4267 which passes the golf club.
Parkland course.
18 holes, 6150 yards, S.S.S.70
Club founded in 1890.
Visitors: welcome except on competition days, Bank Holidays and when Societies on course.
Green fees: £10 weekdays; £12 weekends and Bank Holidays.
Society meetings: on application to Sec.
Catering: first class facilities, à la carte menus, bar snacks; lunch

every day.
Hotels: Walton House.

L21 **Glynhir**
☎Llandybie (0269) 850427
Glynhir Rd, Llandybie, Ammanford, Dyfed SA18 2TF.
1.25 miles N from Ammanford on A483 Llandybie road, turn right up Glynhir Rd and continue for almost 2 miles to club.
Undulating parkland/meadowland course.
18 holes, 6090 yards, S.S.S.70
Course designed by F.W. Hawtree.
Club founded in 1964.
Visitors: welcome weekdays; by permission weekends in summer.
Green fees: £6 weekdays, £8 weekends in summer; £3 weekdays, £5 weekends in winter.
Society meetings: weekdays welcome; weekends on occasions all by prior appointment.
Catering: restaurant, bar meals except Mon.
Hotels: The Mill; Golf Clubhouse; Cawdon; Red Lion.

L22 **Glynneath**
☎Glynneath (0639) 720452
Penycraig, Pontneathvaughan, Neath, W Glam SA11 5AG.
Off A4109 10 miles N of Neath.
Hillside course.
12 holes, 5385 yards, S.S.S.67
Club founded in 1931.
Visitors: welcome.
Green fees: on application.
Society meetings: welcome weekdays.
Catering: by arrrangement.
Hotels: Plas-y-Felin.

L23 **Haverfordwest**
☎Haverfordwest (0437) 3565
Arnolds Down, Narberth Rd, Haverfordwest, Dyfed SA61 1JB.
A40 Carmarthen to Haverfordwest, on right hand side of A40, 1 mile before town.
Undulating meadowland course.
18 holes, 5908 yards, S.S.S.70
Club founded in 1910.
Visitors: welcome.
Green fees: £6.50, (£5.50 with member) weekdays; £8.50, (£6.50 with member) weekends.
Society meetings: welcome by appointment.
Catering: hot or cold bar snacks; meals also available.
Hotels: County; St Brides, Saundersfoot.

L24 **Knighton**
☎Knighton (0547) 528646
The Ffrydd, Knighton, Powys LD7 1EF.
0.5 mile S of Knighton.
Undulating course.
9 holes, 5320 yards, S.S.S.66
Course designed by Harry Vardon.
Club founded in 1913.
Visitors: welcome.
Green fees: £3 weekdays; £5 weekends, unrestricted.
Society meetings: by prior arrangement with Sec.
Catering: snacks available weekends, other by prior arrangement.
Hotels: Red Lion.

L25 **Llangland Bay**
☎Swansea (0792) 366023
Llangland Bay, Swansea, W Glam SA3 4QR.
M4 to Swansea, 6 miles W.
Seaside parkland course.
18 holes, 5827 yards, S.S.S.69
Club founded in 1904.
Visitors: welcome if member of recognised club.
Green fees: winter £7, (£4 with member); summer £11, (£10 with member).
Society meetings: welcome if booked in advance, maximum 40.
Catering: bar meals available; cooked meals to order before playing.
Hotels: Osborne; Caswell.

L26 **Llandrindod Wells**
☎Llandrindod Wells (0597) 2010
Llandrindod Wells, Powys.
Signposted from A483, half mile E of town, above lake.
Mountain course.
18 holes, 5749 yards, S.S.S.68
Course designed by Harry Vardon.
Club founded in 1907.
Visitors: welcome at all times.
Green fees: on application.
Society meetings: catered for at all times by prior arrangement.
Catering: lunch and snacks served by arrangement with Steward.
Hotels: Metropole; Commodore, Glen Usk.

L27 **Llanishen**
☎Cardiff (0222) 755078
Cwm, Lisvane, Cardiff CF4 5UD.
5 miles to N of Cardiff city centre, 1.5 miles N of Llanishen church via Heol Hir.
Parkland course.

18 holes, 5296 yards, S.S.S.66
Club founded in 1905.
Visitors: weekdays unlimited,
weekends and Bank Holidays with
member only, handicap certificate
required.
Green fees: £10.
Society meetings: Thurs only by
previous arrangement.
Catering: full facilities except Mon.
Hotels: Phoenix, Cardiff.

L28 Llantrisant & Pontyclun

☎Llantrisant (0443) 22148/228169
Lanelay Rd, Talbot Green,
Pontyclub, Mid Glam CF7 8HZ.
On A4119 10 miles from Cardiff.
12 holes, 5712 yards, S.S.S.68
Club founded in 1927.
Visitors: welcome weekdays.
Green fees: £7, (£4 with member)
weekdays; £7 with member
weekends and Bank Holidays.
Society meetings: catered for
weekdays.
Catering: bar meals on request
except Wed. Three course meals
with 24 hour notice.

Hotels: Heronstone; New Inn; City
Inn.

L29 Llanwern

☎Newport (0633) 412029
Golf House, Tenyson Ave, Llanwern,
Gwent NP6 2DY.
Leave M4 at Junction 24, after
quarter mile turn left into Llanwern
village.
Meadowland course.
18 holes, 6206 yards, S.S.S.70
9 holes, 5674 yards.
Club founded in 1928.
Visitors: welcome weekdays (jacket
and tie to be worn in evenings).
Green fees: on application.
Society meetings: by arrangement.
Catering: full facilities available.
Hotels: Ladbroke Mercury.

L30 Machynlleth

☎Machynlleth (0654) 2000
Newtown Rd, Machynlleth, Powys.
0.5 mile from Machynlleth on A489 to
Newtown.
Undulating course.
9 holes, 5726 yards, S.S.S.67
Course designed by James Braid.

Club founded in 1907.
Visitors: welcome apart from
competition days; welcome Sun.
Green fees: £5 weekdays,
weekends.
Society meetings: not at weekends.
Catering: on by arrangement.
Hotels: Wynstan.

L31 Maesteg

☎Maesteg (0656) 732037
Mount Pleasant, Neath Rd, Maesteg,
Mid Glam.
Adjacent to main Maestag to Port
Talbot road.
Moorland course.
18 holes, 5845 yards, S.S.S.69
Club founded in 1912.
Visitors: no restrictions.
Green fees: £6 weekdays; £7
weekends and Bank Holidays.
Society meetings: by arrangement.
Catering: meals available.
Hotels: Sarn Services.

L32 Merthyr Tydfil

☎Merthyr Tydfil (0685) 3308
Clothall Lane, Cefn Coed, Merthyr
Tydfil, Mid Glam.

Off the Heads of the Valley road A465 at Cefn Coed.
Mountain course.
9 holes, 5794 yards, S.S.S.68
Club founded in 1908.
Visitors: welcome.
Green fees: £4 per day, (£3 with member); £8 weekends and Bank Holidays, (£5 with member).
Society meetings: welcome weekdays.
Catering: snacks and bar meals served.
Hotels: Castle; Baverstocks.

L33 **Milford Haven**
☎Milford Haven (064 62) 2368
Woodbine House, Hubberston, Milford Haven.
Clubhouse situated 0.75 mile from town centre to W.
Meadowland course.
18 holes, 6071 yards, S.S.S.71
Course designed by D. Snell.
Visitors: welcome all times.
Green fees: £6 weekdays; £7 weekends.
Society meetings: welcome.
Catering: full facilities available.
Hotels: Lord Nelson; Sir Benfro.

L34 **Monmouth**
☎Monmouth (0600) 2212
Leasebrook Lane, Monmouth, Gwent.
1 mile along A40 Monmouth - Ross road.
Parkland course.
9 holes, 5454 yards, S.S.S.66
Club founded in 1921.
Visitors: welcome.
Green fees: £6 weekdays; £10 weekends and Bank Holidays.
Society meetings: by arrangement with Sec.
Catering: every day except Mon.
Hotels: Leasebrook Country; Pilgrim.

L35 **Monmouthshire**
☎Abergavenny (0873) 2606 Sec, 3171 Club, 2532 Pro.
Llanfoist, Abergavenny, Gwent NP7 9HE.
M4 to Newport then A4042, take road to Llanfoist between Llanfoist and Llanellen.
Meadowland course.
18 holes, 6054 yards, S.S.S.69.
Course designed by James Braid.
Club founded in 1892.
Visitors: must have proof of membership of recognised club and handicap certificate.

Green fees: £10 weekdays; £14 weekends and Bank Holidays.
Society meetings: Mon and Fri only application before Dec of preceding year.
Catering: full facilities except Tues.
Hotels: The Angel; Llanwenarth Arms.

L36 **Morlais Castle**
☎Merthyr (0685) 2822
Pant, Dowlais, Merthyr Tydfil, Mid Glam CF48 2UY.
Follow signs for Brecon Mountain Railway.
Moorland course.
9 holes, 3129 yards, S.S.S.70
Club founded in 1900.
Visitors: welcome except Sat pm.
Green fees: on application.
Catering: lunch or evening meals served every day.
Hotels: Castle; Baverstocks.

L37 **Morriston**
☎Swansea (0792) 71079.
160 Clasemont Rd, Morriston, Swansea, West Glam SA6 6AJ.
3 miles N of Swansea city centre on A4067, then 0.5 mile W along A48.
Parkland course.
18 holes, 5734 yards, S.S.S.68
Club founded in 1919.
Visitors: welcome at all times.
Green fees: £8 weekdays; £10.35 weekends and Bank Holidays.
Reduction of 25 per cent if with member.
Society meetings: on application.
Catering: lunch available except Mon.
Hotels: Dragon; Dolphin; Ladbroke; Forest Motel.

L38 **Mountain Ash**
☎Mountain Ash (0443) 472265
Cefnpennar, Mountain Ash, Mid Glam CF45 4ES.
A470 to Abercynon, then A4059 to Mountain Ash.
Mountain course.
18 holes, 5485 yards, S.S.S.68
Club founded in 1908.
Visitors: welcome.
Green fees: £7 weekdays; £9 weekends; (reduction of £3 with member).
Society meetings: welcome.
Catering: full facilities except Mon.
Hotels: Baverstocks.

L39 **Neath**
☎Neath (0639) 3615
Cadoxton, Neath, West Glam

SA10 7AH.
3 miles from Neath, opposite Cadexton Church.
Mountain course.
18 holes, 6465 yards, S.S.S.72
Course designed by James Braid.
Club founded in 1934.
Visitors: welcome without reservation.
Green fees: £6 weekdays; £8 weekends.
Society meetings: welcome by arrangement with Sec.
Catering: full facilities except Mon.
Hotels: Glynclydach.

L40 **Newport**
☎Newport (0633) 892643
Great Oak, Rogerstone, Newport, Gwent NR1 6FX.
From M4 junction 27 take B4591 (signposted Highcross), after 1.25 miles turn right at Vixen Garage.
Undulating parkland course.
18 holes, 6370 yards, S.S.S.71
Club founded in 1903.
Visitors: welcome weekdays, members of recognised club only.
Green fees: £12 weekdays.
Society meetings: welcome Wed, Thurs and Fri.
Catering: lunch 12-1.30pm; evening meal 6.30-9pm; except Tues; sandwiches, rolls, pies available.
Hotels: Harris.

L41 **Newport (Pembs)**
☎Newport (0239) 820244
Newport. Dyfed SA42 0NR.
Follow signs to Newport Sands from Newport.
Seaside course.
9 holes, 6178 yards (for 18), S.S.S.69
Club founded in 1925.
Visitors: welcome.
Green fees: £6.
Society meetings: by arrangement.
Catering: snacks served.
Hotels: Golden Lion; Fishguard.

L42 **Palleg**
☎Glantawe (0639) 842524
Palleg Rd, Lower Cwmtwrch, Swansea
15 miles N of Swansea on Brecon road A4067, turn left at Aubrey Arms roundabout, course is 1 mile from here.
Undulating meadowland/moorland course.
9 holes, 3260 yards, S.S.S.72
Course designed by C.K. Cotton.
Club founded in 1930.

Visitors: welcome except during major competitions.
Green fees: on application.
Society meetings: welcome except Bank Holidays.
Catering: by arrangement except Mon.
Hotels: Ganafon; Abercrave Inn.

L43 **Pennard**
☎Bishopton (044 128) 3131
2 Southgate Rd, Southgate, Swansea. West Glam SA3 2BT.
8 miles W of Swansea on B4436.
Undulating seaside course.
18 holes, 6266 yards, S.S.S.71
Club founded in 1908.
Visitors: welcome at all times.
Green fees: £25 weekly ticket; £8, (£6 with member) weekdays; £9, (£7 with member) weekends and Bank Holidays.
Society meetings: by arrangement.
Catering: bar snacks; lunch and evening meals by prior arrangement with Stewardess.
Hotels: Osborne.

L44 **Pontardawe**
☎Pontardawe (0792) 863118
Cefn Llan, Pontardawe, Swansea.
4 miles N of M4 on A4067.
Meadowland course.
18 holes, 6061 yards, S.S.S.69
Club founded in 1924.
Visitors: welcome.
Green fees: £5 weekdays; £7.50 weekends and Bank Holidays.
Society meetings: on application.
Catering: lunch served except Mon.
Hotels: Inn on the Lake.

L45 **Pontnewydd**
☎Cwmbran (063 33) 2170
West Pontnewydd, Cwmbran, Gwent NP4 4AR.
Follow signs for West Pontnewydd or Upper Cwmbran, 2 miles N of Cwmbran.
Meadowland course.
10 holes, 5340 yards, S.S.S.67
Club founded in 1875.
Visitors: welcome weekdays, weekends only with member.
Green fees: £6, (£3 with member).
Society meetings: by previous arrangement.
Catering: lunchtimes and evening meals except Mon.
Hotels: Parkway; Commodore, Cwmbran.

L46 **Pontypool**
☎Pontypool (049 55) 3655

Trevethin, Pontypool, Gwent NP4 8DJ.
1 mile N of town centre.
Undulating parkland/moorland course.
18 holes, 6058 yards, S.S.S.69
Club founded in 1903.
Visitors: welcome.
Green fees: £6 weekdays; £7 weekends and Bank Holidays.
Society meetings: welcome.
Catering: available daily.
Hotels: Commodore; Parkway, Cwmbran.

L47 **Pontypridd**
☎Pontypridd (0443) 402359
Ty-Gwyn, The Common, Pontypridd, Mid Glam.
9 miles from Cardiff, take A470 N to Pontypridd and Merthyr.
Undulating mountain course.
18 holes, 5650 yards, S.S.S.68
Course designed by Bradbeer.
Club founded in 1905.
Visitors: welcome.
Green fees: £6, (£4 with member) weekdays; £9, (£6 with member) weekends.
Society meetings: by arrangement.
Catering: snacks served, meals by arrangement.
Hotels: many in Cardiff.

L48 **Pyle & Kenfig**
☎Porthcawl (065 671) 3093
Waun-y-Mer, Kenfig, Mid Glam CF33 4PU.
Leave M4 at Junction 37, follow Porthcawl.
Seaside links course.
18 holes, 6640 yards, S.S.S.73
Club founded in 1922.
Visitors: welcome weekdays, guest of members at weekends and Bank Holidays.
Green fees: £10; £7 with member.
Society meetings: on application to Sec.
Catering: full facilities available.
Hotels: Seabank; Rose and Crown; Fairways; Atlantic.

L49 **Radyr**
☎Radyr (0222) 842408 Manager, 842442 Members.
Drysgol Rd, Radyr, Cardiff CF4 8BS.
Off A470 at Taffs Well.
Parkland course.
18 holes, 6031 yards, S.S.S.70 summer 18 holes, 5616 yards, S.S.S.68 winter.
Club founded in 1902.
Visitors: weekdays with handicap

certificate; weekends with members only.
Green fees: £10 per day.
Society meetings: Wed and Fri.
Catering: full dining facilities except Thurs.
Hotels: numerous in Cardiff.

L50 **Rhondda**
☎Tonypandy (0443) 433204
Pontygwaitn, Ferndale, Rhondda, Mid Glam CF43 3PW.
On Cardiff to Rhondda Rd 3 miles from Porth.
Mountain top course.
18 holes, 6428 yards, S.S.S.70
Club founded in 1904/1910.
Visitors: welcome weekdays, weekends with member.
Green fees: on application.
Society meetings: by arrangement.
Catering: meals except Mon, preferably ordered before play.
Hotels: Dunraven; Gordon.

L51 **The Rolls of Monmouth**
☎Monmouth (0600) 5353
The Hendre, Monmouth, Gwent MP5 4HG.
3.25 miles W of Monmouth on B4233 (Abergavenny Rd).
Undulating parkland course.
18 holes, 6723 yards, S.S.S.72
Course designed by Urbis Planning.
Club founded in 1982.
Visitors: welcome.
Green fees: £12.50, (£5 with member) weekdays; £15, (£5 with member) weekends.
Society meetings: welcome.
Catering: full facilities 7 days.
Hotels: Kings Head; Priory Motel; Pilgrim.

L52 **Royal Porthcawl**
☎Porthcawl (065 671) 2251
Porthcawl, Mid Glam CF36 3UW.
Leave M4 junction 37 winding through A4229 to reach Porthcawl via South Cornelly and Nottage.
Heathland/downland course.
Championship course - 18 holes, 6605 yards, S.S.S.74.
Course designed by Charles Gibson.
Club founded in 1891.
Visitors: welcome with introduction of member or club Sec.
Green fees: on application.
Society meetings: by arrangement.
Catering: lunch, tea available; evening meals by arrangement.
Hotels: Atlantic; Seabank; Fairways; Maid of Sker; Seaways.

L53 **St Giles**
☎Newtown (0686) 25844
Pool Rd, Newtown, Powys
SY16 3AJ.
1 mile E of Newtown on main
Welshpool to Newtown road, A483.
Undulating parkland course.
9 holes, 5864 yards, S.S.S.68
Club founded in 1910.
Visitors: welcome weekdays, some weekends.
Green fees: £4 weekdays; £5 weekends and Bank Holidays. Per week, £20.
Society meetings: contact Sec.
Catering: meals available from Steward except Mon.
Hotels: Elephant & Castle; Bear.

L54 **St Idloes**
☎Llanidloes (055 12) 2559
Pen-Rhallt, Llanidloes, Powys
Off B4569 N out of Llanidloes.
Hillside, slightly undulating course.
9 holes, 5320 yards, S.S.S.66
Visitors: welcome.
Green fees: on application.
Society meetings: by appointment.
Catering: by appointment.
Hotels: Lloyds; Trewythen Arms.

L55 **St Mellons**
☎Castleton (0633) 680408 Sec,
680101 Pro, 680401 Club.
St Mellons, Cardiff, Gwent CF3 8XS.
On A48 between Newport and Cardiff on left, follow yellow sign for St Mellons C.C.
Parkland course.
18 holes, 6250 yards, S.S.S.70
Visitors: welcome weekdays; with member at weekends.
Green fees: £10.
Society meetings: by arrangement.
Catering: meals served.
Hotels: Wentloog Castle; St Mellons CC.

L56 **St Pierre G & CC**
☎Chepstow (0291) 23564
St Pierre Park, Chepstow, Gwent
NP6 6YA.
On A48, 1 mile from Chepstow roundabout.
Old course parkland, new course meadowland.
Old-18 holes, 6700 yards, S.S.S.73
New-18 holes, 5762 yards, S.S.S.68
Old course designed by C.K. Cotton, new by Bill Cox.
Club founded in 1964.

Visitors: welcome, handicap certificate required. Booking advised for starting time.
Green fees: on application.
Society meetings: Mon-Fri, weekends residential only.
Catering: restaurant and coffee shop.
Hotels: St Pierre, residential 110 beds.

L57 **Southerdown**
☎Southerdown (0656) 880476.
Ewenny, Bridgend, Mid Glam CF35 5BT.
4 miles from Bridgend on B4265 S to Ewenny, then W on B4524 to Ogmore.
Downland course.
18 holes, 6613 yards, S.S.S.73
Club founded in 1905.
Visitors: weekdays; weekends with member.
Green fees: £10 weekdays; £13 weekends.
Society meetings; weekdays only by arrangement with Sec.
Catering: facilities daily.
Hotels: Sea Lawns; Sea Bank; Court Colman.

Tenby

Enthusiastic, often obsessive, a liking for a golf course is hard to restrain. Golfers enjoy sharing delights they have experienced, hoping that their pleasure will rub off on those following their recommendations. Naturally, we don't all look for the same things. Carnoustie or Wentworth off the back tees for instance, may be alright for the giants but, for the less sadistically inclined, it is hardly heaven on earth. Attempting the impossible is not everyone's taste but, when it comes to a combination of good golf, enjoyment, a holiday atmosphere and scenic glory, the tempter is on far surer ground where Tenby is concerned.

On the West Wales coast, it offers all of these pleasures. It is a seaside links of unrivalled joy and beauty and, for the historically minded, has an important extra qualification — it is the oldest constituted Club in the Principality. Host to countless championships, home for the fortunate legions who choose it as a permanent base, it is equally attractive to those who get there only now and then.

It lies at the west end of a charming town in typically seaside terrain with which not many in the golfing world are familiar. The game for them conjures up more tree-lined fairways, sinister water features and other inhibiting hazards. Tenby's freedom and invigorating air can be sampled with one deep breath although that is not to say that the control of shots is not paramount. It is essentially a course which rewards good driving, the basic art of the game, but, for those who err, the cost is limitless. Apart from acquiring mastery of the wind, the ability to flight the ball and overcome a variety of lies and stances are prime requirements.

Examining the whole range of strokemaking is rare these days but Tenby achieves it without making it seem overburdensome. It defies the tenet which holds that modern tests need a plethora of par 5s. It has only one, while its four short holes are within range of all. This is a sign of strength not weakness.

It is important to stand on the 1st tee refreshed and fully aware that Tenby gets to the heart of the matter straight away. The first four holes are as demanding a quartet of par 4s as you will find, the 1st (the old 2nd) calling for two mighty hits, the 3rd earning a public compliment from Dai Rees after whom the hole is named and the 4th, where only the fairway will do from the tee.

There is unusual change of direction at these holes. The second shot to the 4th belongs to the category 'shots to a hidden green' but it is one that our forefathers relished. Today too, they must be revered not reviled.

The 5th, of more modest dimensions, offers welcome relief and another change of direction with a slightly diagonal attack to a distinctive green. The 6th is the first short hole, a shortish iron which needs to be got airborne quickly. Then follow two more 4s to the furthest point, before another lovely par 3 ends the outward 9.

The 10th goes back and the 11th out again to the tee of the short 12th, where there is the distraction of a glorious sea view. It affords quite a geography lesson of the West Wales but there is still unfinished business. The 14th is the lone par 5 and, though the next three on the other side of the railway are of more meadowy character, the short 17th starts the eye wandering to the landscape again. Then it is on to a unique back tee at the 18th, a lofty pulpit set on stone, and a last inviting drive to a fairway below.

L58 **South Pembrokeshire**
☎Pembroke (0646) 683817
Defensible Barracks, Pembroke
Dock, Dyfed.
1.5 miles S of Hobbs Point at W end
of A477, 0.5 mile from Pembroke
Dock.
Seaside parkland course.
9 holes, 5804 yards, S.S.S.69
Club founded in 1970.
Visitors: welcome.
Green fees: £5 per day, (£4 with
member) weekdays; £15 per week
weekdays; juniors £2 per day.
Society meetings: by prior
arrangement with Sec.
Catering: meals available by
arrangement with Stewardess, bar
facilities except Mon lunchtime.
Hotels: Cleddau Bridge.

L59 **Swansea Bay**
☎Skewen (0792) 814153
Jersey Marine, Neath, West Glam
SA10 6JP.
Just off main A48 road between
Neath and Swansea.
Links course.
18 holes, 6302 yards, S.S.S.70
Club founded in 1892.
Visitors: welcome.
Green fees: on application.
Society meetings: catered for.
Catering: meals served except Wed.
Hotels: Dragon, Swansea.

L60 **Tenby**
☎Tenby (0834) 2978/2787
The Burrows, Tenby, Dyfed
SA70 7NP.
A40 from Carmarthen to St Clears,
then A477 and A478 W of Tenby
town centre.
Links course.
18 holes, 6232 yards, S.S.S.71
Club founded in 1888.
Visitors: welcome.
Green fees: £8.50 weekdays; £10
weekends and Bank Holidays; cheap
winter rates and weekly tickets
available.
Society meetings: welcome with
prior booking.
Catering: full facilities, bar snacks
pre-booked.
Hotels: Kinloch Court; Imperial.

L61 **Tredegar & Rhymney**
☎Rhymney (0685) 840743
Cwmtysswg, Rhymney, Mid Glam.

B4256 1.5 miles from Rhymney
Undulating mountain course.
9 holes, 2788 yards, S.S.S.67
Club founded in 1921.
Visitors: welcome.
Green fees: £5, (£3 with member).
Society meetings: weekdays only.
Catering: no catering daytime;
evening by arrangement.
Hotels: County Ebbe Vale.

L62 **Tredegar Park**
☎Newport (0633) 894433 Sec,
895219 Club.
Bassaleg Rd, Newport, Gwent
NP9 3PX.
Leave M4 at Junction 27, to
Newport, first right in Western Ave.
Parkland course.
18 holes, 6044 yards, S.S.S.70
Course designed by James Braid.
Club founded in 1923.
Visitors: must be member of
affiliated club; and produce evidence
thereof.
Green fees: £9 weekdays; £11
weekends and Bank Holidays.
Society meetings: by arrangement.
Catering: for members and visitors
only.
Hotels: The Kings; Celtic Manor,
Newport.

L63 **Welshpool**
☎Castle Caereinion (0938) 83249
Golfa Hill, Welshpool, Powys.
4 miles from Welshpool on A458.
Mountain course.
18 holes, 5708 yards, S.S.S.69
Course designed by James Braid.
Club founded in 1922.
Visitors: welcome.
Green fees: £5 weekdays; £7 week-
ends and Bank Holidays.
Society meetings: by arrangement.
Catering: facilities available.
Hotels: Golfa Hall; Royal Oak,
Welshpool.

L64 **Wenvoe Castle**
☎Cardiff (0222) 594371 Sec,
593649 Pro.
Wenvoe, Cardiff CF5 6BE.
A48 W from Cardiff, left after 3 miles
onto A4050, course 2 miles on right.
Parkland course.
18 holes, 6411 yards, S.S.S.71
Club founded in 1936.
Visitors: welcome with member or
production of recognised club card.

Green fees: on application.
Society meetings: catered for Mon,
Thurs and Fri.
Catering: lunch and dinners
available except Tues.
Hotels: several in Cardiff.

L65 **West Monmouthshire**
☎Brynmawr (0495) 310233
Pond Rd, Nantyglo, Gwent NP3 4JX.
Turn off A467 at Dunlop Semtex Ltd.
signposted.
Mountain course.
18 holes, 6097 yards, S.S.S.69
Club founded in 1909.
Visitors: welcome.
Green fees: on application.
Society meetings: welcome.
Catering: full service available.
Hotels: Griffin, Brynmawr.

L66 **Whitchurch**
☎Cardiff (0222) 620125
Pantmawr Rd, Whitchurch, Cardiff,
S Glam CF4 6XD.
Off M4 at Exit 32, 500 yards S on
A470, filter left at lights to meet club
entrance.
Parkland course.
18 holes, 6245 yards S.S.S.70
Course re-designed by James Braid
Club founded in 1915.
Visitors: weekdays handicap
certificate required; weekends and
Bank Holidays with member only.
Green fees: £11 weekdays; £13
weekends and Bank Holidays.
Society meetings: Thurs only.
Catering: facilities every day.
Hotels: Masons Arms.

L67 **Whitehall**
☎Abercynon (0443) 740245
Nelson, Treharris, Mid Glam.
Take Treharris and Nelson exit at
roundabout on A470, turn right and
head S for 0.25 mile, take first left
turning up Mountain Rd.
Mountain course.
9 holes, 5750 yards, S.S.S.68
Club founded in 1922.
Visitors: welcome weekdays; with
member at weekends.
Green fees: on application.
Society meetings: none.
Catering: lunch and dinners served
by arrangement.
Hotels: Castle, Merthyr.

St Pierre

In the summer of 1987, St Pierre celebrated its 25th anniversary. In a game which goes back centuries, that might not seem much of a landmark but St Pierre earned itself pride of place by being the first post-war championship course to be built in Britain — the herald of a new era.

When it comes to personal sentiment, it was the first new course I saw under construction. In the winter of 1961-2, Ken Cotton was invited to design two courses in the border county of England and Wales, one in the old deer park alongside the main road to Newport and Cardiff and the other in unpromising woodland at Ross-on-Wye. He thought a visit to see how it was done would be a good experience for a young writer — and how right he was.

The two courses could not possibly have been more of a contrast. St Pierre was largely ready-made in terms of fairways whereas Ross-on-Wye, a miracle of enterprise by a devoted band, had to be stripped root by root before the holes took shape.

That Cotton succeeded in both instances showed that he was a master of his craft. You can only judge the results if you knew the original terrain, the difficulties encountered and the budgets available. Both St Pierre and Ross-on-Wye were built on the thinnest of shoestrings. Bill Graham, who had long dreamed of a course in the lovely park in St Pierre, drove past one day, and discovering that it was on the market, proved himself a man of action by buying it.

The land, the ancient manor house where the crown jewels were stored during the Battle of Agincourt, and the cost of construction of the course amounted to something under £30,000. However absurdly modest that seems nowadays, one or two sacrifices had to be made but Graham's reasons for purchasing had to be commercially based and here he showed how valid his instincts were. Floodlit golf proved to be one of his few ideas to misfire. When St Pierre was built, the motorway systems were already well launched, and the opening of the Severn Bridge only a few years away. St Pierre was and, indeed, is, wonderfully accessible from London, Birmingham and Bristol as well as South Wales.

It wasn't given long to settle down before it was much in demand. Dunlop made it a frequent home for their much lamented Masters and in 1980 the Ladies Golf Union paid it the ultimate compliment by holding the Curtis Cup there. Regular calls have been made upon it by organisers of small tournaments and company days, all of whom flock to take advantage of its residential amenities and a host of other sporting facilities.

The addition of the second course brought alteration to Cotton's original design, and more land was purchased on higher ground. However, nothing destroyed Cotton's first impression that, for Club golfers at large, it is a delightful place to play.

Stately ancient trees feature strongly. After a mild introduction to them at the 1st, the 2nd is dominated by them although there follows a break on the loftier reaches of the 3rd to the 6th.

At the 6th, the eye is caught by the distant sights but with the 7th the trees return and, from then on, there is no let-up.

There is talk of one or two changes and a few new back tees to make the professionals flex their muscles a little more than in the past. However, one hole where no change is contemplated, and certainly none required, is the 18th across the lake. One of golf's oldest clichés is that nothing is certain until the last putt is holed. Nowhere is that more apt than at St Pierre.

M NorthWales

M1 Aberdovey

☎Aberdovey (0654) 72493
Aberdovey, Gwynedd LL35 0RT.
On A493, adjoining Aberdovey
Station.
Championship links course.
18 holes, 6445 yards, S.S.S.71
Course designed by James Braid.
Club founded in 1892.
Visitors: welcome.
Green fees: £9.50 weekdays; £11
weekends and Bank Holidays.
Society meetings: catered for by
prior arrangement.
Catering: Bar meals, lunch, dinners
by arrangement; restricted Mon.
Hotels: Trefeddian; Bodfor; Bryn
Morwydd; Harbour; Maybank.

M2 Abergele & Pensarn

☎Abergele (0745) 824034
Tan-y-Goppa Rd, Abergele, Clwyd.
Through the market town of Abergele
from A55, turn left after passing
through town in direction of
Llanddulas.

Parkland course.
18 holes, 6086 yards, S.S.S.69
Course designed by Hawtree and
Sons
Club founded in 1910.
Visitors: welcome.
Green fees: £8 weekdays; £10
weekends and Bank Holidays.
Society meetings: by prior
arrangement.
Catering: full restaurant facilities
except Mon.
Hotels: Kinmel Manor; Hotel 70;
Medeer.

M3 Abersoch

☎Abersoch (075 881) 2622
Pwlhelli, Gwynedd LL53 7EY.
6 miles from Pwlhelli; beyond village
turn left into Golf Rd.
Links course.
9 holes, 5792 yards, S.S.S.68
Course designed by Harry Vardon.
Club founded in 1910.
Visitors: welcome.
Green fees: on application.

Society meetings: by arrangement.
Catering: meals served.
Hotels: Egryn; Wylsa; Riverside.

M4 Anglesey

☎Rhosneigr (0407) 810219
Station Rd, Rhosneigr, Gwynedd
LL64 5QT.
Left off A5 about 8 miles from
Holyhead.
Seaside course.
18 holes, 5573 yards, S.S.S.69
Club founded in 1911.
Visitors: welcome.
Green fees: £5 weekdays; £6
weekends.
Society meetings: by arrangement.
Catering: meals served.
Hotels: Maelog Lake, Rhoslan.

M5 Bala

☎Bala (0678) 520359
Penlan, Bala, Gwynedd LL23 7SR.
A494, first right out of Bala for
Dolgellau towards lake.
Mountainous course.

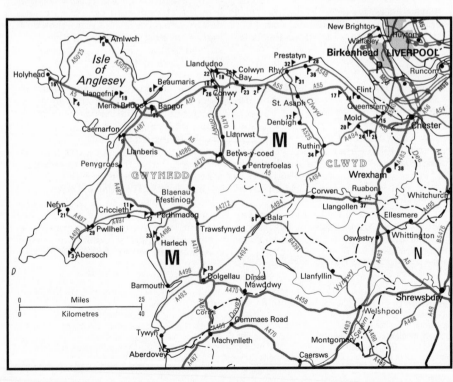

19 holes, 4970 yards, S.S.S.64
Club founded in 1974.
Visitors: welcome.
Green fees: £5, (£2.50 with member) weekdays; £7, (£3.50 with member) weekends and Bank Holidays; £15 weekly ticket.
Society meetings: catered for weekdays by prior arrangement.
Catering: available only by prior arrangement.
Hotels: Plas Goch; White Lion; Pale Hall, Bala.

M6 **Baron Hill**
☎Beaumaris (0248) 810231
Beaumaris, Gwynedd LL58 8YN.
Signposted from Beaumaris, 0.75 mile S of town centre.
Undulating seaside course.
9 holes, 5564 yards, S.S.S.67
Club founded in 1895.
Visitors: welcome.
Green fees: on application.
Society meetings: welcome on application to Hon Sec.
Catering: light snacks and sandwiches.
Hotels: Henllys Hall; Bulkeley Arms; Bishopgate House; Liverpool Arms.

M7 **Betws-y-Coed**
☎Betws-y-Coed (069 02) 556
Betws-y-Coed, Gwynedd.
Just off main A5 road in the middle of village of Betws-y-Coed.
Parkland course.
18 holes, 4996 yards, S.S.S.64
Club founded in 1977.
Visitors: welcome.
Green fees: £6 weekdays; £7.50 weekends; reduction for parties.
Society meetings: arrangements to be made in writing to Sec.
Catering: everyday except Mon.
Hotels: Royal Oak; Plas Hall.

M8 **Bull Bay**
☎Amlwch (0407) 830960
Bull Bay Rd, Amlwch, Anglesey LL68 9RY.
A5025 15 miles from Menai Bridge.
Undulating seaside course.
18 holes, 6160 yards, S.S.S.70
Course designed by Herbert Fowler. and Walton Heath.
Club founded in 1913.
Visitors: no restrictions.
Green fees: £5 summer, £3 winter weekdays; £7 summer, £5 winter weekends.
Society meetings: by arrangement with Hon Sec. 20% discount for parties of 12 or more.

Catering: full facilities available.
Hotels: Trecastell; Gadlys; Bull Bay; Erw Felin.

M9 **Caernarfon**
☎Caernarfon (0284) 3783
Llanfaglan, Caernarfon, Gwynedd.
0.5 miles S of town along the Menai Straits.
Parkland course.
18 holes, 5860 yards, S.S.S.69
Club founded in 1907.
Visitors: welcome.
Green fees: £6 per day.
Society meetings: by arrangement.
Catering: snacks in season; meals by arrangement.
Hotels: Black Boy; The Stables.

M10 **Conwy (Caernarvonshire)**
☎Conwy (0492) 593400
Morfa, Conwy, Gwynedd.
From Conwy, A55 to Bangor, down Morfa Drive over cattle grid, clubhouse 300 yards on left.
Championship links course.
18 holes, 6901 yards, S.S.S.73
Club founded in 1890.
Visitors: welcome weekdays; restrictions on weekends and Bank Holidays.
Green fees: £8 per day weekdays; £10 per day weekends and Bank Holidays. 5 day ticket Mon-Fri £30; (£3.50 with member).
Society meetings: catered for on application to Sec.
Catering: available except Mon evening; all day Tues.
Hotels: Castle Bank; Bryn Cregin; Caerlyr.

M11 **Criccieth**
☎Criccieth (076 671) 2154
Ednyfed Hill, Criccieth, Gwynedd.
A497, 4 miles from Portmadoc, turn right past Memorial Hall, 0.5 mile up hill.
Undulating hilltop course.
18 holes, 5787 yards, S.S.S.68
Club founded around 1904.
Visitors: welcome.
Green fees: on application.
Society meetings: welcome.
Catering: meals and snacks served by arrangement with Steward.
Hotels: George IV.

M12 **Denbigh**
☎Denbigh (074 571) 4159 (coin box) Henllan Rd, Denbigh, Clwyd.
B5382 Denbigh to Henllan road, 1 mile out of Denbigh.

Undulating parkland course.
18 holes, 5650 yards, S.S.S.67
Club founded in 1922.
Visitors: welcome - telephone Pro shop for reservation.
Green fees: £7 weekdays; £9 weekends and Bank Holidays.
Society meetings: welcome; write to Sec for details.
Catering: restaurant - booking advisable.
Hotels: Bull; Llanrhaeadr Hall, Denbigh; Oriel, St Asaph; Kinmel Manor, Abergele.

M13 **Dolgellau**
☎Dolgellau (0341) 422603
Pencefn, Golf Road, Dolgellau, Gwynedd LL40 1SL.
Turn off the town by-pass onto the old A494 road, turn right 25 yards past top of main bridge, signposted from there on. Approx 0.5 mile from town centre.
Parkland course.
Course played twice with alternate tees. 9 holes, 4512 yards, S.S.S.62
Club founded in 1911.
Visitors: welcome weekdays; ring Sat.
Green fees: £5 per day weekdays; £6 weekends.
Society meetings: by arrangement.
Catering: available throughout year.
Hotels: Royal Ship; Bontoon Hall.

M14 **Flint**
☎Flint (035 26) 2327
Cornist Park, Flint, Clwyd CH6 5HJ.
About 1 mile from A548 coast road, turn right at Town Hall, follow signs to Cornist Park.
Parkland course.
9 holes, 5829 yards, S.S.S.68
Club founded in 1966.
Visitors: welcome weekdays; weekends with member only.
Green fees: £4 per day.
Society meetings: £10 per day including lunch, evening meal and green fee.
Catering: meals available if previously booked.
Hotels: Chequers; Northop Hall.

M15 **Hawarden**
☎Hawarden (0244) 531447
Greemsdale Lane, Hawarden, Deeside, Clwyd CH5 3EH.
A55 9 miles W of Chester, first left after Hawarden station.
Parkland course.
9 holes, 5735 yards, S.S.S.68
Club founded in 1911.

Visitors: with member only, others by arrangement with Sec.
Green fees: £4.
Society meetings: by arrangement with Sec.
Catering: full facilities.
Hotels: numerous in Chester.

M16 Holyhead

☎Holyhead (0407) 3279
Trearddur Bay, Holyhead, Gwynedd LL65 2YG.
Follow A5 from Bangor, turn left at Valley traffic lights on B4545, through Trearddur Bay, on left hand side.
Undulating course.
18 holes, 6058 yards, S.S.S.70
Club founded in 1912.
Visitors: welcome handicap certificate required.
Green fees: £7 weekdays; £8 weekends and Bank Holidays (half price with member).
Society meetings: recognised societies welcome subject to prior arrangement with Sec.
Catering: lunchtime bar snacks; evening meals by arrangement except Mon winter months.
Hotels: Treadour Bay, Gwynedd.

M17 Holywell

☎Holywell (0352) 710040
Brynford, Holywell, Clwyd.
Turn left at traffic lights on A55 from Chester at Holywell, then proceed 1 mile to crossroads, turn right at Brynford, signpost to Pantasaph.
Moorland course.
9 holes, 6484 yards, S.S.S.71
Club founded in 1906.
Visitors: welcome except on competition days.
Green fees: on application.
Society meetings: catered for on weekdays.
Catering: lunch and evening meals served if booked in advance.
Hotels: Miners Arms; Fielding Arms.

M18 Llandudno

☎Llandudno (0492) 76450
Hospital Rd, Llandudno, Gwynedd LL30 1HU.
Alongside the main Llandudno Hospital, approx 1 mile from town centre.
Seaside parkland course.
Course designed by Tom Jones.
Club founded in 1915.
Visitors: welcome must be members of recognised clubs.
Green fees: £8 weekdays; £10

weekends and Bank Holidays; (half price if playing with member).
Society meetings: accepted providing members of recognised club; limited to 30 players at weekends.
Catering: each day during season May - Sept; subject to prior booking with Steward.
Hotels: St Georges; Imperial; Bryn Cregin; Gogarath Abbey.

M19 Llangefni (Public)

☎Llangefni, Anglesey (0248) 722193
Llangefni, Anglesey, N Wales.
A5 to Llangefni.
9 holes, 1467 yards, S.S.S.28
Course designed by Hawtree & Sons.
Club founded in 1983.
Visitors: welcome.
Green fees: £1.25 adults; 70p juniors and OAPs, weekdays; £1.85; 85p juniors and OAPs, weekends.
Society meetings: none.
Catering: none.
Hotels: Bull; Ship; Market.

M20 Mold

☎Mold (0352) 740318
Cilcain Road, Pantymwyn, Mold, Clwyd.
3 miles from Mold. Leave on the Denbigh road, turn left at the Clegg Arms, turn right at the T-junction and club is 2.5 miles on left.
Undulating parkland course.
18 holes, 5521 yards, S.S.S.69
Club founded in 1909.
Visitors: welcome.
Green fees: £8 per day weekdays; £11 per day weekends and holidays.
Society meetings: welcome.
Catering: bar snacks, full facilities.
Hotels: Bryn Awel; Chequers.

M21 Nefyn & District

☎Nefyn (0758) 720218
Morfa Nefyn, Pwllheli, Gwynedd LL53 6DA.
1 mile W of Nefyn.
Seaside course.
18 holes, 6335 yards, S.S.S.71
Club founded in 1907.
Visitors: unrestricted, but must arrange with Sec.
Green fees: £8.50 per day; £10 weekends.
Society meetings: by prior arrangement with Sec.
Catering: full services available.
Hotels: Caeau Capel; Linksway.

M22 North Wales

☎Llandudno (0492) 75325
72 Bryniau Rd, West Shore, Llandudno, Gwynedd LL30 2DZ.
0.5 mile from town centre.
Seaside links course.
18 holes, 6132 yards, S.S.S.69
Club founded in 1890.
Visitors: accepted subject to prior reservation.
Green fees: £9 weekdays; £11 weekends and Bank Holidays.
Society meetings: accepted subject to prior reservation.
Catering: full facilities available.
Hotels: numerous in area.

M23 Old Colwyn

☎Colwyn Bay (0492) 515581
Woodland Ave, Old Colwyn, Clwyd LL29 9NL
200 yards off A55 in Old Colwyn, turn into Boddelwyddan Ave between chapel and M and K Garage.
Undulating meadowland course.
9 holes, 5800 yards, S.S.S.66
Club founded in 1907.
Visitors: welcome except on Sat afternoons and on Tues and Wed evenings.
Green fees: weekdays £5, weekends and Bank Holidays £6. (Half price with member).
Society meetings: by arrangement except Sat.
Catering: dinner available on weekdays and lunch or dinner at weekends by arrangement with Stewardess.
Hotels: Lyndale.

M24 Old Padeswood

☎Buckley (0244) 547401
Station Rd, Padeswood, Mold, Clwyd CH7 4JL
2.5 miles S of Mold, 8 miles W of Chester on A5118.
Meadowland course.
18 holes, 6728 yards, S.S.S.72
Course designed by Arthur Joseph.
Club founded in 1933.
Visitors: welcome on weekdays and weekends (except on competition days)
Green fees: £6 weekdays (£5 with member) £7 weekends (£6 with member)
Society meetings: Societies welcome by appointment. Ring for details.
Catering: Bar snacks. 3-course meals catered for Societies of 11 or more.
Hotels: Bryn Awel Hotel, Mold; The Arches, New Brighton, Mold.

M25 Padeswood & Buckley

☎Buckley (0244) 542537 Office,
543636 Pro and Members
The Caia, Station Lane, Padeswood,
Mold Clwyd CH7 4JD
Off A5118, 3 miles E of Mold, 2 miles
S of Buckley, 2nd club on right.
Parkland/meadowland course.
18 holes.
Club founded in 1933.
Visitors: welcome on weekdays
before 9am until 4.30pm; on Sun
permission of Captain required in
advance.
Green fees: £7 weekdays (£4 with
member); £9 weekends (£6 with
member). Juniors Mon-Fri, £3.50
(£2.50 with member), Juniors
Weekends/Bank Holidays, £4.50
(with member £3.50).
Society meetings: welcome
weekdays.
Catering: snacks, lunch and evening
meals except Mon and Tues.
Hotels: The Druid; The Arches;
Chequers.

M26 Penmaenmawr

☎Penmaenmawr (0492) 623330
Conwy Old Rd, Penmaenmawr,
Gwynedd LL34 6RD
Main A55 from Conwy to Penmaen-
mawr turn left at Mountain View
Hotel along Conwy Old Rd for 1 mile.
Undulating parkland course.
9 holes, 5031 yards, S.S.S.65
Club founded in 1910.
Visitors: Welcome. Green fees for
parties by arrangement.
Green fees: £5 daily, £7 weekends,
(half price with member).
Society meetings: welcome. Fees
by arrangement.
Catering: only by previous
arrangement.
Hotels: Caerlyr Hotel, Conway Old
Road, Penmaenmawr. Sychnant
Pass Hotel, Sychnant Pass,
Conway.

M27 Portmadoc

☎Portmadoc (0776) 512037
Morfa Bychan, Portmadoc, Gwynedd
LL49 9UU
1.5 miles from Portmadoc, take road
to Morfa Bychan.
Seaside course.
18 holes, 5838 yards, S.S.S.68
Visitors: welcome.
Green fees: on application.
Society meetings: by arrangement.
Catering: meals and snacks served.
Hotels: Royal Sportsman; Tyddyn
Lywyn.

M28 Prestatyn

☎Prestatyn (0745) 4320
Marine Rd East, Prestatyn, Clwyd
Follow A548 coast road to Prestatyn,
cross railway bridge and turn right
at Pontins, Prestatyn Sands.
Seaside course.
18 holes, 6764 yards, S.S.S.72
Course designed by S. Collins.
Club founded in 1905.
Visitors: welcome, except Sat and
Tues mornings.
Green fees: £7 weekdays; £9
weekends and Bank Holidays.
Society meetings: by arrangement
with the Sec only. No Sats.
Catering: full facilities.
Hotels: Bryn Gwalia, Prestatyn.
Nant Hall, Prestatyn.
Kinmel Manor, Abergele.

M29 Pwllheli

☎Pwllheli (0758) 612520
Gold Rd, Pwllheli, Gwynedd LL53
5PS
Turn into Cardiff Rd in town centre,
bear right at first fork.
Seaside parkland course.
18 holes, 6110 yards, S.S.S.69
Club founded in 1900.
Visitors: welcome
Green fees: £7 weekdays (£3.50
with member); £8 weekends and
Bank Holidays (£4 with member).
Society meetings: catered for any
day
Catering: resident Steward.
Hotels: Caeau Capel Hotel, Nefyn;
Crown Hotel; Tower Hotel.

M30 Rhos-on-Sea

☎Llandudno (0492) 49641
Penrhyn Bay, Llandudno, Gwynedd
LL30 3PU
Between Colwyn Bay and Llandudno
on promenade.
Undulating seaside course.
18 holes, 6064 yards, S.S.S.69
Club founded in 1899.
Visitors: unrestricted by
arrangement.
Green fees: £6.50
Society meetings: welcome by
arrangement.
Catering: snacks & coffee served
all day. Lunch 12 noon-2pm.
Evening meals available if booked.
Hotels: on site. Dormy House Hotel.
Residential.

M31 Rhuddlan

☎Rhuddlan (0745) 590217
Meliden Rd, Rhuddlan, Clwyd.
On A525, 1 mile S of Rhyl.
Parkland course.
18 holes, 6045 yards, S.S.S.69
Club founded in 1930.
Visitors: welcome.
Green fees: on application.
Society meetings: welcome, except
Tues or at weekends from April-Sep.
Catering: lunch and dinners served
except Mon.
Hotels: numerous hotels in Rhyl.

M32 Rhyl

☎Rhyl (0745) 53171
Coast Rd, Rhyl, Clwyd.
1 mile from station on A548 to
Prestatyn.
Seaside course.
9 holes, 6153 yards. S.S.S.70
Club founded in 1890.
Visitors: welcome (except at
competition times)
Green fees: £5 weekdays; £6 week-
ends and Bank Holidays.
Society meetings: by arrangement.
Catering: bar snacks and meals
available during bar hours (excluding
Mon).
Hotels: Westminster Hotel; Grange
Hotel, East Parade.

M33 Royal St. David's

☎Harlech (0766) 780361 Sec,
780857 Pro
Harlech, Gwynedd LL46 2UB
Between Barmouth and Portmadoc
on A496.
Seaside course.
18 holes, 6427 yards, S.S.S.71
Club founded in 1894
Visitors: welcome on weekdays and
weekends but prior arrangements
advisable.
Green fees: £10 per day; £12 Sat,
Sun and Bank Holidays.
Society meetings: catered for
Catering: full catering facilities
available.
Hotels: St David's Hotel; Maes y
Neuadd Hotel, Talsarnau; Noddfa
Hotel, all in Harlech.

M34 Ruthin Pwllglas

☎Ruthin (082 42) 4658
Ruthin Pwllglas, Ruthin, Clwyd.
2.5 miles S of Ruthin in A494, right
fork before Pwllglas village.
Parkland/moorland course.
9 holes, 5418 yards, S.S.S.67
Course designed by David Lloyd
Rees.
Club founded in 1906.
Visitors: welcome.
Green fees: £4.
Society meetings: by arrangement.

Catering: parties by arrangement.
Hotels: Ruthin Castle.

M35 **St. Deiniol**
☎Bangor (0248) 353098
Penybryn, Bangor, Gwynedd
LL57 2LX.
Off A5 on E outskirts of Bangor, at
top of Beach Rd overlooking
Penrhyn Harbour, turn left and
immediately left again up a hill, golf
club signposted.
Undulating parkland course.
18 holes, 5500 yards, S.S.S.67
Course designed by James Braid.
Club founded in 1906.
Visitors: welcome at any time.
Parties by arrangement.
Green fees: £4 weekdays; £5 weekends.
Society meetings: welcomed but by
prior arrangement.
Catering: full catering service
provided.
Hotels: British Hotel, High Street,
Bangor; Castle Hotel, High Street;
Bangor; Gwynedd Hotel, Llanberis.

M36 **St. Melyd**
☎Prestatyn (074 56) 4405
The Paddock, Prestatyn LL19 9NB
Situated between Prestatyn and
Melidlen village on main road A547.
Undulating meadowland course.
9 holes, 5805 yards, S.S.S.68
Club founded in 1922.
Visitors: welcome.
Green fees: £6 weekdays; £8
weekends and Bank Holidays.
Society meetings: catered for on
weekdays and limited weekends.
Catering: lunch and restaurant
except Tues.
Hotels: Pontins Holiday Village;
Grand; Nant Hall; Bryn Gwalia.

M37 **Vale of Llangollen**
☎Llangollen (0978) 860040
Llangollen, Clwyd LL20 7PR
On A5, 1 mile S of Llangollen.
Parkland course.
18 holes, 6617 yards, S.S.S.72
Club founded in 1908.
Visitors: welcome weekdays and

some weekends.
Green fees: £7.50 weekdays; £9
weekends.
Society meetings: weekdays and
some weekends.
Catering: full catering
Hotels: The Royal; The Hand,
The Tyn y Wern, all in Llangollen.

M38 **Wrexham**
☎Wrexham (0978) 364268/261033/
351476
Holt Rd, Wrexham, Clwyd LL13 9SB
Situated on A534 2 miles E of
Wrexham.
Undulating sandy course.
18 holes, 6139 yards, S.S.S.69
Course designed by James Braid.
Club founded in 1923.
Visitors: welcome
Green fees: on application
Society meetings: Mon and Fri.
Catering: full
Hotels: Holt Lodge Hotel, Holt Rd,
Wrexham.

N Cheshire, Staffordshire, Shropshire and Derbyshire

This is a section offering a mighty contrast in the golf. Apart from the seaside tradition of Royal Liverpool, which is the oldest club by far in Cheshire (or should it be Wirral or Merseyside?), the county is largely flat, green and leafy. Derbyshire, on the other hand, undulates considerably. Shropshire is perhaps a mixture of the two while Staffordshire contains more attraction than you might expect of a county with an industrial heart.

Of the courses on the Wirral peninsula, Royal Liverpool takes pride of place. Wallasey, home of Dr Frank Stableford and his points system, has some fine, bold dunes while Caldy enjoys some holes along the shores of the Dee Estuary with marvellous views of North Wales.

To the east of Chester, I can speak highly of Delamere Forest and Sandiway and,

crossing over the M6, a round at Mere, Wilmslow or Prestbury is always rewarding. Before the days of the M6, the journey to Hoylake took you up close to Shrewsbury with thought of a round at Hawkstone Park which has earned extra notoriety by producing an Open champion in Sandy Lyle. With a fine hotel to accompany two 18 hole courses, it is one of the best courses in Shropshire. Staffordshire were a playing force in the land a few years ago, their players owing their prowess to playing on courses like Little Aston, Whittington Barracks, Beau Desert and Trentham.

Players in Derbyshire are not quite so lucky. I fear my knowledge of golf there is not as complete as it should be, but I can speak well of Burton-on-Trent and Matlock, and I hear good things of Kedleston Park, Cavendish and Sickleholme.

N1 **Alderley Edge**
☎Wilmslow (0625) 585583
Brook Lane, Alderley Edge, Cheshire SK9 7RU
From Alderley Edge, turn left off A34 opposite Tower Garage, towards Mobberley/Knutsford
Undulating parkland course.
9 holes, 5839 yards, S.S.S.68
Course designed by T. G. Renouf
Club founded in 1907.
Visitors: welcome without reservation subject to proof of handicap.
Green fees: £8 weekdays; £10 weekends and Bank Holidays.
Society meetings: catered for on Thurs.
Catering: full catering facilities except Mon.
Hotels: De Trafford Arms Hotel, Alderley Edge.

N2 **Alfreton**
☎Alfreton (0773) 832070

Highfields, Wingfield Rd, Oakthorpe, Derbys DE5 7DH
Take the Matlock road out of Alfreton, about 0.75 mile.
Parkland course.
9 holes, 5012 yards, S.S.S.65
Club founded in 1893
Visitors: Sat, Sun and Mon with member only. Welcome at any other time.
Green fees: £6 per round; £7.50 per day.
Society meetings: catered for weekdays
on consultation with Sec.
Hotels: Swallow Hotel, South Normanton

N3 **Allestree Park**
☎Derby (0332) 550616
Allestree Hall, Allestree, Derbys.
Leave Derby on A6, 4 miles from city centre, signposted Allestree Park.
Undulating parkland course.
18 holes, 5749 yards, S.S.S.68

Club founded in 1940.
Visitors: welcome at all times, except for competition days or Sun mornings.
Green fees: on application.
Society meetings: welcome.
Catering: available by prior arrangement.
Hotels: Clovelly, Kedleston Rd, Derby.

N4 **Ashbourne**
☎Ashbourne (0335) 42078
Clifton, Nr Ashbourne, Derbys DE6 4BN.
1 mile S of Ashbourne on A515 to Sudbury and Lichfield.
Undulating parkland course.
9 holes, 5359 yards, S.S.S.66
Course designed by Frank Pennink
Club founded in 1910.
Visitors: welcome.
Green fees: £6 weekdays; £8 Sat Sun and Bank Holidays.
Society meetings: small.

Catering: by arrangement with Stewards, excluding Thurs.
Hotels: Green Man Hotel, Ashbourne.

N5 **Astbury**
☎Congelton (0260) 272772
Peel Lane, Astbury, Nr Congleton, Cheshire CW12 4RE
On the outskirts of Congleton, reached by leaving A34 Congleton to Newcastle Road at Astbury village.
Meadowland course.
18 holes, 6269 yards, S.S.S.70
Club founded in 1925
Visitors: members of recognised Golf Clubs welcome. Must be accompanied by a member at the weekend.
Green fees: £9 per day.
Society meetings: Thurs only by prior arrangement
Catering: by prior arrangement only
Hotels: Bulls Head Hotel, Mill Street, Congleton. Lion and Swan Hotel, Swan Bank, Congleton.

N6 **Bakewell**
☎Bakewell (062 981) 2307
Station Rd, Bakewell, Derbys DE4 1GB
Three quarter mile from Bakewell Square, cross bridge over River Wye on A619 Sheffield to Chesterfield road, left up Station Rd and after a 0.33 mile turn right before Industrial Estate.
Hilly parkland course.
9 holes, 4808 yards, S.S.S.64
Course designed by George Low.
Club founded in 1899.
Visitors: welcome.
Green fees: £6 weekdays, £10 weekends. (With member £3 weekdays £5 weekends).
Society meetings: by arrangement
Catering: Meals available and bar except Mon.
Hotels: Rutland, The Square, Bakewell.

N7 **Beau Desert**
☎Hednesford (054 38) 2626 or 2492 Pro.
Hazelslade, Hednesford, Cannock, Staffs WS12 5PT
Take A460 from Cannock through Hednesford, right at traffic lights. signposted Hazelslade, and next left.
Moorland course.
18 holes, 6300 yards, S.S.S.71
Club founded in 1921
Visitors: Mon-Fri. Weekends telephone Pro

Green fees: £11.50 per round, £13.15 per day
Society meetings: yes
Catering: yes
Hotels: Cedar Tree, Rugeley.
Roman Way on A5 to Cannock.

N8 **Birchwood**
☎Padgate (0925) 818819
Kelvin Close, Risley, Warrington, Cheshire WA3 7PB.
M62, junction 11, follow A574 for Risley/Birchwood. Entrance opposite Data-General.
Parkland course.
18 holes, 6850 yards, S.S.S.73
Course designed by T. J. McAuley
Club founded in 1979
Visitors: welcome weekdays.
Green fees: £8-£11
Society meetings: Mon, Wed, Thurs.
Catering: A la carte/bar snacks 7 days
Hotels: Lord Daresbury.

N9 **Branston**
☎Burton-on-Trent (0283) 43207
Burton Rd, Branston, Burton-on-Trent DE14 3DP
Take A5121 off the A38 towards Burton-on-Trent, pass church on right, over railway bridge, pass petrol station on right, entrance to club 200 yards on right.
Undulating course.
18 holes, 6458 yards, S.S.S.71
Club founded in 1976.
Visitors: welcome weekdays
Green fees: £7 weekdays; £9 weekends (£4 with member).
Society meetings: catered for weekdays.
Catering: full catering, except Mon.
Hotels: Riverside Hotel; Dog & Partridge

N10 **Breadsall Priory G & CC**
☎Derby (0332) 832235
Moor Rd, Morley, Derby
3 miles NE of Derby off A61, towards Breadsall, turn left into Rectory Lane and right onto Moor Rd.
Undulating parkland course.
18 holes, 6402 yards, S.S.S.71
Course designed by David Cox, John Flanders and Richard Lambert.
Club founded in 1977.
Visitors: weekdays.
Green fees: £10 per day.
Society meetings: Catered for on weekdays
Catering: lunch and dinner.

Hotels: Breadsall Priory Hotel, situated within grounds.

N11 **Bridgnorth**
☎Bridgnorth (074 62) 3315
Stanley Lane, Bridgnorth, Salop WV16 4SF
Through High St, along Broseley Rd for some 400 yards, right into Stanley Lane.
Parkland course.
18 holes, 6668 yards, S.S.S.72
Club founded in 1889.
Visitors: daily.
Green fees: £8 weekdays; £12 weekends & Bank Holidays (half price with member).
Society meetings: catered for weekdays by arrangement with Sec.
Catering: full catering daily except Mon.
Hotels: Falcon; Kings Head; Croft; Whitburn Grange.

N12 **Brocton Hall**
☎Stafford (0785) 662627
Brocton, Staffs ST17 0TH
4 miles S of Stafford on A34, turn left at crossroads signposted Brocton, club entrance 300 yards on left.
Parkland course.
18 holes, 6095 yards, S.S.S.69
Course designed by Harry Vardon.
Club founded in 1923
Visitors: accepted.
Green fees: £12 weekdays; £14 weekends and Bank Holidays.
Society meetings: bookings accepted on Tues and Thurs.
Catering: by arrangement.
Hotels: Tillington Hall, Eccleshall Rd.

N13 **Burslem**
☎Stoke-on-Trent (0782) 837006
Wood Farm, High Lane, Tunstall, Stoke-on-Trent ST6 7JT.
2 miles N of Hanley, situated on High Lane.
Moorland course.
11 holes, 5527 yards, S.S.S.67
Club founded in 1907.
Visitors: weekdays; Sat with member; not Sun.
Green fees: £6 per day, (£2.50 with member).
Society meetings: weekdays as and when required.
Catering: apply to Steward.
Hotels: Sneyd Arms, Tunstall; George Hotel, Burslem; Grand, Hanley.

N14 **Burton-on-Trent**
☎Burton-on-Trent (0283) 44551.

43 Ashby Rd East, Burton-on-Trent
DE15 0PS.
Off A50 on road to Ashby.
Meadowland course.
18 holes, 6555 yards, S.S.S.71
Club founded in 1894.
Visitors: welcome - reservation
advisable or letter of introduction;
bona fide handicaps.
Green fees: £9 weekdays; £13
weekends and Bank Holidays.
Society meetings: catered for.
Catering: full facilities except Mon.
Hotels: Stanhope Arms, Bretby.

N15 Buxton & High Peak

☎Buxton (0298) 3453 or 6263
Waterswallows Rd,
Fairfield, Buxton, Derbys.
1 mile from Buxton station, heading
N, on A6.
Meadowland course.
18 holes, 5954 yards, S.S.S.69

Club founded in 1887.
Visitors: welcome.
Green fees: £8 weekdays; £10
weekends.
Society meetings: by arrangement
with Sec.
Catering: full facilities and supper
licence.
Hotels: Buckingham; Palace;
Portland; Edgerton.

N16 Cavendish

☎Buxton (0298) 3494 or 5052 Pro.
Gadley Lane, Buxton, Derbys
SK17 6XD.
0.75 mile from town centre going W
on A53 St John's Rd to Leek, right
on Carlisle Rd, then left on Watford
Rd.
Parkland/downland course.
18 holes, 5815 yards, S.S.S.68
Course designed by Dr Alister
Mackenzie.

Club founded in 1925.
Visitors: welcome.
Green fees: £8 weekdays; £10
weekends; (half price with member).
Society meetings: catered for
weekdays and some weekends by
arrangement with Pro.
Catering: snacks available at all
times and meals by arrangement.
Hotels: Lee Wood; Buckingham;
Portland; Egerton.

N17 Chapel-en-le-Frith

☎Chapel (0298) 813943 Sec,
812118 Club.
The Cockyard, Manchester Rd,
Chapel-en-le-Frith, Stockport
SK12 6UH.
A6 from Stockport through Disley
and onto A5002 for Whaley Bridge,
turn left at second set of traffic lights
in Whaley Bridge towards Chapel-
en-le-Frith for 2 miles, club is on right

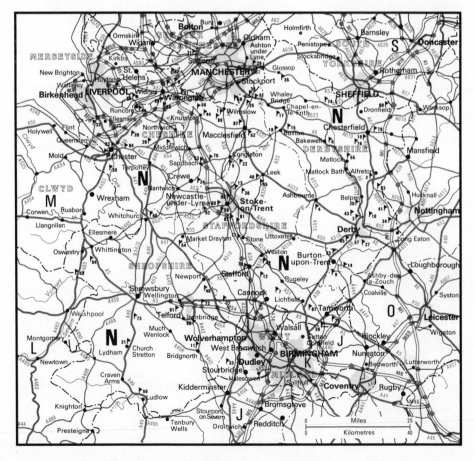

hand side, almost opposite Hanging Gate Public House.
Meadowland course.
18 holes, 6065 yards, S.S.S.69
Club founded in.1906.
Visitors: welcome, small numbers without reservation.
Green fees: £8 weekdays; £12 weekends and Bank Holidays.
Society meetings: catered for by arrangement.
Catering: all meals any day except Mon.
Hotels: Kings Arms.

N18 **Chester**
☎Chester (0244) 677760
Curzon Park North, Chester
CH4 8AR.
1 mile from centre of Chester, off A55, course located behind Chester Racecourse.
Parkland course.
18 holes, 6487 yards, S.S.S.71
Club founded in 1901.
Visitors: welcome by arrangement.
Green fees: £10 weekdays; £12 weekends.
Society meetings: welcome by arrangement.

Catering: full facilities.
Hotels: many in area.

N19 **Chesterfield**
☎Chesterfield (0246) 79256
Walton, Chesterfield, Derbyshire
S42 7LA.
2 miles from town centre on Matlock Rd A632.
Parkland course.
18 holes, 6326 yards, S.S.S.70
Club founded in 1909.
Visitors: welcome weekdays.
Green fees: on application.
Society meetings: catered for on weekdays if booked in advance.
Catering: lunch and dinner every day.
Hotels: Chesterfield; Portland.

N20 **Chevin**
☎Derby (0332) 841864
Golf Lane, Duffield, Derby DE6 4EE.
5 miles N of Derby on A6.
Undulating parkland/moorland course.
18 holes, 6043 yards, S.S.S.69
Club founded in 1894.
Visitors: welcome weekdays; with member at weekends.

Green fees: £10.
Society meetings: welcome except Mon.
Catering: meals served except Mon.
Hotels: Kedleston; Strutt Arms, Milford.

N21 **Church Stretton**
☎Church Stretton (0694) 722281
Hunters Moon, Trevor Hill, Church Stretton, Salop SY6 7AA.
0.5 mile off A49 W of town.
Undulating moorland course.
18 holes, 5008 yards, S.S.S.65
Course designed by James Braid.
Club founded in 1898.
Visitors: welcome weekdays and Sat, weekends by arrangement.
Green fees: £6 weekdays; £8 weekends and Bank Holidays.
Society meetings: by arrangement.
Catering: by arrangement with Steward.
Hotels: Denehurst; Sandford.

N22 **Congleton**
☎Congleton (0260) 273540
Biddulph Rd, Congleton, Cheshire
SW12 3LZ.
1 mile SE of Congleton Station on

main Congleton to Biddulph road A527.
Parkland course.
9 holes, 5080 yards, S.S.S.65
Club founded in 1898.
Visitors: welcome daily, telephone first for competition days.
Green fees: on application.
Society meetings: Mon.
Catering: snack meals, ring first for full meals. Not Mon.
Hotels: Lion and Swan; Bull's Head.

N23 Craythorne
☎(0283) 64329
Craythorne Rd, Stretton DE13 0AZ.
N of Burton, turn off A521, follow signs to Stretton.
18 holes, 5230 yards, S.S.S.66
Course designed by Cyril Johnson.
Club founded in 1972.
Visitors: welcome.
Green fees: £4 weekdays; £5 Sat; £6 Sun.
Society meetings: welcome by appointment.
Catering: full facilities.
Hotels: on site - please ring.

N24 Crewe
☎Crewe (0270) 584099
Fields Rd, Haslington, Crewe, Cheshire CW1 1TB.
1 mile S off A534 at Haslington, between Crewe and Sandbach.
Parkland/meadowland course.
18 holes, 6277 yards, S.S.S.70
Club founded in 1911.
Visitors: weekdays only.
Green fees: £12 visitor, (£5 with member weekday); (£6 with member weekends).
Society meetings: Tues only by prior arrangement.
Catering: bar snacks, lunch, dinner.
Hotels: Crewe Arms; Saxon Cross Motel; Lamb.

N25 Davenport
☎Stockport (0625) 876951 Sec, 877321 Club, 877319 Pro.
Worth Hall, Middlewood Rd, Higher Poynton, Stockport SK12 1TS.
From Stockport take A6 to Rising Sun at Hazel Grove, then take A523 Macclesfield road, at Poynton traffic lights turn left into Park Lane, club is approx 1.5 miles.
Undulating parkland course.
18 holes, 6006 yards, S.S.S.69
Course designed by Fraser Middleton.
Club founded in 1913.
Visitors: welcome most days -

telephone Pro to check.
Green fees: £10 weekdays; £12 weekends; (half price with member).
Society meetings: Thurs.
Catering: by arrangement with Steward.
Hotels: Belfry; Belgrade.

N26 Delamere Forest
☎Sandway (0606) 882807
Station Rd, Delamere, Northwich, Cheshire CW8 2JE.
From A556 Manchester to Chester road, W from Northwich, take B5152 towards Frodsham; the lane to club is on right, approx 1 mile from A556, immediately by Delamere station.
Undulating heathland course.
18 holes, 6287 yards, S.S.S.70
Course designed by Herbert Fowler.
Club founded in 1910.
Visitors: welcome; 2 balls only weekends and Bank Holidays.
Green fees: £12 weekdays, £15 weekends and Bank Holidays; (£3 & £7 with member).
Society meetings: Tues and Thurs; small parties up to 24 on Wed.
Catering: bar snacks, restaurant if booked in advance.
Hotels: Hartford Hall; Swan; Willington Hall.

N27 Derby
☎Derby (0332) 766462
Shakespeare St, Sinfin, Derby DE2 9HD.
1 mile off A5111 at Normanton.
Parkland municipal course.
18 holes, 6183 yards, S.S.S.69
Club founded in 1923.
Visitors: welcome.
Green fees: £2.80 weekdays; £3.80 weekends and Bank Holidays.
Society meetings: catered for by arrangement weekdays.
Catering: meals available every day.
Hotels: numerous in Derby.

N28 Drayton Park
☎Tamworth (0827) 251139
Drayton Park, Tamworth, Staffs B78 3TN.
2 miles S of Tamworth on A4091.
Parkland course.
18 holes, 6214 yards, S.S.S.71
Course designed by James Braid.
Club founded in 1897.
Visitors: by arrangement weekdays.
Green fees: £12.50 per day/round.
Society meetings: Tues and Thurs.
Catering: full facilities from 10.30am.
Hotels: Gungate; Castle.

N29 Dukinfield
☎061-338 2340
Yew Tree Lane, Dukinfield, Cheshire SK16 5DF.
From Ashton Rd 1 mile then right into Yew Tree Lane, club 1 mile on right, on hill behind Senior Service Factory.
Hillside course.
18 holes, 5544 yards, S.S.S.67
Club founded in 1913.
Visitors: welcome weekdays except Wed pm.
Green fees: on application.
Society meetings: by arrangement with Sec.
Catering: meals by prior arrangement.
Hotels: York House.

N30 Eaton
☎Chester (0244) 680474
Eaton Park, Eccleston, Chester.
About 2 miles S of Chester on A483 Wrexham road.
Parkland course.
18 holes, 6446 yards, S.S.S.71
Course designed by Hawtree.
Club founded in 1965.
Visitors: by arrangement only.
Green fees: £8 per round weekdays; £10 per round weekends; (half price with member).
Society meetings: weekdays only - maximum 40.
Catering: full facilities.
Hotels: Grosvenor.

N31 Ellesmere
☎061-790 2122 Clubhouse, 7908591 Pro.
Old Clough Lane, Worsley, Manchester M28 5HZ.
5 miles W of Manchester, on A580, adjacent to Junction 14 on M62.
Undulating parkland course.
18 holes, 5957 yards, S.S.S.69
Club founded in 1913.
Visitors: members of recognised club welcome by arrangement with Pro, except during club competitions.
Green fees: £7.50, (£3.50 with member) weekdays; £8.50, (£4 with member) weekends and Bank Holidays.
Society meetings: catered for weekdays; apply in writing to Hon Sec.
Catering: facilities available at all times; by prior arrangement with Steward's wife.
Hotels: numerous in Manchester.

N32 **Ellesmere Port**
☎051-339 7689.
Chester Rd, Hooton, S Wirral,
L66 1QH.
Approximately 9 miles N of Chester,
on main A41 road to Birkenhead,
clubhouse at the rear of St Paul's
Church, Hooton, opposite Burleydam
Nurseries.
Parkland/meadowland course.
18 holes, 6432 yards, S.S.S.71
Course designed by Cotton,
Pennink, Lawrie and Partners.
Club founded in 1971.
Visitors: welcome weekdays and
weekends.
Green fees: £2.40 weekdays; £2.95
weekends and Bank Holidays.
Society meetings: catered for
weekdays and weekends.
Catering: food is available.
Hotels: St Andrews, Hooton.

N33 **Enville**
☎Kinver (0384) 872074 Sec and
Manager, 872551 Club, 872585 Pro.
Highgate Common, Enville,
Stourbridge, W Midlands DY7 5BN.
Off A458 Bridgnorth road, past Fox
Inn and turn right to Halfpenny Green
airport.
Moorland course.
Highgate-18 holes, 6541 yards,
S.S.S.72
Ledge-18 holes, 6207 yards,
S.S.S.70
Club founded in 1935.
Visitors: welcome weekdays and
with member at weekends.
Green fees: £15 per day, (£3.50 with
member).
Society meetings: by arrangement
a year in advance if possible;
weekdays only.
Catering: full facilities except Mon.
Hotels: Anchor, Kinver.

N34 **Erewash Valley**
☎Ilkeston (0602) 323258
Stanton-by-Dale, Ilkeston, Derbys.
From M1, Junction 25, follow signs to
Stanton Ironworks Co Ltd through
Sandiacre.
Meadowland/parkland course.
18 holes, 6487 yards, S.S.S.71
Club founded in 1905.
Visitors: welcome weekdays.
Green fees: £9 weekdays; £14
weekends and Bank Holidays.
Society meetings: catered for
weekdays.
Catering: lunch, evening meals by
arrangement.
Hotels: Post House; Novotel,
Sandiacre.

N35 **Glossop & District**
☎Glossop (045 74) 3117
Hurst Lane, off Sheffield Rd,
Glossop, Derbys SK13 8RH.
1 mile out of town on A57 Sheffield
road.
Moorland course.
11 holes, 5726 yards, S.S.S.68
Club founded in 1895.
Visitors: welcome.
Green fees: £6 per day, (£4 with
member) weekdays; £7, (£4 with
member) weekends and Bank
Holidays; £15 per week.
Society meetings: welcome.
Catering: meals served by
arrangement.
Hotels: Hurst Lee Guest House.

N36 **Greenway Hall**
☎Stockton Brook (0782) 503158
Stockton Brook, Stoke-on-Trent
ST9 9LI.
Off A53 Stoke-Leek road, approxi-
mately 5 miles from Stoke.
Meadowland course.
18 holes, 5676 yards, S.S.S.67
Club founded in 1908.
Visitors: welcome with member
only.
Green fees: on application.
Society meetings: by appointment
only.
Catering: by prior arrangement with
Steward.
Hotels: many in area.

N37 **Hawkstone Park Hotel**
☎Lee Brockhurst (093 924) 611
Weston, Shrewsbury SY4 5UY.
Junction 4, M54, easy access M6.
Parkland courses 2 x 18 hole.
Hawkstone-18 holes, 6203 yards,
S.S.S.71
Weston-18 holes, 5063 yards,
S.S.S.66
Visitors: welcome.
Green fees: on application.
Society meetings: minimum 12
persons, from £5.50.
Catering: snacks and full meals.
Hotels: own hotel on premises.

N38 **Hazel Grove**
☎061-483 3978
Buxton Rd, Hazel Grove, Stockport,
Cheshire SK7 6LU.
Buxton Rd is on A6.
Moorland course.
18 holes, 6300 yards, S.S.S.70
Club founded in 1913.
Visitors: welcome weekdays.
Green fees: £11, (£3.50 with
member) weekdays; £14, (£5 with

member) weekends and Bank
Holidays.
Society meetings: catered for
Thurs, Fri.
Catering: every day except Mon.
Hotels: numerous in area.

N39 **Helsby**
☎Helsby (092 82) 2021
Towers Lane, Helsby, Warrington,
Cheshire WA6 0JB.
Junction 14, off M56, to Helsby, turn
into Primrose Lane, first right into
Towers Lane.
Parkland course.
18 holes, 6262 yards, S.S.S.70
Course designed by James Braid.
Club founded in 1902.
Visitors: welcome weekdays.
Green fees: £12 per day; £9 per
round.
Society meetings: catered for Mon
and Thurs only.
Catering: full service except Tues.
Hotels: Grosvenor; Queens,
Chester.

N40 **Hill Valley G & CC**
☎Whitchurch (0948) 3584
Terrick Rd, Whitchurch, Salop
SY13 4JZ.
Off A49, 1 mile N from centre of
Whitchurch, signposted.
Undulating parkland course.
18 holes, 6050 yards, S.S.S.69
Course designed by P. Alliss &
D. Thomas.
Club founded in 1975.
Visitors: welcome.
Green fees: £8 weekdays; £12
weekends.
Society meetings: catered for at all
times.
Catering: breakfasts, lunch, dinner
served daily; conferences, wedding
receptions.
Hotels: Terrick Hall Country Hotel.

N41 **Ilkeston Borough**
☎Ilkeston (0602) 320304 Sec.
Peewit West End Drive, Ilkeston,
Derby.
0.5 mile W of Ilkeston market place.
Meadowland municipal course.
9 holes, 4000 yards, S.S.S.60
Club founded in 1929.
Visitors: welcome.
Green fees: £3.
Society meetings: welcome.
Catering: not available.
Hotels: Rutland, Bath St.

N42 **Ingestre Park**
☎Weston (0889) 270061

Ingestre, Weston, Stafford
ST18 0RE.
5 miles E of Stafford, via Great or Little Haywood, off A51.
Undulating meadowland course.
18 holes, 6376 yards, S.S.S.70
Club founded in 1977.
Visitors: welcome daily, but at weekends only with member.
Green fees: on application.
Society meetings: by arrangement with Sec except Mon or Bank Holidays.
Catering: full facilities daily except Mon.
Hotels: numerous in Stafford.

N43 Kedleston Park
☎Derby (0332) 840035
Kedleston, Quarndon, Derby
DE6 4JD.
Follow RAC signs to Kedleston Hall, 4 miles N of Derby off A5111.
Parkland course.
18 holes, 6611 yards, S.S.S.72
Course designed by James Braid. and J.S.F. Morrison.
Club founded in 1947.
Visitors: weekdays, weekends with member; only spiked shoes allowed on course.
Green fees: £13 per day; £11 per round.
Society meetings: on application.
Catering: full services available.
Hotels: Kedleston; Mundy Arms.

N44 Knutsford
☎Knutsford (0565) 55444
Mereheath Lane, Knutsford.
2 miles from Junction 19 on M6, make for Knutsford entrance to Tatton Park club a few yards on right down Mereheath Lane.
Parkland course.
9 holes, 6288 yards, S.S.S.70
Club founded in 1891.
Visitors: welcome weekdays by arrangement with Sec.
Green fees: on application.
Society meetings: catered for on certain weekdays mainly Thurs.
Catering: by arrangement with Steward.
Hotels: George; Angel; Cottons; Rose and Crown; Swan.

N45 Leek
☎Leek (0538) 384779 Sec, 385889 Club
Cheddleton Rd, Leek, Staffs
ST13 5RE.
0.75 mile S of Leek on A520.
Moorland course.

18 holes, 6229 yards, S.S.S.70
Club founded in 1892.
Visitors: welcome weekdays before 3pm.
Green fees: £12 weekdays; £16 weekends.
Society meetings: Wed only.
Catering: lunch served except Sun; evening meals except Sun and Mon.
Hotels: Abbey Inn; Three Horse-shoes; Jester.

N46 Leek Westwood
☎Leek (0583) 383060
Newcastle Rd, Leek, Staffs
ST13 7AA.
0.5 mile W of Leek on A53.
Moorland course.
9 holes, 5567 yards, S.S.S.67
Visitors: welcome weekdays.
Green fees: on application.
Society meetings: by arrangement.
Catering: by arrangement.
Hotels: Jester, Leek.

N47 Leigh
☎Culcheth (092 576) 3130
Kenyon Hall, Broseley Lane, Culcheth, Warrington WA3 4BG.
5 minutes from Culcheth village centre.
Parkland course.
18 holes, 5861 yards, S.S.S.68
Club founded in 1906.
Visitors: anytime except during club competitions.
Green fees: £9 weekdays; £12 weekends and Bank Holidays.
Society meetings: Tues on application.
Catering: bar snacks/full catering.
Hotels: Greyhound Motel.

N48 Lilleshall Hall
☎Telford (0952) 604776
Lilleshall, Newport, Salop TF10 9AS.
About 5 miles from Newport turn off A41 into Sheriffhales Rd, 2 miles later turn right into Abbey Rd.
Parkland course.
18 holes, 5906 yards, S.S.S.68
Course designed by H.S. Colt.
Club founded in 1937.
Visitors: weekdays unaccompanied; weekends with members only.
Green fees: £8 per day, (£3 with member) weekdays; £12 per day Bank Holidays.
Society meetings: by prior arrangement, maximum 32.
Catering: 7 days a week 9am-6.30pm.
Hotels: The Royal Victoria.

N49 Llanymynech
☎Llanymynech (0691) 830542
Pant, Oswestry, Salop SY10 8LB.
1 mile W of A483 Welshpool to Oswestry road and 6 miles S of Oswestry, turn by Cross Guns Inn, signposted to club in village of Pant.
Upland course.
18 holes, 6114 yards, S.S.S.69
Club founded in 1933.
Visitors: welcome, restrictions on competition days.
Green fees: £6 weekdays; £8 weekends and Bank Holidays.
Society meetings: by prior arrangement with Sec.
Catering: lunch and evening meal, except Mon.
Hotels: Wynnstay Hotel, Oswestry.

N50 Ludlow
☎Bromfield (058 477) 285
Bromfield, Ludlow, Salop SY8 2BT.
Take A49 Ludlow to Shrewsbury road, turn right 2 miles out of Ludlow, signposted.
Parkland course.
18 holes, 6239 yards, S.S.S.70
Club founded in 1889.
Visitors: welcome.
Green fees: on application.
Society meetings: welcome weekdays, write for details.
Catering: snacks and meals available by arrangement.
Hotels: Overton Grange; Angel; Feathers.

N51 Lymm
☎Lymm (092 575) 5020
Whitbarrow Rd, Lymm, Cheshire
WA13 9AM.
5 miles SE of Warrington.
Parkland course.
18 holes, 6319 yards, S.S.S.70
Club founded in 1907.
Visitors: welcome.
Green fees: £9.50, (£4 with member) weekdays; £11.50, (£5.50 with member) weekends and Bank Holidays.
Society meetings: usually on Wed.
Catering: meals available.
Hotels: Lymm; Statham Lodge; Dingle.

N52 Macclesfield
☎Macclesfield (0625) 23227
The Hollins, Macclesfield, Cheshire
SK11 7EA.
Off Windmill St in Macclesfield (A523 Macclesfield-Leek road).
Hilly course.
9 holes, 5974 yards, S.S.S.69

Club founded in 1889.
Visitors: welcome weekdays.
Green fees: £7, (£4 with member).
Society meetings: weekdays.
Catering: lunch except Tues.
Hotels: Belgrade, Bollington.

N53 Malkins Bank
☎Crewe (0270) 765931
Betchton Rd, Sandbach, Cheshire.
1.5 miles from Junction 17, off M6.
Parkland municipal course.
18 holes, 6071 yards, S.S.S.69
Course designed by Hawtree and
Son.
Club founded in 1980.
Visitors: welcome 7 days.
Green fees: £3 weekdays; £3.75
weekends.
Society meetings: catered for 7
days.
Catering: bar and catering provided
7 days.
Hotels: Old Hall, Sandbach.

N54 Market Drayton
☎Market Drayton (0630) 2266
Sutton, Market Drayton, Salop.
1.5 miles S of town.
Undulating meadowland course.
13 holes, 6230 yards, S.S.S.70
Club founded in 1911.
Visitors: welcome except Sun and
Bank Holidays.
Green fees: £6 weekdays; £8 per
day Sat.
Society meetings: welcome on
application to Sec.
Catering: by arrangement with Sec.
Hotels: Corbet Arms, Market
Drayton; Bear Inn, Hodnet.

N55 Matlock
☎Matlock (0629) 2191
Chesterfield Rd, Matlock, Derbyshire
DE4 5LF.
On A632 Matlock-Chesterfield road,
1.5 miles out of Matlock.
Moorland/parkland course.
18 holes, 5871 yards, S.S.S.68
Club founded in 1907.
Visitors: welcome weekdays.
Green fees: £10 weekdays; £13
weekends and Bank Holidays.
Society meetings: catered for
weekdays.
Catering: snacks available, meals to
order except Mon.
Hotels: Peacock; New Bath.

N56 Mere G & CC
☎Bucklow Hill (0565) 830155
Chester Rd, Mere, Knutsford,
Cheshire WA16 6LJ.

From Junction 19 off M6 take A556
for 2 miles, from Junction 7 off M55
take A556 past Swan at Bucklow Hill.
Parkland course.
18 holes, 6849 yards, S.S.S.73
Course designed by George Duncan
& James Braid.
Club founded in 1934.
Visitors: by prior arrangement Mon,
Tues and Thurs.
Green fees: £16.
Society meetings: Mon, Tues,
Thurs.
Catering: very extensive; breakfast,
lunch and dinner 7 days a week.
Hotels: Swan.

N57 Mickleover
☎Derby (0332) 512092
Uttoxeter Rd, Mickleover, Derby.
3 miles W of Derby, take A516 out of
Derby, join B5020 to Mickleover.
Meadowland course.
18 holes, 5709 yards, S.S.S.67
Club founded in 1923.
Visitors: welcome.
Green fees: £9 weekdays; £12
weekends and Bank Holidays.
Society meetings: Tues and Thurs.
Catering: facilities available.
Hotels: The Crest; International.

N58 Mirrlees
☎061-449 9513 Hon Sec.
Bramhall Moor Lane, Hazel Grove,
Stockport SK7 5AH.
From Stockport follow A6 to Hazel
Grove, turn right into New Moor
Lane, course is 0.25 mile on right
hand side.
Parkland course.
9 holes, 6102 yards, S.S.S.69
Club formed in 1925.
Visitors: welcome with member.
Green fees: on application.
Society meetings: none.
Catering: bar snacks available.
Hotels: numerous hotels in area.

N59 Newcastle under Lyme
☎Newcastle (0782) 618526 Pro,
617006 Sec.
Whitmore Rd, Newcastle under
Lyme, Staffs ST5 2QB.
1.5 miles SW from Newcastle under
Lyme on A53.
Parkland course.
18 holes, 6420 yards, S.S.S.71
Club formed in 1910.
Visitors: welcome weekdays.
Green fees: £10, (£3.50 with
member).
Society meetings: catered for Mon,
Wed and Thurs.

Catering: bar snacks, lunch and
evening meals served.
Hotels: Post House; Borough Arms.

N60 Newcastle Municipal
☎Newcastle (0782) 627596.
Keele Rd, Newcastle, Staffs
ST5 2QB.
Off M6 at junction 15 onto A525,
then A525 for 2 miles.
Parkland course.
18 holes, 6256 yards, S.S.S.70
Club formed in 1912.
Visitors: welcome, not weekends
Green fees: £10.
Society meetings: Mon and Wed.
Catering: lunch and dinner by
arrangement.
Hotels: Post House; Clayton Lodge.

N61 New Mills
☎New Mills (0663) 43485
Shaw Marsh, New Mills, Stockport,
Cheshire.
Take St Mary Rd from centre of New
Mills, about 0.75 miles.
Moorland course.
9 holes, 5707 yards, S.S.S.68
Club formed in 1907.
Visitors: welcome weekdays and
Sat am except competition days.
Green fees: on application.
Society meetings: welcome
weekdays by arrangement with Sec.
Catering: snacks and meals
available.
Hotels: Pack Horse and Sportsman;
Moorside.

N62 Onneley
☎Stoke-on-Trent (0782) 750577
Onneley, Crewe, Cheshire
CW3 5QF.
1 mile from Woore on A51.
Undulating meadowland course.
9 holes, 5584 yards, S.S.S.67
Club founded in 1968.
Visitors: welcome Mon, Wed, Thurs,
Fri; Sat only with member.
Green fees: £5 per day, (£2.50 with
member).
Society meetings: welcome by prior
booking with Sec.
Catering: by arrangement with
Stewardess.
Hotels: numerous in area.

N63 Ormonde Fields
G & CC
☎Ripley (0773) 42987 Pro, 44157
Club.
Nottingham Rd, Codnor, Ripley,
Derbys DE5 9RL.
Off M1 at Junction 26, take A610

towards Ripley for about 7.5 miles.
Undulating course.
18 holes, 6007 yards, S.S.S.69
Club founded in 1906.
Visitors: welcome at any time during week, by arrangement with Sec at weekends.
Green fees: on application.
Society meetings: welcome by arrangement.
Catering: full facilities.
Hotels: Sun Inn; Novatel; Post House.

N64 Oswestry
☎Queens Head (069 188) 221 or 535
Aston Park, Oswestry, Salop
SY11 4JJ.
SE of Shrewsbury, just off A5, 2 miles from Oswestry.
Parkland course.
18 holes, 6046 yards, S.S.S.69
Course designed by James Braid.
Club founded in 1930.
Visitors: welcome, must be member of club and hold handicap certificate or play with member.
Green fees: £8 weekdays; £10 weekends; (reduction when playing with member).
Society meetings: catered for on Wed and Fri only.
Catering: every day.
Hotels: Wynstay Arms; Sweeney Hall.

N65 Pastures
☎Derby (0332) 513921 extn 317
Pastures Hospital, Mickleover, Derby
DE3 3DQ.
On A516 4 miles W of Derby.
Undulating meadowland course.
9 holes, 5005 yards, S.S.S.64
Course designed by Frank Pennink.
Club founded in 1969.
Visitors: welcome with member only.
Green fees: on application.
Society meetings: weekdays by special arrangement.
Catering: no catering except for societies.
Hotels: Crest, Derby.

N66 Poulton Park
☎Padgate (0925) 812034
Dig Lane, Cinnamon Brow, Warrington.
Off A574, turn into Crab Lane, 3 miles from Warrington.
Meadowland course.
9 holes, 4918 metres, S.S.S.66
Club formed in 1978.

Visitors: welcome weekdays, restricted weekends.
Green fees: £6.50 weekdays, (£3 with member); £8 weekends, (£4 with member).
Society meetings: welcome weekdays.
Catering: lunch served except Mon.
Hotels: Paddington House.

N67 Prestbury
☎Prestbury (0625) 82824
Macclesfield Rd, Prestbury, Cheshire
SK10 4BJ.
2 miles NW of Macclesfield on Macclesfield Rd leaving Prestbury village.
Undulating meadowland course.
18 holes, 6359 yards, S.S.S.71
Course designed by Colt & Morrison.
Club founded in 1921.
Visitors: welcome weekdays and with member at weekends; advisable to telephone in advance.
Green fees: £12 per day/round, (£5 with member).
Society meetings: welcome Thurs only.
Catering: lunch, dinners and bar snacks served except Mon.
Hotels: Edge; Mottram Hall.

N68 Renishaw Park
☎Eckington (0246) 432044
Station Rd, Renshaw, Sheffield
S31 9UZ.
Junction 30, off M1, take the sign for Eckington, club approximately 1.5 miles on the right.
Parkland course.
18 holes, 6253 yards, S.S.S.70
Course designed by R. Sitwell.
Club founded in 1911.
Visitors: welcome weekdays; ring club for dress code.
Green fees: Winter: £4.75 per round, (£2.50 with member); £5.75 per day, (£3 with member) weekdays. £5.50 per round, (£3.25 with member); £6.75 per day, (£3.50 with member) weekends. Summer: £9.50 per round, (£5 with member); £11.50 per day, (£6 with member) weekdays. £11 per round, (£6.50 with member); £13.50 per day, (£7 with member) weekends.
Society meetings: none.
Catering: full facilities available with 24 hours notice.
Hotels: Sitwell Arms; Mosborough Hall.

N69 Runcorn
☎Runcorn (092 85) 72093 or

74214 Sec.
Clifton Rd, Runcorn, Cheshire
WA7 4SU.
Signposted The Heath off A557.
High parkland course.
18 holes, 6012 yards, S.S.S.69
Club formed in 1909.
Visitors: welcome weekdays.
Green fees: £8 per round weekdays; £9.50 per round weekends and Bank Holidays.
Society meetings: by arrangement.
Catering: by arrangement.
Hotels: Crest.

N70 Sandbach
☎Crewe (0270) 762117
117 Middlewich Rd, Sandbach, Cheshire CW11 9EA.
1 mile N of town centre on A533 Middlewich Rd.
Meadowland course.
Club formed in 1921.
Visitors: welcome weekdays; weekends and Bank Holidays by invitation only.
Green fees: £7 per round/day.
Society meetings: limited to a few each year.
Catering: all days except Mon and Thurs.
Hotels: Saxon Cross Motel; Old Hall.

N71 Sandiway
☎Sandiway (0606) 883247
Chester Rd, Sandiway, Northwick, Cheshire CW8 2DJ.
On A556 14 miles E of Chester, 4 miles from Northwich.
Undulating parkland course.
18 holes, 6435 yards, S.S.S.72
Course designed by Ted Ray.
Club founded in 1921.
Visitors: welcome weekdays and certain weekends with letter of introduction.
Green fees: £15 weekdays; £20 weekends and Bank Holidays.
Society meetings: catered for on Tues.
Catering: meals served every day by arrangement.
Hotels: Hartford Hall, Northwich; Oaklands, Weaverham.

N72 Shifnal
☎Telford (0952) 460330
Decker Hill, Shifnal, Salop
TF11 8QL.
On B4379 1 mile from Shifnal.
Parkland course.
18 holes, 6422 yards, S.S.S.71
Course designed by Frank Pennink.
Club formed in 1929.

Visitors: weekdays.
Green fees: £9 weekdays only; weekends with member.
Society meetings: Tues, Wed or Fri.
Catering: lunch and evening meals.
Hotels: Park House, Shifnal; Jerningham Arms, Shifnal.

N73 **Shrewsbury**
☎Shrewsbury (074 372) 2976
Condover, Salop SY5 7BL.
4 miles SW of Shrewsbury, follow signs for Condover and golf club.
Meadowland course.
18 holes, 6212 yards, S.S.S.70
Course designed by C.K. Cotton, Pennink, Lawrie and Partners.
Club founded in 1890.
Visitors: must have handicap certificates.
Green fees: £8 weekdays; £10 weekends and Bank Holidays.
Society meetings: 3 months notice.
Catering: full facilities available.
Hotels: Lord Hill, Shrewsbury; Deanhurst, Church Stretton.

N74 **Sickleholme**
☎Hope Valley (0433) 51306
Saltergate Lane, Bamford, Sheffield S30 2BH.
On A625, 14 miles W of Sheffield, near Marquis of Granby.
Hillside meadowland course.
18 holes, 6064 yards, S.S.S.69
Club founded in 1895.
Visitors: welcome but not Wed am.
Green fees: £10 weekdays; £12.50 weekends and Bank Holidays.
Society meetings: catered for on weekdays.
Catering: by arrangement.
Hotels: Marquis of Granby; The Derwent; Rising Sun, Bamford.

N75 **Stafford Castle**
☎Stafford (0785) 223821
Newport Rd, Stafford.
0.5 mile from Stafford main street.
Meadowland course.
9 holes, 6347 yards, S.S.S.70
Club founded in 1907.
Visitors: welcome weekdays.
Green fees: £5.
Society meetings: by prior arrangement.
Catering: bar meals available daily, others by arrangement except Mon.
Hotels: Swan, Stafford; Tillington Hall, Stafford; Vine, Stafford.

N76 **Stanedge**
☎Chesterfield (0246) 566156

Walton Hay Farm, Walton, Chesterfield, Derbys S45 0LW.
5 miles SW of Chesterfield, at top of long hill on A632, turn on to B5057; the turning to club is 300 yards W of Red Lion Inn.
Undulating moorland course.
9 holes, 4867 yards, S.S.S.64
Club founded in 1931.
Visitors: welcome Mon-Fri mornings, with member afternoons. With member only on Sat and Bank Holidays. No visitors Sun.
Green fees: £5, (£3 with member) weekdays; £4.50 Sat and Bank Holidays, with member only.
Society meetings: welcome Mon-Fri, subject to prior arrangement.
Catering: can be provided for parties by prior arrangement.
Hotels: The Chesterfield; Portland; Glen Stuart, Chesterfield.

N77 **Stone**
☎Stone (0785) 813103
Filleybrooks, Stone, Staffs ST15 0NB.
0.5 mile N of Stone on A34 next to Wayfarer Hotel.
Meadowland course.
9 holes, 6140 yards, S.S.S.69
Club founded in 1900.
Visitors: welcome weekdays.
Green fees: £7.
Society meetings: welcome weekdays.
Catering: lunch and evening meal except Mon.
Hotels: Stonehouse, on A34; Crown, High Street.

N78 **Tamworth**
☎Tamworth (0827) 53850
Eagle Drive, Tamworth, Staffs B77 4EG.
Off B5000 Tamworth to Polesworth road, signposted from Railway Arches at Tamworth roundabout.
Undulating moorland course.
18 holes, 6083 yards, S.S.S.72
Club founded in 1975.
Visitors: welcome 7 days per week.
Green fees: £3.35 per round.
Society meetings: Mon-Fri advance booking.
Catering: 7 days per week and licenced.
Hotels: Tamworth Hotel Directory.

N79 **Tapton Park**
☎Chesterfield (0246) 73887
Murray House, Crow Lane, Chesterfield.
0.5 mile from Chesterfield station.

Parkland course.
18 holes, 6048 yards, S.S.S.69
Visitors: by arrangement with Pro J. Delaney.
Green fees: £2.60 weekdays; £3.40 weekends.
Society meetings: by arrangement.
Catering: full bar and catering facilities.
Hotels: Chesterfield.

N80 **Telford Hotel G & CC**
☎Telford (0952) 585642
Great Hay, Telford, Salop TF7 4DT.
Off A442 at Sutton Hill, S of Telford.
Undulating meadowland course.
18 holes, 6274 yards, S.S.S.70
Course designed by John Harris.
Club founded in 1981.
Visitors: welcome with handicap certificate.
Green fees: £12.50 weekdays; £17.50 weekends.
Society meetings: by arrangement.
Catering: meals served every day.
Hotels: Telford Hotel Golf & Country Club.

N81 **Trentham**
☎Stoke-on-Trent (0782) 658109
14 Barlaston Old Rd, Trentham, Stoke-on-Trent ST4 8HB.
3 miles S of Newcastle under Lyme on A34, turn at the Trentham round-about onto A5035 to Uttoxeter, take first turning on right by National Westminster Bank, club is immediately on right.
Parkland course.
18 holes, 6644 yards, S.S.S.72
Club founded in 1895.
Visitors: welcome weekdays; weekends with permission of the Secretary.
Green fees: £13 weekdays; £16 weekends.
Society meetings: catered for on weekdays.
Catering: lunches served, bar snacks and evening meals by arrangement.
Hotels: Post House; Clayton Lodge, Stoke; Stonehouse, Stone.

N82 **Trentham Park**
☎Stoke-on-Trent (0782) 658800
Trentham Park, Trentham.
Stoke-on-Trent ST4 8AE.
4 miles S of Newcastle under Lyme on A34, 1 mile from Junction 15 on M6.
Parkland course.
18 holes, 6403 yards, S.S.S.71
Club founded in 1936.

Visitors: welcome weekdays.
Green fees: £9.
Society meetings: Wed and Fri.
Catering: full facilities.
Hotels: Clayton Lodge; Post House, Newcastle.

N83 Upton-by-Chester

☎Chester (0244) 381183
Upton Lane, Upton-by-Chester, Chester CH2 1EE.
1.5 miles N of Chester off Liverpool Road.
Parkland course.
18 holes, 5875 yards, S.S.S.68
Club founded in 1934.
Visitors: welcome - Tues-Fri.
Green fees: £10 (£12 weekends).
Society meetings: Tues-Fri.
Catering: full restaurant facilities except Mon.
Hotels: Pied Bull, Chester.

N84 Vicars Cross

☎Chester (0244) 335174
Tarvin Rd, Littleton, Chester CH3 7HN.
A51 2 miles E of Chester.
Meadowland course.
18 holes, 5876 yards, S.S.S.68
Course designed by E. Parr.
Club founded in 1939.
Visitors: welcome.
Green fees: £10 per day weekdays; £12 per day weekends and Bank Holidays.
Society meetings: full facilities available.
Hotels: Oaklands, Chester.

N85 Walton Hall

☎Warrington (0925) 66775
Warrington Rd, Higher Walton, Warrington WA4 5LU.
4 miles SW from Warrington along A56, 0.5 mile from M56.
Undulating parkland course.
18 holes, 6801 yards, S.S.S.73
Club founded in 1972.
Visitors: welcome.
Green fees: on application.
Society meetings: catered for by appointment.
Catering: bar snacks available during licensed hours and meals available by arrangement with Steward.
Hotels: Lord Daresbury.

N86 Warrington

☎Warrington (0925) 61775 Sec, 65431 Pro.
London Rd, Appleton, Warrington, Cheshire WA4 5HR.
On A49 from M56 or S on A49 through town, 3 miles S of Warrington.
Undulating parkland course.
Long-18 holes, 6217 yards, S.S.S.70
Short-18 holes, 5890 yards, S.S.S.68
Course designed by James Braid.
Club founded in 1902.
Visitors: welcome.
Green fees: on application.
Society meetings: welcome by arrangement; Wed over 30; Thurs up to 30.
Catering: meals and snacks available except Mon.
Hotels: Hill Cliffe Hydro; Old Vicarage.

N87 Whittington Barracks

☎Whittington (0543) 432317 Sec, 432317 Club, 432261 Pro.
Tamworth Rd, Lichfield WS14 9PW.
On A51 2.5 miles from Lichfield station.
Moorland course.
18 holes, 6457 yards, S.S.S.71
Club founded in 1886.
Visitors: welcome weekdays with handicap certificate or letter of introduction.
Green fees: £13 per day/round.
Society meetings: held on Wed/Thurs maximum 40.
Catering: snack lunch, evening meals available except Mon.
Hotels: George, Bird St; Little Barrow, Beacon St; Swan, Bird St; all in Lichfield.

N88 Widnes

☎051-424 2995
Highfield Rd, Widnes, Cheshire.
Near town centre.
Parkland course.
18 holes, 5688 yards, S.S.S.67
Club founded in 1923/4
Visitors: welcome weekdays.
Green fees: on application.
Society meetings: welcome weekdays, except Tues.
Catering: meals served by arrangement.

Hotels: Hillcrest.

N89 Wilmslow

☎Mobberley (056 587) 2148
Great Warford, Mobberley, Knutsford, Cheshire WA16 7AY.
2 miles from Wilmslow on B5085.
Parkland course.
18 holes, 6500 yards, S.S.S.71
Club founded in 1899.
Visitors: limited.
Green fees: on application.
Society meetings: Tues and Thurs.
Catering: facilities available.
Hotels: Edge, Macclesfield Rd; Mottram Hall, Mottram St Andrew, Prestbury; Belfry, Handforth, Wilmslow.

N90 Wolstanton

☎Stoke-on-Trent (0782) 622413 Sec, 616995 Clubhouse.
Dimsdale Old Hall, Hassam Parade, Newcastle-under-Lyme, Staffs ST5 9DR.
1.5 miles NW of Newcastle-under-Lyme on A34, turn off at Lymelight Hotel into Dimsdale Parade, then first right into Hassam Parade.
Meadowland/parkland course.
18 holes, 5807 yards, S.S.S.68
Club founded in 1925.
Visitors: welcome weekdays.
Green fees: on application.
Society meetings: welcome Mon and Fri.
Catering: lunch served except Fri.
Hotels: Crest.

N91 Wrekin

☎Telford (0952) 44032
Ercall Woods, Wellington, Telford TF6 5BX.
M54 onto A5, take Golf Links Lane off A5.
Parkland course.
18 holes, 5699 yards, S.S.S.67
Club founded in 1905.
Visitors: welcome weekdays.
Green fees: £8 per day weekdays; £12 weekends and Bank Holidays.
Society meetings: catered for weekdays except Mon.
Catering: arranged if booked in advance with Stewardess.
Hotels: Charlton; Buckatree.

O Nottinghamshire, Leicestershire and Lincolnshire

There are few inland courses to match the Notts GC (Hollinwell), or Woodhall Spa in Lincolnshire, both places where a round never disappoints. They are the pick of their respective counties although Sherwood Forest and Coxmoor are near neighbours of Hollinwell that can be highly recommended.

Newark, Worksop, Stanton-on-the-Wolds and Oxton have their admirers, too, and, driving from Newark into Lincolnshire, the Lincoln Club at Torksey is a good stopping point. Further south, Burghley Park at Stamford enjoys stately surroundings and Luffenham Heath is as fine an example of heathland golf as you will find.

In the north, Market Rasen is very pleasant while Seacroft at Skegness is a notable seaside links in contrast to the heart of Leicestershire which is parkland in character. Rothley Park and the Leicestershire club are perhaps the best and Longcliffe and the nine holes at Charnwood Forest extol the virtues more of heathland.

O1 **Beeston Fields**
☎Nottingham (0602) 257062
Beeston Fields, Nottingham
NG9 3DD.
Off A52 4 miles W of Nottingham
4 miles from M1 Exit 25.
Parkland course.
18 holes, 6346 yards, S.S.S.70
Course designed by
Tom Williamson.
Club founded in 1922.
Visitors: daily, by arrangement.
Green fees: to be revised.
Society meetings: catered for Mon and Wed.
Catering: meals served every day.
Hotels: The Priory; Hylands; Novotel, Nottingham.

O2 **Belton Park**
☎Grantham (0476) 67399
Belton Lane, Londonthorpe Rd,
Grantham, Lincs NG31 9SH.
A607 from Grantham signposted to
Sleaford and Lincoln, turn right at
traffic lights at Park signposted
Londonthorpe, golf club is 1 mile on
left.
Parkland courses.
Brownlow-9 holes, 6412 yards,
S.S.S.71
Belmont-9 holes, 5857 yards,
S.S.S.68
Course designed by Dave Thomas & Peter Alliss.
Club founded in 1892.

Visitors: welcome.
Green fees: £11, (£5.50 with member) weekdays; £13.50, (£6.75 with member) weekends; (18 holes only).
Society meetings: Mon, Wed, Thurs, Fri. Special arrangements for 18/27/36 holes.
Catering: snacks, lunch and dinner available every day.
Hotels: George; Angel and Royal; King's; all in Grantham.

O3 **Birstall**
☎Leicester (0533) 674322
Station Rd, Birstall, Leicester
LE4 3BB.
3 miles N of town just off A6.
Parkland course.
18 holes, 5988 yards, S.S.S.69
Club founded in 1900.
Visitors: not weekends.
Green fees: £10.
Society meetings: Wed and Fri.
Catering: not Mon.
Hotels: Goscote Hall, Birstall.

O4 **Blankney**
☎Metheringham (0526) 20263
Blankney, Lincoln, Lincs LN4 3AZ.
On B1188 10 miles S from Lincoln,
1 mile past Metheringham.
Parkland course.
18 holes, 6232 yards, S.S.S.70
Course designed by Lt Col Hotchkin.
Club founded in 1903.

Visitors: weekdays no restrictions; reservations required at weekends.
Green fees: £9 per day; £7 per round.
Society meetings: not Tues or weekends.
Catering: full facilities.
Hotels: Moor Lodge, Branston; Golf Hotel, Woodhall Spa.

O5 **Boston**
☎Boston (0205) 50589 Sec, 62306 Club
Cowbridge, Horncastle Rd, Boston, Lincs PE22 7EL.
2 miles N of Boston on B1183, look for sign on right when crossing first bridge.
Parkland/moorland course.
18 holes, 5795 yards, S.S.S.68
Course designed by B.S. Cooper and extended by Donald Steel.
Club founded in 1962.
Visitors: welcome.
Green fees: £8 weekdays; £10 weekends and Bank Holidays.
Society meetings: welcome weekdays.
Catering: full facilities except Wed when only bar snacks available.
Hotels: White Hart, Bridge Ford, New England, Wide Bargate, Boston.

O6 **Bulwell Forest**
☎Nottingham (0602) 278008

Hucknall Rd, Bulwell, Nottingham NG5 9LQ.
4 miles N of city centre, follow signs for Bulwell or Hucknall, 3 miles from M1, Junction 26.
Moorland course.
18 holes, 5572 yards, S.S.S.67
Club founded in 1902.
Visitors: welcome.
Green fees: £3.20 per round.
Society meetings: by arrangement.
Catering: by arrangement.
Hotels: Savoy; Royal.

O7 Burghley Park
☎Stamford (0780) 53789
St Martins Without, Stamford, Lincs PE9 3JX.
Leave A1 at roundabout S of town, course entrance is first gateway on the right, 1 mile S of Stamford.

Parkland course.
18 holes, 6200 yards, S.S.S.70
Club founded in 1890.
Visitors: welcome weekdays; only after 3pm weekends and Bank Holidays.
Green fees: £8.
Society meetings: welcome weekdays (preference given to Wed).
Catering: lunch and teas, dinner for Societies and by arrangement.
Hotels: George of Stamford; Crown; Cavalier, Collyweston.

O8 Canwick Park
☎(0522) 22166
Canwick Park, Washingborough Rd, Lincoln LN4 1EF.
2 miles S of city centre.
Parkland course.

18 holes, 6257 yards, S.S.S.70
Course designed by Hawtree & Sons.
Club founded in 1973.
Visitors: welcome weekdays.
Green fees: £6 per day.
Society meetings: catered for weekdays.
Catering: lunch and evening meals except Mon.
Hotels: Eastgate; Brierley House.

O9 Carholme
☎Lincoln (0522) 23725
Carholme Rd, Lincoln LN1 1SE.
On A57, 1 mile from city centre.
Parkland course.
18 holes, 6086 yards, S.S.S.69
Visitors: welcome weekdays and Sat.
Green fees: on application.

Society meetings: welcome weekdays.
Catering: lunch served except Mon.
hotels: numerous in Lincoln.

O10 **Charnwood Forest**
☎Woodhouse Eaves (0509) 890259
Breakback Lane, Woodhouse Eaves, Loughborough, Leics.
B591 off A6 at Quorndon, follow signs to Woodhouse Eaves, 3 miles SE.
Undulating heathland course.
9 holes, 6202 yards, S.S.S.70
Club founded in 1890.
Visitors: welcome.
Green fees: £8 weekdays; £10 weekends and Public Holidays.
Society meetings: catered for weekdays.
Catering: full facilities; light catering Mon and Thurs.
Hotels: Kings Head, Lougborough; Quorn Country, Quorn.

O11 **Chilwell Manor**
☎Nottingham (0602) 258958
Meadow Lane, Chilwell, Nottingham NG9 6AE.
4 miles W of Nottingham, near Beeston, on A6005.
Parkland course.
18 holes, 6379 yards, S.S.S.69
Club founded in 1906.
Visitors: welcome weekdays, restricted to 4 per hour.
Green fees: £10, (£5 with member). Not weekends and Bank Holidays.
Society meetings: catered for Mon.
Catering: lunch served weekdays, evening meals by arrangement.
Hotels: Post House; Novotel (UK) Ltd, Bostocks Lane, Long Eaton.

O12 **Cosby**
☎Leicester (0533) 864759
Chapel Lane, Cosby, Leics.
A46 or A426 out of Leicester, in Cosby village take Broughton Rd.
Parkland course.
18 holes, 6270 yards, S.S.S.70
Club founded in 1895.
Visitors: welcome weekdays and with member at weekends.
Green fees: on application.
Society meetings: by arrangement.
Catering: meals served except Mon.
Hotels: Charnwood; Four Seasons; both in Narborough.

O13 **Coxmoor**
☎Mansfield 021-444 3584
Coxmoor Rd, Sutton-in-Ashfield, Notts NG17 5LF.
On A611 2 miles SW of Mansfield,

5 miles from M1, Exit 27.
Heathland course.
18 holes, 5800 yards, S.S.S.68
Club founded in 1927.
Visitors: must book tee off time one week in advance.
Green fees: £3.40 per (18 holes); £2.40 per (9 holes) weekdays; £4 weekends.
Society meetings: must be booked well in advance.
Catering: Birmingham City caterers open daily.
Hotels: Midland.

O14 **Edwalton Municipal**
☎Nottingham (0602) 234775
Edwalton Village, Nottingham.
Left at A606 from Nottingham at Edwalton Hall Hotel.
Parkland course.
Main-9 holes, 3336 yards, S.S.S.36
Par 3-9 holes, 1592 yards, S.S.S.27
Course designed by Frank Pennink.
Course opened in 1981.
Visitors: welcome.
Green fees: Main - £2 weekdays; £2.40 weekends; Par 3 - £1.10 weekdays; £1.50 weekends.
Society meetings: catered for on weekdays.
Catering: lunch and evening meals.
Hotels: Edwalton Hall.

O15 **Glen Gorse**
☎Leicester (0533) 714159
Glen Rd, Oadby, Leicester LE2 4RF.
Follow main road A6 towards Market Harborough, club on right hand side just past Oadby.
Parkland course.
18 holes, 6641 yards, S.S.S.72
Club founded in 1933.
Visitors: welcome weekdays.
Green fees: £12 per day, (£6 with member) weekdays; weekends only with member.
Society meetings: catered for weekdays; snacks or full meals available.
Catering: snack meals, sandwiches, full meals served except Mon.
Hotels: Moat House, Oadby.

O16 **Hinckley**
☎Hinckley (0455) 615124
Leicester Rd, Hinckley, Leics LE10 3DR.
NE boundary of Hinckley on A47.
Parkland course.
18 holes, 6462 yards, S.S.S.71
Club founded in 1894.
Visitors: Mon, Wed, Thurs and Fri and Sun after 12 noon.

Green fees: on application.
Society meetings: welcome Mon, Wed, Thurs and Fri.
Catering: lunch daily; evening meals served except Sun.
Hotels: Sketchley Grange, Burbage; Hinckley Island.

O17 **Kibworth**
☎Kibworth (053 753) 2301
Weir Rd, Kibworth, Beauchamp, Leics LE8 0LP.
8 miles SE of Leicester on A6.
Meadowland course.
18 holes, 6282 yards, S.S.S.70
Club founded in 1962.
Visitors: welcome weekdays.
Green fees: £9 per day, (£4 with member).
Society meetings: welcome mid-week.
Catering: full facilities; special all in package for societies including morning coffee, lunch and dinner.
Hotels: Angel, Market Harborough.

O18 **Kirby Muxloe**
☎Leicester (0533) 393457
Station Rd, Kirby Muxloe, Leicester LE9 9EN.
On A47 3 miles W of Leicester.
Parkland course.
18 holes, 6303 yards, S.S.S.70
Club founded in 1910.
Visitors: weekdays only; weekends with Captain's permission only.
Green fees: on application.
Society meetings: Wed, Thurs 24-30 only; Fri 24-30 only.
Catering: available.
Hotels: Post House; Moat House.

O19 **Leicestershire**
☎Leicester (0533) 738825
Evington Lane, Leicester LE5 6DJ.
Make for Evington village in SE district of Leicester, 2 miles from city centre.
Parkland course.
18 holes, 6312 yards, S.S.S.70
Club founded in 1891.
Visitors: welcome.
Green fees: £12, (£4 with member) weekdays; £13 weekends and Bank Holidays.
Society meetings: welcome weekdays by prior arrangement.
Catering: lunch and tea daily.
Hotels: Daval; Rowans; Thornwood; Stanfre House; Gordon Lodge, all on London Rd A6.

O20 **Lincoln**
☎Torksey (042 771) 210
Torksey, Lincoln LN1 2EG.

Off A156, 12 miles NW of Lincoln.
Undulating meadowland course.
18 holes, 6400 yards, S.S.S.70
Club founded in 1891.
Visitors: welcome with reservation
and letter of introduction.
Green fees: £8 per round, £12 per
day weekdays; £10 per round, £15
per day weekends.
Society meetings: weekdays by
arrangement.
Caatering: meals served by
arrangement.
Hotels: White Hart; Grand, Lincoln.

O21 **Lindrick**
☎Worksop (0909) 475282
Lindrick, Worksop, Notts S81 8BH.
On A57, 4 miles W of Worksop.
Heathland course.
18 holes, 6615 yards, S.S.S.72
Course designed by Willie Park and
W.H. Fowler.
Club founded in 1891.
Visitors: welcome weekdays prior
notice required.
Green fees: Nov-Mar: £10 per
round/day weekdays, £15 per round
weekends. Apr-Oct £16 per round,
£20 per day weekdays; £18 per
round, £22 per day weekends.
Society meetings: catered for
weekdays.
Catering: lunch served most days.
Evening meals for visiting societies/
parties. Prior notice required.
Hotels: Red Lion, Todwick;
Fourways, Blyth; Charnwood, Blyth;
Olde Bell, Barnby Moor.

O22 **Lingdale**
☎Woodhouse Eaves (0509) 890035
Clubhouse, 890703 Sec.
Joe Moores Lane, Woodhouse
Eaves, Leics LE12 8TF.
5 miles S of Loughborough on
B5330.
Undulating parkland course.
9 holes, 6114 metres, S.S.S.72
Course designed by D.W. Tucker.
Club founded in 1967.
Visitors: welcome.
Green fees: £8 per day, £6 per
round weekdays; £10 per day, £8 per
round weekends.
Society meetings: Mon-Fri by prior
arrangement with Sec.
Catering: clubhouse closed Mon,
full catering facilities.
Hotels: Kings Head; De Montford,
Loughborough.

O23 **Longcliffe**
☎Loughborough (0509) 239129
Snell's Nook Lane, Nampantan,

Loughborough, Leics LE11 3YA.
Adjacent to M1 motorway, leave M1
at Junction 23 and follow A512
towards Loughborough, within 0.25
mile turn right into Snell's Nook Lane,
golf course is 0.75 mile on right.
Undulating heathland course.
18 holes, 6551 yards, S.S.S.71
Club founded in 1904.
Visitors: welcome weekdays.
Green fees: £13 per day, (£5 with
member).
Society meetings: Mon-Fri
excluding Tues, (Ladies day).
Catering: meals available via
Stewardess not available Mon.
Hotels: Kings Head, Loughborough.

O24 **Louth**
☎Louth (0507) 603681
Crowtree Lane, Louth, Lincs
LN11 9LJ.
From Lincoln or Gainsborough turn
right at Trout Farm on outskirts of
Louth, from Sleaford turn left by the
Grammar School, course is situated
in Hubbard Hills 1 mile outside of
Louth.
Undulating meadowland course.
18 holes, 6477 yards, S.S.S.71
Club founded in 1965.
Visitors: welcome.
Green fees: £7 per round, £9 per
day weekdays; £8 per round, £10 per
day weekends.
Society meetings: catered for
weekdays.
Catering: lunch, bar snacks every
day.
Hotels: Priory; Kings Head; Masons
Arms.

O25 **Luffenham Heath**
☎Stamford (0780) 720205
Ketton, Stamford, Lincs PE9 3UU.
6 miles SW of Stamford on A6121 by
Fosters Bridge, off A47 at Morcott
onto A6121.
Undulating heathland course.
18 holes, 6254 yards, S.S.S.70
Course designed by James Braid.
Club founded in 1911.
Visitors: by prior arrangement.
Green fees: £10.50 weekdays; £16
weekends and Bank Holidays.
Society meetings: welcome
weekdays.
Catering: by arrangement.
Hotels: George, Stamford; Falcon,
Uppingham.

O26 **Lutterworth**
☎Lutterworth (045 55) 2532
Rugby Rd, Lutterworth, Leics
LE17 5HN.

0.5 mile from M1, Exit 20 on A426.
Undulating course.
18 holes, 5570 yards, S.S.S.67
Course designed by D. Snell.
Club founded in 1904.
Visitors: welcome weekdays;
weekends with member only.
Green fees: £7.50, (£2.50 with
member) weekdays; £3.50
weekends.
Society meetings: Mon-Fri.
Catering: full facilities 7 days per
week.
Hotels: Denbigh, Lutterworth.

O27 **Mapperley**
☎Nottingham (0602) 265611
Central Ave, Mapperley Plains,
Nottingham NG3 5RH.
From Nottingham take Woodborough
Rd, B684. Central Ave is about 4
miles NE of Nottingham, turn right at
Speeds (Volvo) Garage.
Hilly meadowland course.
18 holes, 6224 yards, S.S.S.70
Club founded about 1905.
Visitors: welcome.
Green fees: £6.50 weekdays; £7.50
weekends.
Society meetings: welcome
weekdays.
Catering: lunch and evening meals
served except Wed, when only
snacks available.
Hotels: many around Nottingham.

O28 **Market Harborough**
☎Market Harborough (0858) 63684
Oxendon Rd, Market Harborough,
Leics.
1 mile S of town on A508
Northampton Rd.
Parkland course.
9 holes, 6168 yards, S.S.S.69
Club founded in 1898.
Visitors: welcome Mon-Sat with
member only Sun.
Green fees: £6.
Society meetings: welcome with
prior arrangement.
Catering: facilities available.
Hotels: The Three Swans, High St,
Market Harborough.

O29 **Market Rasen & District**
☎Market Rasen (0673) 842416
Legsby Rd, Market Rasen, Lincs
LN8 3DZ.
Off A631, 1 mile S of racecourse.
Moorland course.
18 holes, 6043 yards, S.S.S.69
Club founded in 1922.
Visitors: welcome weekdays; with

members at weekends.
Green fees: on application.
Society meetings: Tues and Fri by arrangement with Secretary.
Catering: lunch available except Mon.
Hotels: Gordon Arms, The Chase.

O30 Melton Mowbray
☎Melton Mowbray (0664) 62118
Waltham Rd, Thorpe Arnold, Melton Mowbray, Leics LE14 4SD.
On A609 between Melton Mowbray and Grantham, 2 miles NE of Melton Mowbray.
Undulating course.
9 holes, 6168 yards, S.S.S.69
Visitors: welcome.
Green fees: £7 weekdays; £8 weekends.
Society meetings: by arrangement on weekdays.
Catering: bar meals available.
Hotels: George, Melton Mowbray; Harborough, Melton Mowbray.

O31 Newark
☎Fenton Claypole (063 684) 282/ 492/241.
Coddington, Newark, Notts NG24 2QX.
4 miles E of Newark on A17 toward Sleaford, off A1 1 mile E of Coddington.
Parkland course.
18 holes, 6486 yards, S.S.S.71
Club founded in 1901.
Visitors: welcome.
Green fees: £9 per round/day weekdays; £15 per round/day weekends and Bank Holidays.
Society meetings: by arrangement on weekdays.
Catering: bar snacks and meals by prior arrangement except Fri.
Hotels: Robin Hood, Newark.

O32 North Shore
☎Skegness (0754) 3298
North Shore Rd, Skegness, Lincs PE25 1DN.
1 mile N of town on Seaward side of Ingoldmells Rd.
Links/parkland course.
18 holes, 6134 yards, S.S.S.69
Course designed by James Braid.
Club founded in 1910.
Visitors: welcome if bona fide members of recognised club.
Green fees: £8 per round/day weekdays; £9 per round/day weekends and Bank Holidays.
Society meetings: catered for.
Catering: normal hotel services.

Hotels: North Shore on site.

O33 Nottingham City
☎Nottingham (0602) 278021
Lawton Drive, Bulwell, Nottingham NG6 8BL.
2 miles off M1 at Junction 26.
Parkland municipal course.
18 holes, 6120 yards, S.S.S.70
Club founded in 1910.
Visitors: welcome weekdays and by booking at weekends.
Green fees: £3.20 per day weekdays.
Society meetings: welcome weekdays except Fri.
Catering: meals served.
Hotels: numerous in Nottingham.

O34 Nottinghamshire
☎Mansfield (0623) 753225
Hollinwell, Derby Rd, Kirkby-in-Ashfield, Notts NG17 7QR.
Leave M1 at Junction 27, then 2 miles N on A611.
Undulating moorland course.
Course designed by Willie Park.
Club founded in 1887.
Visitors: reserved for members 12.30-2.30pm on Wed; Lady members until 12.30am Fri. No visitors Sat.
Green fees: currently £5 per round/ day.
Society meetings: by arrangement.
Catering: full facilities every day.
Hotels: Swallow; Pine Lodge.

O35 Oadby
☎Leicester (0533) 709052
Leicester Rd, Oadby, Leicester LE2 4AB.
On A6 from Leicester, just outside city limits.
Moorland course.
18 holes, 6228 yards, S.S.S.70
Club founded in 1975.
Visitors: welcome.
Green fees: £2.50, OAPs/Juniors £2 weekdays; £3, OAPs/Juniors £2.50 weekends.
Society meetings: on application to Oadby and Wigston Borough Council, Station Rd, Wigston, Leics.
Catering: on application to Steward.
Hotels: numerous in Leicester.

O36 Oxton
☎Nottingham (0602) 653545
Oaks Lane, Oxton, Southwell, Notts NG25 0RH.
Take the A6097, 10 miles NE of Nottingham then off A614.
Meadowland course.

18 holes, 5681 metres, S.S.S.72
Course designed by Frank Pennink.
Club founded in 1965.
Visitors: welcome but should make reservation at weekends.
Green fees: £6.50 per round, £12 per day weekdays; £7.50 per round, £14 per day weekends and Bank Holidays; (reduction if under 16 or over 60).

O37 Radcliffe-on-Trent
☎Radcliffe-on-Trent (0673) 3000, 5771
Dewberry Lane, Cropwell Rd, Radcliffe-on-Trent, Notts NG12 2JH.
Off A52 Nottingham to Grantham road, 7 miles E of Nottingham.
Undulating parkland course.
18 holes, 6434 yards, S.S.S.71
Course designed by F. Pennink.
Club founded in 1909.
Visitors: welcome except Tues or weekends.
Green fees: £9 per (18 holes) weekdays; £12 per (36 holes).
Society meetings: subject to written application.
Catering: available - contact Steward.
Hotels: Bridgford Lodge, Nottingham.

O38 Retford
☎Retford (0777) 703733
Ordsall, Retford, Notts.
S off A620.
Woodland course.
9 holes, 5697 metres, S.S.S.70
Visitors: welcome weekdays, with members only at weekends.
Green fees: on application.
Catering: full meal facilities.
Hotels: West Retford; Ye Olde Bell.

O39 Rothley Park
☎Leicester (0533) 302809 Sec, 302019 Club, 303023 Pro.
Westfield Lane, Rothley, Leicester LE7 7LH.
6 miles N of Leicester, W of A6.
Parkland course.
18 holes, 6487 yards, S.S.S.71
Club founded in 1912.
Visitors: welcome but must be member of recognised club with handicap.
Green fees: £12 per person weekdays; £15 per person weekends and Bank Holidays.
Society meetings: apply to Sec.
Catering: full catering except Mon.
Hotels: Rothley Court, Westfield Lane, Rothley.

THE SHERWOOD FOREST GOLF CLUB LTD

EAKRING ROAD, MANSFIELD, NOTTS. NG18 3EW
Club House Telephone No. 23327

Secretary: K. Hall Tel: 26689
Professional: K. Hall Tel: 27403
Stewardess: Mrs. J. Mottershead (Mansfield 23327)

Full catering service available with dining for up to 70 persons at one sitting.
Course is heathland, set in the very heart of Robin Hood country, and was designed by James Braid. Yellow markers distance is 6,286 yds. SSS 71. White markers distance is 6,710 yds. SSS 73.
The Course is the venue for the
Midland Region Qualifying Round for the Open Championship 1990 — 1995.
Green fees for 1988 — Round £14.00 — Day £18.00 — Weekend £20.00
All applications to be made with the secretary.
Within a few miles of places of interest — such as the Major Oak (Robin Hood's Larder), Newstead Abbey, Thoresby Hall, Clumber Park, and 14 miles from the centre of Nottingham.

O40 **RAF North Luffenham**
☎Stamford (0780) 720041 ext 313.
North Luffenham, Oakham, Leics LE15 8RL.
Follow signposts for RAF North Luffenham from A606, station is close to Rutland Water.
Meadowland course.
9 holes, 5997 yards, S.S.S.69
Club founded in 1975.
Visitors: book in at Guardroom prior to proceeding to course.
Green fees: £3.
Society meetings: can be arranged through Sec.
Catering: only light refreshments.
Hotels: George, Stamford; Crown, Oakham.

O41 **Rushcliffe**
☎East Leake (050 982) 2959
Stocking Lane, East Leake, Loughborough, Leics LE12 5RL.
Off M1 at Junction 24, follow signs to Nottingham, then Gotham and East Leake.
Undulating parkland course.
18 holes, 6057 yards, S.S.S.69
Club founded in 1911.
Visitors: welcome, not Tues (Ladies Day).

Green fees: on application.
Society meetings: welcome weekdays only. If over 16 must be booked before Jan.
Catering: bar snacks and meals served.
Hotels: numerous in area.

O42 **Sandilands**
☎Sutton-on-Sea (0521) 41432/41617
Sea Lane, Sandilands, Sutton-on-Sea, Mablethorpe, Lincs LN12 2RJ.
4 miles S of Mablethorpe on A52 coast road, course runs next to sea wall.
Seaside course.
18 holes, 5995 yards, S.S.S.69
Club founded in 1901.
Visitors: welcome any time.
Green fees: £7 per round, £8 per day weekdays; £8 per round, £9 per day weekends and Bank Holidays; 3 days £18; weekly £30; fortnightly £40.
Society meetings: welcome on application.
Catering: bar meals except Wed.
Hotels: Grange & Links, Sea Lane.

O43 **Scraptoft**
☎Leicester (0533) 419000
Beeby Rd, Scraptoft, Leicester LE7 9SJ.
Turn off A47, main Leicester-Peterborough road, to Scraptoft at Thurnby.
Meadowland course.
18 holes, 6146 yards, S.S.S.69
Visitors: welcome.
Green fees: £10, (£5 with member) weekdays; £12 per day, (£6 with member) weekends and Bank Holidays.
Society meetings: welcome.
Catering: meals served except Mon.
Hotels: White House, Scraptoft; Grand.

O44 **Seacroft**
☎Skegness (0754) 3741
Drummond Rd, Skegness, Lincs PE25 3AU.
1 mile S of Skegness alongside road to Gibraltar Rd Bird Sanctuary.
Moderately undulating links course.
18 holes, 6490 yards, S.S.S.71
Club founded in 1895.
Visitors: welcome from bona fide club with handicap.

Green fees: £9 per round, £12 per day weekdays; £11 per round, £15 per day weekends.
Society meetings: welcome as for visitors.
Catering: available except Tues.
Hotels: Vine; Crown.

O45 **Sherwood Forest**
☎Mansfield (0602) 26689
Eakring Rd, Mansfield, Notts, NG18 3EW.
On A617 2.5 miles SE of Mansfield.
Wooded heathland course.
18 holes, 6710 yards, S.S.S.73
Course designed by James Braid.
Club founded in 1904.
Visitors: welcome any day by prior arrangement.
Green fees: £15 per (36 holes), £12 per (18 holes) weekdays; £20 weekends.
Society meetings: Mon-Fri only.
Catering: full facilities.
Hotels: Ravensdale; Pine Lodge, Mansfield; Budleways, Forest Town, Nottingham.

O46 **Sleaford**
☎South Rauceby (052 98) 273
South Rauceby, Sleaford, Lincs NG34 8PL.
On A153 Sleaford-Grantham road, 2 miles W of Sleaford.
Heathland course.
18 holes, 6443 yards, S.S.S.71
Course designed by James Braid.
Club founded in 1905.
Visitors: unrestricted generally.
Green fees: £8.50 weekdays; £12 weekends, holidays. (Reductions when playing with member).
Society meetings: Mon-Fri by prior arrangement.
Catering: bar facilities, meals and snacks available.
Hotels: Carre Arms, Sleaford.

O47 **Spalding**
☎Surfleet (0775 85) 234
Surfleet, Spalding, Lincs PE11 4DG.
4 miles N of Spalding off A16.
Meadowland course.
18 holes, 5847 yards, S.S.S.68
Club founded circa 1920.
Visitors: members of recognised clubs. Advise prior telephone enquiry.
Green fees: on application.
Society meetings: Thurs only on application.
Catering: full facilities except Tues.
Hotels: numerous in Spalding.

O48 **Stanton-on-the-Wolds**
☎Plumtree (060 237) 2006
Stanton-on-the-Wolds, Keyworth, Notts NG12 5AH.
Off A606 at Blue Star Garage 8 miles SE of Nottingham.
Meadowland course.
18 holes, 6437 yards, S.S.S.71
Course designed by Tom Williamson.
Club founded in 1906.
Visitors: weekdays if no competitions in progress.
Green fees: £9 per round, £11 per day weekdays; £12 weekends and Bank Holidays.
Society meetings: write to Sec, H.G. Gray FCA, 29 Arboretum St, Notts.
Catering: ring Steward in advance.
Hotels: Edwalton, Notts.

O49 **Stoke Rochford**
☎Great Ponton (047 683) 275
Stoke Rochford, Grantham, Lincs.
Off A1 5 miles S of Grantham, entrance at Roadhog service station.
Parkland course.
18 holes, 6204 yards, S.S.S.70
Course designed by C. Turner.
Club founded in 1926.
Visitors: welcome any day. Cannot tee off before 10.30am Sat or Sun unless playing with member.
Green fees: £10, (£5 with member) weekdays; £14, (£6 with member) weekends and Bank Holidays.
Society meetings: catered for Mon, Tues, Thurs and Fri only.
Catering: lunch and evening meals served upon request.
Hotels: many in Grantham.

O50 **Sutton Bridge**
☎Holbeach (0406) 350323
New Rd, Sutton Bridge, Spalding, Lincs.
On A17 10 miles W of Kings Lynn.
Parkland course.
9 holes, 5820 yards, S.S.S.68
Club founded in 1914.
Visitors: weekdays only.
Green fees: £8.
Society meetings: not catered for.
Catering: meals, sandwiches not Mon.
Hotels: none recommendable.

O51 **Thonock**
☎Gainsborough (0427) 2278
Thonock, Gainsborough, Lincs.
1 mile E of town centre.
Parkland course.
18 holes, 5824 yards, S.S.S.68
Visitors: welcome. Advisable to ring first.
Green fees: £6 per round, £8 per day weekdays; £10 weekends.
Society meetings: welcome weekdays by arrangement.
Catering: meals served except Tues.

O52 **Ullesthorpe**
☎Leire (0455) 209023 or 202361
Frolesworth Rd, Ullesthorpe, Lutterworth, Leics.
B577 off A5 to Claybrooke and Ullesthorpe, follow signs to course.
Meadowland course.
18 holes, 6048 yards, S.S.S.70
Visitors: welcome.
Green fees: £6.50 weekdays; £8.50 weekends.
Society meetings: welcome, details on application.
Catering: bar snacks and restaurant.
Hotels: Island, Watling St; Denbigh Arms, Lutterworth.

O53 **Western Park**
☎Leicester (0533) 872339
Scudamore Rd, Braunstone Frith, Leicester LE3 1UQ.
Off A47, 2 miles W of city centre.
Parkland course.
18 holes.
Course designed by F.W. Hawtree.
Club founded in c1900.
Visitors: welcome.
Green fees: £2.60 weekdays; £3.70 weekends. Book at weekends.
Society meetings: welcome.
Catering: 7 days a week.
Hotels: Post House.

O54 **Willesley Park**
☎Ashby-de-la-Zouch (0530) 414596.
Tamworth Rd, Ashby-de-la-Zouch, Leics LE6 5PF.
On A453, approx 1.5 miles from centre of Ashby-de-la-Zouch S towards Tamworth.
Undulating parkland/heathland course.
18 holes, 6310 yards, S.S.S.70
Course designed by C.K. Cotton.
Club founded in 1921.
Visitors: with reservation, must be bona fide members of another club.
Green fees: to be revised.
Society meetings: Wed, Thurs, Fri (April- Sept).
Catering: full facilities.
Hotels: Royal.

O55 **Woollaton Park**
☎Nottingham (0602) 787574
Woollaton Park, Nottingham
NG8 1BT.
Parkland course.
18 holes, 6494 yards, S.S.S.71
Course designed by T. Williamson.
Club founded in 1927.
Visitors: welcome weekdays.
Green fees: £8.60 per round, £12 per day weekdays.
Society meetings: Tues and Fri.
Catering: daily except Mon.
Hotels: variety in Nottingham.

O56 **Woodhall Spa**
☎Woodhall Spa (0526) 52511
The Broadway, Woodhall Spa, Lincs
LN10 6PU.

On B1191, 6 miles SW of Horncastle, 18 miles SE of Lincoln, 18 miles NE of Sleaford.
Heathland course.
18 holes, 6866 yards, S.S.S.73
Course designed by Col S.V. Hotchkin.
Club founded in 1905.
Visitors: welcome all week by prior arrangement with Sec.
Green fees: £11 per round, £15 per day weekdays; £13 per round, £17 per day weekends and Bank Holidays.
Society meetings: welcome all week by prior arrangement with Sec.
Catering: full facilities 7 days a week.
Hotels: Golf; Petwood; Dower House.

O57 **Worksop**
☎Worksop (0909) 477731 or 477732
Windmill Lane, Worksop, Notts
S80 2SQ.
On S of town, from town centre approach via Lowtown St and Netherton Rd, course is adjacent to Worksop College.
Sandy heathland course.
18 holes, 6651 yards, S.S.S.72
Club founded in 1904.
Visitors: welcome, telephone first.
Green fees: £11 per round/day weekdays; £13 per round weekends and Bank Holidays.
Society meetings: by arrangement.
Catering: full, with notice.
Hotels: Van Dyk; Olde Bull; Regency.

P Merseyside

P1 Allerton Municipal
☎051-428 1046
Allerton, Liverpool L18.
From city centre on Allerton Rd.
Undulating parkland course.
9 holes, 1845 yards, S.S.S.34
18 holes, 5494 yards, S.S.S.67
Visitors: welcome.
Green fees: (9 holes) £1.60 adult,

80p Juniors/OAPs; (18 holes) £2.20
adult, £1.10 Juniors/OAPs.
Catering: snacks served.
Hotels: in Liverpool.

P2 Arrowe Park
☎051-677 1527
Arrowe Park, Woodchurch,
Birkenhead, Merseyside.

3 miles from town centre, take
Borough Rd, Woodchurch Rd and
then opposite Landicon Cemetery.
Public parkland course.
18 holes, 6377 yards, S.S.S.70
Club founded in 1932.
Visitors: welcome, telephone first for
state of tee.
Green fees: £2.80.

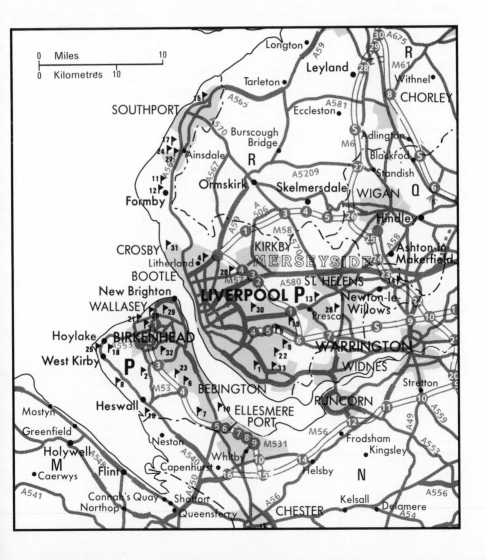

Society meetings: arrange with Pro.
Catering: no facilities.

P3 **Bidston**
☎051-638 3412
Scoresby Rd, Leasowe, Wirral,
Merseyside L46 1QQ.
A551 from Wallasey, 0.75 mile.
Parkland course.
18 holes, 6207 yards, S.S.S.70
Club founded in 1913.
Visitors: welcome weekdays.
Green fees: £6.
Society meetings: weekdays only.
Catering: full facilities.
Hotels: Leasowe Castle.

P4 **Bootle**
☎051-928 6196
Dunnings Bridge Rd, Bootle,
Merseyside L30 2PP.
A565, 5 miles from Liverpool.
Seaside/links course.
18 holes, 6362 yards, S.S.S.70
Course designed by F. Stephens.
Club founded in 1934.
Visitors: welcome.
Green fees: £2.30 weekdays; £3.40
weekends
Society meetings: by arrangement.
Catering: meals served.
Hotels: Park, Netherton.

P5 **Bowring**
☎051-489 1901
Bowring Park, Roby Rd, Huyton,
Liverpool L36 4HD.
4.5 miles from city centre.
Parkland course.
9 holes, 2500 yards, S.S.S.66
Club founded in c.1911.
Visitors: welcome.
Green fees: £2.20; £1.10 juniors and
OAP's.
Hotels: Edenhurst (adjacent).

P6 **Brackenwood**
☎051-608 3093
Bracken Lane, Bebington, Wirral,
Merseyside.
Off M56 at Junction 4, signposted.
Parkland course.
18 holes, 6285 yards, S.S.S.70
Club founded in 1885.
Visitors: welcome.
Green fees: £2.80.
Society meetings: by arrangement.
Catering: pending.
Hotels: in area.

P7 **Bromborough**
☎051-334 2155, 334 4499 Pro.
Raby Hall Rd, Bromborough, Wirral,

Merseyside L63 0NW.
0.5 mile from Bromborough station,
0.75 mile from A41 Birkenhead-
Chester road. Parkland course.
18 holes, 6650 yards, S.S.S.73
Club founded in 1904.
Visitors: welcome weekdays;
advisable to book at weekends.
Green fees: £11, (£6 with member)
weekdays; £14, (£6 with member)
weekends and Bank Holidays.
Society meetings: catered for Wed,
early booking essential.
Catering: snacks available every
day and lunch except Sun, meals by
arrangement.
Hotels: Dibbinsdale, Bromborough;
Thornton Hall, Wirral.

P8 **Caldy**
☎051-625 5660
Links Hey Rd, Caldy, Wirral,
Merseyside, L48 1NB.
A540 from Chester turn left at Caldy
crossroads.
Seaside/parkland course.
18 holes, 6665 yards, S.S.S.73
Course designed by James Braid.
Club founded in 1907.
Visitors: casual welcome weekdays,
(Tues Ladies Day); not weekends
without member.
Green fees: 1987 £12.50 per day;
£10 after 2pm (£5 with member).
Society meetings: Thurs is main
day; not Wed.
Catering: lunch facilities, dinner by
arrangement.
Hotels: Parkgate; Ship Inn; Green
Lodge.

P9 **Childwall**
☎051-487 0654
Naylor's Rd, Liverpool, Merseyside
L27 2YB.
Junction of M57 and M62, 2 miles on
A5080 Huyton exit.
Parkland course.
18 holes, 6425 yards, S.S.S.71
Course designed by James Braid.
Club founded in 1912.
Visitors: weekdays only (except
Tues).
Green fees: £8.50 per day.
Society meetings: most welcome
20 and over, green fees £7.50 per
day.
Catering: lunch and evening meals.
Hotels: in Liverpool.

P10 **Eastham Lodge**
☎051-327 3003 Sec, 3008 Pro.
117 Ferry Rd, Eastham, Wirral
L62 0AP.

Off A41 to Eastham Country Park,
6 miles from Birkenhead.
Parkland course.
15 holes, 6444 yards, S.S.S.68
Course designed by Hawtree & Sons.
Club founded in 1975.
Visitors: welcome on weekdays.
Green fees: £6.50 per day/round,
(£3.25 with member).
Society meetings: Thurs only.
Catering: bar snacks or full meal
pre-ordered.
Hotels: Dresden; Mercury.

P11 **Formby**
☎Formby (07048)72164
Golf Rd, Formby, Liverpool L37 1LQ.
6 miles S of Southport off A565.
Links course.
18 holes, 6871 yards, S.S.S.74
Club founded in 1884.
Visitors: welcome weekdays,
advance reservation advisable.
Green fees: £21 weekdays; £24
weekends and Bank Holidays.
Society meetings: Tues, Thurs, Fri.
Catering: lunch served except Mon.
Hotels: Tree Tops, Formby.

P12 **Formby Ladies**
☎Formby (070 48) 73493 Sec,
74127 Club.
Golf Rd, Formby, Liverpool L37 1LQ.
6 miles S of Southport off A565.
Seaside course.
18 holes, 5374 yards, S.S.S.71
Club founded in 1896.
Visitors: welcome, advisable to ring
first.
Green fees: £12 weekends; £15
weekends.
Society meetings: by arrangement.
Catering: bar snacks and salads.
Hotels: Prince of Wales; Royal
Clifton; Scarisbrick; Bold, Southport.

P13 **Grange Park**
☎St Helens (0744) 26318
Prescot Rd, St Helens, Merseyside
WA10 3AD.
On A58 1 mile from town centre
towards Prescot.
Parkland course.
18 holes, 6429 yards, S.S.S.71
Club founded in 1891.
Visitors: welcome weekdays (Ladies
day Tues) by arrangement
weekends.
Green fees: £9.50 weekdays; £12
weekends.
Society meetings: Mon, Wed,
Thurs, Fri.
Catering: full restaurant facilities.
Hotels: Fleece, St Helens.

GolfCentres Limited

17 Market Place, Oundle, Nr Peterborough PE8 4BA

We provide comprehensive facilities for the enjoyment of golf in excellent locations. Golf societies and company golf clubs especially welcome. Beginners and advanced tuition. Attractive golf courses of a good standard with modern clubhouse facilities.

LONDON AREA

CRAY VALLEY GOLF CLUB
Sandy Lane, St Paul's Cray, Kent
Tel: 0689 39677
18 hole and 9 hole courses

CROYDON GOLF CENTRE
175 Long Lane, Addiscombe, Croydon
Tel: 01 656 8396
golf range, 24 bays

FINCHLEY GOLF CENTRE
444 High Road, Finchley
Tel: 01 445 9677
golf range, 24 bays, shortly to be developed as a 32 bay indoor golf dome

LOUGHTON GOLF CLUB
Clays Lane, Debden Green,
Loughton, Essex
Tel: 01 502 2923
*9 hole short course &
12 bay driving range*

MERSEYSIDE

BOOTLE GOLF COURSE
Dunnings Bridge Road, Bootle
Tel: 051 928 1371
18 hole course

**Further particulars on application:
Telephone: 0832 72303**

P14 **Haydock Park**
☎Newton-le-Willows (0952) 4389
Golborne Park, Newton-le-Willows,
Merseyside WA12 oHX.
M6 to A580, then 1 mile E.
Parkland course.
18 holes, 6043 yards, S.S.S.69
Club founded in 1877.
Visitors: welcome weekdays except Tues.
Green fees: £10 per day/round.
Society meetings: weekdays except Tues.
Catering: as requested.
Hotels: Kirkfield, Church St.

P15 **Hesketh**
☎Southport (0704) 36897 Sec,
30050 Pro.
Cockle Dicks Lane, off Cambridge Rd, Southport, Merseyside PR9 9QQ.
1 mile N of Southport town centre on the main Preston road, A565.
Links course.
Yellow-18 holes, 6160 yards, S.S.S.70
White-18 holes, 6478 yards, S.S.S.72.
Club founded in 1885.

Visitors: welcome weekdays; occasionally weekends; advance booking for societies.
Green fees: £9 per round, £12 per day weekdays; £11 per round, £15 per day weekends.
Society meetings: catered for weekdays.
Catering: bar snacks always available; dining room - prior notice required.
Hotels: Southport is a holiday town with plenty of accommodation.

P16 **Heswall**
☎051-342 1237/7431
Cottage Lane, Gayton Heswall, The Wirral, Merseyside L60 8PB.
Leave M53. At roundabout turn into Well Lane, leads into Cottage Lane.
Meadowland course.
18 holes, 6472 yards, S.S.S.72
Club founded in 1901.
Visitors: welcome anytime - telephone call advisable.
Green fees: £11 per day weekdays; £15 per day weekends and Bank Holidays.
Society meetings: Wed and Fri

only; full catering, minimum 24.
Catering: bar snacks every day, full facilities except Mon.
Hotels: Craxton Wood; Mollington Banastre; Thornton Hall; Woodhey.

P17 **Hillside**
☎Southport (0704) 67169
Hastings Rd, Hillside, Southport PR8 2LU.
Take A565 Southport-Liverpool road, turn right before Hillside railway station, club at end of Hastings Rd.
Parkland links course.
18 holes, 6850 yards, S.S.S.74
Course designed by Fred Hawtree.
Club founded in 1923.
Visitors: by appointment.
Green fees: on application.
Society meetings: by appointment.
Catering: facilities continuous.
Hotels: numerous in Southport.

P18 **Hoylake**
☎051-632 2956/4883
Carr Lane, Hoylake, Merseyside
Off M53, 10 miles SW of Liverpool, follow signs for Hoylake, 100 yards from Hoylake station.
Parkland course.

18 holes, 6330 yards, S.S.S.70
Course designed by James Braid.
Club founded in 1933.
Visitors: unrestricted; telephone for weekends one week in advance; A/C block bookings in operation.
Green fees: £2.80 per round.
Society meetings: unrestricted, telephone Pro.
Catering: hot snacks, meals, bar meals.
Hotels: Stanley; Green Lodge.

P19 **Huyton & Prescot**
☎051-489 3948
Hurst Park, Huyton Lane, Huyton, Liverpool L36 1UA.
Approx 10 miles from Liverpool city centre, just off M57.
Parkland course.
18 holes, 5738 yards, S.S.S.68
Club founded in 1905.
Visitors: must be members of recognised golf clubs.
Green fees: £7.25 per round, £9.50 per day; (with member only weekends).
Society meetings: by arrangement weekdays only.
Catering: every day.
Hotels: Derby Lodge; Hillcrest.

P20 **Kirkby**
☎051-546 5435
Ingoe Lane, Kirkby, Liverpool L32 4SS
M57 exit B5192.
Meadowland course.
18 holes, 6571 yards, S.S.S.71
Club founded in 1967.
Visitors: welcome everyday.
Green fees: £2.20 weekends and weekdays; £1.10 Juniors/OAPs.
Society meetings: tee booking required weekends.
Catering: only at weekends.
Hotels: Golden Eagle, Cherryfield Drive, Liverpool.

P21 **Leasowe**
☎051-677 5852
Leasowe Rd, Moreton, Wirral L46 3RD.
Take Wallasey turn off M53 1 mile after Queensway tunnel, 1 mile W of Wallasey village.
Seaside course.
18 holes, 6204 yards, S.S.S.71
Club founded in 1891.
Visitors: welcome weekdays; weekends by arrangement.
Green fees: £9 weekdays; £12 weekends.
Society meetings: welcome by arrangement.
Catering: restaurant, bar snacks.
Hotels: Leasowe Castle.

P22 **Lee Park**
☎051-487 3882 Sec.
Childwall Valley Rd, Gateacre, Liverpool L27 3YA.
On B5171 off A562, next to Netherley Comprehensive School.
Parkland course.
18 holes, 6024 yards, S.S.S.69
Course designed by Frank Pennink.
Club founded in 1950.
Visitors: weclome with reservation.
Green fees: £7.50 weekdays; £10 weekends; (£3.50 with member).
Society meetings: by arrangement.
Catering: bar snacks served and meals by arrangement.
Hotels: Gateacre Hall, Halewood Rd.

P23 **Prenton**
☎051-608 1053/1461
Golf Links Rd, Prenton, Birkenhead, Wirral L42 8LW.
2 miles W of Birkenhead off A552. Junction 3 off M53.
Flat parkland course.
18 holes, 6411 yards, S.S.S.71
Course designed by Colt Mackenzie & Co.
Club founded in 1905.
Visitors: welcome any day except competition days (Saturday in summer).
Green fees: £10, (£5 with member) weekdays; £15 weekends and Bank Holidays; £30 weekly rate (Mon-Fri).
Society meetings: Wed; small societies Mon and Fri.
Catering: full service available.
Hotels: Leasowe Castle; Riverhill, Oxton; Bowler Hat, Oxton.

P24 **Royal Birkdale**
☎Southport (0604) 67920 Sec, 69903/69928.
Waterloo Rd, Birkdale, Southport, Merseyside PR8 2LX
1.5 miles S of Southport on A565.
Seaside course.
18 holes, 6711 yards, S.S.S.73
Course designed by Hawtree & Taylor.
Club founded in 1889.
Visitors: letter of introduction required from visitor's home club together with confirmation of handicap.
Green fees: Winter: £18 weekdays, £35 weekends. Summer: £25 per day, £35 Sun.

Society meetings: welcome weekdays by arrangement.
Catering: light lunch and afternoon tea served, full lunch and dinner by arrangement.
Hotels: in Southport.

P25 **Royal Liverpool**
☎051-632 3101
Meols Drive, Hoylake, Wirral, Merseyside L47 4AL.
A553 to Hoylake, 10 miles W of Liverpool.
Seaside links course.
18 holes, 6737 yards, S.S.S.74
Club founded in 1869.
Visitors: welcome weekdays and weekends with letter of introduction from club or handicap certificate.
Green fees: £18, (£7 with member) weekdays; £19.50, (£8 with member) weekends.
Society meetings: welcome weekdays.
Catering: bar snacks available every day and lunches on Sun.
Hotels: Green Lodge; Bowler Hat; Craxton Wood.

P26 **Sherdley Park**
☎St Helens (0744) 813149
Elton Head Rd, St Helens, Merseyside.
2 miles from town centre on Warrington Rd.
Undulating parkland course.
18 holes, 5941 yards, S.S.S.69
Course designed by P.R. Parkinson.
Club founded in 1973.
Visitors: welcome.
Green fees: on application.
Society meetings: by arrangement.
Hotels: Fleece.

P27 **Southport & Ainsdale**
☎Southport (0704) 78000
Bradshaws Lane, Ainsdale, Southport, Merseyside PR8 3LG.
3 miles S of Southport on A565, 0.5 mile from Ainsdale railway station.
Championship links course.
18 holes, 6603 yards, S.S.S.73
Course designed by James Braid.
Club founded in 1907.
Visitors: weekdays only, must be members of a golf club, advance booking recommended.
Green fees: £15 per day, £11 per round.
Society meetings: weekdays only, must be members of a golf club, advance booking essential.
Catering: full facilities.
Hotels: Prince of Wales; Scarisbrick.

──── Royal Liverpool ────

There are people who never give a thought for the past, and with golf they miss so much. Where would a club's history be without romantic tales of its origins? When chroniclers come to tell the story of their Clubs, these form the major part of the romance but, for a combination of proud traditions, the challenge of its links and the eminence of its golfing sons, none can stand comparison with Hoylake, home of the Royal Liverpool.

Sadly, there are some who write off Hoylake because of its loss to the Open Championship rota. If, as seems likely, it has gone for good, at least its final act remains a vivid memory. For the heartstrings it tugged and the tears it evoked, there were few championships to match the long-awaited triumph of Roberto de Vicenzo in 1967.

He did what only a handful managed in the 1960s — hold off the challenge of Jack Nicklaus and Gary Player. However, Hoylake's inability to supply vast acres of car parking and a tented village should not rule it out. The practical demands of a modern Open have been too much for many fine courses where the test of strokemaking and the calls on heart and nerve shine as brightly as ever.

Hoylake is undoubtedly the frontrunner. In the last 20 years, it has housed two Amateur championships, one English, and two English strokeplay championships, the last in 1977 won by Sandy Lyle. The English Ladies have played there twice and among professional tournaments staged on a ground which was once a racecourse, was the 1981 European Open. But above all it was the 1983 Walker Cup match which delighted lovers of Hoylake and friends of the Club.

It was the one significant honour that was missing: in 1921, the first men's match between Britain and the United States was held at Hoylake, giving George H Walker the idea of inaugurating a series whose subsequent influence has been nothing but good. In a match sixty-two years after that first unofficial contest, the United States pulled away to victory in the last couple of hours or so. As with so many American teams, the fascination for the observer had been to see the team's reaction to a course totally foreign to them.

At first sight, Hoylake is not imposing. All that appears from a distance is a vast expanse divided up by a series of cops and banks, partly enclosed by roads and houses with the Welsh hills on the horizon. The other jolt to an American's system is the virtual absence of trees but when the individual holes are tackled, the mind is concentrated on a task which remains as testing and refreshing as it did when John Ball and Harold Hilton were performing heroic deeds in the Club's glorious early days.

Few opening holes are as daunting as Hoylake's with its right-angled dogleg following the out-of-bounds of the practice ground. In years gone by, it was possible to go out-of-bounds on something like a dozen holes but, like many famous links, Hoylake has undergone a fair amount of change.

The 3rd and 4th are cases in point. The 3rd is now a par 5 curving left and the 4th a pleasant short hole to a raised, well-guarded target. When J H Taylor mastered a gale to win the 1913 Open, it was fashionable for the holes to be known by their names, the 5th being Telegraph, the 6th being Briars (although it might just as easily have been Orchard) and the 7th known as Dowie.

The old orchard juts into the fairway necessitating a formidable carry in a head or cross wind from the championship tee, even today. The Dowie, perhaps the most controversial hole, is a flat, short hole with an out-of-bounds over the bank to the left, often within a few yards of the hole. The 8th, which cost Bobby Jones 7 in the final round of the 1930 Open, is the second par 5, taking us out to the point furthest from the clubhouse. But the true test of Hoylake is its par 4s.

The 9th, 10th and 12th, following the line of the shore of the Dee estuary, are excellent examples although the Alps (the 11th) is a magnificent one-shotter. It is from this raised tee that the most comprehensive view of the surroundings can be obtained — but Hoylake's sting has always been in the tail.

The 14th and 16th have been lengthened and strengthened to combat modern equipment. They are three-shot holes to all except the mighty although the 15th, a long par 4, can be just as devilish. The 17th (named Royal after the much lamented Royal Hotel which stood on the opposite side of the road from the green) is as good a 17th as you will find. The drive is not too overpowering but it must be well positioned to ensure the second shot is correctly in line for an angled green. A shade too far left and the second shot must be aimed directly at the road; the slightest pull with the second shot and bunkers await.

The 18th is not the hardest of finishing holes but let the last word belong to Tom Simpson, the celebrated golf course architect. In conversation with Henry Longhurst, he remarked 'No golf course can be truly great without out-of-bounds'. Longhurst remarked 'I take it then you regard Hoylake as the best in England'; 'Without any doubt' came Simpson's reply.

P28 **Wallasey**
☎051-691 1024
Bayswater Rd, Wallasey, Merseyside L45 8LA.
Via M53 through Wirral or 15 minutes from Liverpool centre via Wallasey Tunnel.
Seaside course.
18 holes, 6607 yards, S.S.S.73
Course designed by Tom Morris Snr.
Club founded in 1891.
Visitors: welcome weekdays, limited weekends.
Green fees: £11, (£5 with member) weekdays; £13, (£6 with member) weekends and Bank Holidays.
Society meetings: catered for Weekdays.
Catering: every day except Mon evening meals for societies by arrangement.
Hotels: Leasowe Castle; Belvedere.

P29 **Warren**
☎051 639 5730
The Grange, Grove Rd, Wallasey, Merseyside.
500 yards up Grove Rd, beyond Grove Rd station.
Municipal links course.
9 holes, 2700 yards, S.S.S.34(68)
Club founded in 1911.
Visitors: welcome weekdays, telephone first at weekends.
Green fees: £2.70 per (18 holes);

£1.35 per (9 holes).
Catering: lunch and tea in cafe in clubhouse.
Hotels: Grove House.

P30 **West Derby**
☎051-254 1034 Sec, 220 5478 Pro.
Yew Tree Lane, Liverpool L12 9HQ.
4 miles E of Liverpool centre, 1 mile S of West Derby village.
Parkland course.
18 holes, 6333 yards, S.S.S.70
Club founded in 1896.
Visitors: welcome Mon-Fri.
Green fees: £9.
Society meetings: by arrangement.
Catering: facilities.
Hotels: Derby Lodge.

P31 **West Lancashire**
☎051-924 1076
Hall Rd West, Blundellsands, Liverpool L23 8SZ.
M57 to Aintree, A567 to Seaforth, then A565 to Crosby, follow signs to club, by Hall Rd station.
Seaside links course.
18 holes, 6756 yards, S.S.S.73
Course designed by C.K. Cotton.
Club founded in 1873.
Visitors: welcome except competition days.
Green fees: £13 weekdays; £16 weekends.
Society meetings: Wed, Thurs, Fri.

Catering: lunch Tues-Sun, other by arrangement.
Hotels: Blundellsands.

P32 **Wirral Ladies**
☎051-652 1255, 652 1255 Sec
93 Budston Rd, Oxton, Birkenhead, Merseyside L43 6TS.
On A41 adjacent to M53 Exit 3.
Moorland course.
18 holes, 4539 yards, S.S.S.70
Course designed by H. Hilton.
Club founded in 1894.
Visitors: welcome anytime.
Green fees: £8 per round.
Society meetings: apply to Sec.
Catering: meals served at all times.
Hotels: Bowler Hat, River Hill.

P33 **Woolton**
☎051-486 2298
Doe Park, Speke Rd, Woolton, Liverpool L25 7TZ.
6 miles from City Centre.
Parkland course.
18 holes, 5706 yards, S.S.S.68
Club founded in 1901.
Visitors: welcome.
Green fees: £8.50 weekdays; £13 weekends.
Society meetings: catered for weekdays, not Tues.
Catering: by arrangement.
Hotels: in Liverpool.

Q Greater Manchester

Q1 Acre Gate
☎061-748 1226
Pennybridge Lane, Flixton,
Manchester.
From Urmston take Flixton Rd, then
left at Bird in Hand public house.
Parkland course.
Club founded in 1974.
Visitors: municipal open to public.
Green fees: £2.75 weekdays; £3.60
weekends.
Society meetings: welcome.
Catering: weekends only. Summer
88 catering daily.
Hotels: many in area.

Q2 Altrincham
☎061-928 0761
Stockport Rd, Timperley, Altrincham,
Cheshire WA15.
On A560 1 mile E of Altrincham.
Undulating parkland course.
18 holes, 6162 yards, S.S.S.69
Club founded in 1935.
Visitors: welcome at all times in
week, advance bookings at
weekends.
Green fees: £2.75 weekdays; £3.75
weekends.
Society meetings: none.
Catering: no facilities at club,
Beefeater restaurant next door.
Hotels: Cresta Court; Woodlands
Park, Altrincham.

Q3 Ashton-in-Makerfield
☎Ashton-in-Makerfield (0942)
724229
Garswood Park, Liverpool Rd,
Ashton-in-Makerfield WN4 9LL.
On A58, off M6 0.5 mile to course.
Parkland course.
18 holes, 6160 yards, S.S.S.69
Course designed by F.W. Hawtree.
Club founded in 1902.
Visitors: welcome weekdays except
Wed, and with member at weekends.
Green fees: on application.
Society meetings: catered for on
Tues.
Catering: meals available except
Mon.
Hotels: Trust House Forte;
Cranberry.

Q4 Ashton on Mersey
☎061-973 3220
Church Lane, Sale, Cheshire

M33 5QQ.
2 miles from Sale station.
Parkland course.
9 holes, 6202 yards, S.S.S.70
Club founded in 1897.
Visitors: welcome, except Tues after
3pm (Ladies Day).
Green fees: on application.
Society meetings: by arrangement.
Catering: snacks and lunches.
Hotels: Cresta Court.

Q5 Ashton-under-Lyne
☎061-330 1537
Gorsey Way, Ashton-under-Lyne,
Greater Manchester.
From Ashton take Mossley Rd, left at
Queens Rd and right at Kings Rd.
Moorland course.
18 holes, 6209 yards, S.S.S.70
Club founded in 1913.
Visitors: Sat and Sun only with
member.
Green fees: £10.
Society meetings: by arrangement,
not Wed or weekends.
Catering: full facilities except Mon.
Hotels: York House, Ashton; Birch
Hall, Oldham.

Q6 Blackley
☎061-643 2980
Victoria Ave East, Blackley,
Manchester M9 2HW.
Parkland course.
18 holes, 6237 yards, S.S.S.70
Club founded in 1907.
Visitors: Mon-Fri; weekends and
Bank Holidays with member only.
Green fees: £8 per day.
Society meetings: Mon, Tues, Wed
and Fri, special all in fee including
light lunch and evening meal £12.
Catering: all types available.
Hotels: numerous in Manchester.

Q7 Bolton
☎Bolton (0204) 43067
Lostock Park, Chorley New Rd,
Bolton BL6 4AJ.
Leave M61 at Exit 6, off main road
halfway between Bolton and
Horwich.
Parkland course.
18 holes, 6215 yards, S.S.S.70
Club founded in 1912.
Visitors: welcome any day.
Green fees: £10 Mon, Tues, Thurs,
Fri; £12 Wed, Sat, Sun, Bank

Holidays.
Society meetings: Thurs and Fri.
Catering: all day.
Hotels: Crest, Beaumont Rd, Bolton.

Q8 Brackley
☎061-790 6076
Bullows Rd, Little Hulton, Worsley,
Manchester.
9 miles from Manchester on A6, turn
right at White Lion Hotel into
Highfield Rd, left into Captain Fold
Rd, left into Bullows Rd.
Parkland course.
9 holes, 3003 yards, S.S.S.69
Club founded in 1976.
Visitors: welcome.
Green fees: £8 per day.
Hotels: Crest, Bolton; Wendover,
Morton.

Q9 Bramhall Park
☎061-485 3119
20 Manor Rd, off Carr Wood Rd,
Bramhall, Stockport SK7 3LY.
8 miles S of Manchester, A6 to
Bramhall Lane, then A5102 to Carr
Wood Rd.
Parkland course.
18 holes, 6214 yards, S.S.S.70
Club founded in 1894.
Visitors: not Fri (no catering).
Green fees: £9 weekdays; £11
weekends.
Society meetings: Tues for up to 70
players; Thurs small parties up to 25.
Catering: full except Fri.
Hotels: Raven, Cheadle Hulme;
Alma Lodge, Buxton Rd.

Q10 Bramhall
☎061-439 4057 or 6092 Sec.
Ladythorn Rd, Bramhall, Stockport,
Cheshire SK7 2EY.
Near Bramhall station, 8 miles S of
Manchester on A5102.
Meadowland course.
18 holes, 6293 yards, S.S.S.70
Club founded in 1905.
Visitors: welcome, subject to
members competitions.
Green fees: £10 weekdays; £12
weekends and Public Holidays.
Society meetings: catered for on
Wed.
Catering: à la carte menu and bar
snacks.
Hotels: Moat House, Bramhall.

Q11 Breightmet

☎Bolton (0204) 27381
Red Bridge, Ainsworth, Bolton, Lancs.
From Bolton 3 miles on main road to Bury and turn left to Red Bridge.
Parkland course.
9 holes, 6448 yards, S.S.S.71
Course designed by Alliss & Thomas.
Club founded in 1912.
Visitors: welcome weekdays except Wed.
Green fees: £6, (£3 with member) weekdays; £8, (£4 with member) weekends and Bank Holidays.
Society meetings: welcome Tues, Thurs, Fri.
Catering: each day except Mon.
Hotels: Pack Horse, Bolton.

Q12 Brookdale

☎061-681 4534/2655
"Ashbridge", Woodhouses, Failsworth, Manchester M35 9WM.
5 miles NE of Manchester.
Parkland, meadowland course.
18 holes, 6040 yards, S.S.S.68
Club founded in 1962.
Visitors: welcome.
Green fees: £5.50, (£4.50 with member) weekdays; £7.50, (£5.50 with member) weekends.
Society meetings: welcome by prior arrangement with Sec. Special package can be arranged.
Catering: available daily except Mon.
Hotels: The Belgrade, Oldham; The Bower, Chadderton, Oldham.

Q13 Bury

☎061-766 4897
Unsworth Hall, Blackford Bridge, Bury BL9 9TJ.
On A56 7 miles N of Manchester.
Undulating moorland course.
18 holes, 5953 yards, S.S.S.69
Club founded in 1889.
Visitors: welcome with reservation.
Green fees: £7.50 weekdays.
Society meetings: catered for Wed, Thurs and Fri.
Catering: daily except Mon.
Hotels: Woolfield; Hazeldine; White Lion, Bury.

Q14 Castle Hawk

☎Rochdale (0706) 40841
Heywood Rd, Castleton, Rochdale.
Leave Rochdale on Castleton road, in Castleton turn right directly before railway station, follow until reach Heywood Rd (dirt track).

Undulating parkland/meadowland course.
18 holes, 3158 yards, S.S.S.65
Course designed by T. Wilson.
Club founded in 1965.
Visitors: welcome.
Green fees: on application.
Society meetings: welcome.
Catering: snacks and lunch available; evening meals by arrangement.
Hotels: Norton Grange, Castleton.

Q15 Cheadle

☎061-428 2160
Shiers Drive, Cheadle, Cheshire SK8 1HW.
1 mile S of Cheadle village, 1 mile N of Cheadle Hulme railway station.
Undulating parkland course.
9 holes, 5006 yards, S.S.S.65
Course designed by R. Renouf.
Club founded in 1885.
Visitors: must be members of golf club and hold official handicap. Not Tues or Sat.
Green fees: £8, (£4 with member) weekdays; £10 per day Sun and Bank Holidays.
Society meetings: by arrangement with Sec.
Catering: lunchtime catered daily except Thurs, at other time by arrangement with Stewardess.
Hotels: Alma Lodge, Stockport.

Q16 Chorlton cum Hardy

☎061-881 3139, 881 5830 Sec, 881 9911 Pro.
Barlow Hall Rd, Chorlton, Manchester M21 2JJ.
3 miles from city centre, on A5103, near Southern Cemetery.
Meadowland course.
18 holes, 6004 yards, S.S.S.69
Club founded in 1903.
Visitors: telephone Pro.
Green fees: £12.
Society meetings: Thurs.
Catering: sandwiches only Mon, bar snacks, evening meals as ordered other days.
Hotels: Longford Park, Chorlton; Trust House; Post House; Northenden.

Q17 Crompton & Royton

☎061-642 2154
Highbarn, Royton, Oldham, Lancs Ol2 6RW.
Off A627 at Royton centre.
Moorland course.
18 holes, 6187 yards.
Club founded in c.1936.

Visitors: welcome.
Green fees: £7, (£4 with member) weekdays; £8, (£6 with member) weekends.
Society meetings: welcome by arrangement.
Hotels: Belgrade, Oldham.

Q18 Davyhulme Park

☎061-748 2260 Sec, 748 2856 Club.
Gleneagles Rd, Davyhulme, Urmston, Manchester M31 2SA.
8 miles S of Manchester, adjacent to Park Hospital, Moorside Rd.
Parkland course.
18 holes, 6237 yards, S.S.S.70
Club founded in 1910.
Visitors: welcome except competition days.
Green fees: £8 weekdays; £10 weekends and Bank Holidays.
Society meetings: Tues, Thurs, Fri catered for by arrangement.
Catering: except Mon.
Hotels: numerous in Manchester.

Q19 Denton

☎051-336 3218
Manchester Rd, Denton, Manchester M34 2NU.
A57, 5 miles SE of Manchester.
Parkland course.
18 holes, 6290 yards, S.S.S.70
Club founded in May 1909.
Visitors: welcome weekdays and at weekends with member.
Green fees: on application.
Society meetings: catered for Mon, Wed, Thurs and Fri.
Catering: lunch served except Mon.
Hotels: Old Rectory, Haughton Green, Denton, Manchester.

Q20 Didsbury

☎061-998 9278 Sec, 998 2811 Pro.
Ford Lane, Northenden, Manchester M22 4NQ.
Off M63 at Junction 9, near Northenden Church, club sign on wall.
Parkland course.
18 holes, 6273 yards, S.S.S.70
Club founded in 1891.
Visitors: (Ladies day Tues); not weekends unless by arrangement.
Green fees: £10, (£5 with member) weekdays; £12, (£6 with member) weekends.
Society meetings: Thurs and Fri.
Catering: restaurant and snacks.
Hotels: Post House, Northenden; Britannia, Northenden.

Q21 Disley

☎Disley (0633) 62071
Stanley Hall Rd, Jackson's Edge,
Disley, Stockport, Cheshire
SK12 2JX.
A6, 6 miles South from Stockport.
Moorland, meadowland course.
18 holes, 6015 yards, S.S.S.69
Course designed by James Braid.
Club founded in 1889.
Visitors: welcome Mon-Fri without
member except Bank Holidays.
Green fees: £7 per round.
Society meetings: private
arrangement with Secretary.
Catering: any day except Monday.
Hotels: Moorside, Stockport.

Q22 Dunham Forest G & CC

☎061-928 2605
Oldfield Lane, Altrincham, Cheshire
WA14 4TY
2 miles N of Junction 7, off M56,
proceed in direction of Manchester,
golf course is on left of main road.
Parkland course.
18 holes, 6800 yards, S.S.S.72
Club founded in 1961.
Visitors: welcome.
Green fees: £11.50.
Society meetings: weekdays except
Thurs.
Catering: meals served except Mon.
Hotels: Moorside.

Q23 Dunscar

☎Bolton (0204) 51090
Longworth Lane, Bromley Cross,
Bolton BL7 9QY.
N of Bolton about 2 miles off A666
Blackburn road, golf course signed to
left at Dunscar Bridge.
Parkland/moorland course.
18 holes, 5957 yards, S.S.S.70
Club founded in 1908.
Visitors: welcome, stewards day off
Mon; weekends by special
arrangement.
Green fees: £7, (£3 with member)
weekdays; £8.50, (£4 with member)
weekends.
Society meetings: welcome, details
from Secretary.
Catering: lunch, dinner except Mon.
Hotels: Last Drop; Egerton House,
Egerton.

Q24 Fairfield G & Sailing C.

☎061-370 1641, 2292 Pro.
Booth Rd, Audenshaw, Manchester
M34 5GA.
A635 6 miles from city centre.
Meadowland course.
18 holes, 5654 yards, S.S.S.68

Club founded in 1892.
Visitors: welcome weekdays, with
reservation at weekends, club
competitions Wed afternoon, Thurs
and weekends mornings.
Green fees: on application.
Society meetings: by arrangement,
preferably not Wed and Thurs.
Catering: full facilities available by
arrangement.
Hotels: Trough House.

Q25 Gathurst

☎Appley Bridge (025 75) 2861.
Miles Lane, Shevington, Wigan
WN6 8EW.
1 mile S of Junction 27 on M6.
Meadowland course.
9 holes, as 18 holes 6308 yards,
S.S.S.70
Club founded in 1913.
Visitors: welcome Mon, Tues, Thurs
and Fri.
Green fees: £6.90 per day.
Society meetings: by arrangement.
Catering: lunch except Mon and
Tues.
Hotels: Lindley, Parbold; The
Beeches, Standish.

Q26 Gatley

☎061-437 2091 or 436 2830 Pro.
Waterfall Farm, off Styal Rd, Heald
Green, Cheadle, Ches SK8 3TW.
Off Yew Tree Grove and Styal Rd 2
miles from Cheadle, 1 mile from
Manchester Airport.
Parkland course.
9 holes, 5934 yards, S.S.S.68
Club founded in 1912.
Visitors: welcome weekdays except
Tues.
Green fees: on application.
Society meetings: welcome by
arrangement with Sec on weekdays
only.
Catering: full facilities; societies
should book in advance.
Hotels: Excelsior, Manchester
Airport; Post House, Northenden;
Belfry, Hanforth.

Q27 Great Lever & Farnworth

☎Bolton (0204) 651637
Lever Edge Lane, Bolton BL3 3EN.
1.5 miles from town centre.
Meadowland course.
18 holes, 5958 yards, S.S.S.69
Club founded in 1917.
Visitors: welcome weekdays.
Green fees: £4.50, (£3.50 with
member) weekdays; £6.50, (£5.50
with member) weekends and Bank

Holidays.
Society meetings: catered for
weekdays by prior arrangement.
Catering: lunch served except Mon.
Hotels: Crest, Bolton.

Q28 Haigh Hall

☎Wigan (0942) 831107
Haigh Country Park, Haigh, Wigan.
Off B5238 or B5239, 6 miles NE of
Wigan.
Parkland municipal course.
18 holes, 6400 yards, S.S.S.71
Club founded in 1973.
Visitors: welcome anytime;
telephone first for tee off time.
Green fees: £2.50 weekdays; £3.25
weekends.
Society meetings: none.
Catering: cafe run by Wigan Metro.
Hotels: Brockett Arms.

Q29 Hale

☎061-980 4225
Rappax Rd, Hale, Altrincham,
Cheshire WA15 0NU.
2 miles SE of Altrincham.
Undulating parkland course.
9 holes, 5780 yards, S.S.S.68
Club founded in 1903.
Visitors: weekdays except Thurs;
weekends and Public Holidays only
with member.
Green fees: weekdays without
member £10.
Society meetings: by arrangement
with Hon Sec.
Catering: lunch daily by arrange-
ment with Steward except Tues and
Thurs.
Hotels: Bowdon; Ashley.

Q30 Heaton Moor

☎061-432 2134
Heaton Mersey, Stockport, Cheshire
SK4 3NX.
2 miles from Stockport.
Parkland course.
18 holes, 5876 yards, S.S.S.68
Visitors: welcome except Tues and
Wed.
Green fees: £7.50, (£3.75 with
member), £2.50 after 5pm week-
days; £9, (£4 with member)
weekends.
Society meetings: by arrangement.
Catering: meals served except Mon.
Hotels: many in area.

Q31 Heaton Park

☎061-798 0295
Prestwich, Manchester.
Leave M62 at Exit 19, right at A576,
200 yards on right.

Undulating parkland course.
18 holes, 5849 yards, S.S.S.68
Course designed by C.H. Taylor.
Club founded in 1912.
Visitors: welcome, but book in
advance.
Green fees: £3.50 per round
weekdays; £5 per round weekends.
Society meetings: by arrangement.
Catering: none available.
Hotels: numerous in area.

Q32 Hindley Hall
☎Wigan (0942) 55131/55991 Pro
Hall Lane, Hindley, Wigan, Lancs
WN2 2SQ.
Junction 6, off M61, onto A6, take
Dicconson Lane, then after 1 mile,
left at church into Hall Lane, club just
after lake.
Moorland course.
18 holes, 5875 yards, S.S.S.68
Club founded in 1895.
Visitors: welcome if member of
recognised club, advisable to check
with Pro in advance.
Green fees: on application.
Society meetings: by arrangement.
Catering: meals served by
arrangement except Mon.
Hotels: Brockett Arms, Wigan.

Q33 Horwich
☎Horwich (0204) 696980
Victoria Rd, Horwich, Bolton, Greater
Manchester.
1.5 miles from M61.
Parkland course.
9 holes, 2900 yards, S.S.S.67
Club founded in 1895.
Visitors: welcome with member
only.
Green fees: on application.
Society meetings: catered for
weekdays only by application.
Catering: bar snacks only available.
Hotels: Crest, Bolton.

Q34 Houldsworth
☎061-224 5055
Wingate House, Higher Levens-
hulme, Manchester M19 3JW.
M63 to Stockport finishing point, turn
left onto A6 main Stockport-
Manchester road, right at lights at
Barlow Rd.
Parkland course.
18 holes, 6078 yards, S.S.S.69
Course designed by T.G. Renouf.
Club founded in 1911.
Visitors: welcome weekdays (Ladies
Day Tues 1.30-3.30pm).
Green fees: £6-£8 inclusive of VAT

weekends and holidays (half price
with member).
Society meetings: welcome but
advance booking only.
Catering: full facilities. Requirements provided prior notice for large
parties is given.
Hotels: numerous in Manchester.

Q35 Lobden
☎Rochdale (0706) 343228
Lobden Moor, Whitworth, Rochdale.
A671 4 miles from Rochdale, 0.5
mile from centre of village.
Moorland course.
9 holes, 5750 yards, S.S.S.68
Club founded in 1888.
Visitors: welcome weekdays and
Sun.
Green fees: on application.
Society meetings: none.
Catering: by arrangement with
Stewardess.
Hotels: hotels in area.

Q36 Lowes Park
☎061-764 1231
Hill Top, Walmersley, Bury, Lancs.
Take A56 Walmersley Road from
Bury centre, after about 1.5 miles
turn right past Bury General Hospital

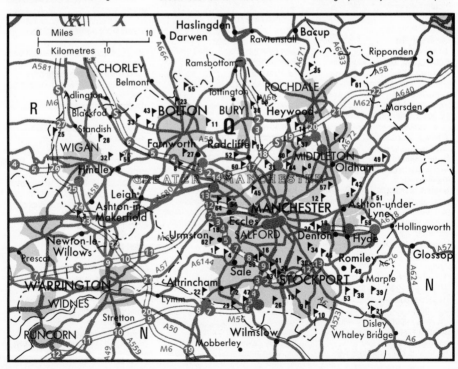

into Lowes Rd. follow road until course signposted.
Moorland course.
9 holes, 6035 yards, S.S.S.69
Club founded in 1930.
Visitors: welcome weekdays, except Wed (Ladies Day) and by invitation on Sun.
Green fees: £5 weekdays; £4 weekends (by invitation).
Society meetings: welcome Mon, Tues or Thurs.
Catering: full facilities except Mon.
Hotels: Woolfield House, Wash Lane.

Q37 Manchester
☎061-643 3202
Hopwood Cottage, Rochdale Rd, Middleton, Manchester M24 2QP.
7 miles N of city on A664, 2 miles from exits 19 and 20, off M62.
Undulating moorland course.
18 holes, 6540 yards, S.S.S.72
Course designed by J.H. Taylor.
Club founded in 1882.
Visitors: welcome weekdays.
Green fees: £10 per day.
Society meetings: welcome weekdays.
Catering: full facilities available.
Hotels: Normandy, Norton Grange, Midway.

Q38 Marple
☎061-427 2311
Hawk Green, Marple, Stockport, Cheshire SK6 7EL.
Off A6 at High Lane for 2 miles, left at Hawk Green.
Parkland/meadowland course.
18 holes, 5700 yards, S.S.S.67
Club founded in 1892.
Visitors: welcome, not competition days.
Green fees: £7.50 weekdays; £9.50 weekends; (reduction if playing with member).
Society meetings: Tues and Wed only. Special package to societies 12 or more, £12.50 green fee, lunch and evening meal.
Catering: full facilities.
Hotels: West Towers, Church Lane, Marple.

Q39 Mellor & Townscliffe
☎061-427 2208
Tarden, Gibb Lane, Mellor, Stockport Cheshire.
Off A626 opposite Devonshire Arms on Longhurst Lane, Mellor.
Parkland/moorland course.
18 holes, 5925 yards, S.S.S.69

Club founded in 1894.
Visitors: welcome, except Sat with member only.
Green fees: £7, (£3.50 with member) weekdays; £9, (£4.50 with member) weekends and Bank Holidays.
Society meetings: welcome except Sat by arrangement.
Catering: full facilities, except Tues.
Hotels: West Towers, Marple.

Q40 New North Manchester
☎061-643 9033 Sec, 2941 Club, 7094 Pro.
Rhodes House, Manchester Old Rd, Middleton, Manchester M24 4PE.
5 miles N of Manchester, exit 18 off M62.
Moorland/parkland course.
18 holes, 6527 yards, S.S.S.72
Club founded in 1894.
Visitors: welcome weekdays and by arrangement at weekends.
Green fees: on application.
Society meetings: welcome weekdays.
Catering: full service except Tues.
Hotels: Bower, Hollinwood Ave, Chadderton, Oldham; Birch, Manchester Rd, Heywood.

Q41 Northenden
☎061-998 4738 Sec, 998 2934 Steward and Members, 998 4079/945 3386 Pro.
Palatine Rd, Northenden, Manchester M22 4FZ.
Exit 9 off M63, 1 mile into Northenden
Parkland course.
18 holes, 6435 yards, S.S.S.71
Club founded in 1914.
Visitors: by arrangement except Sat.
Green fees: £9, (£4.50 with member) weekdays; £12, (£5.50 with member) weekends.
Society meetings: catered for Tues and Fri.
Catering: snacks every day, lunch and evening meals by arrangement.
Hotels: Trust House Forte, Northenden.

Q42 Oldham
☎061-624 4986/626 8346
Lees New Rd, Oldham OL4 5EN.
Just off minor road between Oldham and Ashton-under-Lyne or on A669 turn right at Lees.
Moorland/parkland course.
18 holes, 5045 yards, S.S.S.65
Club registered in 1891.

Visitors: unlimited, but telephone for arrangements on competitions being played.
Green fees: £6 weekends; £7 weekends and Bank Holidays.
Society meetings: by arrangement.
Catering: full facilities.
Hotels: Birch Hall.

Q43 Old Links
☎Bolton (0204) 43089
Chorley Old Rd, Bolton BL1 5SU.
On B6226 just N of A58.
Moorland course.
18 holes, 6406 yards, S.S.S.72
Club founded in 1891.
Visitors: welcome except competition days.
Green fees: £9 weekdays; £12 weekends and Bank Holidays.
Society meetings: by prior arrangement on weekdays.
Catering: daily except Mon.
Hotels: Crest, Beaumont Road; Pack Horse, Bolton.

Q44 Pike Fold
☎061-740 1136
Cooper Lane, Victoria Ave, Blackley, Manchester M9 2QQ.
4 miles N of city centre off Rochdale road.
Undulating meadowland course.
9 holes, 5789 yards, S.S.S.68
Club founded in 1909.
Visitors: welcome weekdays without reservation.
Green fees: £5 per round/day weekdays, (£2.50 with member); £3 per round weekends.
Society meetings: welcome by appointment.
Catering: full facilities available.
Hotels: Piccadilly; Midland.

Q45 Prestwich
☎061-773 4578
Hilton Lane, Prestwich, Manchester M25 8SB.
On A6044 0.25 mile W of junction with A56.
Parkland course.
18 holes, 4712 yards, S.S.S.63
Club founded in 1908.
Visitors: welcome.
Green fees: on application.
Society meetings: welcome except Tues (Ladies Day).
Catering: snacks and meals by arrangement with Steward except Mon.
Hotels: Village Squash, George St, Prestwich; Hazel Dean, Bury New Rd, Kersal, Salford.

Q46 **Reddish Vale**
☎061-480 2359
Southcliffe Rd, Reddish, Stockport,
Cheshire SK5 7EE.
1.5 miles N of Stockport, off Reddish
Rd.
Undulating course in valley.
18 holes, 6086 yards, S.S.S.69
Course designed by Dr A.
Mackenzie.
Club founded in 1912.
Visitors: welcome weekdays (not
12.30-1.30pm) with member only at
weekends.
Green fees: £7.50.
Society meetings: weekdays (very
occasional weekends) by prior
arrangement.
Catering: generally available during
normal bar opening hours.
Hotels: Belgrade, Stockport; Old
Rectory, Haughton Green.

Q47 **Ringway**
☎061-980 2630, 980 4468
Stewardess.
Hale Mount, Hale Barns, Altrincham,
Cheshire WA15 8SW.
8 miles S of Manchester, off M56,
Junction 6, follow signs for Hale,
course is just through Hale Barns
village.
Parkland course.
18 holes, 6494 yards, S.S.S.71
Club founded in 1909.
Visitors: welcome, not Fri.
Green fees: £11.50, (£4.80 with
member) weekdays; £16, (£4.80 with
member) weekends.
Society meetings: catered for Thurs
only from May-Sept.
Catering: full facilities by arrange-
ment with Stewardess.
Hotels: Cresta Court, Altrincham;
Four Seasons, Ringway, Hale.

Q48 **Romiley**
☎061-430 2392
Goosehouse Green, Romiley,
Stockport SK6 4LJ.
On B6101 off A560, 0.75 mile from
Romiley Station.
Undulating parkland course.
18 holes, 6335 yards, S.S.S.70
Club founded in 1897.
Visitors: welcome except Thurs
(Ladies Day).
Green fees: £9; £12 weekends and
Bank Holidays.
Society meetings: by prior
arrangement with Hon Sec.
Catering: full service except Mon.
Hotels: West Towers, Marple;
various in Stockport.

Q49 **Saddleworth**
☎Saddleworth (045 77) 2059/3653
Mountain Ash, Ladcastle Rd,
Uppermill, Oldham.
5 miles from Oldham, signposted off
A670 Ashton to Huddersfield road at
bend where road crosses railway
bridge.
Moorland course.
18 holes, 5976 yards, S.S.S.69
Club founded in 1904.
Visitors: welcome.
Green fees: £7.50 weekdays; £9.50
weekends.
Society meetings: catered for
weekdays.
Catering: facilities daily.
Hotels: Old Bell Inn, Delph, Oldham.

Q50 **Sale**
☎061-973 3404, 1638 Sec.
Sale Lodge, Golf Rd, Sale, Cheshire
M33 2LU.
Boundary of Sale, 1 mile from Sale
station.
Parkland course.
18 holes, 6346 yards, S.S.S.70
Club founded in 1913.
Visitors: welcome any day,
telephone for confirmation.
Green fees: £9 weekdays; £13
weekends and Public Holidays.
Society meetings: by arrangement
with Secretary.
Catering: bar snacks, main meals
every day but Mon. (No service
Mon.)
Hotels: Post House, Wythenshawe
Rd; Normanhurst, Brookland Rd.

Q51 **Stamford**
☎Mossley (045 75) 2126, 4829 Pro.
Oakfield House, Huddersfield Rd,
Heyheads, Stalybridge, Cheshire
SK15 3ET.
On B6175 Huddersfield Rd, 3 miles
from Ashton-under-Lyne.
Undulating moorland course.
18 holes, 5619 yards, S.S.S.67
Club founded in 1900.
Visitors: welcome weekdays (Ladies
Day Tues afternoon).
Green fees: £6, (£3 with member)
weekdays; £10, (£5 with member)
weekends.
Society meetings: catered for
weekdays, except Mon and Tues.
Catering: meals served except Mon.
Hotels: York House, York Place, off
Richmond St, Ashton-under-Lyne.

Q52 **Stand**
☎061-766 2388
The Dales, Ashbourne Grove,

Whitefield, Manchester M25 7NL.
1 mile N of M62, exit 17.
Undulating parkland course.
Course designed by Alex Herd.
Club founded in 1904.
Visitors: welcome weekdays.
Green fees: £8, (£4 with member)
weekdays; £10, (£5 with member)
weekends and Bank Holidays.
Society meetings: catered for
weekdays; Mon, Wed and Fri
preferred.
Catering: lunch/snacks served
except Mon.

Q53 **Stockport**
☎061-427 2001
Offerton Rd, Offerton, Stockport
SK2 5HL.
From Stockport-Marple on A626 then
1 mile on A627 to Hazel Grove.
Parkland course.
18 holes, 6319 yards, S.S.S.71
Club founded in 1908.
Visitors: members of other clubs
welcome.
Green fees: £11 per day weekdays;
£12.50 per day weekends.
Society meetings: Wed and Thurs.
Catering: restaurant (closed Mon).
Hotels: several in area.

Q54 **Swinton Park**
☎061-794 1785
East Lancashire Rd, Swinton,
Manchester M27 1LX.
On A580 Manchester-Liverpool road,
about 4 miles from Manchester.
Parkland course.
18 hole, 6675 yards, S.S.S.72
Course designed by Braid & Taylor.
Club founded in 1926.
Visitors: welcome weekdays only.
Green fees: £9.
Society meetings: by arrangement
Tues.
Catering: bar snacks, meals
available throughout day (excluding
Mon).
Hotels: many small hotels in area
plus large hotels in Manchester.

Q55 **Turton**
☎Bolton (0204) 852235
Wood End Farm, Chapeltown Rd,
Bromley Cross, Bolton, Lancs
BL7 9QH.
3 miles N of Bolton on A676,
adjacent to Last Drop Hotel.
Moorland course.
9 holes, 5805 yards, S.S.S.68
Course designed by James Braid.
Club founded in 1908.
Visitors: welcome except Wed

12.30-4.00pm; Sat, competition days.
Green fees: £6 per day weekdays; £8 per day weekends.
Society meetings: welcome by arrangement.
Catering: resident Steward & Stewardess every day except Mon.
Hotels: Last Drop; Egerton House.

Q56 **Walmersley**
☎061-764 0018
Garretts Close, Walmersley, Bury.
On A56 about 2.5 miles N of Bury.
Moorland course.
9 holes, 3057 yards, S.S.S.70
Club founded in 1906.
Visitors: Wed, Thurs and Fri. Sun with member.
Green fees: £5, (£3 with member).
Society meetings: by arrangement weekdays.
Hotels: Royal Hotel, Bury; Old Mill, Ramsbottom.

Q57 **Werneth (Oldham)**
☎061-624 1190
Green Lane, Garden Suburb, Oldham, Lancs OL8 3AZ.
5 miles from Manchester, take A62 to Hollinwood and then A6104.
Moorland course.
18 holes, 5363 yards, S.S.S.66
Club founded in 1908.
Visitors: welcome weekdays only.
Green fees: £6 weekdays.
Society meetings: catered for weekdays.
Hotels: Bower; Hollinwood.

Q58 **Werneth Low**
☎061-368 2503
Werneth Low Rd, Hyde, Cheshire SK14 3AF.
2 miles from Hyde town centre via Gee Cross and Joel Lane.
Undulating course.
9 holes, 5734 yards, S.S.S.68
Club founded in 1918.
Visitors: welcome except Sun.
Green fees: £7.50, (£3 with member) weekdays; £11.50, (£4 with

member) Sat.
Society meetings: welcome by arrangement.
Catering: daily, except Wed.
Hotels: numerous in Stockport.

Q59 **Westhoughton**
☎Westhoughton (0942) 811085
Long Island, Westhoughton, Bolton, Lancs.
4 miles SW of Bolton on A58.
Meadowland course.
9 holes, 5834 yards, S.S.S.68
Visitors: welcome weekdays, with member only at weekends.
Green fees: on application.
Society meetings: by arrangement.
Catering: snacks and meals except Mon.
Hotels: Mercury.

Q60 **Whitefield**
☎061-766 2904
81/83 Higher Lane, Whitefield, Manchester M25 7EZ.
Leave M62 at Exit 17 onto A56, club is 200 yards on left in Higher Lane.
Parkland course.
18 holes, 2580 yards, S.S.S.68
Club founded in 1932.
Visitors: welcome.
Green fees: on application.
Society meetings: welcome, special rates on application.
Catering: meals served.
Hotels: Bolton Crest, Beaumont Rd, Bolton; Hazeldean, 467 Bury New Rd, Salford.

Q61 **Whittaker**
☎Littleborough (0706) 78310
Whittaker Lane, Littleborough, Lancs.
1.5 miles from town centre.
Undulating moorland course.
9 holes, S.S.S.67
Club founded in 1906.
Visitors: welcome except Sun.
Green fees: £3.50, (£3 with member) weekdays; £5 weekends.
Society meetings: arrange with Sec.
Catering: none available.

Hotels: Sun; Derbley Cottage.

Q62 **William Wroe**
☎061-748 8680
Penny Bridge Lane, Flixton, Manchester M31.
M63, Exit 4, B5214, then B5158 to Flixton Rd.
Parkland course.
18 holes, 4395 yards, S.S.S.61
Visitors: welcome.
Green fees: £2.60 weekdays; £3.75 weekends.
Society meetings none.
Catering: none.
Hotels: many in area.

Q63 **Withington**
☎061-445 9544
243 Palatine Rd, West Didsbury, Manchester M20 8UD.
From Manchester S on A5103 then B5166 through Northenden.
Parkland course.
18 holes, 6411 yards, S.S.S.71
Club founded in 1892.
Visitors: welcome weekdays.
Green fees: on application.
Society meetings: catered for weekdays except Thurs.
Catering: full facilities available Telephone 061-434 8716.
Hotels: Post House, Northenden; Britannia Ringway, Didsbury.

Q64 **Worsley**
☎061-789 4202
Stableford Ave, Monton, Eccles, Manchester M30 8AP.
1 mile from junction of M62 and M63.
Parkland course.
18 holes, 6217 yards, S.S.S.70
Course designed by James Braid.
Club founded in 1894.
Visitors: welcome if member of golf club with official handicap.
Green fees: £10 per day.
Society meetings: catered for Mon, Wed and Thurs.
Catering: service available from 12 noon.
Hotels: Wendover, Monton Rd, Monton.

R Lancashire and Isle of Man

Lancashire is renowned for the wonderful stretch of coastal courses; first of all, those between Liverpool and Southport and then the group in the Fylde area between Lytham and Blackpool.

There are enough championship links to satisfy the most avid golfers although not everyone should be tempted to try the championship tees even if permission is granted to do so. My own favourite is Formby. The dunes, pine and heather indicate easy walking on a sandy base and make an ideal combination of features. There is seclusion and beauty in so many of the holes and a variety in their challenge of which one never tires. Its first tee is almost on the platform of Freshfield Station, but first time travellers will have already spotted West Lancashire at Blundellsands; and Southport, Ainsdale and Hillside are the next stops up the line from Freshfield. There is a glimpse too, of the clubhouse of Royal Birkdale set in an almost continuous avenue of dunes; Hesketh and Southport Municipal lie on the other side of Southport, journey's end for the train.

Another line, however, the one from Preston, provides a good view of Royal Lytham and St Annes which, if seaside in character, is hidden from the sea. It has been a regular home of the Open championship since 1926 and, more recently, has been fortunate in having such splendid qualifying courses as St Annes Old, Fairhaven, Lytham Green Drive and Blackpool North Shore.

From Blackpool, it is an easy hop to the Isle of Man which deserves the attention of golfers. Castletown wears the crown but Ramsey held the northern counties championship in 1985 while Douglas Municipal was designed by Alister Mackenzie and Peel, like Ramsey, by James Braid.

Lancashire's inland golfing attractions are bound to suffer but Manchester is surrounded by plenty of choice while Bolton boasts two fine courses, Bolton GC and Old Links.

R1 Accrington & District
☎Accrington (0254) 32734
New Barn Farm, Devon Ave, West End, Oswaldtwistle, Accrington, Lancs BB5 4LR.
On A679 5 miles from Blackburn.
Moorland course.
18 holes, 5954 yards, S.S.S.69
Visitors: welcome at any time.
Green fees: £6, (£3.50 with member) weekdays; £7.50, (£5 with member) weekends.
Society meetings: catered for any time by arrangement.
Catering: full facilities.
Hotels: Kendal, Accrington; Moat House, Blackburn.

R2 Ashton & Lea
☎Preston (0772) 726480/735282
Tudor Ave, off Blackpool Rd, Lea, Preston PR4 0XA.
3 miles from Preston centre on A584 Blackpool road, turn right opposite Pig and Whistle.
Parkland course.
18 holes, 6289 yards, S.S.S.70
Club founded in 1913.

Visitors: weekdays; telephone weekends.
Green fees: £9.50 weekdays; £11 weekends.
Society meetings: welcome weekdays except Thurs.
Catering: full facilities available except Mon.
Hotels: Crest; Tickled Trout (junction 31 on M6).

R3 Bacup
☎Bacup (0706) 873170
Maden Rd, Bacup, Lancs OL13 8HM.
Off A671, 7 miles N of Rochdale, 0.5 mile from Bacup centre.
Meadowland course.
9 holes, 5652 yards, S.S.S.67
Club founded in 1911.
Visitors: welcome weekdays, except Tues, and at weekends after competitions.
Green fees: on application.
Society meetings: welcome weekdays except Tues.
Catering: full facilities.
Hotels: Burwood, Bacup; Royal, Waterfoot.

R4 Beacon Park
☎Up Holland (0695) 622700
Beacon Lane, Dalton, Up Holland, Wigan, Lancs WN8 7RU.
Signposted from centre of Up Holland on A577 and from A5209 near Parbold, located on side of Ashurst Beacon Hill overlooking Skelmersdale.
Undulating/hilly parkland course.
18 holes, 5996 yards, S.S.S.69
Course designed by Donald Steel.
Club founded in 1982.
Visitors: welcome at any time.
Green fees: £2.60 weekdays; £2.95 weekends; Mon, Tues, Thurs before 11am, £1.50.
Society meetings: welcome during week and by arrangement at weekends.
Catering: bar meals during bar hours; other meals by arrangement.
Hotels: Balcony Farm, Skelmersdale.

R5 Bentham
☎Bentham (0468) 61018
Robin Lane, Bentham, Lancaster

Castletown, Isle of Man

When the weather is fine, the greens holding and there is no wind, seaside links often present fewer problems than other types of course. In the 1980 Open championship, Muirfield suffered all sorts of indignities when its guard was lowered. Isao Aoki posted a 63 while Tom Watson and Horacio Carbonetti helped themselves to a 64; but the moment the wind stirred it was another matter.

Tales of the 1979 PGA Cup match at Castletown in the Isle of Man centred largely on days of sunshine, the ball running a mile and unanimous agreement that it was an idyllic spot. My baptism was a little more severe, a near gale springing up overnight and rain slanting in from the Irish Sea — all on the Longest Day of 1985, if you please. The clear outline of mountain peaks disappeared and there was a remoteness, almost a loneliness, on the little peninsula of land in the south-east corner of the island.

It was the sort of day when long par fives down the wind play shorter than modest par fours against it but the raw state is the true revealer of character and not even a princely soaking could dampen my enjoyment or admiration. Unless conditions blurred my judgment, its position as one of the great courses of the British Isles is undoubted.

Its modern version owes everything to Mackenzie Ross whose task of restoration after the war was similar to the miracle he wrought at Turnberry. To a greater degree than on most seaside links, good driving is essential. On such as the 7th and 8th, the fairway is the only place to be; yet the line from the championship tees involves quite a carry.

Castletown's hazards are entirely natural — gorse, bracken, rough, rocks and beach which gives the course more coastal frontage than perhaps any other in the world. Apart from a clump of forlorn palms behind the 8th green, and some planting to mask the wall behind the 4th — a relic of a wartime firing range — there isn't a tree to be seen. Though the

golfer has nothing to shield him, there is nothing to obscure the magnificent panoply of views either; the sea, two great sweeps of bay, the small boats, the many landmarks including the castle which gave the place its name and, on a good day, the Cumbrian Hills.

In days gone by, it was the residence of the Earl of Derby who, when Lord of Man (what an all embracing title), started the Derby at Castletown prior to taking it to Epsom. The 10th, nearly three furlongs in length, was the actual site, the hole not surprisingly assuming the name of 'Racecourse'. In this, Castletown has something in common with Hoylake and Torquay whose courses were originally homes of racing.

Castletown deserves the undivided attention of those who play it although the start is no indication of what lies ahead. The 1st is a short, uphill par four, one yard, in fact, over the par 3 limit, and the 2nd a somewhat plain two shotter. It is when you turn away down the long 5th, a dogleg round the corner of a stone wall, with a second shot (or third or fourth) between a large mound and an old pill box, that the course really begins.

The 5th, not quite such a good par five as the 3rd, sandwiches the 4th where the drive must be left to obtain the correct angle to negotiate the slope of the green and to miss the guardian bunkers on the right. Castletown's short holes make a wonderful set, the 6th, the shortest of them, providing an inviting shot even if the green is encircled by trouble. The same applies to the drive at the 7th and the second shot to a green typical of Mackenzie Ross's imaginative designs and shapes.

However, the 8th is no easier. The fairway may present a nice target at a lower level but it is also alarmingly narrow and the road is only a thin strip separating errant drives from the beach on which golf balls, pebbles and boulders are indistinguishable. This is Derbyhaven Bay with Derbyhaven village beckoning on the right of the 10th. But, before that is reached, the drive at the 9th must be aimed on the outline of King William's College, a solid fortress of Manx stone, although, having made what may have been the home turn in the first Derby down by the 10th green, Castletown Bay hoves in sight to further goad the golfer. There is no let-up.

At the delightful short 11th and the next two par fours, it is all too simple to let a tee shot drift to the right and, if the 14th is a shade less of a threat in this regard, the tee marker tells the bad news that it is 468 yards. On the 15th, a stone wall denotes out of bounds and the contouring of the greens foils those playing too safe to the left; but the best is yet to come — notably

the 17th with its gaping gorge in front of the tee and resplendent rocks to the right introducing a touch of Cypress Point.

The 18th is a challenging finishing hole set against the square form of the welcoming Links Hotel which was purpose built in the last century. Those who originally spied out the land certainly knew what they were doing but a slight questioning word must be levelled at Manx folk lore and the island's emblem of the Three Legs of Man. It has as its motto 'whichever way you throw me, I shall stand' but did they ever experiment on the championship tee at the 17th with a gale off the sea?

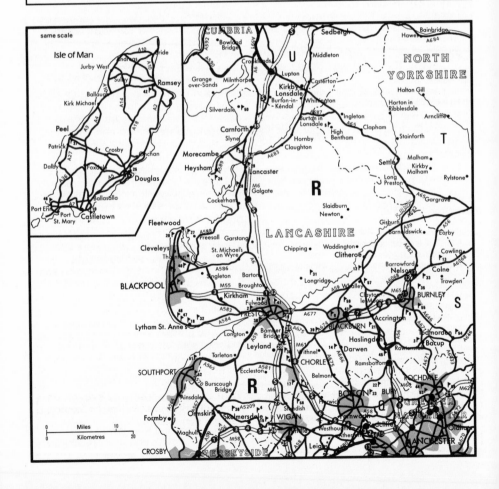

LA2 7LF.
Halfway between Lancaster and Settle on B6480, 13 miles E of junction 34, off M6.
Undulating meadowland course.
9 holes, 5752 yards, S.S.S.69
Club founded in 1922.
Visitors: welcome.
Green fees: £5 per day, (£2.50 with member) weekdays; £6.50, (£3.25 with member) weekends and Bank Holidays.
Society meetings: welcome by arrangement.
Catering: snacks, meals in bar hours.
Hotels: Black Bull, Bentham; Post House,Lancaster.

R6 Blackburn
☎Blackburn (0254) 51122
Beardwood Brow, Blackburn, Lancs BB2 7AX.
Situated in W end of town off Revidge Rd, from Moat House Hotel on A677 proceed to traffic lights and turn left, at Dog Hotel turn left to clubhouse.
Undulating meadowland course.
18 holes, 6100 yards, S.S.S.70
Club founded in 1894.
Visitors: welcome weekdays.
Green fees: £8.50, (£3.50 with member) weekdays; £11, (£4 with member) weekends and Bank Holidays.
Society meetings: catered for weekdays.
Catering: daily except lunch Monday.
Hotels: Moat House, Blackburn.

R7 Blackpool North Shore
☎Blackpool (0253) 51017, 52054 Sec
Devonshire Rd, Blackpool FY2 0RD.
On A587 N of town centre behind North Promenade.
Undulating parkland course.
18 holes, 6442 yards, S.S.S.71
Club founded in 1904.
Visitors: unlimited but some restrictions Thurs and weekends.
Green fees: £11 weekdays; £12 weekends.
Society meetings: special party rates including meals.
Catering: full service of meals or snacks.
Hotels: Sheraton; Queens Prom; Boston, Queens Prom.

R8 Blackpool - Stanley Park
☎Blackpool (0253) 33960
North Park Drive, Blackpool, Lancs FY3 8LS.

1.5 miles E of centre of Blackpool.
Parkland course.
18 holes, 6060 yards, S.S.S.69
Course designed by Dr Mackenzie.
Club founded in 1926.
Visitors: welcome anytime.
Green fees: £3.25 weekdays; £4.30 weekends.
Society meetings: welcome weekdays.
Catering: every day except Tues.
Hotels: numerous in Blackpool.

R9 Burnley
☎Burnley (0282) 21045
Glen View, Burnley BB11 3RW.
Off A56 to Glen View Rd, after 300 yards turn right.
Moorland/meadowland course.
18 holes, 5900 yards, S.S.S.69
Club founded in 1905.
Visitors: mid-week and Sun; limited Sat.
Green fees: £6.50 weekdays; £8 weekends and Bank Holidays (per day).
Society meetings: mid-week and Sun.
Catering: snacks and full meals except Mon.
Hotels: Kierby; Rosehill House; Oaks.

R10 Castletown
☎Castletown (0624) 822201
Fort Island, Castletown, Isle of Man
1.5 miles E of Castletown.
Seaside course.
18 holes, 6804 yards, S.S.S.73
Course designed by Mackenzie Ross.
Visitors: welcome.
Green fees: details by request.
Society meetings: by arrangement.
Catering: meals served every day in hotel.
Hotels: Castletown Golf Links adjoining Golf course.

R11 Chorley
☎Adlington (0257) 480263
Hall o'th'Hill, Heath Charnock, Chorley, Lancs PR6 9HX.
On A673 100 yards S of junction with A6 at Skew Bridge traffic lights.
Undulating course.
18 holes, 6277 yards, S.S.S.71
Course designed by J.A. Steer.
Club founded in 1898.
Visitors: advisable to ring Pro.
Green fees: £9, (£4.50 with member) weekdays; £13, (£6 with member) weekends and Bank Holidays.

Society meetings: weekdays by arrangement.
Catering: arrange with Steward.
Hotels: Hartwood Hall, Preston Rd, Chorley.

R12 Clitheroe
☎Clitheroe (0200) 22292 Sec, 22618 Club, 24242 Pro.
Whalley Rd, Pendleton, Clitheroe BB7 1PP.
Off A59 2 miles S of Clitheroe.
Undulating parkland course.
18 holes, 6311 yards, S.S.S.71
Course designed by James Braid.
Club founded in 1891.
Visitors: welcome subject to competition days on Sat and Thurs.
Green fees: £11 weekdays; £13 weekends.
Society meetings: welcome by arrangement, maximum 24 on Sun.
Catering: meals served.
Hotels: Roefield; Swan and Royal; Fairway; Stirk House, Clitheroe.

R13 Colne
☎Colne (0282) 863391
Law Farm, Skipton Old Rd, Colne, Lancs BB8 7EB.
0.75 mile off A56 at Colne Cricket Club.
Moorland course.
9 holes, 5961 yards, S.S.S.69
Club founded in 1901.
Visitors: except competition days. Please ring.
Green fees: £6 weekdays; £7 weekends and Bank Holidays.
Society meetings: by arrangement.
Catering: as required.
Hotels: many in area.

R14 Darwen
☎Darwen (0254) 71287
Winter Hill, Darwen, Lancs.
1.5 miles from Darwen town centre, off A666 Bolton to Blackburn road.
Moorland course.
18 holes, 5752 yards, S.S.S.68
Club founded in 1893.
Visitors: welcome weekdays and with advance bookings at weekends.
Green fees: £6.90, (£3.45 with member) weekdays; £9.20, (£4.60 with member) weekends.
Society meetings: catered for any day.
Catering: full, except Mon.
Hotels: Whitehall and Country Club.

R15 Dean Wood
☎Up Holland (0695) 622219 Sec, 622980 Clubhouse.

Lafford Lane, Up Holland, Skelmersdale, Lancs WN8 0QZ.
Exit 26 from M6, 1.5 miles on A577 to Up Holland.
Undulating parkland course.
18 holes, 6129 yards, S.S.S.70
Course designed by James Braid.
Club founded in 1922.
Visitors: welcome weekdays; weekends by introduction.
Green fees: £9 weekdays; £12.50 weekends.
Society meetings: weekdays only by arrangement.
Catering: daily.
Hotels: Holland Hall, Up Holland.

R16 Douglas
☎Douglas (0624) 75952
Pulrose Rd, Douglas, Isle of Man.
1 mile from Douglas town centre, clubhouse situated near to large cooling tower for Electricity Dept Power Station.
Parkland municipal course.
18 holes, 6080 yards, Par 70, S.S.S.69
Course designed by Dr Mackenzie.
Club founded in 1927.
Visitors: welcome.

Green fees: winter: £2.20 per round/day; £13 per week; summer: £4 per round/day; £14 per week.
Society meetings: welcome.
Catering: meals and snacks served from 11am-11pm from May-end Sept.
Hotels: numerous in Douglas.

R17 Duxbury Park
☎Chorley (025 72) 65380
Duxbury Park, Chorley, Lancs
1.5 miles S of Chorley, off A6, 200 yards along A5106 Chorley-Wigan road.
Parkland municipal course.
18 holes, 6390 yards, S.S.S.70
Club founded in 1970.
Visitors: municipal course, booking accepted by telephone.
Green fees: £2.40 weekdays; £4 weekends.
Society meetings: catered for.
Catering: separate facilities from the club.
Hotels: Hartwood Hall, Chorley; Kilhey Court, Wigan Rd, Worthington.

R18 Fairhaven
☎Lytham (0253) 736976
Lytham Hall Park, Ansdell, Lytham

St Annes FY8 4JU.
On B5261 2 miles from Lytham.
Semi links course.
18 holes, 6810 yards, S.S.S.73
Course designed by James Braid.
Club founded in 1895.
Visitors: welcome by arrangement.
Green fees: on application.
Society meetings: welcome by prior arrangement.
Catering: meals served except Mon when sandwiches are available from bar.
Hotels: Clifton Arms, Lytham; Grand, St Annes; Dalmeney, St Ives; Fearnlee, St Annes.

R19 Fishwick Hall
☎Preston (0772) 795870/796866
Glenluce Drive, Farringdon Park, Preston, Lancs PR1 5TB.
Leave M6 at junction 31, then take A59 towards Preston, past Tickled Trout Hotel, Glenluce Drive is first left at top of hill.
Undulating meadowland/parkland course.
Club founded in 1912.
Visitors: welcome. Parties by arrangement.

Green fees: £7.50 weekdays; £9.50 weekends; less with member.
Society meetings: welcome by arrangement weekdays; also some weekends.
Catering: full facilities, closed Mon.
Hotels: Tickled Trout Hotel; Crest, Preston Centre.

R20 Fleetwood
☎Fleetwood (039 17) 3661
Princes Way, Fleetwood, Lancs FY7 8AF.
On A587, 7 miles N of Blackpool.
Seaside links course.
18 holes, 6437 yards, S.S.S.71
Club founded in 1932.
Visitors: welcome without reservation.
Green fees: £8; £10.
Society meetings: yes.
Catering: not Monday.
Hotels: Euston.

R21 Green Haworth
☎Accrington (0254) 37580
Green Haworth, Accrington, Lancs BB5 3SL.
From Accrington town centre take main road to Blackburn, turn left on Willows Lane, follow road for 2-3 miles, sign just past Red Lion Hotel.
Moorland course.
9 holes, 5470 yards, S.S.S.67
Club founded in 1914.
Visitors: welcome, restricted to weekdays; Saturday with reservation.
Green fees: £6.
Society meetings: catered for.
Catering: by arrangement.
Hotels: Moat House, Blackburn.

R22 Greenmount
☎Tottington (020 488) 3712
Greenhalgh Fold Farm, Greenmount, Bury BL8 4LA.
Off M66 towards Ramsbottom on Bolton road, left at T-junction, club 1 mile on right.
Undulating parkland/moorland course.
9 holes, 4915 yards, S.S.S.64
Club founded in 1920.
Visitors: welcome weekdays and with member at weekends.
Green fees: on application.
Society meetings: catered for on weekdays except Tues.
Catering: full service except Mon.
Hotels: Old Mill, Ramsbottom.

R23 Harwood
☎Bolton (0204) 22878

Springfirlys, Roaming Brook Rd, Harwood, Bolton, Lancs.
On B6391 off A666 4 miles NE of Bolton town centre.
Undulating parkland course.
9 holes, 5958 yards, S.S.S.69
Club founded in 1926.
Visitors: welcome, but must be members of recognised club.
Green fees: £7, (£2 with member).
Society meetings: none.
Catering: only by request.
Hotels: Last Drop, Village; Bromley Cross, Bolton.

R24 Heysham
☎Lancaster (0524) 51011
Trumacar Park, Heysham, LA3 3JH.
Drive S along Morecambe Promenade for 2.5 miles and golf club is on right hand side on main road to Middleton.
Parkland course.
18 holes, 6340 yards, S.S.S.70
Club founded in 1910.
Visitors: welcome; parties by arrangement weekdays and weekends.
Green fees: £6.50 per round; £9 per day weekdays; £12 per day weekends (half price with a member).
Society meetings: catered for by arrangement.
Catering: standard menu and à la carte. 7 day catering.
Hotels: Midland; Clarendon, Morecambe; Post House, Lancaster.

R25 Howstrake
☎Douglas (0624) 20430
Groudle Rd, Onchan, Isle of Man.
On A11, 2 miles NE of Douglas.
Moorland/seaside course.
18 holes, 5255 yards, S.S.S.66
Club founded in 1914.
Visitors: welcome Mon-Sat; Sun by arrangement.
Green fees: £4.
Society meetings: catered for weekdays.
Catering: full services 10am-10pm daily.
Hotels: Empress; Douglas.

R26 Ingol G & Squash Club
☎Preston (0772) 734556
Tanterton Hill Rd, Ingol, Preston, Lancs PR2 7BY.
From A6 to Preston turn right down Lightfoot Lane, take second turn on left and first left again, signposted.
Parkland course.
18 holes, 6345 yards, S.S.S.70
Course designed by Cotton,

Pennink, Lawrie & Partners.
Club founded in 1980.
Visitors: welcome any day.
Green fees: Summer £8, (£4 with member) weekdays; £10, (£5 with member) weekends.
Society meetings: welcome by arrangement.
Catering: full facilities.
Hotels: Barton Grange; Broughton; Bartle Hall.

R27 Knott End
☎Knott End (0253) 810576
Wyreside, Knott End, Blackpool FY6 0AA.
Take A588, Fleetwood road, off M55, and then B2588 to Knott End.
Meadowland course.
18 holes, 5852 yards, S.S.S.68
Course designed by James Braid.
Club founded in 1911.
Visitors: welcome weekdays not before 9.30am or between 12.30pm and 1.30pm.
Green fees: £9 weekdays; £11 weekends.
Society meetings: by arrangement.
Catering: every day.
Hotels: Bourne Arms, Knott End.

R28 Lancaster
☎Lancaster (0524) 751247
Ashton Hall, Ashton-with-Stodday, Lancaster LA2 0AJ.
On A588 2.5 miles SW of Lancaster.
Undulating parkland course.
18 holes, 6422 yards, S.S.S.72
Course designed by James Braid.
Visitors: welcome but restricted at weekends.
Green fees: on application.
Society meetings: welcome by arrangement.
Catering: meals served.
Hotels: Post House, Lancaster.

R29 Lansil
☎Lancaster (0524) 39269 Club
Caton Rd, Lancaster, Lancs LA1 3PE.
2 miles E of Lancaster centre on A683.
Parkland/meadowland course.
9 Holes, 5608 yards, S.S.S.67
Club founded in 1947.
Visitors: welcome but not before 1pm Sun.
Green fees: £4 weekdays; £6 weekends.
Society meetings: welcome weekdays.
Catering: light refreshments only.
Hotels: Farmers Arms, Penny St, Lancaster.

R30 **Leyland**
☎Leyland (0772) 421359
Wigan Rd, Leyland, Lancs PR2 5UD.
Off A49, 0.25 mile from Exit 28 off M6.
Meadowland course.
18 holes, 6105 yards, S.S.S.69
Club founded in 1923.
Visitors: weekdays unrestricted;
weekends with member.
Green fees: £8.
Society meetings: by arrangement
with Sec.
Catering: daily except Mon.
Hotels: Ladbroke Mercury Hotel &
Conference Centre, Leyland Way,
Leyland.

R31 **Longridge**
☎Longridge (077 478) 3291
Fell Barn, Jeffrey Hill, Longridge,
Preston, Lancs PR3 2TU.
B6243 to B5269 to Longridge, climb
through village, continue climbing for
1.5 miles.
Moorland course.
18 holes, 5800 yards, S.S.S.68
Club founded in 1877.
Visitors: welcome at all times.
Green fees: £6 weekdays; £8
weekends and Bank Holidays.
Society meetings: welcome at all
times.
Catering: full facilities available
except Mon.
Hotels: Shireburn Arms; Gibbon
Bridge; Black Moss Guest House,
Preston.

R32 **Lytham Green Drive**
☎Lytham (0253) 737390
Ballam Rd, Lytham, Lancs FY8 4LE.
0.75 mile from Lytham centre.
Parkland course.
18 holes, 6038 yards, S.S.S.69
Club founded in 1924.
Visitors: mid-week only, handicap
certificate required.
Green fees: £11 weekdays, (£5.50
with member).
Society meetings: accepted on
application to Sec.
Catering: full service daily.
Hotels: Clifton Arms, Lytham.

R33 **Marsden Park**
☎Nelson (0253) 67525
Downhouse Rd, Nelson, Lancs
BB9 8GD
Off A56, 4 miles N of Burnley.
Undulating meadowland course.
18 holes, 5806 yards, S.S.S.68
Course designed by C.K. Cotton &
Partners.
Club founded in 1968.

Visitors: welcome.
Green fees: on application.
Society meetings: by arrangement.
Catering: snacks in evenings, all
day weekends.
Hotels: Great Marsden.

R34 **Morecambe**
☎Morecambe (0524) 412841 Sec,
418050 Members, 415596 Pro.
Bare, Morecambe, Lancs LA4 6AJ.
5 miles from M6 at Carnforth, follow
signs to Morecambe.
Seaside/parkland course.
18 holes.
Course designed by Dr Clegg.
Club founded in 1922.
Visitors: welcome by arrangement.
Green fees: on application.
Society meetings: welcome by
arrangement with Sec, if members of
recognised golf clubs.
Catering: full catering available
except Mon when bar snacks only.
Hotels: Elms; Strathmore.

R35 **Nelson**
☎Nelson (0282) 64583
King's Causeway, Brierfield, Nelson,
Lancs BB9 0EU.
Off A56 2 miles E of Brierfield.
Moorland course.
18 holes, 5679 yards, S.S.S.69
Visitors: welcome weekdays except
Thurs pm; weekends and Bank
Holidays by application.
Green fees: £7, (£3.50 with
member) weekdays; £8, (£4 with
member) weekends.
Society meetings: by arrangement.
Catering: lunch served except Mon,
evening meals except Mon or Fri.
Hotels: Kierby, Burnley; Oaks,
Reedley, Burnley.

R36 **Ormskirk**
☎Ormskirk (0695) 72112
Cranes Lane, Lathom, Ormskirk,
Lancs L40 5UV.
2 miles E of Ormskirk.
Parkland course.
18 holes, 6333 yards, S.S.S.71
Club founded in 1899.
Visitors: advanced booking advised.
Green fees: Mon, Tues, Thurs, Fri
£13.50; Wed, Sun and Bank
Holidays £16.
Society meetings: to be booked in
advance.
Catering: daily except Mon.
Hotels: numerous in area.

R37 **Peel**
☎Peel (0624) 843456 (Mon-Fri

mornings).
Rheast Lane, Peel, Isle of Man.
On A1, signposted on outskirts of
Peel, coming from Douglas.
Moorland course.
18 holes, 5914 yards, S.S.S.68
Course designed by A. Herd.
Club founded in 1895.
Visitors: welcome weekdays; by
arrangement weekends - after
10.30am.
Green fees: £6 per day weekdays; £8
per day weekends and Bank
Holidays.
Society meetings: by arrangement
with Sec.
Catering: meals and light snacks as
required and arrangement with
Steward.
Hotels: many on Island.

R38 **Penwortham**
☎Preston (0772) 744630
Blundell Lane, Penwortham, Preston,
Lancs PR1 0AX.
Off A59 at Penwortham traffic lights,
1 mile from Preston.
Parkland course.
18 holes, 5915 yards, S.S.S.68
Club founded in 1908.
Visitors: welcome weekdays (not
Tues).
Green fees: £9, (£3.75 with member)
weekdays; £10.60, (£4.75 with
member) weekends and Bank
Holidays.
Society meetings: weekdays (not
Tues).
Catering: lunch and evening meals
except Mon.
Hotels: Crest; The Ringway, Preston.

R39 **Pleasington**
☎Blackburn (0254) 22177
Pleasington, Blackburn, Lancs
BB2 5JF.
3 miles from Blackburn off A674.
Undulating parkland course.
18 holes, 6417 yards, S.S.S.71
Club founded in 1891.
Visitors: Mon, Wed, Fri by prior
arrangement. Handicap certificate
required.
Green fees: £12 weekdays; £15
weekends and Bank Holidays per
person inclusive of VAT.
Society meetings: Mon, Wed and
Fri.
Catering: full facilities.
Hotels: Moat House Motel,
Blackburn.

R40 **Poulton-le-Fylde.**
☎Poulton-le-Fylde (0253) 893150

Myrtle Farm, Breck Rd, Poulton-le-Fylde, Lancs.
2 miles from Poulton via Breck Rd.
Meadowland course.
9 holes, 5958 yards, S.S.S.69
Club founded in 1976.
Visitors: welcome including weekends.
Green fees: £1.90 weekdays; £3.20 weekends and Bank Holidays.
Society meetings: by arrangement.
Catering: daily lunch.
Hotels: Imperial, Blackpool.

R41 Preston
☎Preston (0772) 700011
Fulwood Hall Lane, Fulwood, Preston, Lancs PR2 4DD.
N of Preston off Watling Street Rd.
Undulating course.
18 holes, 6233 yards, S.S.S.71
Course designed by James Braid.
Club founded in 1892.
Visitors: welcome by arrangement; occasionally weekends.
Green fees: £10 weekday; £12 weekends; (half price with member).
Society meetings: Mon, Wed, Fri. Not Saturday.
Catering: breakfast, lunch, dinner, snacks.
Hotels: Broughton Park, Barton, Preston.

R42 Ramsey
☎Ramsey (0624) 812244
Brookfield, Ramsey.
12 miles N of Douglas, 5 minutes walk from town centre.
Parkland course.
18 holes, 6019 yards, S.S.S.69
Course designed by James Braid.
Club founded in 1890.
Visitors: societies accepted.
Green fees: £5 per day weekdays; £6 per day weekends.
Society meetings: none.
Catering: lunch daily. Full meals by request.
Hotels: Grand Island.

R43 Rishton
☎Blackburn (0254) 884442
Eachill Links, Rishton, Blackburn, Lancs BB1 4HG.
Past Blackburn towards new M65, halfway to Accrington, turn off at roundabout near Red Lion Public House.
Undulating meadowland course.
9 holes, 6094 yards, S.S.S.69
Course designed by Alliss & Thomas.
Club founded in 1928.

Visitors: welcome weekdays; weekends and Bank Holidays with member.
Green fees: £4, (£2 with member).
Society meetings: welcome by prior arrangement with Sec.
Catering: available by prior arrangement.
Hotels: Dunkenhalgh.

R44 Rochdale
☎Rochdale (0706) 43818 Sec, 46024 Club.
Edenfield Rd, Bagslate, Rochdale.
3 miles from exit 20, off M62, on A680.
Parkland course.
18 holes, 5981 yards, S.S.S.69
Club founded in 1888.
Visitors: welcome.
Green fees: on application.
Society meetings: catered for on Wed and Fri.
Catering: coffee, lunch and evening meals served except Mon.
Hotels: Royal, Waterfoot; Queens Arms, Rawtenstall.

R45 Rossendale
☎Rossendale (0706) 213056
Ewood Lane Head, Haslingden, Rossendale, Lancs BB4 6LH.
16 miles from Manchester off A56.
Moorland/meadowland course.
18 holes, 6267 yards, S.S.S.70
Club founded in 1903.
Visitors: welcome weekdays and Sun.
Green fees: £8 weekdays; £10 Sun.
Society meetings: welcome.
Catering: full facilities except Mon.
Hotels: Queen's, Rawtenstall; Royal, Waterfoot.

R46 Rowany
☎Port Erin (0624) 834108
Rowany Drive, Port Erin, Isle of Man.
Off Promenade.
Seaside course.
18 holes, 5840 yards, S.S.S.69
Visitors: welcome.
Green fees: £4.50 per day, weekdays; £6 (with member only) weekends. 25% discount for groups and visitors staying locally.
Catering: restaurant - evening meals, lunch, bar snacks.
Hotels: Ocean Castle, Promenade, Port Erin.

R47 Royal Lytham & St Annes
☎St Annes (0253) 724206

Links Gate, St Annes on Sea, Lytham St Annes, Lancs FY8 3LQ.
1 mile from centre of St Annes on Sea.
Links course.
18 holes, 6673 yards, S.S.S.73
Club founded in 1886.
Visitors: weekdays by arrangement; not weekends.
Green fees: £25 per round or day.
Society meetings: by arrangement.
Catering: yes.
Hotels: many in the area.

R48 St Annes Old Links
☎St Annes (0253) 723597
Highbury Rd, St Annes, Lytham St Annes, Lancs FY8 2LD.
On A584 coast road towards St Annes turn right at traffic lights past holiday camp, club is 400 yards on left.
Links course.
18 holes, 6616 yards, S.S.S.72
Course designed by James Herd.
Club founded in 1901.
Visitors: welcome weekdays; restricted Tues and weekends.
Green fees: £13 weekdays.
Society meetings: by arrangement with Sec.
Catering: lunch, tea, dinner daily.
Hotels: St Ives, South Promenade, St Annes; Warwick, South Shore, Blackpool.

R49 Shaw Hill C & CC
☎Chorley (025 76) 4300
Whittle-le-Woods, Chorley, Lancs PR6 7PP.
On A6 1.5 miles N of Chorley.
Parkland course.
18 holes, 6467 yards, S.S.S.71
Course re-designed by T.J. McCauley.
Club founded in 1925.
Visitors: welcome 7 days a week.
Green fees: £10 weekdays; £12 weekends.
Society meetings: welcome weekdays.
Catering: restaurant and bar snacks.
Hotels: own 3 star hotel. All rooms en suite.

R50 Silverdale
☎Carnforth (0524) 701300
Red Bridge Lane, Silverdale, Carnforth, Lancs LA5 0SP.
Off M6 at Carnforth, course opposite Silverdale railway station via Carnforth and Warton.
Hilly heathland course.
9 holes, 5262 yards, S.S.S.67

Club founded in 1906.
Visitors: welcome, not competition days (Sun, Men), (Wed, Ladies).
Green fees: £5 weekdays, (£3 with member); £7.50 (£5 with member) weekends and Bank Holidays.
Society meetings: catered for.
Catering: usually by special arrangement.
Hotels: Wheatsheaf, Beetham, Milnthorpe; Silverdale, Silverdale.

R51 **Southport Municipal**
☎Southport (0704) 35286
Park Rd, West, Southport, Merseyside.
N end of Promenade.
Seaside course.
18 holes, 5939 yards, S.S.S.70
Visitors: welcome.
Green fees: £2.92, £1.22 juniors, weekdays; £3.05 weekends; booking required.
Society meetings: by arrangement.
Catering: meals served.
Hotels: in Southport.

R52 **Southport Old Links**
☎Southport (0704) 28207
Moss Lane, Southport, Merseyside PR9 7QS.
From town centre take Lord St to roundabout at Law Courts, turn right into Manchester Rd, into Roe Lane and into Moss Lane.
Seaside course.
9 holes, 6486 yards, S.S.S.72
Club founded in 1920.
Visitors: preferably not Wed or weekends.
Green fees: £7.50 weekdays; £10 weekends.
Society meetings: by arrangement if party 12 or more.
Catering: snacks or light cooked meals as arranged with Steward.
Hotels: Bold, Lord St.

R53 **Springfield**
☎Rochdale (0706) 49801
Springfield Park, Bolton Road, Rochdale, Lancs.
3 miles from M62.
Parkland course.
18 holes, 5209 yards, S.S.S.66
Club founded in 1927.
Visitors: welcome anytime.
Green fees: £2.75 weekdays and weekends.
Catering: none.
Hotels: Midway, Manchester Rd, Castleton, Nr Rochdale.

R54 **Todmorden**
☎Todmorden (0706) 812986
Rive Rocks, Cross Stone Rd, Todmorden, Lancs.
Ascend Cross Stone Rd off A646 Halifax Road, 0.75 mile from town centre.
Moorland course.
9 holes, 5818 yards, S.S.S.68
Club founded in 1895.
Visitors: welcome weekdays and Sun.
Green fees: £4, (£2 with member) weekdays; £6, (£3 with member) weekends and Bank Holidays.
Society meetings: catered for weekdays and Sun.
Catering: full facilities except Mon.
Hotels: Queens, Todmorden.

R55 **Towneley**
☎Burnley (0282) 38473 Pro, 51636 Clubhouse.
Todmorden Rd, Burnley, Lancs BB11 3ED.
Leaving Burnley town centre following Halifax and Todmorden signs, turn right at traffic lights near Burnley Football Ground, about 1 mile on left.
Parkland/meadowland course.
18 holes, 5862 yards, S.S.S.68
Course designed by Burnley Council
Club founded in 1932.
Visitors: welcome anytime.
Green fees: £2.50 weekdays; £3.35 weekends and Bank Holidays.
Society meetings: catered for by prior arrangement.
Catering: lunch and bar snacks except Mon.
Hotels: Oaks Hotel & Leisure Centre, Colne Rd; Alexander, Tarleton Ave, Burnley.

R56 **Tunshill**
☎Rochdale (0706) 342095
Kiln Lane, Milnrow, Lancs.
Follow Kiln Lane out of Milnrow town centre and continue along narrow lane to clubhouse.
Moorland course.
9 holes, 2902 yards, S.S.S.68
Club founded in 1943.
Visitors: welcome weekdays except Tues evening and with special permission at weekends.
Green fees: on application.
Society meetings: welcome weekdays.
Catering: by prior arrangement.
Hotels: Midway; Castleton; Rochdale.

R57 **Whalley**
☎Whalley (025 482) 2236
Portfield Lane, Whalley, Blackburn, Lancs BB6 9DR.
A59 to Whalley, then S of town on road to Accrington.
Parkland course.
9 holes, 5953 yards, S.S.S.69
Club founded in 1912.
Visitors: welcome except Thurs 12.30pm to 4pm (Ladies Day) and Sat April-Sept.
Green fees: £5, (£2.50 with member) weekdays; £7, (£3.50 with member) weekends and Public Holidays.
Society meetings: 20% discount on green fees for parties over 20.
Catering: lunch, teas and dinners except Mon.
Hotels: Moat House, Blackburn; Dunkenhalgh, Accrington.

R58 **Wigan**
☎Standish (0257) 421360
Arley Hall, Haigh, Wigan WN1 2UH.
On B5239 3.5 miles N of Wigan, through Standish and turn left at traffic lights on Canal Bridge, opposite Crawford Arms Public House.
Parkland course.
9 holes, 6058 yards, S.S.S.69
Club founded in 1898.
Visitors: welcome weekdays except Tues (Ladies Day).
Green fees: on application.
Society meetings: applications considered.
Catering: snack lunch and evening meals available.
Hotels: Bellingham, Wigan Lane, Wigan; Brockett Arms, Mesnes Rd, Wigan.

R59 **Wilpshire**
☎Blackburn (0254) 48260
72 Whalley Rd, Wilpshire, Blackburn, Lancs BB1 9LF.
On A666 4 miles N of Blackburn.
Moorland course.
18 holes, 5911 yards, S.S.S.69
Club founded in 1898.
Visitors: welcome weekdays.
Green fees: £7, (£3.50 with member) weekdays; £8.50, (£4.25 with member) weekends.
Society meetings: catered for weekdays.
Catering: lunch daily, except Mon.
Hotels: Moat House, Blackburn; Trafalgar, Salmesbury, Blackburn.

S West and South Yorkshire

S1 Abbeydale
☎Sheffield (0742) 360763
Twentywell Lane, Dore, Sheffield,
S Yorks S17 4QA.
Off A621 Sheffield-Baslow road at
Dore and Totley station.
Parkland course.
18 holes, 6419 yards, S.S.S.71
Visitors: welcome any day by
arrangement.
Green fees: £11.50 weekdays;
£13.50 weekends.
Society meetings: Tues and Fri by
arrangement.
Catering: bar snacks and restaurant.
Hotels: Beauchief.

S2 Alwoodley
☎Leeds (0532) 681680
Wigton Lane, Alwoodley, Leeds,
W Yorks.
5 miles N of Leeds via A61.
Heathland course.
18 holes, 6301 yards, S.S.S.70
Course designed by Dr A Mackenzie.
Club founded in 1907.
Visitors: welcome weekdays subject
to prior notice.
Green fees: on application.
Society meetings: by arrangement
weekdays.
Catering: by arrangement.
Hotels: Harewood Arms, Harewood.

S3 Austerfield Park
☎(0302) 710841/710850.
Cross Lane, Austerfield, Nr Bawtry,
S Yorks DN10 6RF.
Off A614, 4 miles N of Bawtry.
Moorland course.
18 holes, 6828 yards, S.S.S.73
Course designed by E & M Baker
Ltd.
Club founded in 1974.
Visitors: welcome mid-week and
weekends.
Green fees: £6, £3 Eurogolf and
guest weekdays; £8, £4 Eurogolf and
guest weekends.
Society meetings: special rates
apply based on packages from
£5.50.
Catering: full restaurant and bar
snacks.
Hotels: Crown; Mount Pleasant;
Punches.

S4 Baildon
☎Bradford (0274) 584266

Moorgate, Baildon, Shipley, W Yorks
BD17 5PP.
5 miles N of Bradford, A6037 to
Shipley, 0.75 mile NE on A6038, left
at Junction Hotel.
Moorland course.
18 holes, 6178 yards, S.S.S.69
Club founded in 1896.
Visitors: welcome weekdays and at
weekends by arrangement.
Green fees: £6, (£3 with member)
weekdays; £8, (£5 with member)
weekends.
Society meetings: welcome.
Catering: lunches available except
Mon.
Hotels: Bankfield, Cottingley.

S5 Barnsley
☎Barnsley (0226) 382856
Wakefield Rd, Staincross, Nr
Barnsley, S Yorks S75 6JZ.
On A61 3 miles from Barnsley.
Undulating meadowland course.
18 holes, 6048 yards, S.S.S.69
Club founded in 1928.
Visitors: welcome.
Green fees: £2.80 weekdays; £3.50
weekends.
Society meetings: by arrangement
with Pro.
Catering: bar meals.
Hotels: Queens, Barnsley; Ardley
Moat House, Barnsley.

S6 Beauchief
☎Sheffield (0742) 620648
Abbey Lane, Sheffield S8 0DB.
5 miles from city centre, Abbeydale
Rd is on A625 to Baslow.
Meadowland municipal course.
18 holes, 5423 yards, S.S.S.66
Club founded in 1925.
Visitors: welcome by arrangement.
Green fees: on application.
Society meetings: welcome by
arrangement.
Catering: meals served except
Tues.
Hotels: many good hotels in
Sheffield.

S7 Ben Rhydding
☎Ilkley (0943) 608759
High Wood, Ben Rhydding, Ilkley, W
Yorks LS29 8SB.
Keep left after passing Wheatley
Hotel to top of hill.
Moorland course.

9 holes, 4711 yards, S.S.S.64
Club founded in 1947.
Visitors: welcome except Sun
morning.
Green fees: on application.
Society meetings: none.
Catering: no facilities.
Hotels: Wheatley, Ben Rhydding;
Craiglands, Ilkley.

S8 Bingley St Ives
☎Bradford (0274) 562436
The Mansion, St Ives Estate,
Bingley, W Yorks BD16 1AT.
Turn off A650, Bingley town centre
on Harden/Cullingworth Road. 0.5
mile on right hand side, turn right into
Estate.
Wooded parkland/moorland course.
18 holes, 6480 yards, S.S.S.70
Club founded in 1931.
Visitors: welcome weekdays.
Green fees: £3.95 per round, £6.20
per day weekdays; £7.25 per round,
£11.20 per day weekends.
Society meetings: catered for on
weekdays.
Catering: meals available every day
except Mon.
Hotels: Bankfield, Bradford Rd,
Bingley.

S9 Bradford
☎Guiseley (0943) 75570 Sec.
Hawksworth Lane, Guiseley, Leeds
LS20 8NP.
From Shipley 3.5 miles NE of A6038,
left to Hawksworth Lane.
Moorland/parkland course.
18 holes, 6259 yards, S.S.S.70
Club founded in 1891.
Visitors: weekdays, unlimited;
weekends, not before noon.
Green fees: £11.
Society meetings: on weekdays
welcome.
Catering: full facilities.
Hotels: Chevin Lodge, Yorkgate,
Otley.

S10 Bradford Moor
☎Bradford (0274) 5638313
Scarr Hall, Pollard Lane, Bradford
BD2 4RW.
2 miles from Bradford.
Undulating meadowland course.
9 holes, S.S.S.68
Club founded in 1907.
Visitors: welcome.

Green fees: on application.
Catering: meals served.
Hotels: good hotels in area.

S11 Bradley Park

☎Huddersfield (0484) 539988
Bradley Rd, Huddersfield, W Yorks
HD2 1DZ.
M62 runs along boundary of course
between junction 24, Huddersfield
and junction 25, Huddersfield W;
boundary borders on A6107 Bradley
Rd, Huddersfield, entrance to course
is signposted midway along Bradley
Rd.
Hilly parkland course.
18 holes, 6202 yards, S.S.S.70
Course designed by Cotton (CK)
Pennink, Lawrie & Partners.
Club founded in 1977.
Visitors: welcome anytime mid-
week or weekends.
Green fees: £3 weekdays; £4.25
weekends; half price OAP & juniors
weekdays.
Society meetings: mid-week

bookings acceptable only.
Catering: full facilities.
Hotels: Ladbroke; George.

S12 Branshaw

☎Haworth (0535) 43235
Branshaw Moor, Keighley, W Yorks.
B6143 2 miles SW of Keighley.
Moorland course.
18 holes, 5121 yards, S.S.S.65
Club founded in 1912.
Visitors: welcome weekdays.
Green fees: £3.50 weekdays; £5
weekends.
Society meetings: catered for
weekdays except Mon and Sun.
Catering: meals served except Mon,
prior notice required for larger
parties.
Hotels: Black Bull, Haworth; Fleece
Inn, Oakworth.

S13 City of Wakefield

☎Wakefield (0924) 360282 Pro
shop.
Lupset Park, Horbury Rd, Wakefield,

W Yorks WF2 8QS.
Approximately 2 miles from M1
junctions 39 or 40, course situated
on A642 Huddersfield Rd, turn at
Empire Mail Order Stores.
Parkland course.
18 holes, 6405 yards, S.S.S.71
Club founded in 1936.
Visitors: welcome.
Green fees: £3.10 weekdays; £4.80
weekends.
Society meetings: by arrangement
with Sec.
Catering: meals and snacks served
for groups, arrange with Sec.
Hotels: Swallow, Wakefield; Post
House; Cedar Court.

S14 Clayton

☎Bradford (0274) 880047
Thornton View Rd, Clayton,
Bradford, W Yorks BD14 6JX.
On A647 from Bradford, then turn
right and follow signs to Clayton.
Moorland course.
9 holes, 5518 yards, S.S.S.67

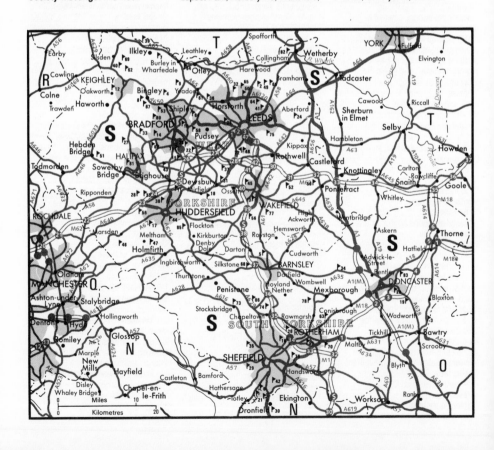

Club founded in 1906.
Visitors: welcome weekdays and Sat unless tee closed for competition.
Green fees: £3 weekdays with or without member; £5 weekends (not before 4pm Sun).
Society meetings: catered for by arrangement with Sec.
Catering: bar available daily except Mon, bar snacks available. Other catering by arrangement.
Hotels: Norfolk Gardens; Victoria.

s15 Cleckheaton & District

☎Cleckheaton (0274) 874118
Bradford Rd, Cleckheaton, W Yorks BD19 6BU.
Exit 26, from M62, onto A638 towards Bradford.
Parkland course.
18 holes, 5847 yards, S.S.S.69
Club founded in 1900.
Visitors: welcome.
Green fees: £9, (£4 with member) weekdays; £14, (£5 with member) weekends.
Society meetings: catered for weekdays.
Catering: full facilities available; morning coffee, lunch, afternoon tea, dinner every day but not Mon.
Hotels: Novotel, Merrydale Rd, Bradford.

s16 Concord Park

☎Sheffield (0742) 613605 Sec.
Shiregreen Lane, Sheffield S5.
Off A6135, 3.5 miles N of Sheffield, next to Concord Sports Centre, Shiregreen.
Undulating parkland course.
18 holes, 4302 yards, S.S.S.62
Club founded in 1952
Visitors: welcome.
Green fees: £4.20.
Society meetings: none.
Catering: none.
Hotels: good hotels in Sheffield.

s17 Crosland Heath

☎Huddersfield (0484) 653216
Felt Stile Rd, Crosland Heath, Huddersfield HD4 7AF.
Take A62 Huddersfield-Oldham road for 3 miles then follow signs for Goodalls Caravans.
Moorland course.
18 holes, 5962 yards, S.S.S.70
Visitors: welcome by arrangement.
Green fees: £6.50, (£2.50 with member) weekdays; (£8.50 weekends.
Society meetings: welcome except Tues and Sat contact Sec.

Catering: full facilities except Tues.
Hotels: Dryclough, Crosland Moor, Huddersfield; Durker Roods, Meltham, Huddersfield.

s18 Dewsbury District

☎Mirfield (0924) 492399, 496033 Pro.
The Pinnacle, Sands Lane, Mirfield, W Yorks WF14 8HJ.
Off A644, 2.5 miles from Dewsbury, at Swan Hotel turn left into Steanard Lane, sign at Sands Lane.
Undulating meadowland/moorland course.
18 holes, 6256 yards, S.S.S.71
Course redesigned by Peter Alliss & Dave Thomas (1970).
Club founded in 1891.
Visitors: welcome weekdays by prior arrangement, also certain weekends.
Green fees: £7 weekdays; £9 weekends.
Society meetings: welcome.
Catering: full facilities except Mon.
Hotels: Little Chef, Cooper Bridge, Mirfield; The Cottage, Huddersfield Rd, Mirfield.

s19 Doncaster

☎Doncaster (0302) 868316 Club, 868404 Pro.
278 Bawtry Rd, Bessacarr, Doncaster, S Yorks DN4 7PD.
Easy to locate between Doncaster and Bawtry on A638.
Undulating heathland course.
18 holes, 6015 yards, S.S.S.69
Club founded in 1894.
Visitors: welcome with or without member, not weekends.
Green fees: on application.
Society meetings: welcome weekdays by prior arrangement with Sec.
Catering: main meals available by prior arrangement daily except Wed.
Hotels: Punch's, Bawtry Rd; Danum, High St, Doncaster.

s20 Doncaster Town Moor

☎Doncaster (0302) 535286
Neatherds House, Belle Vue, Doncaster, S Yorks DN4 5HU.
400 yards S of racecourse roundabout on A638 travelling towards Bawtry.
Parkland course.
18 holes, 5923 yards, S.S.S.68
Club founded in 1900.
Visitors: welcome except Sun before 11.30am.
Green fees: £5 weekdays; £6

weekends.
Society meetings: by arrangement with Sec.
Catering: lunches except Mon.
Hotels: Danum, High St, Doncaster; Earl of Doncaster, Bennetthorpe, Doncaster; Punches, Bawtry Rd, Bessacarr, Doncaster; Rockingham, Bennetthorpe, Doncaster.

s21 Dore & Totley

☎Bradway (0742) 360492
Bradway Rd, Sheffield S17 4QR.
Off A61 Sheffield-Chesterfield on Holmesfield road.
Parkland course.
18 holes, 6301 yards, S.S.S.70
Club founded in 1913.
Visitors: welcome by prior arrangement.
Green fees: £8 per round; £12 per day.
Society meetings: catered for weekdays by prior arrangement.
Catering: full facilities available every day except Mon.
Hotels: Beauchief, Abbey Lane, Sheffield.

s22 East Bierley

☎Bradford (0274) 681023
South View Rd, Bierley, Bradford, W Yorks
3 miles SE of Bradford on Wakefield-Heckmondwike road.
9 holes, 4692 yards, S.S.S.62
Club founded in 1909.
Visitors: no restrictions except Sun.
Green fees: £5 per round weekdays; £7 per round weekends.
Society meetings: welcome, write for details.
Catering: by prior arrangement.
Hotels: in Bradford.

s23 Elland

☎Elland (0422) 72505
Hammerstones, Leach Lane, Elland, W Yorks HX5 0QP.
Leave M62 at junction 24, head for Blackley, golf club is 1 mile on left.
Parkland/meadowland course.
9 holes, 5526 yards, S.S.S.66
Club founded in 1912.
Visitors: welcome weekdays and now, competition days.
Green fees: on application.
Society meetings: none.
Catering: bar snacks, except Mon.
Hotels: Ladbroke Mercury, Elland; The Rock, Holywell Green.

s24 Garforth

☎Garforth (0532) 862021
Long Lane, Garforth, Leeds

LS25 2DS.
6.5 miles E of Leeds on A63, then left onto A642.
Parkland course.
18 holes, 6296 yards, S.S.S.70
Club founded in 1913.
Visitors: welcome weekdays.
Green fees: £11.
Society meetings: during the week.
Catering: all days except Tues.
Hotels: Ladbroke, Garforth.

S25 **Gott's Park**
☎Leeds (0532) 638232
Armley Ridge Rd, Leeds LS12 2QX.
About 3 miles W of city centre.
Parkland course.
18 holes, 4449 yards, S.S.S.62
Visitors: welcome.
Green fees: £2.95 weekdays; £3.20 weekends; juniors, OAPs, unemployed, £1.60 before 5pm otherwise £1.40.
Society meetings: booked through Council.
Catering: meals served.
Hotels: Queens; Dragonara.

S26 **Grange Park**
☎Rotherham (0709) 558884 and 559497
Upper Wortley Rd, Rotherham S61 2SJ.
2 miles W of town on A629.
Parkland municipal course.
18 holes, 6461 yards, S.S.S.71
Club founded in 1971.
Visitors: no restrictions.
Green fees: £2.20 weekdays; £2.80 weekends.
Society meetings: not catered for.
Catering: available on request.
Hotels: many nearby.

S27 **Halifax**
☎Halifax (0422) 244171
Union Lane, Ogden, Halifax HX2 8XR.
4 miles from town centre on A629 to Keighley.
Moorland course.
18 holes, 6030 yards, S.S.S.70
Club founded in 1900.
Visitors: welcome weekdays and by prior appointment at weekends.
Green fees: £6 per day weekdays; £9 per day weekends.
Society meetings: welcome by prior arrangement with reduced party rates.
Catering: full range of catering services available at most times except Mon.
Hotels: Holdsworth House,

Holmfield, Halifax; Princess, Princess St, Halifax.

S28 **Halifax Bradley Hall**
☎Elland (0422) 74108
Stainland Rd, Holywell Green, Halifax.
Halfway between Halifax and Huddersfield on B6112.
Moorland course.
18 holes, 6213 yards, S.S.S.70
Visitors: welcome.
Green fees: on application.
Society meetings: welcome.
Catering: full catering, except Tues.
Hotels: Old Golf House, Outlane, Huddersfield; hotels in Halifax or Huddersfield.

S29 **Hallamshire**
☎Sheffield (0742) 302153
Sandygate, Sheffield S10 4LA.
A57 from centre of Sheffield, left fork at Crosspool (3 miles from centre), 1 mile to course.
Moorland course.
18 holes, 6396 yards, S.S.S.71
Club founded in 1897.
Visitors: weekdays and limited weekends.
Green fees: £12; £14 weekends and Bank Holidays.
Society meetings: catered for weekdays.
Catering: full dining facilities except Tues.
Hotels: Hallam Towers; Post House, Sheffield; Rutland, Sheffield.

S30 **Hallowes**
☎Dronfield (0246) 413734 Sec, 411196 Pro.
Hallowes Lane, Dronfield, Sheffield S18 6UA.
Take A61 Sheffield to Chesterfield road into Dronfield (do not take the by-pass), turn sharp right under railway bridge, club signposted.
Undulating moorland course.
18 holes, 6134 yards, S.S.S.71
Club founded in 1892.
Visitors: check with Professional.
Green fees: on application.
Society meetings: limited.
Catering: by arrangement with the Stewardess.
Hotels: Chantrey; Blue Stoops, Dronfield; Hallam Towers; The Grosvenor House.

S31 **Hanging Heaton**
☎Dewsbury (0924) 461606
White Cross Rd, Bennett Lane, Dewsbury, W Yorks WF12 7HJ.

On A653 1 mile from Dewsbury town centre.
Parkland course.
9 holes, 5874 yards, S.S.S.68
Visitors: welcome weekdays.
Green fees: on application.
Society meetings: welcome weekdays.
Catering: lunch served except Mon.
Hotels: numerous in area.

S32 **Headingley**
☎Leeds (0532) 679573 Sec, 675100 Pro.
Back Church Lane, Adel, Leeds LS16 8DW.
At roundabout on Leeds ring road take A660 towards Otley, turn right at traffic lights, course is just past Adel Church.
Undulating moorland course.
18 holes, 6238 yards, S.S.S.70
Club founded in 1892.
Visitors: largely unrestricted.
Recognised golfing societies by previous arrangement.
Green fees: £11 per round/day weekdays; £13 per round, £15 per day weekends and Bank Holidays.
Society meetings: recognised societies welcome if previous arrangements made with Sec.
Catering: full facilities (restricted Fri).
Hotels: Post House, Leeds Road, Bramhope, Nr Leeds; Parkway, Oxley Rd, Leeds.

S33 **Headley**
☎Bradford (0274) 833481
Headley Lane, Thornton, Bradford, W Yorks BD13 3AJ.
4 miles W of Bradford, on B6145 Thornton road. Course in village of Thornton.
Moorland course.
9 holes, 2457 yards, S.S.S.64
Club founded in 1906.
Visitors: unlimited not Sun.
Green fees: £3 per weekday; £6 weekends.
Society meetings: by arrangement.
Catering: by arrangement.
Hotels: Norfolk Gardens, Bradford.

S34 **Hickleton**
☎Rotherham (0709) 892496
Hickleton, Doncaster, S Yorks.
7 miles out of Doncaster on A635 to Barnsley.
Undulating meadowland course.
18 holes, 6361 yards, S.S.S.70
Course designed by Huggett, Coles & Dyer.
Club founded in 1909.

Visitors: welcome if members of recognised club.
Green fees: on application.
Society meetings: welcome weekdays.
Catering: by arrangement except Mon.
Hotels: in Doncaster.

s35 **Hillsborough**
☎Sheffield (0742) 349151
Worrall Rd, Sheffield S6 4BE.
Moorland/parkland course.
18 holes, 5518 metres, S.S.S.69
Club founded in 1920.
Visitors: welcome weekdays.
Green fees: £10.50; £15 weekends.
Society meetings: by prior arrangement.
Catering: soup/sandwiches any lunchtime except Fri. Any full meals by prior arrangement.
Hotels: Grosvenor, Sheffield; Rutland, Sheffield.

s36 **Horsforth**
☎Leeds (0532) 586819
Layton Rd, Horsforth, Leeds, W Yorks LS18 5EX.
A65 Leeds-Ilkley road, Layton Rd is on right after crossing A6120 Leeds ring road, course is after Rawdon Crematorium on left.
Undulating moorland course.
18 holes, 6243 yards, S.S.S.70
Club founded in 1905.
Visitors: any time except Sat.
Green fees: £9 per day; £12 weekends.
Society meetings: weekdays and Sun.
Catering: full service available.
Hotels: Post House, Bramhope, Otley Rd, Nr Leeds.

s37 **Howley Hall**
☎Batley (0924) 472432.
Scotchman Lane, Morley, Leeds LS27 0NX.
From A650, main Bradford-Wakefield Rd, take B6123, situated in Morley.
Parkland course.
18 holes, 6420 yards, S.S.S.71
Club founded in 1900.
Visitors: welcome except Sat.
Green fees: £8 per round, £10 per day weekdays; £12 per round/day weekends.
Society meetings: catered for weekdays.
Catering: every day except Mon.
Hotels: Post House, Ossett.

s38 **Huddersfield**
☎Huddersfield (0484) 26203 Sec,

20110 Club.
Fixby Hall, Fixby, Huddersfield HD2 2EP.
From M62, exit 24, follow A643 to Clough House Inn then first right down Lightridge Rd, clubhouse gates on right.
Parkland course.
18 holes, 6424 yards, S.S.S.71
Club founded in 1891.
Visitors: welcome but time restricted Sun.
Green fees: £12.50, (£5 with member) weekday; £15, (£5 with member) weekends.
Society meetings: by prior arrangement with Sec.
Catering: lunch, à la carte dinner.
Hotels: Ladbroke Motor Motel; George.

s39 **Ilkley**
☎Ilkley (0943) 600214 Sec, 607277 Steward, 607463 Pro.
Myddleton, Ilkley, W Yorks LS29 0BE.
On A65 18 miles NW of Leeds.
Parkland course.
18 holes, 6256 yards, S.S.S.70
Club founded in 1890.
Visitors: welcome by arrangement.
Green fees: £14 weekdays; £18 weekends and Bank Holidays.
Society meetings: by arrangement weekdays only.
Catering: full facilities.
Hotels: Craiglands, Cow Pasture Rd, Ilkley; Grove, The Grove, Ilkley.

s40 **Keighley**
☎Keighley (0535) 604778/603179
Howden Park, Utley, Keighley, W Yorks BD20 6DA.
1 mile N of Keighley on A650 Skipton road, between the River Aire and the canal.
Parkland course.
18 holes, 6139 yards, S.S.S.70
Club founded in 1904.
Visitors: not Sat, limited Sun.
Green fees: £10 weekdays; £12 weekends and Bank Holidays.
Society meetings: by prior arrangement.
Catering: every day except Mon.
Hotels: Dalesgate, Skipton Rd, Utley, Keighley; Beeches, Bradford Rd, Keighley.

s41 **Leeds**
☎Leeds (0532) 658775
Elmete Lane, Leeds LS8 2LJ
Off A58 4 miles from Leeds.
Parkland course.
18 holes, 6097 yards, S.S.S.69

Club founded in 1896.
Visitors: weekdays, weekends with member only.
Society meetings: catered for weekdays.
Catering: as required except Mon.
Hotels: Queens; Hotel Metropole.

s42 **Lees Hall**
☎Sheffield (0742) 552900 Sec, 554402 Club.
Hemsworth Rd, Norton, Sheffield S8 8LL.
3 miles S of Sheffield, A61 then B6054 towards Gleadless, first exit at roundabout, follow road to next roundabout passing water tower on left, take first exit, course 300 yards on right.
Parkland/meadowland course.
18 holes, 6137 yards, S.S.S.69
Visitors: always welcome.
Green fees: £7 per round, £8 per day weekdays; £9 per round weekends and Bank Holidays.
Society meetings: weekdays subject to prior booking.
Catering: no catering on Tues.
Hotels: Grosvenor House; Hallam Towers.

s43 **Lightcliffe**
☎(0422) 202459
Knowle Top Rd, Lightcliffe, Halifax.
On A58 Leeds-Halifax road, in Lightcliffe/Hipperholme village 4 miles E of Halifax.
Parkland course.
9 holes, 5388 yards, S.S.S.68
Club founded in 1907.
Visitors: welcome not Wed and Sat.
Green fees: £6, (£3 with member) weekdays; £8, (£4 with member) weekends.
Society meetings: catered for on weekdays except Wed.
Catering: lunch and evening meals except Thurs.

s44 **Longley Park**
☎Huddersfield (0484) 22304
Maple St, off Somerset Rd, Huddersfield HD5 9AX.
0.5 mile from town centre.
Parkland course.
9 holes, 5269 yards, S.S.S.66
Club founded in 1911.
Visitors: welcome weekdays except Thurs. Restricted weekends.
Green fees: £3.50 weekdays; £5.50 weekends.
Society meetings: by arrangement except Sat.
Catering: except Mon by arrangement.

Hotels: Huddersfield, Huddersfield (1 mile).

S45 **Low Laithes**
☎Ossett (0924) 273275 Club, 274667 Pro.
Parkmill Lane, Flushdyke, Ossett, W Yorks.
Leave M1 at exit 40, follow signs to Low Laithes and Flushdyke, about 1 mile.
Undulating course.
18 holes, 6448 yards, S.S.S.71
Course designed by McKenzie.
Club founded in 1925.
Visitors: parties welcome weekdays. No parties weekends. Individual visitors welcome.
Green fees: £6 weekdays; £8 weekends and Bank Holidays; (2/3rd price with member).
Society meetings: by arrangement, full facilities available.
Catering: full facilities by previous arrangement.
Hotels: Post House, Queens Drive, Ossett; Mews, Dale St, Ossett; Swallow, Wakefield.

S46 **Marsden**
☎Huddersfield (0484) 844253
Mount Rd, Hemplow, Marsden, Huddersfield HD7 6NN.
Off A62, 8 miles out of Huddersfield towards Manchester.
Moorland course.
9 holes, 5702 yards, S.S.S.68
Course designed by Dr Mackenzie.
Club founded in 1920.
Visitors: welcome weekdays.
Green fees: £4, (£2.50 with member) weekdays; £6, (£3 with member) weekends and Bank Holidays.
Society meetings: catered for by arrangement weekdays.
Catering: lunch except Tues, evening meals by arrangement.
Hotels: Durker Roods, Meltham.

S47 **Meltham**
☎Huddersfield (0484) 850227
Thick Hollins, Meltham, Huddersfield HD7 3DQ.
5 miles from Huddersfield on B6108, in Meltham take B6107.
Moorland/parkland course.
18 holes, 6145 yards, S.S.S.70
Club founded in 1908.
Visitors: any day except Wed and Sat.
Green fees: £8 weekdays; £10 Sun and Bank Holidays.
Society meetings: welcomed weekdays.
Catering: all days except Tues.
Hotels: Durker Roods, Meltham; Old Bridge, Holmfirth, Huddersfield.

S48 **Middleton Park**
☎Leeds (0532) 700449
Middleton Park, Leeds.
3 miles S of city centre.
Parkland course.
18 holes, 5233 yards, S.S.S.69
Course designed by Leeds City Council.
Club founded in 1932.
Visitors: welcome.
Green fees: £3 per round.
Society meetings: can be booked.
Catering: none.
Hotels: many in Leeds city centre.

S49 **Moor Allerton**
☎Leeds (0532) 661154 or 661155
Coal Rd, Wike, Leeds LS17 9NH.
Take A61 Harrogate Road, about 1 mile past intersection with A6120 ring road, turn right onto Wigton Lane, at T-junction take first left, then first right then signposted.
Undulating parkland course.

1-18 The Lakes-6045 yards,
S.S.S.71
10-27 Blackmoor-6222 yards,
S.S.S.72
1-9/19-27 High course-6930 yards,
S.S.S.75
Course designed by Robert Trent
Jones.
Club founded in 1923.
Visitors: welcome weekdays and
with reservation weekends.
Green fees: £16.50 per day
weekdays; £25 per day Sat and
Bank Holidays.
Society meetings: any weekdays,
maximum 24 Sat and Bank Holidays.
Not Sundays.
Catering: lunch every day except
Sun. Dinner - Tues, Wed, Thurs -
unlimited numbers. Mon, Fri -
minimum 40 required.
Hotels: Harewood Arms, Harewood;
Windmill, Seacroft; Post House,
Bramhope; Ladbroke, Wetherby;
Dragonara, Leeds; Granby,
Harrogate; Parkway, Otley Road.

s50 Moortown
☎Leeds (0532) 681682
Harrogate Rd, Leeds LS17 7DB.
On A61 main Leeds-Harrogate road.
Moorland course.
18 holes, 6503 yards, S.S.S.72
Course designed by Dr Mackenzie.
Club founded in 1909.
Visitors: welcome weekdays and at
weekends by arrangement with Sec
and Pro.
Green fees: on application.
Society meetings: welcome
weekdays.
Catering: lunch served except Mon,
other meals by arrangement.
Hotels: Harewood Arms, Harewood;
Post House, Bramhope.

s51 Mount Skip
☎Hebden Bridge (0422) 842896
Wadsworth, Hebden Bridge, W
Yorks HX7 8PH.
1 mile E of Hebden Bridge on
Birchcliffe Rd.
Moorland course.
9 holes, 5114 yards, S.S.S.66
Club founded in 1930.
Visitors: welcome.
Green fees: £5 (half price with
member, further discount for juniors).
Society meetings: welcome except
Mon.
Catering: restaurant available
except Mon.
Hotels: Hebden Lodge, New Rd,
Hebden Bridge; Carlton, Albert St,

Hebden Bridge.

s52 Normanton
☎Wakefield (0924) 892943
Syndale Rd, Normanton, Wakefield,
W Yorks WF6 1PA.
Off M62 at junction 31 0.5 mile from
Normanton centre.
Flat meadowland course.
9 holes, 5184 yards, S.S.S.66
Club founded in 1903.
Visitors: weekdays and Sat.
Members only Sun.
Green fees: £5, (£4 with member)
weekdays; £7, (£6 with member)
Saturday.
Society meetings: weekdays only
(full catering available).
Catering: full facilities.
Hotels: The Village Motel, Castleford
Rd, Normanton.

s53 Northcliffe
☎Bradford (0274) 596731 Sec,
584085 Club, 587193 Pro.
High Bank Lane, Shipley, W Yorks
BD18 4LJ.
Take A650 Bradford to Keighley road
to Saltaire roundabout, turn up
Moorhead Lane, leading to High
Bank Lane, club 0.5 mile on left.
Undulating parkland course.
18 holes, 6065 yards, S.S.S.69
Course designed by Sidney Weldon.
Club founded in 1920.
Visitors: welcome at all times except
Sat. (Tues Ladies Day - no visiting
parties).
Green fees: £8 weekdays; £10
weekends and Bank Holidays.
Society meetings: except Mon (no
catering or bar service except Tues
and Sat).
Catering: except Mon. Coffee, bar
snacks, dinner by arrangement with
Steward.
Hotels: Bankfield, Shipley; Regency
and Norfolk Gardens, Bradford.

s54 Otley
☎Otley (0943) 465329 Sec, 461015
Club, 463403 Pro.
West Busk Lane, Otley, W Yorks
LS21 3NG.
On Otley-Bradford road 1.5 miles
from Otley.
Meadowland course.
18 holes, 6225 yards, S.S.S.70
Club founded in 1906.
Visitors: welcome.
Green fees: £10.50 weekdays; £13
weekends.
Society meetings: by arrangement.
Catering: full facilities available

except Mon.
Hotels: Post House, Bramhope;
Devonshire Arms, Bolton Abbey.

s55 Outlane
☎Elland (0422) 74762
Slack Lane, Outlane, Huddersfield,
W Yorks.
Off A640 Rochdale road, 4 miles out
of Huddersfield, through village of
Outlane, turn left under motorway.
Moorland course.
18 holes, 5590 yards, S.S.S.67
Club founded in 1906.
Visitors: welcome.
Green fees: £6, (£3.50 with
member) weekdays; £8, (£5 with
member) weekends.
Society meetings: by prior
arrangement.
Catering: meals daily except Tues.
Hotels: Old Golf House, Outlane,
Huddersfield; Ladbroke Mercury,
Ainley Top, Huddersfield.

s56 Painthorpe House
☎Wakefield (0924) 255083
Painthorpe Lane, Crigglestone,
Wakefield.
1 mile from junction 39 off M1.
Meadowland course.
9 holes, 4100 yards, S.S.S.60
Club founded in 1961.
Visitors: welcome except Sun.
Green fees: £2 per day.
Catering: meals served.
Hotels: Cedar Court.

s57 Phoenix
☎Rotherham (0709) 382624
Pavilion Lane, Brinsworth,
Rotherham.
1 mile along Bawtry turning from
Tinsley roundabout on M1.
Undulating meadowland course.
18 holes, 6145 yards, S.S.S.69
Club founded in 1932.
Visitors: welcome if members of
recognised golf clubs.
Green fees: £8 per day, (£3 with
member) weekdays; £10, (£4 with
member) weekends and Bank
Holidays.
Society meetings: welcome.
Catering: full on request.
Hotels: Carlton Park, Rotherham;
Brecon, Rotherham.

s58 Phoenix Park
☎Bradford (0274) 667178, 662369
Sec.
Phoenix Park, Dick Lane, Thornbury,
Bradford, W Yorks.
From Bradford take Leeds road for

2.5 miles to Thornbury roundabout, course situated at side of roundabout.
Undulating parkland course.
9 holes, 4776 yards, S.S.S.63
Visitors: welcome weekdays only.
Green fees: on application.
Society meetings: by prior arrangement with Sec.
Catering: by arrangement with Steward prior to visit.
Hotels: many good hotels in Bradford.

S59 Pontefract & District
☎Pontefract (0977) 792241
Park Lane, Pontefract, W Yorks WF8 4QS.
Exit 32 on M62, course on B6134.
Parkland course.
18 holes, 6227 yards, S.S.S.70
Club founded in 1900.
Visitors: welcome weekdays.
Green fees: £8.50 weekdays; £9 weekends.
Society meetings: catered for weekdays except Wed.
Catering: daily, except Mon.
Hotels: Red Lion, Market Place, Pontefract; Wentbridge House, Wentbridge, Pontefract.

S60 Queensbury
☎Bradford (0276) 882155
Brighouse Rd, Queensbury, Bradford, W Yorks BD13 1QF.
4 miles from Bradford on A647.
Undulating parkland course.
9 holes, 5102 yards, S.S.S.65
Club founded in 1923.
Visitors: bona fide golfers welcome.
Green fees: £4 weekdays; £7 weekends.
Society meetings: by arrangement.
Catering: during normal licensing hours.
Hotels: Norfolk Gardens, Bradford; White Swan, Halifax.

S61 Rawdon
☎(0532) 506040
Buckstone Drive, Rawdon, Leeds LS19 6BD.
On A65 6 miles from Leeds.
Undulating parkland course.
9 holes, 5964 yards, S.S.S.69
Club founded in 1896.
Visitors: welcome weekdays.
Green fees: £7.50 per day.
Society meetings: welcome weekdays by arrangement.
Catering: lunch served except Mon.
Hotels: Peas Hill; Robin Hood, Yeadon.

S62 Riddlesden
☎Keighley (0535) 602148
Howden Rough, Elam Wood Rd, Riddlesden, Keighley, W Yorks.
A650 Keighley-Bradford road, left into Bar Lane, left into Scott Lane for 2 miles.
Moorland course.
18 holes, 4185 yards, S.S.S.61
Club founded in 1927.
Visitors: unlimited except before 10am on Sun.
Green fees: £3; (£2 introduced by member) weekdays; £4; (£3 introduced by member) weekends.
Society meetings: none.
Catering: by prior arrangement or during normal bar hours at weekend.
Hotels: Beeches, Bradford Rd, Keighley.

S63 Rotherham
☎Rotherham (0709) 850812 Sec, 850466 Pro.
Thrybergh Park, Thrybergh, Rotherham S65 4NU.
On main road from Doncaster-Rotherham, from A1 (M), 3 miles from M18 at Bramley, 7 miles from M1 at junction 35.
Parkland course.
18 holes, 6324 yards, S.S.S.70
Club founded in 1903.
Visitors: casuals by arrangement with Pro. Societies (16 or more) booked through Sec.
Green fees: £11.50 per day weekdays; £14 weekends and Bank Holidays.
Society meetings: not Wed, limited at weekends.
Catering: full facilities every day.
Hotels: Brecon, Moorgate, Rotherham.

S64 Roundhay
☎Leeds (0532) 662695
Park Lane, Leeds LS8 2EJ.
A58 to Oakwood Clock, then Princes Ave, Street Lane, right at Park Lane, 4 miles from city centre.
Parkland municipal course.
9 holes, 5166 yards, S.S.S.65
Club founded in 1921.
Visitors: unrestricted.
Green fees: £3 weekdays; £3.30 weekends.
Society meetings: by arrangement with Leeds City Council.
Catering: restaurant Tues-Sun evenings. Snacks available Sat, Sun.
Hotels: Beech Wood, 34 Street Lane, Leeds.

S65 Sand Moor
☎Leeds (0532) 685180.
Alwoodley Lane, Leeds LS17 7DJ.
A61 from Leeds city centre 6 miles.
Turn left into Alwoodley Lane 0.5 mile on right.
Undulating parkland/moorland course.
18 holes, 6429 yards, S.S.S.71
Course designed by N. Barnes.
Club founded in 1926.
Visitors: welcome weekdays.
Members reserved times 12.00-1.30pm; Tues 9.30-10.30am; Thurs 9.00-12.00am.
Green fees: £13 per round, £15 per day weekdays; £18 weekends.
Society meetings: catered for weekdays.
Catering: full facilities on all days except Mon when lunch and snacks only served.
Hotels: Harewood Arms, Harewood; Parkway, Otley Road, Leeds; Post House, Bramhope, Nr Leeds.

S66 Scarcroft
☎Leeds (0532) 892263 or 892311.
Syke Lane, Leeds LS14 3BQ.
On A58 NE of Leeds, immediately after the New Inn on the left is Syke Lane.
Parkland course.
18 holes, 6426 yards, S.S.S.71
Course designed by Major Charles Mackenzie.
Club founded in 1937.
Visitors: welcome weekdays, weekends by prior arrangement only.
Green fees: £12.50 per day/round, (£5.50 with member) weekdays; £20 per day/round, (£5.50 with member) weekends.
Society meetings: welcome weekdays by arrangement.
Catering: meals every day except Mon.
Hotels: Angel, High Street, Wetherby; Brunswick, High Street, Wetherby.

S67 Shipley
☎Bradford (0274) 568652 Sec, 563212 Club, 563674 Pro.
Beckfoot Lane, Cottingley Bridge, Bingley, W Yorks BD16 1LX.
Situated on A650 Bradford-Keighley road at Cottingley Bridge, Bingley.
Parkland course.
18 holes, 6203 yards, S.S.S.70
Course designed by Colt, Alison and Mackenzie assisted by James Braid.
Club founded in 1896.
Visitors: welcome except Tues

Yorkshire

Yorkshire, as the biggest county, has a lot to offer with much contrast, too. Its coastal courses are rather more of the cliff-top variety than embossed with great dunes but it possesses four of our very finest inland courses — Alwoodley, Ganton, Lindrick and Moortown.

To avoid accusations of partiality, I list them alphabetically as any attempt to grade them on merit would be extremely difficult. Alwoodley is perhaps the least well known because she used to guard her secrets jealously. It wasn't until 1965 that the Yorkshire championship was granted leave to be held there but it was the home course of Alister Mackenzie, the celebrated course architect, and its lovely moorland character undoubtedly left its mark on his thinking.

As it happened, Mackenzie was also responsible for Moortown which lies just across the Harrogate Road from Alwoodley and was part of the same moor until becoming more or less surrounded by housing developments, a course which used to rub shoulders with Moor Allerton and Sand Moor. For many years, Moortown was a suburb of Leeds rather than now, it seems, part of it. By contrast no setting could be more rurally splendid or scenically glorious than Ganton which lies in the Vale of Pickering between Malton and Scarborough. Everything about it bears such an air of elegance that nobody could fail to enjoy the challenge of the golf over a course that has housed countless national championships as well as the Ryder Cup of 1949. Moortown, Ganton and Lindrick have all, in fact, hosted the Ryder Cup. Lindrick followed the unforgettable scenes of the British victory in 1957 by staging the Curtis Cup of 1960.

Lindrick's delights, conveying the virtues of heath and common, extol the best of South Yorkshire, so far south, to be strictly accurate, that the river behind the famous 4th green forms the boundary with Nottinghamshire. From Lindrick, along the A57, it is a short journey to Sheffield where Hallamshire and Abbeydale are well worth a visit and, edging north and a little west, I have a soft spot for the Huddersfield Club at Fixby and for Woodsome Hall.

However, to complete the county of many acres and many courses, Ilkley, Otley and Bradford are equally pleasant; Harrogate is well served by Pannal, the Harrogate Club and Oakdale while travellers to the coast should never overlook Fulford at York or, moving further afield, some of the more isolated clubs out in the country.

---

before 2pm. Saturdays before 4pm.
Green fees: £10.50 per day; £13 weekends and Bank Holidays; (£5 with member) at any time.
Society meetings: by arrangement with the Hon Sec.
Catering: except Mon, bar snacks and evening meals by arrangement with the Steward.
Hotels: Bankfield, Bradford Rd, Bingley; Oakwood Hall, Lady Lane, Bingley; Hall Bank, Beck Lane, Bingley.

S68 **Silkstone**
☎Barnsley (0226) 790328, 790128 Pro.
Field Head, Silkstone, Barnsley, S Yorks S75 4OD.
Leave M1 at junction 37, then 1 mile

on A628 towards Manchester.
Undulating meadowland course.
Club founded in 1905.
Visitors: welcome weekdays.
Green fees: £8 per round/day.
Society meetings: catered for weekdays.
Catering: full facilities except Mon.
Hotels: Ardsley Moat House, Doncaster Rd, Ardsley, Barnsley; Brooklands Motel, Dodworth, Barnsley.

S69 **Silsden**
☎Steeton (0525) 52998
High Brunthwaite, Silsden, Keighley BD20 0NH.
A629, 4 miles from Keighley, on to A6034 to Silsden town centre, turn right at canal.

Moorland/meadowland course.
14 holes, 4870 yards, S.S.S.64
Club founded in 1913.
Visitors: welcome weekdays and at weekends with restrictions on Sat afternoons and Sun mornings.
Green fees: £5, (£2.10 with member) weekdays; £8, (£4 with member) weekends.
Society meetings: none.
Catering: none.
Hotels: Steeton Hall, Station Rd, Steeton.

S70 **Sitwell Park**
☎Rotherham (0709) 541046
Shrogswood Rd, Rotherham, S Yorks S60 4BY.
Exit 33 (M1), or Exit 18, off A631, 2 miles SE of Rotherham.

Undulating parkland course.
18 holes, 6203 yards, S.S.S.70
Course designed by Dr Mackenzie.
Club founded in 1913.
Visitors: welcome.
Green fees: £8 per round, £10 per
day weekdays; £10 per round, £12
per day weekends.
Society meetings: welcome
weekdays.
Catering: meals served except
Tues.
Hotels: Moat House, Brecon,
Brentwood.

s71 South Bradford
☎Bradford (0274) 679195
Pearson Rd, Odsal, Bradford
BD6 1BH.
From Odsal roundabout take
Stadium Rd (first road left down
Cleckheaton Rd) then Pearson Rd to
club.
Undulating meadowland course.
9 holes, 6004 yards, S.S.S.69
Club founded in 1906.
Visitors: welcome weekdays.
Green fees: £5, (£2.50 with
member) weekdays; £8, (£5 with
member) weekends.
Society meetings: welcome
weekdays.
Catering: lunches and evening
meals served except Mon.
Hotels: Novotel, Euroway Estate,
Bradford.

s72 South Leeds
☎Leeds (0532) 700479
Gipsy Lane, Beeston Ring Rd, Leeds
LS11 5TU.
Take Leeds-Dewsbury road to traffic
lights at Tommy Wass Hotel, follow
ring road for 100 yards then left into
Gipsy Lane, leading to clubhouse.
Parkland course.
18 holes, 5890 yards, S.S.S.68
Club founded in 1914.
Visitors: welcome any time with
member or by arrangement.
Green fees: £8 weekdays; £11
weekends.
Society meetings: welcome by
application to Sec except Tues.
Catering: every day except Mon.
Hotels: Dragonara; Queens; Red
Lion; all in Leeds City Centre.

s73 Stocksbridge & District
☎Stocksbridge (0742) 882003
30 Royd Lane, Townend, Deepcar,
Sheffield S30 5RZ.
On Sheffield-Manchester road, A616,
9 miles from Sheffield to Deepcar.

Moorland course.
15 holes, 5055 yards, S.S.S.65
Club founded in 1925.
Visitors: welcome any time.
Green fees: £6 per day.
Society meetings: on request.
Catering: on request except Mon.
Hotels: Grosvenor, Sheffield; Hallam
Towers, Sheffield.

s74 Tankersley Park
☎Sheffield (0742) 468247
High Green, Sheffield S30 4LG.
Leave M1 at junction 35 to
Chapeltown, then 1 mile off A6135 N
of Chapeltown.
Parkland course.
18 holes, 3204 yards, S.S.S.79
Club founded in 1903.
Visitors: weekdays unlimited, Sat
and Sun after 3pm.
Green fees: £6 per round; £8 per
day; (£3 per round with member).
Society meetings: catered for
weekdays.
Catering: bar snacks and/or full
dinner.
Hotels: Staindrop Lodge, Lane End,
Chapeltown, Sheffield.

s75 Temple Newsam
☎Leeds (0532) 645624
Temple Newsam Rd, Leeds LS15.
On A63 Selby road, 5 miles from
Leeds centre, follow signs for
Temple Newsam House.
Undulating parkland course.
18 holes, 6448 yards, S.S.S.71
18 holes, 6029 yards, S.S.S.72
Club founded in 1923.
Visitors: welcome.
Green fees: on application.
Society meetings: welcome.
Catering: meals served at
weekends.
Hotels: Windmill, Scarcroft, Leeds;
Mercury, Garforth, Leeds.

s76 Tinsley Park
☎Sheffield (0742) 560237
High Hazel Park, Darnall, Sheffield
S9.
Take A57 off M1 at junction 33. At
traffic lights turn right on Greenland
Rd and right by bus depot.
Parkland course.
18 holes, 6045 yards, S.S.S.69
Club founded in 1921.
Visitors: unrestricted.
Green fees: £4.20 any time.
Society meetings: cannot book
block times.
Catering: any day except Tues.
Hotels: Royal Victoria.

s77 Wakefield
☎Wakefield (0924) 258778 Sec,
255104 Club, 255380 Pro.
Woodthorpe Lane, Sandal,
Wakefield WF2 6JH.
3 miles S of Wakefield on A61, from
M1 Exit 39.
Parkland course.
18 holes, 6626 yards, S.S.S.72
Course designed by Alex (Sandy)
Herd.
Club founded in 1891.
Visitors: by arrangement.
Green fees: £11 weekdays; £13
weekends.
Society meetings: by arrangement
with Sec.
Catering: except Mon.
Hotels: Cedar Court; Swallow.

s78 Wath
☎Rotherham (0709) 878677
Abdy, Blackamoor, Rotherham,
S Yorks S62 7SJ.
Off A633 in Wath upon Dearne, 7
miles N of Rotherham. Course only
open Mar-Oct.
Meadowland course.
9 holes, (as 18 holes) 5614 yards,
S.S.S.67
Visitors: welcome weekdays, with
member at weekends.
Green fees: £6 per day, (£3 with
member).
Society meetings: welcome by
arrangement.
Catering: snacks and bar food
available.
Hotels: Marquis Hotel in village.

s79 West Bowling
☎Bradford (0274) 724449
Newall Hall, Rooley Lane, Bradford,
W Yorks BD5 8LB.
On Bradford inner ring road, 2 miles
from town centre, adjacent to M606
and M62.
Parkland/meadowland course.
18 holes, 5770 yards, S.S.S.68
Club founded in 1898.
Visitors: welcome weekdays.
Green fees: £6.50, (£3.25 with
member) weekdays; £10, (£5 with
member) weekends.
Society meetings: Wed, Thurs, Fri.
Catering: every day lunches and
evening meals except Mon.
Hotels: Norfolk Gardens, Bradford;
Guide Post, Low Moor.

s80 West Bradford
☎Halifax (0274) 42767
Chellow Grange, Haworth Rd,
Bradford, W Yorks BD9 6NP.

B6144 3 miles from Bradford on Haworth road.
Meadowland course.
18 holes, 5752 yards, S.S.S.68
Club founded in 1900.
Visitors: welcome weekdays.
Green fees: £6 including VAT weekdays; £8 including VAT weekends and Bank Holidays.
Society meetings: catered for weekdays.
Catering: meals served except Mon.
Hotels: Norfolk Gardens, Bradford.

S81 **West End**
☎Halifax (0422) 53608
The Racecourse, Paddock Lane, Highroad Well, Halifax, W Yorks.
Take A61 Burnley road from town centre. At traffic lights complex at King Cross, 1 mile from town, turn sharp right at sign to Warley and ascend Warley road to T-junction in 0.75 mile. Turn left to Highroad Well village then right at end of village, up Court Lane, signposted.
Moorland course.
18 holes, 6003 yards, S.S.S.69
Club founded in 1906.
Visitors: welcome.
Green fees: £7 weekdays, (£3 with member); £9 weekends, (£3.50 with member).
Society meetings: catered for weekdays.
Catering: full facilities available every day except Mon.
Hotels: Holdsworth House, Holmfield, Halifax; Princess, Princess St, Halifax.

S82 **Wetherby**
☎Wetherby (0937) 63375
Linton Lane, Wetherby, LS22 4JF.
Off A1 at Wetherby.
Parkland course.
18 holes, 6235 yards, S.S.S.70
Club founded in 1910.

Visitors: subject to 12.15-1.15pm reservation for members. Welcome at all times.
Green fees: £9 per round, £11.50 per day weekdays; £13 per round, £16 per day weekdays. (Half price with member.)
Society meetings: Wed, Thurs, Fri. 9.30am and 2pm starting times.
Catering: lunch served except Mon.
Hotels: Ladbroke Mercury, Wetherby (plus all Harrogate hotels).

S83 **Wheatley**
☎Doncaster (0302) 831655
Armthorpe Rd, Doncaster, S Yorks DN2 5QB.
Follow S ring road on A18 E along boundary of St Leger racecourse to next crossroads, clubhouse is on right opposite large water tower.
Undulating parkland course.
18 holes, 6345 yards, S.S.S.70
Course designed by George Duncan.
Club founded in 1913.
Visitors: welcome.
Green fees: £8 per round, £10.50 per day weekdays; £10 per round, £12.50 per day weekends and Bank Holidays.
Society meetings: visiting societies weekdays only by arrangement.
Catering: restaurant facilities.
Hotels: Balmoral, Thorne Rd; Earl of Doncaster, Bennetthorpe; Punches, Bawtry Road.

S84 **Woodhall Hills**
☎Leeds (0532) 554594
Woodhall Rd, Calverley, Pudsey, W Yorks.
Adjacent to main Leeds-Bradford road, 6 miles from Leeds.
Undulating parkland course.
18 holes, 6102 yards, S.S.S.69
Club founded in 1905.
Visitors: welcome most days, restricted Sat.

Green fees: £8 per day, £6 per round weekdays; £10 per day, £8 per round weekends and Bank Holidays.
Society meetings: contact Sec.
Hotels: many in area.

S85 **Woodsome Hall**
☎Huddersfield (0484) 602971, 602739 Sec.
Fenay Bridge, Huddersfield, W Yorks HD8 0LQ.
5 miles SE of Huddersfield on A629 Sheffield to Penistone road.
Parkland course.
18 holes, 6068 yards, S.S.S.69
Club founded in 1922.
Visitors: welcome weekdays, Tues after 4pm and limited number at weekends.
Green fees: £11.50 weekdays; £14 weekends and Public Holidays.
Society meetings: catered for weekdays.
Catering: full facilities except Mon.
Hotels: The George; The Ladbroke Mercury.

S86 **Wortley**
☎Sheffield (0742) 885294 Sec, 882139 Steward.
Hermit Hill Lane, Wortley, Sheffield S30 4DF.
Off M1 at junction 35, take A629 through Wortley village, course first right.
Undulating wooded parkland course.
18 holes, 5983 yards, S.S.S.69
Club founded in 1894.
Visitors: not restricted but parties are arranged on Wed and Fri.
Green fees: £10 and £11.
Society meetings: arrangements can be made for Wed and Fri.
Catering: by arrangement.
Hotels: Hallam Towers, Sheffield.

T North Yorkshire and Humberside

T1 Bedale

☎Bedale (0677) 22568
Leyburn Rd, Bedale, N Yorks
DL8 1EZ.
On A684 0.25 mile N of Bedale.
Parkland course.
18 holes, 5599 yards, S.S.S.66
Club founded in 1884.
Visitors: welcome weekdays/
weekends.
Green fees: £6 weekdays; £10
weekends.
Society meetings: weekdays only.
Catering: served daily except Mon.
Hotels: Leeming Motel, Leeming
Bar, Northallerton; The Old Vicarage,
Crakehall, Bedale.

T2 Beverley & East Riding

☎Beverley (0482) 868757
Ante Mill, The Westwood, Beverley
HU17 8RG.
On Beverley to Walkington road.
Undulating course.
18 holes, 5937 yards, S.S.S.69
Course designed by Dr J.J. Fraser.
Club founded in 1889.
Visitors: welcome weekdays.
Green fees: £5, (£3 with member)
weekdays; £7, (£4 with member)
weekends and Bank Holidays.
Society meetings: catered for
weekdays.
Catering: lunch served except Wed.
Hotels: Beverley Arms, Beverley;
Lairgate, Beverley.

T3 Boothferry

☎Howden (0430) 430364
Spaldington, Howden, Goole
DN14 7NG.
A63 towards Howden then B1228 to
Bubwith for 3 miles.
Meadowland course.
18 holes, 6651 yards, S.S.S.72
Course designed by Cotton,
Pennink, Lawrie & Partners.
Club founded in 1982.
Visitors: welcome weekdays,
weekends and Bank Holidays except
Christmas day (public golf course).
Green fees: £3 per round, £4.50 per
day weekdays; £6.40 per round,
£8.80 per day weekends and Bank
Holidays.
Society meetings: catered for any
day except certain club competitions
days - reduced rates for societies of
12 players or more.

Catering: meals and snacks served
all lunchtimes except Christmas Day,
and summer season evenings
except Mon.
Hotels: Bowmans, Bridgegate,
Howden; Wellington, Bridgegate,
Howden; Farmhouse B & B
available.

T4 Bridlington

☎Bridlington (0262) 672092 and
606367
Belvedere Rd, Bridlington,
N Humberside YO15 3NA.
1.5 miles S of Bridlington station, off
A165.
Seaside course.
18 holes, 6320 yards, S.S.S.70
Course designed by James Braid.
Club founded in 1905.
Visitors: welcome. Parties booked
with Hon Sec.
Green fees: £5 per round, £8 per
day weekdays; £7 per round, £10 per
day weekends and Bank Holidays.
Society meetings: by arrangement.
Catering: full facilites except Tues.
Hotels: Marine, The Spa; Monarch.

T5 Brough

☎Hull (0482) 667291
Cave Rd, Brough, N Humberside
HU15 1HB.
10 miles W of Hull off A63.
Parkland course.
18 holes, 6035 yards, S.S.S.69
Club founded in 1891.
Visitors: weekdays only. Wed after
2.30pm only.
Green fees: £11 weekdays.
Society meetings: Tues and Fri.
Catering: available.
Hotels: Cave Castle, South Cave.

T6 Catterick Garrison

☎Richmond (0748) 833268
Leyburn Rd, Catterick Garrison, N
Yorks DL9 3QE.
6 miles S of Scotch Corner, turn off
A1 at Catterick Bridge, 2.5 miles to
Catterick Garrison.
Undulating moorland/parkland
course.
18 holes, 6332 yards, S.S.S.70
Course designed by Arthur Day.
Club founded in 1930.
Visitors: welcome.
Green fees: £7, (£4 with member)
weekdays; £10, (£6 with member)

weekends and Bank Holidays.
Society meetings: catered for on
application.
Catering: restaurant and snacks
except Mon.
Hotels: Bridge House, Catterick
Bridge; Golden Lion, Market Place,
Leyburn.

T7 Cleethorpes

☎Grimsby (0472) 812059 or
814060
Kings Rd, Cleethorpes, S Humber-
side DN35 0PN.
Off A1031 1 mile S of Cleethorpes.
Meadowland course.
18 holes, 6015 yards, S.S.S.69
Course designed by Harry Vardon.
Club founded in 1896.
Visitors: welcome but must be
members of a recognised club
(Ladies, Wed pm).
Green fees: £7, (£5.50 with
member) weekdays; £10, (£8.50 with
member) weekends.
Society meetings: only by
arrangement.
Catering: full facilities available by
arrangement with Steward.
Hotels: Kingsway, Kingsway,
Cleethorpes; Wellow, Kings Rd,
Cleethorpes; Blundell Park, Grimsby
Rd, Cleethorpes.

T8 Driffield

☎Driffield (0377) 43116
Sunderlandwick, Driffield, N
Humberside.
1 mile from Driffield town centre
towards Hull on A164.
Parkland course.
9 holes, 6227 yards, S.S.S.70
Course due to be extended to 18
holes.
Club founded in 1935.
Visitors: welcome.
Green fees: £4 per round weekdays;
£5 per day or round with member
weekends.
Society meetings: catered for
weekdays.
Catering: not on Mon.
Hotels: Bell, Market Square,
Driffield.

T9 Easingwold

☎Easingwold (0347) 21486 or
21964 Pro.
Stillington Rd, Easingwold YO6 3ET.

0.75 mile off A19, entering
Easingwold from York turn right
immediately past garage.
Parkland course.
18 holes, 6262 yards, S.S.S.70
Club founded in 1930.
Visitors: welcome.
Green fees: £10 per day weekdays;
£14 per day weekends and Bank
Holidays.
Society meetings: by prior
arrangement (not weekends or Bank
Holidays).
Catering: bar, lunch, dinner except
Mon.
Hotels: George, Market Place,
Easingwold.

T10 **Elsham**
☎Barnetby (0652) 688382 or
680291
Barton Rd, Elsham, Brigg, S
Humberside DN20 0LS.
Situated on E side of Brigg-Barton
road, B1206, 3 miles N of Brigg.
Parkland course.
18 holes, 6420 yards, S.S.S.71
Club founded in 1926.
Visitors: welcome weekdays.
Green fees: on application.

T11 **Filey**
☎Filey (0723) 513273
West Ave, Filey, N Yorks YO14 9BQ.
Private road off end of West Ave in S
end of town.
Seaside course.
18 holes, 6030 yards, S.S.S.69
Club founded in 1897.
Visitors: unaccompanied if member
of a golf club.
Green fees: £9 weekdays; £12
weekends.
Society meetings: by arrangement.
Catering: all year round.
Hotels: White Lodge, The Crescent,
Filey.

T12 **Flamborough Head**
☎Flamborough (0262) 850333
Lighthouse Rd, Flamborough,
Bridlington, N Humberside
YO15 1AR.
5 miles NE of Bridlington on B1255,
near lighthouse on headland at
Flamborough.
Undulating course.
18 holes, 5438 yards, S.S.S.66
Club founded in 1932.
Visitors: unrestricted, but not before
11am Sun.
Green fees: £5.50 weekdays; £7.50
weekends and Bank Holidays;

weekly £22 (5 weekdays).
Society meetings: by arrangement
with Sec.
Catering: full facilities available
except Mon.
Hotels: Flaneburg, N Marine Rd,
Flamborough; Timoneer, South Sea
Rd, Flamborough.

T13 **Fulford**
☎York (0904) 413579
Heslington Lane, Heslington, York
YO1 5DY.
Off A19 from York, follow signs to
University.
Parkland course.
18 holes, 6779 yards, S.S.S.72
Course designed by Dr A.
Mackenzie.
Club founded in 1906.
Visitors: by prior arrangement.
Green fees: £17 per day weekdays;
£19 per day weekends and Bank
Holidays.
Society meetings: contact Sec.
Catering: morning coffee, lunch and
evening meal.
Hotels: Alfreda, Heslington Lane,
York.

T14 **Ganstead Park**
☎Hull (0482) 811280.
Longdales Lane, Coniston, Hull
HU11 4LB.
On A165 E of Hull, 2 miles from city
boundary.
Parkland course.
9 holes, 5769 yards, S.S.S.68
Club founded in 1976.
Visitors: any day except Wed and
Sun am.
Green fees: £6, (£4 with member)
weekdays; £9, (£6 with member)
weekends.
Society meetings: by arrangement
only.
Hotels: Hull Marina; Beverley Arms.

T15 **Ganton**
☎Sherburn (0944) 70329
Ganton, Scarborough, N Yorks
YO12 4PA.
11 miles from Scarborough on A64.
Heathland course.
18 holes, 6693 yards, S.S.S.73
Course designed by Dunn, Vardon,
Cotton.
Visitors: by prior arrangement.
Green fees: on application.
Society meetings: by prior
arrangement.
Catering: available.
Hotels: list available on application.

T16 **Ghyll**
☎Earby (0282) 842466
Thornton-in-Craven, N Yorks.
Off A56, 1 mile from Barnoldswick.
Parkland course.
9 holes, 5708 yards, S.S.S.68
Club founded in 1908.
Visitors: Sun usually competitions.
Green fees: £5 weekdays; £6
weekends; (£4 anytime with a
member).
Society meetings: by arrangement.
Catering: bar snacks Fri evening
and Sat lunchtime, parties can be
catered for.
Hotels: Stirk House, Gisburn; The
Black Horse, Skipton.

T17 **Grimsby**
☎Grimsby (0472) 42630 Sec,
42823 Clubhouse, 56981 Pro.
Littlecoates Rd, Grimsby,
S Humberside DN34 4LU.
Turn left off A46 at first roundabout in
Grimsby, 0.75 mile on left, next
to Humber Royal Hotel.
Undulating parkland course.
18 holes, 6058 yards, S.S.S.69
Club founded in 1923.
Visitors: only members of golf clubs
welcome (Ladies Day Tues).
Green fees: £7 weekdays; £9
weekends; (£2.50 reduction if
introduced by member).
Society meetings: Mon and Fri
only.
Catering: bar snacks available,
other meals by arrangement, except
Wed.
Hotels: Humber Royal.

T18 **Harrogate**
☎Harrogate (0423) 863158
Steward, 862999 Sec, 862547 Pro.
Forest Lane Head, Starbeck,
Harrogate, N Yorks HG2 7TF.
About 1 mile from Knaresborough on
Harrogate-Knaresborough road, A59.
Parkland course.
18 holes, 6204 yards, S.S.S.70
Course designed by Sandy Herd.
Club founded in 1892.
Visitors: welcome, parties over 12 in
number by arrangement with Sec.
Green fees: Proposed 1988: £12
weekdays; £17 weekends and Bank
Holidays.
Society meetings: catered for
weekdays only.
Catering: by arrangement.
Hotels: Dower House, Knaresbor-
ough; many hotels in Harrogate.

T19 Hessle

☎Hull (0482) 650171
Westfield Rd, Cottingham, Hull, N
Humberside HU16 5YL.
4 miles W of Hull City Centre.
Undulating meadowland course.
18 holes, 6638 yards, S.S.S.72
Course designed by Peter Allis &
Dave Thomas.
New course opened in June 1975.
Club founded in 1906.
Visitors: not Tues, 9-15am to
1.00pm.
Green fees: £7.50 per round, £10
per day weekdays.
Society meetings: recognised
golfing societies welcome by prior
arrangement with Sec.
Catering: except Mon.
Hotels: Willerby Manor; Grange
Park; Beverley Arms.

T20 Heworth

☎York (0904) 424618, 422389 Pro.
Muncaster House, Muncastergate,
York YO3 9JX.
1.5 miles from city centre, on A164
York-Scarborough road.
Meadowland/parkland course.
11 holes, 6078 yards, S.S.S.69
Club founded in 1911.
Visitors: weekdays, weekends

restricted availability.
Green fees: £6 weekdays; £7
weekends and Bank Holidays; (£4
with member).
Society meetings: weekdays.
Catering: lunches except Mon.
Hotels: many in York.

T21 Holme Hall

☎Scunthorpe (0724) 862078 Office,
840909 Club.
Holme Lane, Bottesford, Scunthorpe,
S Humberside DN16 3RF.
2 miles SE of Scunthorpe near E exit
of M180.
Parkland course.
18 holes, 6475 yards, S.S.S.71
Club founded in 1908.
Visitors: welcome weekdays, with
member weekends.
Green fees: £8, (£4 with member).
Society meetings: weekdays by
arrangement.
Catering: meals by arrangement,
bar snacks daily except Fri.
Hotels: Royal; Wortley; Beverley.

T22 Hornsea

☎Hornsea (040 12) 2020,
4989 Sec.
Rolston Rd, Hornsea, N Humberside
HU18 1XG.

Follow sign for Hornsea Pottery in
Hornsea and clubhouse is approxi-
mately 600 yards past entrance to
pottery on road to Withernsea.
Parkland/moorland course.
18 holes, 6450 yards, S.S.S.71
Course designed by Sandy Herd.
Club founded in 1910.
Visitors: available everyday except
Tues (Ladies Day) ring Pro or Sec.
Green fees: £8 per round, £12 per
round.
Society meetings: by arrangement
with Sec, any day but Tues.
Catering: Stewards day off Mon,
catering available by arrangement.

T23 Hull

☎Hull (0482) 658919
The Hall, 27 Packman Lane, Kirk Ella
Hull HU10 7TJ.
5 miles W of Kingston-upon-Hull, off
A164.
Parkland course.
18 holes, 6242 yards, S.S.S.70
Course designed by James Braid.
Club founded in 1921.
Visitors: Mon-Fri only.
Green fees: £10 per day/round.
Society meetings: catered for on
Tues and Thurs by prior arrangement.
Catering: prior arrangements if

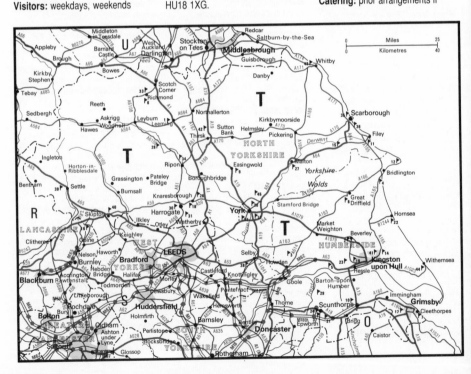

possible, lunches served Mon-Fri.
Hotels: Willerby Manor; Grange Park.

T24 Kingsway
☎Scunthorpe (0724) 840945
Kingsway, Scunthorpe,
S Humberside DN15 7ER.
S of A18 between Berkeley and Queensway roundabouts.
Undulating parkland course.
9 holes, 1915 yards, S.S.S.59
Course designed by R.D. Highfield.
Club founded in 1971.
Visitors: welcome every day.
Green fees: Adult £1.30, Child 65p weekday; Adult £1.60, Child 80p weekend and Bank Holidays.
Catering: snacks available.
Hotels: Royal; Wortley, Scunthorpe.

T25 Kirkbymoorside
☎Kirkbymoorside (0751) 31525
Manor Vale, Kirkbymoorside,
N Yorkshire YO6 6EQ.
On A170 Thirsk to Scarborough road; Helmsley 7 miles, Pickering 7 miles.
Undulating moorland course.
18 holes, 5958 yards, S.S.S.68
Club founded in 1905.
Visitors: welcome at all times.
Green fees: £6, (£4 with member) weekdays; £8, (£5 with member) weekends.
Society meetings: special rates available by arrangement.
Catering: meals and snacks daily.
Hotels: George and Dragon, Kirkbymoorside; Feversham Arms, Helmsley; Feathers, Helmsley.

T26 Knaresborough
☎Harrogate (0423) 862690/863219.
Butterhills, Boroughbridge Rd, Knaresborough HG5 0QQ.
1.5 miles N of Knaresborough off the main Boroughbridge road.
Parkland course.
18 holes, 6281 yards, S.S.S.70
Course designed by Hawtree & Son.
Club founded in 1920.
Visitors: no restrictions.
Green fees: £8 per round, £9.50 per day; £12 weekends and Bank Holidays.
Society meetings: catered for.
Catering: everyday except Tues.
Hotels: Dower House, Knaresborough.

T27 Malton & Norton
☎Malton (0653) 697912 Sec,

692959 Club, 693882 Pro.
Welham Park, Norton, Malton,
N Yorks YO17 9QE.
From Malton and Norton level crossing S on Welham road for 0.75 mile, turn right.
Parkland course.
White-18 holes, 6411 yards, S.S.S.71
Yellow-18 holes, 6141 yards, S.S.S.69
Course designed by Hawtree & Son.
Club founded in 1910.
Visitors: welcome, restricted on club competition days.
Green fees: £9 weekdays; £13 weekends and Public Holidays.
Society meetings: prior arrangement via Sec.
Catering: full facilities, breakfast by arrangement.
Hotels: Talbot, Yorkersgate, Malton; Green Man, Market Square, Malton; Leat House, Welham Road.

T28 Masham
☎Ripon (0765) 89379
Swinton Rd, Masham, Ripon, Yorks.
8 miles NW of Ripon on A6108.
Parkland course.
9 holes, 5244 yards, S.S.S.66
Club founded in 1900.
Visitors: welcome weekdays, weekends with member only.
Green fees: £6 per day.
Society meetings: by arrangement with Sec.
Catering: none.
Hotels: Kings Head, Masham.

T29 Normanby Hall
☎Scunthorpe (0724) 720252 Club, 720226 Pro.
Normanby Park, Normanby, Scunthorpe, S Humberside DN15 9HU.
5 miles N of Scunthorpe adjacent to Normanby Hall.
Parkland course.
18 holes, 6548 yards, S.S.S.71
Course designed by H.F. Jiggens, Hawtree & Sons.
Club founded in 1978.
Visitors: welcome - charge as for green fees.
Green fees: £4 per round; £5.50 per day weekdays; £5.50 weekends.
Society meetings: bookings taken for weekdays, apart from Bank Holidays.
Catering: full facilities available. Telephone Clubhouse for more information.
Hotels: Royal; Wortley House.

T30 Oakdale
☎Harrogate (0423) 502806 or 67162 Sec.
Oakdale, Harrogate HG1 2LN.
Off A61 from Harrogate at Kent Rd, about 0.25 mile from Royal Hall.
Undulating parkland course.
18 holes, 6456 yards, S.S.S.71
Course designed by Dr Mackenzie.
Club founded in 1914.
Visitors: welcome.
Green fees: £12 per day weekdays; £15 per day weekends and Bank Holidays.
Society meetings: catered for weekdays.
Catering: full dining facilities available except Mon at lunchtime, dinner by arrangement.
Hotels: Crown; Fern; Majestic; Studley.

T31 Pannal
☎Harrogate (0423) 871641 or 872628 Sec.
Follifoot Rd, Pannal, Harrogate HG3 1ES.
Just off A61 Leeds-Harrogate road at Pannal.
Parkland/moorland course.
18 holes, 6594 yards, S.S.S.71
Course designed by Sandy Herd.
Club founded in 1906.
Visitors: welcome weekdays.
Green fees: £15 per round, £20 per day.
Society meetings: by arrangement with Sec on weekdays.
Catering: meals served every day.
Hotels: Majestic; Old Swan; Cairn; Granby.

T32 Pike Hills
☎York (0904) 706566
Tadcaster Rd, Copmanthorpe, York YO2 3UW.
On A64 4 miles from York.
Parkland course.
18 holes, 6048 yards, S.S.S.69
Club founded in 1920.
Visitors: weekdays before 4.30pm, Bank Holidays, Sat and Sun only with member.
Green fees: £10 per round/day in summer; £8 per round/day in winter (Oct-Mar).
Society meetings: parties of 12 or more welcome if previously booked, correct dress essential, each member must have a handicap from a recognised club.
Catering: full facilities except Mon.
Hotels: many suitable hotels on Copmanthorpe side of York.

T33 Richmond
☎Richmond (0748) 2457
Bend Hagg, Richmond, N Yorks
DL10 5EX.
A6108 from Scotch Corner, turn right
at traffic lights after 4 miles.
Parkland course.
18 holes, 5704 yards, S.S.S.68
Course designed by Frank Pennink.
Club founded in 1892.
Visitors: welcome.
Green fees: £7 per round, £8 per
day weekdays; £10 weekends and
Bank Holidays.
Society meetings: catered for.
Catering: daily except Mon.
Hotels: Frenchgate, Richmond.

T34 Ripon City
☎Ripon (0765) 3640 Clubhouse,
700411 Pro, 3992 Hon. Sec
Palace Rd, Ripon, N Yorks
HG4 3HH.
1 mile N on A6108 towards Leyburn.
Undulating parkland course.
9 holes, 5752 yards, S.S.S.68
Club founded in 1905.
Visitors: any day.
Green fees: £5 per day weekdays;
£7 per day weekends and Bank
Holidays.
Society meetings: weekdays.
Catering: only for parties, by prior
arrangement.
Hotels: Ripon Spa, Park St, Ripon;
Unicorn, Market Place, Ripon.

T35 Scarborough North Cliff
☎Scarborough (0723) 360786
North Cliff Ave, Burniston Rd,
Scarborough YO12 6PP.
2 miles N of town centre on coast
road (Burniston Rd), turn right along
North Cliff Ave.
Seaside/parkland course.
18 holes, 6425 yards, S.S.S.71
Course designed by James Braid.
Club founded in 1928.
Visitors: no restrictions except
before 10.00 am Sun. Must be
recognised golfers.
Green fees: £8.50 per day
weekdays; £12 per day weekends
and Public Holidays.
Society meetings: mainly weekdays
available prior arrangement with Sec
parties 12-36.
Catering: soup and sandwiches
available to 5.30pm. Bar snacks
lunchtime and 7pm-10pm.
Hotels: Clifton; Majestic; Overdale.

T36 Scarborough South Cliff
☎Scarborough (0723) 374737
Deepdale Avenue, Scarborough,
YO11 2UE.
1 mile S of Scarborough on main
Filey road.
Parkland/seaside course.
18 holes, 6085 yeards, S.S.S.69
Course designed by Dr Mackenzie.
Club founded in 1903.
Visitors: welcome.
Green fees: £9 weekdays; £12.50
weekends and Bank Holidays
inclusive of VAT.
Society meetings: catered for on
weekdays and weekends.
Catering: full catering facilities.
Hotels: Royal; Crown; St Nicholas;
Brooklands; Southlands; Holbeck
Hall.

T37 Scunthorpe
☎Scunthorpe (0724) 866561
Burringham Rd, Scunthorpe, S
Humberside DN17 2AB.
On B1450, adjoining Mallard Hotel.
Parkland course.
18 holes, 6281 yards, S.S.S.71
Club founded in 1936.
Visitors: Mon-Fri.
Green fees: £8 per day.
Society meetings: Mon-Fri.
Catering: full facilities Mon-Thurs,
limited Fri.
Hotels: Royal, Doncaster Rd,
Scunthorpe.

T38 Selby
☎Selby (0757 82) 622
Mill Lane, Brayton Barff, Selby,
N Yorks YO8 9LD.
From Leeds turn right off A63 at the
Wheatsheaf in Hambleton, left at
cemetery then right, next left to
course.
Flat links course.
18 holes, 6246 yards, S.S.S.70
Club founded in 1907.
Visitors: welcome weekdays.
Green fees: £10 weekdays; £15
weekends.
Society meetings: catered for Wed,
Thurs and Fri.
Catering: every day except Mon.
Hotels: Londsborough, Selby.

T39 Settle
☎Settle (072 92) 3912
Buckhaw Brow, Settle, N Yorks
BD24.
Main A65 Settle-Kendal road,

opposite Giggleswick Quarry.
Parkland/moorland course.
9 holes, 4600 yards, S.S.S.62
Club founded in 1891.
Visitors: welcome 6 days, restricted
Sun.
Green fees: £3 weekdays; £5 per
day weekends.
Society meetings: none.
Catering: none.
Hotels: Falcon Manor, Settle.

T40 Skipton
☎Skipton (0756) 3922
Short Lea Lane, Grassington Rd,
Skipton, N Yorks BD23 1LL.
On N by-pass (A59 and A65) 1 mile
from town centre.
Moorland course.
18 holes, 6191 yards, S.S.S.70
Club founded in 1905.
Visitors: welcome except Mon.
Green fees: £8 weekdays; £10
weekends and Bank Holidays.
Society meetings: welcome, special
terms 12 minimum, 40 maximum.
Terms 1988 not yet decided.
Catering: every day except Mon.
Hotels: many in Skipton and District.

T41 Sutton Park
☎Hull (0482) 74242
Saltshouse Rd, Holderness Rd, Hull,
N Humberside HU8 9HF.
4 miles E of city centre on A165
(B1237).
Parkland course.
18 holes, 6251 yards, S.S.S.70
Club founded in 1935.
Visitors: unlimited.
Green fees: £2.50 per round.
Society meetings: on application to
Hull City Council Leisure Services.
Catering: bar snacks lunchtime, full
meals by arrangement.
Hotels: Royal Station.

T42 Thirsk & Northallerton
☎Thirsk (0845) 22170
Thornton-le-Street, Thirsk, N Yorks
YO7 4AB.
2 miles N of Thirsk on A168, the
Northallerton spur 0.5 mile from the
dual carriageway A19.
Meadowland course.
9 holes, 6257 yards, S.S.S.70
Club founded in 1914.
Visitors: individual or parties
welcome.
Green fees: £8 per day, £5 per
round.
Society meetings: catered for

weekdays except Tues.
Catering: full facilities except Tues.
Hotels: Golden Fleece, Thirsk; Three Tuns, Thirsk.

T43 **Whitby**
☎Whitby (0947) 602719 Pro, 600660 Sec.
Low Straggleton, Whitby, N Yorks YO21 3SR.
On main coast road between Whitby and Sandsend.
Seaside course.
18 holes, 5706 yards, S.S.S.69
Club founded in 1892.
Visitors: parties over 12 (experienced golfers) £12.50 weekdays, £13.50 weekends and Bank Holidays, (includes coffee on arrival, soup, sandwiches, lunch, full evening meal, and day of golf).
Green fees: £8 weekdays; £10 weekends and Bank Holidays.

Society meetings: by prior arrangement.
Catering: except Mon.
Hotels: Saxonville, Ladysmith Ave, Whitby; White House, West Cliff, Whitby; Royal, West Cliff, Whitby.

T44 **Withernsea**
☎Withernsea (0964) 612258
Chestnut Ave, Withernsea, N Humberside HU19 2QD.
S end of town.
Seaside course.
9 holes, 5112 yards, S.S.S.64
Club founded in 1909.
Visitors: welcome any time but with certain restrictions on some weekends.
Green fees: £4 OAPs; £2 Juniors; £6 weekdays; £12 weekends.
Society meetings: by prior arrangement with Sec.
Catering: no catering at lunchtime,

but meals served some evenings.
Hotels: Queen's, Queen St.

T45 **York**
☎York (0904) 490304
Lords Moor Lane, Strensall, York YO3 5XF.
6 miles N of York Minster, nr Strensall Barracks and Village.
Woodland course.
18 holes, 6275 yards, S.S.S.70
Course designed by J.H. Taylor (1904).
Club founded in 1890.
Visitors: ring beforehand.
Green fees: £12, (£6 with member) weekdays; £15, (£7.50 with member) weekends.
Society meetings: catered for except Fri and Sat.
Catering: full facilities except Fri.
Hotels: many in York.

U Cumbria, Northumberland, Durham, Tyne & Wear and Cleveland

Mercifully golf has never betrayed the old county nomenclature; Cumberland and Westmorland sound so much nicer and more romantic than Cumbria and it has never occurred to me to regard Tyne and Wear as an acceptable division to anyone except the postal authorities.

Of the counties of the north-east and north-west, Northumberland has been the strongest in terms of golfing numbers which, in view of the area it covers, is hardly surprising. The thickest cluster surrounds Newcastle and includes the Northumberland club, City of Newcastle, Gosforth, Ponteland and Whitley Bay but there is much rewarding exploring to be done along the coast, taking in Dunstanburgh, Seahouses, Bamburgh, Alnmouth and ending up at the home of the Berwick-on-Tweed Club on Goswick which is most appealing.

Morpeth, Hexham and Arcot Hall are well worth a visit but the wise explorers moving north will have already tested the best of Durham. Seaton Carew is the pick but Hartlepool, Brancepeth Castle, Durham City and Eaglescliffe are worthy of a mention in despatches.

Apart from Carlisle, or City of Carlisle, as it used to be known, Cumbria has many attractive outposts and none better than the championship reaches of Silloth on Solway which is an ideal retreat, famous as the course on which Cecil Leitch was raised. Seascale is another treat and I hear good things of the Furness club in Barrow.

U1 **Allendale**
☎(043 483) 412
Thornley Gate, Allendale, Hexham, Northumberland NE47 9LQ.
10 miles SW of Hexham on Menthead Rd.
Meadowland course.
9 holes, 4496 yards, S.S.S.63
Club founded in 1907.
Visitors: no restrictions but competitions have preference, course closed to visitors Aug Bank Holiday Mon.
Green fees: £2.50 weekdays; £3.50 weekends and Bank Holidays, reduced for juniors.
Society meetings: welcome by arrangement.
Catering: kitchen for self catering, charge for electric.
Hotels: Hotspur, Allendale, plus numerous smaller hotels in area.

U2 **Alnmouth**
☎Alnmouth (0665) 830368 Sec.
Foxton Hall, Alnmouth, Alnwick, Northumberland NE66 3BE.
Take Alnmouth road from Alnwick, at Alnmouth turn left, Foxton 1 mile on right.
Seaside meadowland course.
18 holes, 6414 yards, S.S.S.71
Club founded in 1869.
Visitors: welcome.
Green fees: £9 per day including VAT, (£4 with member) weekdays; £12 per day including VAT, (£5 with member) weekends and Bank Holidays.
Society meetings: catered for by arrangement.
Catering: available at all times.
Hotels: Schooner, Alnmouth; White Swan, Alnwick; Club has Dormy house accommodation for up to 16 persons.

U3 **Alnmouth Village**
☎Alnmouth (0665) 830370
Marine Rd, Alnmouth, Northumberland.
From Alnwick on A1 to Alnmouth on A1068.
Undulating seaside course.
9 holes, 6078 yards, S.S.S.70
Club founded in 1869.
Visitors: welcome.
Green fees: on application.
Society meetings: none.
Catering: by arrangement.
Hotels: Marine, Marine Rd.

U4 **Alnwick**
☎Alnwick (0665) 602632, 602499 Sec.
Swansfield Park, Alnwick, Northumberland.
On entering Alnwick from S turn left at Aydon Guest House, follow Bridge St and Swansfield Park Rd to park gates, turn left and first right.
Parkland course.
9 holes, 5379 yards, S.S.S.66
Club founded in 1907.
Visitors: welcome except on competition days.
Green fees: on application.
Society meetings: catered for on application to Committee.
Catering: limited catering service.
Hotels: White Swan.

U5 **Alston Moor**
☎Alston (0498) 81675
The Hermitage, Alston, Cumbria CA9 3DB.
1.75 miles from Alston on B6277.
Meadowland course.
9 holes, 6450 yards, S.S.S.64
Club founded in 1906.
Visitors: welcome anytime.
Green fees: £3.50 weekdays; £4.50

weekends and Bank Holidays.
Society meetings: welcomes special rates.
Catering: can be arranged.
Hotels: Hillcrest; Low Byre Manor; plus local Inns.

U6 Appleby

☎Appleby (0930) 51432
Blackenber Moor, Appleby in Westmorland, Cumbria CA16 6LP.
2 miles S of Appleby on A66.
Moorland course.
18 holes, 5895 yards, S.S.S.68
Club founded in 1902.
Visitors: welcome at any time.
Green fees: £4.50 weekdays; £6 weekends and Bank Holidays.
Society meetings: welcome at any time subject to prior arrangement.
Catering: by arrangement.
Hotels: Tufton Arms; Royal Oak; Appleby Manor.

U7 Arcot Hall

☎Wideopen (091) 2362794
Dudley, Cramlington, Northumberland NE23 7QP.
1 mile E of A1 on A1068.
Parkland course.
18 holes, 6389 yards, S.S.S.70
Course designed by James Braid.
Club founded in 1909.
Visitors: weekdays and non-competition weekends.
Green fees: £10; £12 weekends.
Society meetings: not weekends.
Catering: lunch and teas.
Hotels: Holiday Inn.

U8 Backworth

☎Tyneside (091) 2681048
Backworth Welfare, The Hall, Backworth, Shiremoor, Tyne and Wear NE27 0AH.
Off Tyne Tunnel link road at Holystone roundabout.
Parkland course.
9 holes, 5930 yards, S.S.S.69
Club founded in 1937.
Visitors: welcome with restrictions, ring for details.
Green fees: £5, (£4 with member); 5 day Mon-Fri £15.
Society meetings: none.
Catering: by arrangement with Steward.
Hotels: numerous good hotels in area.

U9 Bamburgh Castle

☎Bamburgh (066 84) 321 Sec, 378 Steward.
The Wynding, Bamburgh. Northum-

berland NE69 7DE.
Turn off A1 between Alnwick and Berwick, on reaching village, turn left opposite Lord Crewe Arms, and travel along The Wynding.
Seaside course.
18 holes, 5465 yards, S.S.S.67
Club founded in 1904.
Visitors: welcome, restricted on Bank Holiday weekends.
Green fees: April-Oct: £7 per day/round (£3 with member) weekdays; £11 per day, £7 per round (£3 with member) weekends and Bank Holidays. Winter: reduced rates.
Society meetings: by arrangement.
Catering: lunch, tea and evening meal except Tues.
Hotels: Sunningdale, Lucker Road, Bamburgh; Mizen Head, Lucker Road, Bamburgh; Victoria, Front Street, Bamburgh; Lord Crewe Arms, Front Street, Bamburgh.

U10 Barnard Castle

☎Barnard Castle (0833) 38355
Harmire Rd, Barnard Castle, Co Durham DL12 8QN.
On N boundary of town on B6278 Barnard Castle-Eggleston road.
Undulating parkland course.
Visitors: welcome except on competition days.
Green fees: on application.
Society meetings: welcome, maximum 40.
Catering: meals and bar snacks served.
Hotels: King's Head, Barnard Castle; Rose and Crown, Romaldkirk.

U11 Barrow

☎Barrow-in-Furness (0229) 25444
Blakesmoor Lane, Hawcoat, Barrow-in-Furness, Cumbria LA14 4QB.
Turn right to Hawcoat off A590 on entering boundary of Barrow.
Undulating meadowland course.
18 holes, 6209 yards, S.S.S.70
Club founded in 1922.
Visitors: welcome.
Green fees: £5.
Society meetings: by arrangement.
Catering: by arrangement.
Hotels: Victoria Park, Barrow; Michaelson House, Fairfield Lane, Barrow; Lisdoonie, Abbey Rd, Barrow.

U12 Beamish Park

☎Durham (091) 3701133
Beamish, Stanley, Co Durham DH9 0RH.

From Chester-le-Street follow signs for Beamish Open Air Museum.
Parkland course.
18 holes, 6000 yards, S.S.S.70
Course designed by Henry Cotton & W. Woodend.
Present course founded in 1951.
Visitors: no visitors Sun, no visitors allowed to play course before 9am on any day.
Green fees: £6.50, (£3 with member) weekdays; £8, (£4 with member) weekends.
Society meetings: catered for weekdays.
Catering: available each day except Mon.
Hotels: Beamish.

U13 Bedlingtonshire

☎Bedlington (0670) 822457 Sec, 822087 Pro.
Acorn Bank, Bedlington, Northumberland.
0.5 mile W of Bedlington on A1068.
Meadowland/parkland course.
18 holes, 6224 metres, S.S.S.73
Course designed by Frank Pennink.
Club founded in April 1972.
Visitors: welcome weekdays from 9am to sunset and weekends from 9.30am to sunset, except on competition days.
Green fees: £5 per round weekdays; £5.25 per round weekends.
Society meetings: on application.
Catering: on request.
Hotels: Holiday Inn, Seaton Burn; Red Lion, Bedlington; Ridge Farm, Bedlington; North Seaton, Ashington.

U14 Bellingham

☎Bellingham (0660) 20530
Boggle Hole, Bellingham, Hexham, Northumberland NE48 2DT.
Off B6320, 16 miles N of Hexham, easy access from A68.
Undulating meadowland course.
9 holes, 5245 yards, S.S.S.66
Course designed by Edward Johnson.
Club founded in 1893.
Visitors: welcome limited Sun.
Green fees: £4 weekdays; £5 weekends; £2 after 5pm.
Society meetings: welcome, limited to 18 holes on Sat, limited Sun.
Catering: parties welcome, individuals by arrangement.
Hotels: Riverdale Hall; Rose & Crown.

U15 Berwick-upon-Tweed

☎Ancroft (0289) 78256/87348.

Goswick, Berwick-upon-Tweed
TD15 2RW.
4 miles S of Berwick-upon-Tweed
E of A1, signposted on A1.
Seaside links course.
18 holes, 6400 yards, S.S.S.71
Club founded in 1890.
Visitors: welcome.
Green fees:£8 per day weekdays;
£10.50 per day weekends and Bank
Holidays.
Society meetings: by arrangement.
Catering: full facilities every day
except Mon.
Hotels: Ladythorn House, Goswick,
Berwick-on-Tweed; Kings Arms,
Berwick.

U16 **Billingham**
☎Billingham (0642) 554494
Sandy Lane, Billingham, Cleveland
TS22 5NA.
E of A19 Billingham by pass, near
town centre.
Undulating parkland course.
18 holes, 6034 yards, S.S.S.71
Course designed by Frank Pennink.
Club founded in 1967.
Visitors: weekdays, with member
only at weekends and Bank
Holidays.
Green fees: £8 per day.
Society meetings: weekdays only
after 9am.
Catering: daily except Mon.

Hotels: Billingham Arms.

U17 **Birtley**
☎Tyneside (091) 4102207
Portobello Rd, Birtley, Co Durham.
A6127 off A1, 6 miles S of
Newcastle.
Parkland course.
9 holes, 5154 yards, S.S.S.67
Visitors: welcome weekdays.
Green fees: £5, (£2 with member)
weekdays; £2, weekends with
members only; £15 per week.
Society meetings: by arrangement.
Catering: snacks and meals
available.
Hotels: Post House, Washington;

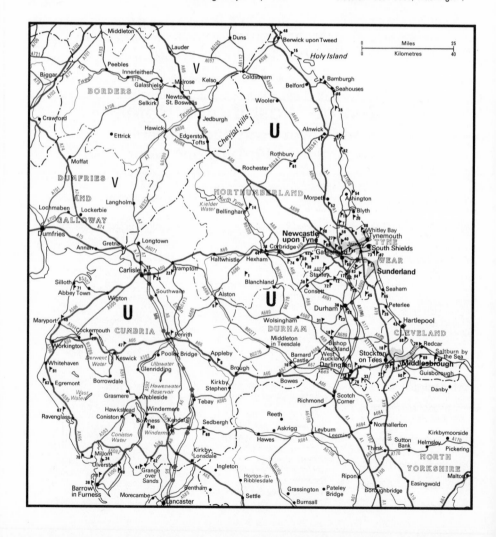

Coach and Horses, Birtley.

U18 **Bishop Auckland**
☎Bishop Auckland (0388) 602198 and 663648.
High Plains, Durham Rd, Bishop Auckland, Co Durham DL14 8DL.
Left side of road going N immediately out of town.
Parkland course.
18 holes, 6420 yards, S.S.S.71
Club founded in 1894.
Visitors: welcome, no societies Sat or Sun.
Green fees: £8 per round, £10 per day weekdays; £10 per round weekends.
Society meetings: welcome Wed, Thurs, Fri.
Catering: lunch and evening meal.
Hotels: Park Head; Queens.

U19 **Blackwell Grange**
☎Darlington (0325) 464464
Briar Close, Blackwell, Darlington, Co Durham DL3 8QX.
1 mile S of Darlington, 0.25 mile W off A66.
Undulating parkland course.

18 holes, 5587 yards, S.S.S.67
Course designed by Frank Pennink.
Club founded in 1930.
Visitors: welcome except Wed afternoon (Ladies Day).
Green fees: on application.
Society meetings: by arrangement on weekdays.
Catering: lunch served except Mon.
Hotels: Blackwell Grange Moat House.

U20 **Blyth**
☎Blyth (067) 367728
New Delaval, Blyth, Northumberland.
14 miles N of Newcastle, 6 miles N of Whitley Bay.
18 holes, 6533 yards, S.S.S.71
Course designed by Hamilton Stutt & Co.
Club founded in 1905.
Visitors: weekdays only.
Green fees: £7 per day, £6 per round; (£4 playing with member).
Society meetings: welcome weekday by arrangement.
Catering: full facilities.
Hotels: Whitley Bay area 6 miles south.

U21 **Boldon**
☎Boldon (0783) 364182
Dipe Lane, E Boldon, Tyne and Wear NE36 0PQ.
On A184, 3 miles NW of Sunderland.
Meadowland course.
18 holes, 6319 yards, S.S.S.70
Club founded in 1925.
Visitors: welcome weekdays, weekends restricted.
Green fees: on application.
Society meetings: by arrangement.
Catering: meals served by arrangement.
Hotels: Sunderland; George Washington; Post House.

U22 **Brampton**
☎Brampton (06977) 2255
Brampton, Cumbria CA8 1HN.
Club is 1.75 miles from centre of Brampton on B6413 Castle Carrock road.
Moorland course.
18 holes, 6420 yards, S.S.S.71
Course designed by James Braid.
Club founded in 1907.
Visitors: welcome.
Green fees: £6 weekdays; £8

weekends.
Society meetings: welcome weekdays; limited number catered for at weekends.
Catering: full facilities available, advance notice preferable.
Hotels: Tarn End, Talkin Tarn, Brampton, Carlisle, Cumbria; Hare & Hounds Inn, Talkin Village, Nr Brampton, Carlisle, Cumbria.

U23 Brancepeth Castle
☎Durham (091) 3780075
Brancepeth Village, Durham DH7 8EH.
4.5 miles SW from Durham City on A690 to Crook.
Parkland course.
18 holes, 6300 yards, S.S.S.70
Course designed by H.S. Colt.
Club founded in 1924.
Visitors: weekdays only for parties, individuals at weekends, catering available.
Green fees: casual £10 weekdays; £15 weekends and Public Holidays.
Society meetings: weekdays, reduced green fees dependent on numbers in party.
Catering: lunch and bar snacks pm, dinners prior booking necessary.
Hotels: Bridge (Bass Charrington), Croxdale, Durham.

U24 Carlisle
☎Scotby (022 872) 303
Aglionby, Carlisle CA4 8AG.
2 miles E of Carlisle, leave M6 at Exit 43 and take A69 for about three quarter mile.
Parkland course.
18 holes, 6278 yards, S.S.S.70
Course designed by Tom Simpson, McKenzie Ross & latterly by Frank Pennink.
Club founded in 1909.
Visitors: welcome, advisable to check availability.
Green fees: on application.
Society meetings: catered for on Wed and Fri.
Catering: meals and snacks available except Mon.
Hotels: Queens Arms, Warwick; Brown, Wetheral; Kilorren, Wetheral.

U25 Castle Eden & Peterlee
☎Wallfield (0429) 836220, 836510 Sec.
Castle Eden, Hartlepool, Cleveland TS27 4SS.
Take Durham to Hartlepool road off A19, follow signs to Castle Eden, course is opposite to Whitbread

Brewery.
Parkland course.
18 holes, 6293 yards, S.S.S.70
Second half of course designed by Henry Cotton.
Club founded in 1927.
Visitors: welcome at all times.
Green fees: £8 per day, (£4 with member).
Society meetings: welcome weekdays.
Catering: every day.
Hotels: Crossways, Thornley, Co Durham; Norseman, Peterlee, Co Durham; Hardwick Manor, Blackhall, Cleveland.

U26 Chester-le-Street
☎Chester-le-Street (091) 3883218
Lumley Park, Chester-le-Street, Co Durham DH3 4NS.
Leave A1(M) to Chester-le-Street, follow A167 signposted Durham, course 0.25 mile E of Chester-le-Street, beside Lumley Castle.
Parkland course.
18 holes, 6245 yards, S.S.S.70
Club founded in 1909.
Visitors: welcome weekdays, not allowed before 10am or between 12-2pm weekends.
Green fees: £8 weekdays; £10 weekends and Bank Holidays.
Society meetings: welcome, not weekends.
Catering: bar snacks, lunch and evening meal.
Hotels: Lumley Castle; Lambton Arms.

U27 City of Newcastle
☎Tyneside (091) 2851775
Three Mile Bridge, Gosforth, Newcastle upon Tyne NE3 2DR.
3 miles N of Newcastle city centre on left hand side of main A1 road heading N, opposite Three Mile Inn.
Parkland course.
18 holes, 6508 yards, S.S.S.71
Course designed by Harry Vardon.
Club founded in 1892.
Visitors: welcome any day.
Green fees: £8, (£3 with member) weekdays; £12, (£4 with member) weekends and Bank Holidays.
Society meetings: Tues, Wed, Thurs and exceptionally other days.
Catering: lunch, bar snacks, sandwiches served every day except Mon.
Hotels: Gosforth Park, High Gosforth Park, Newcastle upon Tyne.

U28 Cleveland
☎Redcar (0642) 471798 Sec, 483693 Club.
Queen St, Redcar, Cleveland TS10 1BT.
From A174 to A1042 to Coatham.
Links championship course.
Club founded in 1887.
Visitors: welcome.
Green fees: £8 weekdays; £12.50 weekends; reductions for playing with a member.
Society meetings: welcome weekdays, brochure available from Sec.
Catering: available.
Hotels: The Park; The Royal.

U29 Cockermouth
☎Bassenthwaite Lake (059 681) 223
Embleton, Cockermouth, Cumbria CA13 9SG.
1 mile E of A66, 4 miles from Cockermouth.
Moorland course.
18 holes, 5496 yards, S.S.S.67
Club founded in 1896.
Visitors: welcome.
Green fees: £6 per day weekdays; £6 weekends.
Catering: snacks and meals by arrangement with Stewardess.
Hotels: Castle Inn, Bassenthwaite; Globe, Cockermouth.

U30 Consett & District
☎Consett (0207) 502186
Elmfield Rd, Consett, Co Durham DH8 5NN.
Off A68 2 miles from Castleside or Allensford; 12 miles from Durham (A691) and Newcastle (A694).
Undulating parkland course.
18 holes, 6001 yards, S.S.S.69
Course designed by Harry Vardon.
Club founded in 1911.
Visitors: welcome except at weekends with competitions.
Green fees: £5, (£2.50 with member) weekdays; £5 weekends.
Society meetings: welcome by arrangement weekdays, Max 40.
Catering: lunch and high tea available every day by arrangement.
Hotels: many good hotels in area.

U31 Crook
☎Bishop Auckland (0388) 762429
Low Jobs Hill, Crook, Co Durham DL15 9AA.
On A690 6 miles W of Durham City.
Moorland/parkland course.
18 holes, 6089 yards, S.S.S.69

Club founded in 1919.
Visitors: welcome all times.
Green fees: £5 weekdays, (£4 with member); £6 weekends and Bank Holidays.
Society meetings: catered for all times by appointment.
Catering: available all days except Tues.
Hotels: Uplands, Crook; Manor House, Auckland.

U32 Darlington
☎Darlington (0325) 463936
Haughton Grange, Darlington,
Co Durham DL1 3JD.
NE of town on A1150.
Parkland course.
18 holes, 6032 yards, S.S.S.70
Course designed by Mackenzie.
Club founded in 1908.
Visitors: welcome weekdays.
Green fees: £8 weekdays; £10 Bank Holidays; (£4 with member).
Society meetings: maximum 40 members.
Catering: full facilities except Mon.
Hotels: Kings Head, Priestgate, Darlington; White Horse, Darlington.

U33 Dinsdale Spa
☎Dinsdale (0325) 332297 Sec, 332515 Pro, 332222 Club.
Middleton St George, Darlington,
Co Durham DL2 1DW.
From A66 or A19 follow signs for Teeside Airport until village of Middleton St George, clubhouse is 1.5 miles from Middleton St George on Neasham road.
Parkland course.
18 holes, 6078 yards, S.S.S.69
Club founded in 1906.
Visitors: welcome weekdays.
Green fees: £6.50; £7.50.
Society meetings: by arrangement.
Catering: available.
Hotels: Devenport, Middleton-one-Row.

U34 Dunnerholme
☎Dalton-in-Furness (0229) 62675
Duddon Rd, Askam-in-Furness,
Cumbria LA16 7AW.
A590 to Askam, over Askam railway crossing towards seashore, turn right over cattle grid.
Links course.
10 holes, 6118 yards, S.S.S.69
Club founded in 1905.
Visitors: welcome but not Sun until after 4.30pm.
Green fees: £5 weekdays; £6 weekends and Bank Holidays; (£2.50

weekdays with member).
Society meetings: welcome.
Catering: by appointment.
Hotels: Railway, Askam-in-Furness; Clarence House, Dalton-in-Furness; Wellington, Dalton-in-Furness.

U35 Dunstanburgh
☎Embleton (0665) 76672
Embleton, Alnwick, Northumberland
NE66 3XQ.
Off A1, 8 miles NE of Alnwick.
Seaside course.
18 holes, 5817 yards, S.S.S.70
Visitors: welcome.
Green fees: on application.
Society meetings: by arrangement.
Catering: meals served by arrangement.
Hotels: Dunstanburgh Castle, Embleton.

U36 Durham City
☎Durham (091) 3780069
Littleburn Farm, Langley Moor,
Durham DH7 8HL.
Off A690 2 miles SW of Durham City.
Meadowland course.
18 holes, 6211 yards, S.S.S.70
Course designed by C.C. Stanton.
Club founded in 1887.
Visitors: welcome weekdays.
Green fees: £8, (£4 with member) weekdays; £12, (£6 with member) weekends and Bank Holidays.
Society meetings: catered for weekdays.
Catering: available all days except Mon.
Hotels: Royal County; Three Tuns; Duke of Wellington - all Durham City.

U37 Eaglescliffe
☎Stockton on Tees (0642) 780098
Yarm Rd, Eaglescliffe, Stockton on Tees, Cleveland TS16 0DQ.
On the left of main road from Stockton on Tees-Yarm road in Eaglescliffe.
Undulating parkland course.
18 holes, 6045 yards, S.S.S.69
Course designed by James Braid, modification by H. Cotton.
Club founded in 1914.
Visitors: welcome weekdays, restricted Tues and Fri (Ladies Days).
Green fees: £10 weekdays; £12.50 weekends.
Society meetings: catered for weekdays, not Tues.
Catering: full.
Hotels: Parkmoor, Yarm Rd, Eaglescliffe; Swallow, Stockton on Tees.

U38 Furness
☎Barrow (0229) 41232
Central Drive, Barrow-in-Furness,
Cumbria LA14 3LN.
A590 to Barrow, follow sign to Walney Island through town, straight ahead at the lights on bridge over channel.
Links course.
18 holes, 6418 yards, S.S.S.71
Club founded in 1872.
Visitors: always welcome.
Green fees: £6 per day.
Society meetings: any weekday except Mon.
Catering: except Mon - afternoon and evening unless previously arranged.
Hotels: White House, Barrow; Abbey House, Barrow; Victoria Park, Barrow.

U39 Garesfield
☎Ebchester (0207) 561278 or 561309
Chopwell, Tyne and Wear
NE17 7AP.
A694 Newcastle to Consett road to Rowlands Gill, take B6315 to High Spen, then take Chopwell road 1 mile on left.
Undulating parkland course.
18 holes, 3338 yards, S.S.S.70
Course designed by William Woodend.
Club founded in 1922.
Visitors: weekdays unrestricted, weekends starting times restricted not before 10.30am and 2.30pm.
Green fees: £6 per day, £4.50 per round weekdays; £8 per day, £6 per round weekends.
Society meetings: reduced fees for parties consisting of 16 players or more. Restricted times as for visitors.
Catering: full facilities available.
Hotels: Five Bridges, Gateshead; Crest, Newcastle upon Tyne.

U40 Gosforth
☎Tyneside 091-285 3495
Broadway East, Gosforth, Newcastle upon Tyne NE3 5ER.
3 miles N of city centre, turn right at first main roundabout after Regent Centre metro station.
Meadowland course.
18 holes, 6043 yards, S.S.S.69
Club founded in 1905.
Visitors: welcome weekdays.
Green fees: £7.50, (£4.50 with member) weekdays; £10, (£5.50 with member) weekends and Bank Holidays.

Society meetings: welcome weekdays.
Catering: full facilities except Mon.
Hotels: Gosforth Park.

U41 Grange Fell
☎Grange-over-Sands (044 84) 2536
Fell Rd, Grange-over-Sands, Cumbria LA11 6HB.
Situated on main road from Grange-over-Sands to Cartmel.
Hillside course.
9 holes, 5278 yards, S.S.S.66
Club founded in 1952.
Visitors: welcome.
Green fees: £5 weekdays; £7 Sun and Bank Holidays.
Society meetings: none.
Catering: none.
Hotels: Grange; Netherwood; Greyrigge; all Grange-over-Sands.

U42 Grange-over-Sands
☎Grange-over-Sands (044 84) 3180
Meathop Rd, Grange-over-Sands, Cumbria LA11 6QX.
Leave A590 at roundabout signposted Grange, course on left hand side just before entering Grange.
Flat parkland course.
18 holes, 5660 yards, S.S.S.68
Club founded in 1921.
Visitors: welcome at any time.
Green fees: £6 per day weekdays; £8 weekends and Bank Holidays.
Society meetings: by arrangement weekdays and weekends.
Catering: except Tues.
Hotels: Grange; Cumbria Grand.

U43 Hartlepool
☎Hartlepool (0429) 274398
Hart Warren, Hartlepool, Cleveland TF24 9QE.
King Oswy Drive, off A1086 at N end of town.
Seaside course.
18 holes, 6255 yards, S.S.S.70
Course designed by James Braid.
Club founded in 1906.
Visitors: unrestricted except Sun.
Green fees: £7.50 weekdays; £9 weekends.
Society meetings: by arrangement except weekends.
Catering: by arrangement with Steward.
Hotels: Grand.

U44 Hexham
☎Hexham (0434) 603072

Spital Park, Hexham, Northumberland NE46 3RZ.
On A69, 1 mile W of Hexham town centre.
Undulating parkland course.
18 holes, 6026 yards, S.S.S.68
Course designed by Harry Vardon.
Club founded in 1907.
Visitors: welcome any day.
Green fees: £7 per round, £9.50 per day weekdays; £8.50 per round, £11 per day weekends.
Society meetings: not Sun.
Catering: full facilities every day.
Hotels: Beaumont, Hexham; Royal, Hexham.

U45 Houghton-le-Spring
☎Houghton-le-Spring 091-584 1198
Copt Hill, Houghton-le-Spring DH5 8LU.
On B1404 Houghton-le-Spring to Seaham Harbour road, 1.5 miles from Houghton-le-Spring.
Undulating moorland course.
18 holes, 6450 yards, S.S.S.71
Club founded in 1912.
Visitors: welcome any day, some restrictions on competition days.
Green fees: £6 weekdays; £8 weekends and Bank Holidays.
Society meetings: welcome prior arrangement for meals.
Catering: available most days.
Hotels: White Lion, Houghton-le-Spring; Ramside Hall, Rainton; Barnes, Durham Rd, Sunderland.

U46 Kendal
☎Kendal (0539) 24079
The Heights, Kendal, Cumbria.
To Kendal on A6 signposted in town.
Moorland course.
18 holes, 5483 yards, S.S.S.67
Club founded in 1903.
Visitors: welcome any time but prior application suggested.
Green fees: £5, (£2.50 with member).
Society meetings: catered for anytime subject to availability.
Catering: full facilities except Mon.
Hotels: County; Woolpack.

U47 Keswick
☎Keswick (07687) 83324 or 72147 Hon Secs office.
Threlkeld Hall, Keswick, Cumbria CA12 4HF.
4 miles E of Keswick on A66.
Undulating moorland/parkland course.
18 holes, 6175 yards, S.S.S.72
Course designed by Eric Brown.

Club founded in 1975.
Visitors: welcome even at most weekends and Bank Holidays.
Green fees: £7 per day.
Society meetings: by arrangement - weekends can be available and Bank Holidays.
Catering: by prior arrangement.
Hotels: Ladore Swiss, Barrowdale, Keswick; Borrowdale, Borrowdale, Keswick; Wordsworth, Grasmere - all have free midweek golf.

U48 Magdalene Fields
☎Berwick (0289) 306384
Berwick-upon-Tweed.
5 minutes walk from town centre.
Seaside course (parkland fairways).
18 holes, 6551 yards, S.S.S.71
Visitors: welcome.
Green fees: on application.
Society meetings: by arrangement.
Catering: meals during summer, at other times by arrangement.
Hotels: Kings Arms; Ravensholme Guest House, Berwick.

U49 Maryport
☎Maryport (0900) 812605
Bank End, Maryport, Cumbria CA15 6PA.
N of Maryport, turn left off A596 onto B5300 (Silloth), course 1 mile.
Seaside links course.
18 holes, 6272 yards, S.S.S.71
Club founded in 1905.
Visitors: welcome at any time.
Green fees: £6 weekdays; £7 weekends and Bank Holidays; (£4 with member).
Society meetings: catered for.
Catering: by prior arrangement.
Hotels: Ellenbank, Birkby, Maryport; The Waverley, Curzon St, Maryport.

U50 Middlesbrough
☎Middlesbrough (0642) 311515/ 316430.
Brass Castle Lane, Marton, Middlesbrough, Cleveland TS8 9EE.
5 miles S of Middlesbrough, 1 mile W of A172.
Parkland course.
18 holes, 6106 yards, S.S.S.69
Course designed by James Braid.
Club founded in 1908.
Visitors: welcome weekdays except Tues.
Green fees: £9, (£4 with member) weekdays; £11, (£6 with member) weekends and Bank Holidays.
Society meetings: catered for Wed, Thurs and Fri.
Catering: full facilities except Mon.

Hotels: Marton Hotel & Country Club, Stokesley Road, Marton, Middlesbrough; Blue Bell Inn, Acklam, Middlesbrough.

U51 Middlesbrough Municipal

☎Middlesbrough (0642) 315533. Ladgate Lane, Middlesbrough, Cleveland TS5 7YZ.
Access from A19 via A174 to Acklam.
Undulating parkland course.
18 holes, 6314 yards, S.S.S.70
Club founded in 1977.
Visitors: welcome but need a starting time.
Green fees: £3.50 weekdays; £4.75 weekends and Bank Holidays.
Society meetings: none.
Catering: lunch and evening meal open to the public.
Hotels: Blue Bell, Acklam Road.

U52 Morpeth

☎Morpeth (0670) 519980 Sec, 512065 Pro.
The Common, Morpeth, NE61 2BT.
On A197 1 mile S of Morpeth.
Parkland course.
18 holes, 6215 yards, S.S.S.70
Course designed by Harry Vardon (1922).
Club founded in 1906.
Visitors: welcome.
Green fees: £7 per round, £10 per day weekdays; £10 per round, £14 per day weekends and Bank Holidays.
Society meetings: catered for weekdays, apply to Sec.
Catering: meals available at Clubhouse, booking advisable.
Hotels: Waterford Lodge, Morpeth.

U53 Mount Oswald

☎Durham (0385) 3867527
South Rd, Durham DH1 3TQ.
Club is SW of Durham on A1050.
Parkland course.
18 holes, 6162 yards, S.S.S.69
Visitors: welcome as singles or groups anytime.
Green fees: £7 per day, £5 per round weekdays; £9 per day, £6 per round weekends.
Society meetings: package deals available for groups over 12 including weekends.
Catering: open for meals from 9.30am-2.30pm and 6.00pm-9.30pm. Coffee/tea and sandwiches always available until close. Sunday lunch to be booked.

Hotels: Royal County; The Bridge; The Three Tuns.

U54 Newbiggin-by-the-Sea

☎Ashington (0670) 817344
Newbiggin-by-the-Sea, Northumberland.
On A197, 9 miles E of Morpeth.
Seaside course.
18 holes, 6423 yards, S.S.S.71
Club founded in 1884.
Visitors: welcome.
Green fees: £4.50 weekdays; £6 weekends and Bank Holidays.
Society meetings: apply to Sec.
Catering: lunches served except Tues.
Hotels: in Newbiggin.

U55 Newcastle United

☎Newcastle-upon-Tyne (0632) 864693
Ponteland Rd, Cowgate, Newcastle upon Tyne, Northumberland NE5 3GW.
1 mile W of city centre.
Moorland course.
18 holes, 6498 yards, S.S.S.71
Club founded in 1890.
Visitors: welcome weekdays.
Green fees: on application.
Society meetings: by arrangement.
Catering: meals by arrangement.
Hotels: in Newcastle.

U56 Northumberland

☎Wideopen (0632) 362498 Sec, 362009 Steward.
High Gosforth Park, Newcastle upon Tyne NE3 5HT.
Situated off A1 4 miles N of Newcastle upon Tyne city centre.
Undulating parkland course.
18 holes, 6640 yards, S.S.S.72
Course designed by H.S. Colt & James Braid.
Club founded in 1898.
Visitors: welcome weekdays by reservation with Sec and letter of introduction.
Green fees: on application.
Society meetings: catered for Tues, Thurs and Fri only.
Catering: luncheon served except Mon.
Hotels: Gosforth Park; Holiday Inn.

U57 Penrith

☎Penrith (0768) 62217
Salkeld Rd, Penrith, Cumbria CA11 8SP.
0.5 mile NE of Penrith.
Parkland course.
18 holes, 6026 yards, S.S.S.69

Club founded in 1890.
Visitors: must be members of a golf club with handicap; very busy April-Oct advisable to telephone first (some restrictions).
Green fees: £8 weekdays; £10 weekends and Public Holidays.
Society meetings: by appointment.
Catering: lunch and evening meals except Mon and Tues.
Hotels: George, Penrith; Edenhill, Langwathby.

U58 Ponteland

☎Ponteland (0661) 22689
53 Bell Villas, Ponteland, Newcastle upon Tyne NE20 9BD.
On A696 road to Jedburgh, 2 miles N of Newcastle Airport.
Meadowland course.
18 holes, 6512 yards, S.S.S.71
Course designed by Harry Ferney.
Club founded in 1927.
Visitors: Mon-Fri.
Green fees: £8 per round; £10 per day.
Society meetings: Tues and Thurs.
Catering: full in bar hours - by prior arrangement at other times.
Hotels: Airport 1.5 miles.

U59 Prudhoe

☎Prudhoe (0661) 32466
Eastwood Park, Prudhoe, Northumberland NE42 5DX.
12 miles W of Newcastle on A695.
Parkland course.
18 holes, 5812 yards, S.S.S.68
Club founded in 1930.
Visitors: welcome weekdays.
Green fees: £5.50 per round, £6 per day weekdays; £6.50 per round/day weekends.
Society meetings: welcome weekdays.
Catering: bar snacks and meals served.
Hotels: Broomhaugh, Riding Mill, Northumberland.

U60 Ravensworth

☎Tyneside 091-487 2843
Moss Heaps, Wrekenton, Gateshead, Tyne & Wear NE9 7UU.
Off A1, 2 miles S of Gateshead.
Moorland/parkland course.
18 holes, 5872 yards, S.S.S.68
Club founded in 1906.
Visitors: welcome weekdays.
Green fees: £5.75, (£3.45 with member) weekdays; £6.90, (£5.18 with member) weekends and Bank Holidays.
Society meetings: catered for

weekdays.
Catering: any day but Mon.
Hotels: Springfield, Durham Rd,
Gateshead.

U61 Rothbury
☎Rothbury (0669) 20718
Old Race Course, Rothbury,
Morpeth, Northumberland
NE65 7UB.
Off A697, 15 miles NE of Morpeth.
Meadowland course.
9 holes, 5146 metres, S.S.S.67
Club founded in 1890.
Visitors: welcome weekdays and
most Sun.
Green fees: on application.
Society meetings: none.
Catering: no facilities.
Hotels: Coquetvale; Queens Head;
Newcastle; all in Rothbury.

U62 Ryton
☎Tyneside 091-413 3737
Dr Stanners, Clara Vale, Ryton, Tyne
&Wear NE40 3TD.
Off A695 8 miles from Newcastle,
follow signs from Ryton to Wylam
then Clara Vale.
Moorland/parkland course.
18 holes, 6034 yards, S.S.S.69
Club founded in 1891.
Visitors: welcome weekdays, by
arrangement weekends.
Green fees: £4.50 weekdays; £6.50
weekends and Bank Holidays.
Society meetings: parties welcome.
Catering: full facilities every day.
Hotels: Ryton Country Club.

U63 St Bees School
☎St Bees (0946) 695
Station Rd, St Bees.
On B5345, 4 miles S of Whitehaven.
Seaside course.
9 holes, S.S.S.65
Club founded in 1942/43.
Visitors: welcome except on
competition days in summer.
Green fees: on application.
Society meetings: no facilities.
Catering: none available.
Hotels: Seacote; Manor House.

U64 Saltburn-by-Sea
☎Guisborough (0287) 22812
Guisborough Rd, Hob Hill, Saltburn-
by-Sea, Cleveland TS12 1NJ.
1 mile from centre of Saltburn on
B1268.
Undulating meadowland course.
18 holes, 5803 yards, S.S.S.68
Visitors: welcome if members of
recognised club.

Green fees: on application.
Society meetings: by arrangement.
Catering: full facilities except Mon.

U65 Seaham
☎Seaham 091-581 2354
Dawdon, Seaham, Co Durham
SR7 7RD.
Off A19, 6 miles S of Sunderland,
take road to Seaham.
Heathland course.
18 holes, 5972 yards, S.S.S.69
Course designed by Dr A.
Mackenzie.
Club founded in May 1911.
Visitors: welcome weekdays.
Green fees: £6, (£5 with member)
weekdays; £7, (£6 with member)
weekends and Bank Holidays.
Society meetings: to be booked
through Sec.
Catering: bar snacks.
Hotels: Harbour View, Seaham.

U66 Seahouses
☎Seahouses (0665) 720794
Beadnell Rd, Seahouses, Northum-
berland NE68 7XT.
Off A1 12 miles N of Alnwick.
Seaside course.
18 holes, 5336 yards, S.S.S.66
Club founded in 1914.
Visitors: welcome at all times.
Green fees: on application.
Society meetings: catered for
weekdays and most weekends.
Catering: lunch, bar meals etc, (late
Mar-Oct except Tues, only).
Hotels: White Swan; Bamburgh
Castle, Main St, Seahouses; Beach
House, Broad Rd, Seahouses.

U67 Seascale
☎Seascale (094 67) 28202
The Banks, Seascale, Cumbria
CA20 1QL.
On coast to N of village.
Seaside links course.
18 holes, 6396 yards, S.S.S.70
Club founded in 1893.
Visitors: unrestricted.
Green fees: £7 weekdays; £9
weekends and Bank Holidays.
Society meetings: by arrangement
with Sec, terms for parties of 12 or
more.
Catering: restricted (by arrange-
ment) Mon, Tues. Full facilities other
days.
Hotels: Scawfell, Seascale; Calder
House, Seascale.

U68 Seaton Carew
☎Hartlepool (0429) 266249

Tees Rd, Seaton Carew, Hartlepool
TS25 1DE.
Off A689 3 miles S of Hartlepool.
Links course.
Course designed by Duncan
McCuaig.
Club founded in 1874.
Visitors: on application to Hon. Sec.
Green fees: £10 weekdays; £12
weekends.
Society meetings: on application to
Hon Sec.
Catering: available.
Hotels: Grand, Hartlepool; Staincliffe
Marine, Seaton Carew.

U69 Sedbergh
☎Sedbergh (0587) 20993 Hon.Sec.
The Riggs, Millthrop, Sedbergh,
Cumbria.
1 mile from Sedbergh on Dent Rd,
via hamlet of Millthrop.
Undulating fell land course.
9 holes, 4134 yards, S.S.S.61
Club founded in 1896.
Visitors: welcome always, no
restrictions. Very limited facilities.
Ring Hon Sec for advice.
Green fees: £2 per day (honesty box
system).
Society meetings: no suitable
facilities.
Catering: none.
Hotels: The Dalesman; The Red
Lion; The Bull.

U70 Silecroft
☎Millom (0657) 4250
Silecroft, Cumbria LA18 4NX.
On A5093 3 miles N of Millom,
through Silecroft village towards
shore.
Seaside course.
9 holes, 5712 yards, S.S.S.68
Club founded in 1903.
Visitors: normally unrestricted on
weekdays weekends often restricted
12.00 noon to 5.30pm same Bank
Holidays.
Green fees: £5 per round/day
weekdays or weekends; £10 weekly
ticket available on caravan site
adjacent.
Society meetings: none.
Catering: none.
Hotels: Bankfield, Kirksanton;
Miners Arms,
Silecroft.

U71 Silloth on Solway
☎Silloth (0965) 31199 Sec/Pro.
31304 Steward.
Silloth on Solway, Carlisle, Cumbria
CA5 4AT.

B5302 at A596 at Wigton, 18 miles W of Carlisle.
Undulating seaside course.
18 holes, 6343 yards, S.S.S.70
Course designed by Dr Leach.
Club founded in 1892.
Visitors: welcome any time.
Green fees: £8 per day weekdays; £12 per day weekends and Bank Holidays; (half price with member).
Society meetings: yes.
Catering: full facilities except Mon.
Hotels: Golf; Queens; Skinburness.

U72 South Moor
☎Stanley (0207) 232848
The Middles, Craghead, Stanley, Co Durham DH9 6AG.
2 miles from Stanley on B6313.
Moorland course.
18 holes, 6445 yards, S.S.S.71
Course designed by Dr Mackenzie.
Club founded in 1923.
Visitors: welcome.
Green fees: on application.
Society meetings: catered for all week.
Catering: lunch and evening meal served except Mon (summer) and Mon and Tues (winter).

Hotels: Post House, Washington; Lumley Castle, Chester le Street; Imperial, Stanley; Beamish Park.

U73 South Shields
☎South Shields 091-456 0475 Club.
Cleadon Hills, South Shields, Tyne & Wear NE34 8EG.
A1018 turn off at Quarry Lane, near Cleadon Chimney.
Seaside course.
18 holes, 6264 yards, S.S.S.70
Club founded in 1893.
Visitors: welcome at all times.
Green fees: £7 weekdays; £10 weekends and Bank Holidays.
Society meetings: any day by arrangement.
Catering: all meals at any time.
Hotels: New Crown; Marsden Inn; Sea Hotel.

U74 Stocksfield
☎Stocksfield (0661) 843041
New Ridley, Stocksfield, Northumberland NE43 7RE.
On A695 between Corbridge and Prudhoe.
Parkland/wooded course.
18 holes, 5594 yards, S.S.S.68

Course designed by Pennink Associates.
Club founded in 1912.
Visitors: welcome any time weekdays, after 10.30am weekends.
Green fees: £6 weekdays; £10 weekends and Bank Holidays.
Society meetings: catered for by arrangement.
Catering: sandwiches, meals by prior booking.
Hotels: Broomhaugh, Riding Mill.

U75 Stonyholme Municipal
☎Carlisle (0228) 34856 Pro, 33208 Clubhouse.
St Aidans Rd, Carlisle.
Off A69, 1 mile W of M6, Junction 43.
Flat meadowland course.
18 holes, 5600 yards, S.S.S.68
Course designed by Frank Pennink.
Club founded in 1974.
Visitors: welcome.
Green fees: £2.20 per round weekdays; £3.60 per round weekends.
Society meetings: welcome.
Catering: meals served.
Hotels: many in Carlisle.

U76 **Stressholme**
☎Darlington (0325) 461002
Snipe Lane, Darlington, Co Durham.
About 8 miles N of Scotch Corner.
Parkland municipal course.
18 holes, 6511 yards, S.S.S.71
Club founded in 1976.
Visitors: welcome.
Green fees: £4.50 weekdays; £5.50 weekends.
Society meetings: by arrangement with Pro.
Catering: lunch daily.
Hotels: Blackwell Moathouse.

U77 **Teesside**
☎Stockton (0642) 616516 Sec, 67249 Club.
Acklam Rd, Thornaby, Cleveland TS17 7JS.
Off A19 take A1130 to Stockton, course is situated 1 mile from A19 on right.
Meadowland course.
18 holes, 6472 yards, S.S.S.71
Club founded in 1901.
Visitors: welcome weekdays before 4.30pm unless playing with a member. Bank Holidays after 11am unless playing with a member.
Green fees: £8 per day, (£5.50 with member); £12 per day, (£7 with member) weekends. To be reviewed.
Society meetings: catered for weekdays.
Catering: full facilities except Mon.
Hotels: Post House, Low Lane, Thornaby; Golden Eagle, Trenchard Ave, Thornaby.

U78 **Tynemouth**
☎North Shields 091-413 2177
Spital Dene, Tynemouth, North Shields, Tyne & Wear NE30 2ER.
On A193 or A1058.
Parkland course.
18 holes, 6351 yards, S.S.S.70
Course designed by Willie Park.
Club founded in 1913.
Visitors: welcome weekdays.
Green fees: £7; (£4 with member per round) weekdays; £10; (£6 with member per round) weekends.
Society meetings: welcome weekdays.
Catering: lunch, tea and snacks served except Mon.
Hotels: Newcastle Mote House, Coast Rd, Wallsend; Park Hotel, Tynemouth.

U79 **Tyneside**
☎Tyneside 091-413 2742 Sec, 413 2177 Clubhouse.

Westfield Lane, Ryton, Tyne & Wear NE40 3QE.
7 miles W of Newcastle upon Tyne on S side of Tyne, on A695, turn N at Ryton. Down to Old Ryton village, turn left, pass Cross Inn, and then right at end of row of old houses on right.
Parkland course.
18 holes, 6055 yards, S.S.S.69
Course designed by H.S. Colt in 1910.
Club founded in 1879.
Visitors: welcome with or without member.
Green fees: £7 per round, £9 per day weekdays; £10 per round weekends.
Society meetings: weekdays only by prior arrangement with Sec.
Catering: bar, tea/coffee, bar snacks, lunch, high tea, dinner. (service 8am - 10pm).
Hotels: Ryton Park Country Club, Holburn Lane, Ryton Park, Ryton.

U80 **Ulverston**
☎Ulverston (0229) 52824
Bardsea Park, Ulverston, Cumbria LA12 92J.
From Ulverston town centre to Bardsea on B5087.
Parkland course.
18 holes, 6142 yards, S.S.S.69
Course designed by W.H. Colt.
Club founded in 1910.
Visitors: welcome daily as individuals or parties for bona fide golfers only.
Green fees: £10 weekdays Mar-Oct inclusive; £12 weekends and Bank Holidays. Any 3 days in 5 (week rates) £25. £6 weekdays Nov-Feb inclusive; £7 weekends.
Society meetings: Glaxochem Ltd, VSEL Barrow, Masonic. Regular visiting societies generally.
Catering: full meals, bar snacks daily except Mon. Full time Steward.
Hotels: Virginia House, Queen St, Ulverston; Sefton House, Queen St, Ulverston; White Water, Backbarrow.

U81 **Wallsend**
☎Tyneside (091) 2621973
Bigges Main, Wallsend-on-Tyne, NE28 8SX.
From Newcastle E along Shields road, turn left at sign to Wallsend Sports Centre.
Parkland course.
18 holes, 6601 yards, S.S.S.72
Club founded in 1905.
Visitors: no restrictions.

Green fees: £3.30 weekdays; £4.20 weekends.
Society meetings: on written request.
Catering: hot or cold snacks.
Hotels: good hotels in area.

U82 **Warkworth**
☎Alnwick (0665) 711596
Warkworth, Northumberland.
Off A1068 to Warkworth, 15 miles N of Morpeth.
Seaside course.
9 holes, 5856 yards, S.S.S.68
Course designed by Tom Morris.
Club founded in 1891.
Visitors: no restrictions except on competition days which are mostly Sat.
Green fees: £5 weekdays; £7 weekends and Bank Holidays.
Society meetings: at committee's discretion.
Catering: by arrangement.
Hotels: Sun; Warkworth House.

U83 **George Washington**
☎(091) 4172626
Ston Cellar Rd, High Usworth, District 12, Washington, Tyne & Wear NE37 1PH.
A1(M), well signposted.
Moorland course.
18 holes, over 6000 yards, S.S.S.72
Club founded in 1975.
Visitors: welcome.
Green fees: £4 weekdays; £5.50 weekends; party rates Mon-Fri £2.70 per person.
Society meetings: welcome.
Catering: full facilities.
Hotels: Washington.

U84 **Wearside**
☎Sunderland (091) 5342518
Coxgreen, Sunderland SR4 9JT.
Take A183 Chester-le-Street road off A19, after 400 yards turn right at Coxgreen sign, left at small T-junction, follow road down hill to Clubhouse.
Meadowland/parkland course.
18 holes, 6216 yards, S.S.S.70
Club founded in 1892.
Visitors: welcome.
Green fees: £7 per round, (£5.50 with member), £9 per day, (£7 with member) weekdays; £10 per day, £6.50 per round, (£8 per day with member) weekends.
Society meetings: on application to Sec. Weekends only during month of Aug.
Catering: full facilities, except Mon when snacks only available.

Hotels: George Washington Sports Centre, Washington; Seaburn, S'Land; Ramside, Belmont, Durham.

U85 Westerhope

☎Newcastle (091) 2869125
Whorlton Grange, Westerhope, Newcastle upon Tyne NE5 1PP.
5 miles W of Newcastle. Airport Rd for 3 miles then follow signs to Westerhope.
Parkland course.
18 holes, 6407 yards, S.S.S.71
Club founded in 1941.
Visitors: Mon-Thurs.
Green fees: £6 weekdays, £7.50 weekends.
Society meetings: catered for Mon-Thurs.
Catering: available except Mon.
Hotels: Gosforth Park; Crest; Swallow; Imperial.

U86 Whickham

☎Tyneside (091) 4887309
Hollinside Park, Whickham, Newcastle upon Tyne NE16 5BA.
5 miles W of Newcastle.
Undulating parkland course.
18 holes, 6129 yards, S.S.S.69
Club founded in 1911.
Visitors: unrestricted weekdays, by arrangement weekends.
Green fees: £7, (£3.50 with member) weekdays; £10, (£5 with member) weekends.
Society meetings: weekdays only.
Catering: snacks, cooked meals by arrangement.
Hotels: Gibside, Whickham.

U87 Whitburn

☎Whitburn (091) 529 2144, 529 4210 Pro.
Lizard Lane, South Shields, Tyne & Wear NE34 7AH.
Halfway between Sunderland and South Shields off coast road.
Parkland course.
18 holes, 6035 yards, S.S.S.69

Club founded in 1932.
Visitors: welcome. At weekends please telephone Pro beforehand to check if competition being played.
Green fees: £6 per round/day weekdays; £7.50 per round, £10 per day weekends.
Society meetings: bookings accepted any weekday except Tues.
Catering: full facilities available.
Hotels: Seaburn, Sunderland; Roker, Sunderland; Sea, South Shields.

U88 Whitley Bay

☎Tyneside (091) 2520180
Claremont Rd, Whitley Bay, Tyne & Wear NE26 3UF.
On A183, 10 miles NE of Newcastle.
Undulating seaside course.
18 holes, 6617 yards, S.S.S.72
Club founded in 1890.
Visitors: welcome weekdays, weekends with a member.
Green fees: £8, (£4 with member).
Society meetings: catered for weekdays.
Catering: full facilities except Mon.
Hotels: Gosforth Park, Gosforth, Newcastle upon Tyne; Holiday Inn, Gt North Rd, Seaton Burn, Newcastle.

U89 Wilton

☎Eston Grange (0642) 465265/ 454626
Wilton Castle, Redcar, Cleveland TS10 4QY.
Off A174, 4 miles W of Redcar, take road for Wilton village and castle.
Parkland course.
18 holes, 6019 yards, S.S.S.69
Club founded in 1947.
Visitors: welcome weekdays and Sun, Bank Holidays not Sat.
Green fees: £8 weekdays; £9 weekends and Bank Holidays.
Society metings: weekdays by arrangement.
Catering: lunches and evening

meals not Sun.
Hotels: Park, Redcar; Hotel Royal York, Redcar.

U90 Windermere

☎Windermere (09662) 3123
Cleabarrow, Windermere, Cumbria LA23 3NB.
From M6, (junctions 36/37), this golf course is 9 miles NW of Kendal.
Turn off A591 at Crooklands round-about to join B5284.
Undulating parkland course.
18 holes, 5006 yards, S.S.S.65
Course designed by George Low.
Club founded in 1891.
Visitors: welcome.
Green fees: £8 weekdays; £10 weekends and Bank Holidays.
Society meetings: catered for by prior arrangement, numbers 8-50.
Catering: full facilities available.
Hotels: Wild Boar, Crook; Low Wood, Windermere.

U91 Workington

☎Workington (0900) 3460
Branthwaite Rd, Workington, Cumbria CA1 4NW.
Off A595 2 miles SE of town centre.
Undulating meadowland course.
18 holes, 6100 yards, S.S.S.70
Course designed by James Braid.
Club founded in 1907.
Visitors: welcome, must be members of golf club and hold current handicap.
Green fees: £7, (£3.50 with member) weekdays; £9, (£4.50 with member) weekends and Bank Holidays. Reductions for parties of 12 or more.
Society meetings: catered for by prior arrangement with Sec.
Catering: full services except Mon and Thurs afternoon.
Hotels: Westlands, Workington; Cross Barrow, Bridgefoot, Workington.

V Lothians, Borders, Dumfries and Galloway

Golfers visiting Scotland traditionally head for St Andrews, Dornoch, Gleneagles, Carnoustie or Muirfield, very often without any idea of what they may be missing elsewhere. So let me do my little bit of voluntary publicity for Southerness, one of the finest in Britain, and for the other courses of Dumfries and Galloway.

They form part of a convenient detour that highlights a lesser known part of a country famous for its golf, and if the subsidiary courses are not on quite the same scale as Southerness, they are highly enjoyable. Powfoot, amid the gorse and within easy reach of Dumfries, ranks nearest to it. Dumfries itself boasts Thornhill and Dumfries and County but, having explored the glories of Southerness, the charms of Portpatrick (Dunskey) and Stranraer are well worth an extra day — maybe en route for Turnberry.

The alternative to heading west from Carlisle along the northern shores of the Solway Firth is the road through the lovely Border country where, again, the scenic beauty makes up for any shortcomings in the golf. Kelos, Hirsel, Innerleithen, Jedburgh, Langholm, St Boswells and Melrose are only nine holes but Galashiels, Moffat, Peebles and Minto are 18 holes and a pleasant way of breaking yourself in for sterner things ahead in the Lothians.

Apart from a variety of courses around Edinburgh, the Lothians embrace the sterling stretch of golfing country from Longniddry through Kilspindie, Luffness, Gullane, Muirfield and North Berwick to Dunbar which is first class. The staging of the Boys championship at Dunbar is testimony to its quality but travellers to Glasgow may well like to break the journey and play some of the West Lothian courses.

V1 **Baberton**
☎031-453 4911
Baberton Avenue, Juniper Green, Edinburgh EH14 3DU.
On main Lanark road from Edinburgh.
Parkland course.
18 holes, 6140 yards, S.S.S.69
Course designed by Willie Park.
Club founded in 1893.
Visitors: on introduction by a member. Visiting societies by arrangement with Sec. (Mon-Fri only).
Green fees: £7 per round, £10 per day.
Society meetings: none.
Catering: full facilities.
Hotels: several in area.

V2 **Bathgate**
☎Bathgate (0506) 630505 Sec, 52232 Club, 630553 Pro.
Edinburgh Rd, Bathgate, West Lothian.
400 yards E from town centre.

Parkland course.
18 holes, 6328 yards, S.S.S.70
Course designed by Willie Park.
Club founded in 1892.
Visitors: unrestricted.
Green fees: £5 weekdays; £7 weekends; (under review).
Society meetings: welcome if previous arrangements made with Sec.
Catering: coffee, lunch, high tea.
Hotels: Golden Circle; Dreadnought.

V3 **Braids United**
☎031-447 3327
22 Braids Hill Approach, Edinburgh EH10.
A702 from city centre (south).
Hillside courses.
18 holes, 5731 yards, S.S.S.68
18 holes, 4832 yards, S.S.S.64
Club founded in 1897.
Visitors: unlimited.
Green fees: £3 per round.
Society meetings: none
Catering: none.

Hotels: Braid Hills.

V4 **Broomieknowe**
☎031-663 9317
36 Golf Course Rd, Bonnyrigg, Midlothian EH19 2HZ.
Take Bonnyrigg road at Eskbank (Dalkeith) roundabout 1 mile to Bonnyrigg.
Gently undulating parkland course.
18 holes, 6046 yards, S.S.S.69
Course designed by James Braid.
Club founded in 1906.
Visitors: welcome weekdays.
Green fees: on application.
Society meetings: welcome weekdays.
Catering: bar lunch available, and evening meal by arrangement with Steward, except Mon.
Hotels: Dalhousie Castle, Bonnyrigg.

V5 **Bruntsfield Links**
☎031-336 1479 Sec, 2006 Clubhouse.

32 Barnton Ave, Davidsons Mains,
Edinburgh EH4 6JH.
Off A90 in Davidsons Mains 2-3
miles W of Edinburgh city centre.
Parkland course.
18 holes, 6407 yards, S.S.S.71
Course designed by Willie Park.
Club founded in 1761.
Visitors: welcome weekdays by
appointment.
Green fees: on application.
Society meetings: by appointment.
Catering: luncheon daily, evening
meals during playing season.
Hotels: Barnton.

v6 Carrickvale
☎031-337 1932
Glendevon Park, Edinburgh

EH12 5VZ.
Opposite the Post House Hotel,
down Balgreen Rd.
Meadowland course.
18 holes, 6299 yards, S.S.S.70
Club founded in 1933.
Visitors: welcome.
Green fees: on application.
Society meetings: by arrangement.
Catering: by arrangement with Sec.
Hotels: Post House.

v7 Castle Douglas
☎Castle Douglas (0556) 2801
Abercromby Rd, Castle Douglas.
400 yards on Ayr road from town
clock.
Parkland course.
9 holes, 5408 yards, S.S.S.66

Green fees: on application.
Catering: bar facilities in evenings.
Hotels: many in town.

v8 Colvend
☎Rockliffe (055 663) 398, (055 662)
685 Sec.
Sandyhills, by Dalbeattie, Kirkcud-
brightshire DG5 4PY.
6 miles from Dalbeattie on A710
Solway coast road.
Undulating meadowland course.
9 holes, 2322 yards, S.S.S.63
Course designed by Willie Fernie
(Troon) 1905 and extended in 1982
with advice from Dave Thomas.
Club founded in 1905.
Visitors: welcome. Course closed
Apr-Sept. at 4.40pm every Tues and

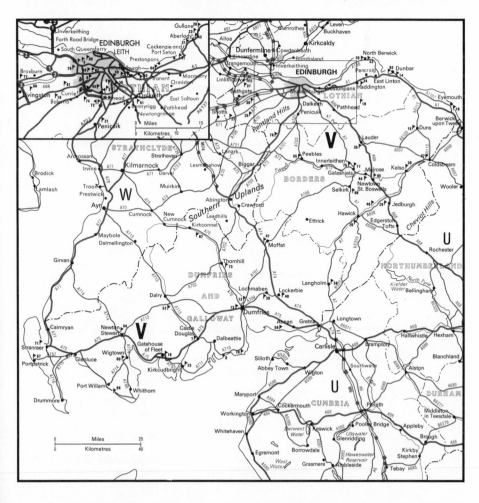

5pm every Thurs.
Green fees: £5 per day. Children under 18 half price except Sat and Sun.
Society meetings: welcome. Contact Sec.
Catering: April-Oct full lunch and dinner facilities. Winter restricted to weekends.
Hotels: Clonyard House, Colvend, Kirkcudbright.

V9 Craigmillar Park
☎031-667 2837 Clubhouse, 0047 Office.
1 Observatory Rd, Edinburgh EH9 3HG.
Approximately 3 miles from city centre close to Royal Observatory, Blackford Hill.
Parkland course.
18 holes, 5846 yards, S.S.S.68
Course designed by James Braid.
Club founded in 1895.
Visitors: non introduced visitors must produce either handicap certificate, letter of introduction or proof of club membership. Off first tee by 3.30pm weekdays. Not allowed weekends or Bank Holidays.
Green fees: £7 per round, £12 per day weekdays.
Society meetings: on application.
Catering: bar lunch, high tea on request.
Hotels: Iona, Strathearn Rd.

V10 Dalmahoy
☎031-333 2055 or 1436
Dalmahoy, Kirknewton, Midlothian EH27 8EB.
On A71 Edinburgh-Kilmarnock road.
Parkland course.
East 18 holes, 6664 yards, S.S.S.72
West 18 holes, 5121 yards, S.S.S.66
Course designed by James Braid.
Club founded in 1922.
Visitors: welcome every day.
Green fees: on application.
Society meetings: catered for every day.
Catering: full facilities every day.
Hotels: Dalmahoy Country Club, set in middle of two golf courses.

V11 Duddingston
☎031-661 768, 4301 Pro.
Duddingston Rd, W Edinburgh EH15 3QD.
3 miles from city centre E of A1.
Parkland course.
18 holes, 6647 yards, S.S.S.72
Course designed by Capability Brown.

Club founded in 1894.
Visitors: Mon-Fri only.
Green fees: £10.35 per round, £14.95 per day.
Society meetings: Tues, Thurs, Fri(am) only £8.05 per round; £10.35 per day.
Catering: lunch, high tea, bar every day.
Hotels: Lady Nairne; King's Manor; Duddingston Mansion House.

V12 Dumfries & County
☎Dumfries (0387) 53585
Edinburgh Rd, Dumfries DG1 1JX.
1 mile N of Dumfries town centre on A701.
Parkland course.
18 holes, 5928 yards, S.S.S.68
Course designed by Willie Fernie.
Club founded in 1912.
Visitors: welcome any day except Sat.
Green fees: £8.50 weekdays; £10 weekends.
Society meetings: by arrangement with Sec.
Catering: full facilities every day.
Hotels: Station; Moreig.

V13 Dumfries & Galloway
☎Dumfries (0387) 63582
Laurieston Ave, Dumfries DG2 7NY.
On A75 W of Dumfries.
Parkland course.
18 holes, 5782 yards, S.S.S.68
Club founded in 1880.
Visitors: welcome without reservation.
Green fees: £6.50; £9 weekends.
Society meetings: catered for.
Catering: full facilities except Mon.
Hotels: Cairndale; Dalston.

V14 Dunbar
☎Dunbar (0368) 62317
East Links, Dunbar EH42 1LT.
0.5 mile from Dunbar centre.
Seaside course.
18 holes, 6426 yards, S.S.S.71
Club founded in 1856.
Visitors: unrestricted.
Green fees: £11 daily weekdays; £15 daily weekends and Bank Holidays.
Society meetings: through Sec in writing.
Catering: full (7 days).
Hotels: Royal Mackintosh, Bellevue, Battleblent.

V15 Duns
☎Duns (0361) 83327 Sec
Hardens Rd, Duns, Berwickshire.

1 mile W of Duns on A6105.
Undulating meadowland course.
9 holes, 5754 yards, S.S.S.68
Club founded in 1898.
Visitors: unrestricted.
Green fees: £4 per day weekdays; £5 weekends; (half price from 1st Nov-15th Mar).
Society meetings: welcomed if previously arranged with Sec.
Catering: none.
Hotels: many in Duns.

V16 Eyemouth
☎Eyemouth (08907) 50551
Gunsgreen House, Eyemouth RD14 4DW.
2.5 miles N of Burnmouth, off A1, signposted on A1107.
Seaside course.
9 holes, 5446 yards, S.S.S.66
Club founded in 1880.
Visitors: unrestricted.
Green fees: £3 weekdays; £4 weekends.
Society meetings: by arrangement.
Catering: by arrangement.
Hotels: Home Arms, Eyemouth; Contented Sole, Eyemouth.

V17 Galashiels
☎Galashiels (0896) 3724
Ladhope Recreation Ground, Galashiels, Selkirkshire.
0.25 mile N of town off A7.
Hilly course.
18 holes, 5309 yards, S.S.S.67
Course designed by James Braid.
Club founded in 1884.
Visitors: no restriction.
Green fees: £4 per round; £4.50 Sun.
Society meetings: none.
Catering: weekend only.
Hotels: Maxwell, Kingsnowes.

V18 Gatehouse
☎Gatehouse (05574) 654 Sec.
Laurieston Rd, Gatehouse-of-Fleet.
First right on entering Gatehouse-of-Fleet from E.
Undulating course.
9 holes, 4796 yards, S.S.S.63
Club founded in 1921.
Visitors: welcome.
Green fees: £4.50 per day.
Hotels: Bank of Fleet, High St; Gatehouse of Fleet.

V19 Gifford
☎Gifford (062 081) 267
c/o Sec, Cawdor Cottage, 11 Station Rd, Gifford, East Lothian EH41 4QL.
4.5 miles S of Haddington off A6137.

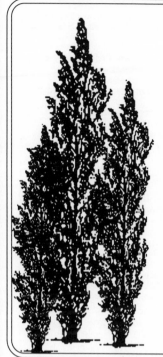

Meadowland/woodland course.
9 holes, 6138 yards, S.S.S.69
Club founded in 1904.
Visitors: welcome, except Tues and Wed from 4pm or Sun from 12 noon.
Green fees: on application.
Society meetings: catered for on weekdays by arrangement with Sec.
Catering: none.
Hotels: Tweeddale Arms, Gifford.

V20 **Glen**
☎North Berwick (0620) 2221
Tantallon Terrace, North Berwick, East Lothian EH39 4LE.
22 miles NE of Edinburgh on A198, follow road along E beach, clubhouse is last building on right.
Seaside/parkland course.
18 holes, 6098 yards, S.S.S.69
Course designed by Mackenzie Ross.
Club founded in 1906.
Visitors: anytime no restrictions.
Green fees: £4.50 per round weekdays; £5.75 per round weekends.
Society meetings: by arrangement with clubmaster.

Catering: bar lunch, high tea, coffee.
Hotels: Royal; Blenheim House, Nether Abbey, all North Berwick.

V21 **Glencorse**
☎Pencuik (0968) 77189
Milton Bridge, Pencuik, Midlothian EH26 0RD.
On A701, 9 miles S of Edinburgh.
Parkland course.
18 holes, 5205 yards, S.S.S.66
Club founded in 1890.
Visitors: welcome.
Green fees: £6 per round, £8 per day; £8 per round weekends.
Society meetings: Tues, Wed (with exception), Thurs, Fri (with exception).
Catering: bar lunch and high tea.
Hotels: Inveravon House, Loanhead; Original, Roslin; Royal, Roslin.

V22 **Greenburn**
☎Fauldhouse (0501) 70292
Bridge St, Fauldhouse, W Lothian EH47 9HG.
Midway between Glasgow and Edinburgh, turn off M8 at Whitburn, 3 miles.

Moorland course.
18 holes, 6210 yards, S.S.S.70
Club founded in 1953.
Visitors: casual mid-week, societies by booking, weekend - societies only by booking.
Green fees: £4.50 per round, weekdays; £6.75 per day, weekdays; £5.50 per round, £8.25 per day weekends.
Society meetings: by prior booking.
Catering: weekends and mid-week when societies are booked in.
Hotels: Whitdale, Whitburn.

V23 **Gullane**
☎Gullane (0620) 842255
Gullane, East Lothian EH31 2BB.
Off A1, on A198 to Gullane.
Links courses.
No. 1-18 holes, 6466 yards, S.S.S.71
No. 2-18 holes, 6127 yards, S.S.S.69
No. 3-18 holes, 5128 yards, S.S.S.65.
Club founded in 1882.
Visitors: welcome on all courses Mon-Fri and on Nos 2 & 3 at all times.
Green fees: on request.
Society meetings: welcome by arrangement (except No. 1 at

──── Four links in one ────

Whenever the question of a centre for a golfing holiday is raised, Gullane in East Lothian is always one of the first that comes to my mind. If anyone feels so inclined, and has the strength and fitness to match, he can play in delightful surroundings on seven different courses in one day.

More likely, however, he will prefer to take a more leisurely look at each or simply stay and sample those absolutely at his doorstep - Luffness New, and the three Gullanes which lie on the other side of Gullane Hill from Muirfield.

Everyone has courses for which he feels unreasoning affection, and Luffness and Gullane No. 1 are two of my favourites.

The incomparable stretch of country on which they stand was introduced to me by a kind uncle during my time at school in Edinburgh when a day at Luffness really was an escape from the problems of Plato and Pythagoras; my earliest recollections are of gloriously smooth, fast putting greens, a blind short hole across a quarry - and a magnificent lunch.

The short hole, at the point where the main road curves sharply for North Berwick, has long since been given a more straightforward approach, but I was glad to see on my last visit that the course, the greens and the lunch had lost none of their appeal.

To my mind the best holes are those from the 8th onwards down nearer Aberlady Bay, where a sense of peace and beauty is complete and the golfer cannot fail to enjoy himself. On a calm day, the demands made upon him are not all that severe, but it is most important to keep straight.

From Luffness it is perfectly possible to hit a ball across the other two Gullane courses — neither of which suffers by comparison with its celebrated neighbour — to Gullane No. 1, and to a stranger the four may at first be indistinguishable from each other. In character they have

much in common but the starts at Gullane are a little more mountainous.

However, when the view is as magnificent as it is from the third tee, or even better from the seventh tee, on Gullane No. 1, it is worth enduring any climb.

It is one of the greatest sights in the whole world of golf and except in grey, wet and windswept conditions, the Firth of Forth and its golden sands, the distant outline of Edinburgh and the two Forth Bridges, the green fields of Fife and an assortment of boats slipping out to sea past the Bass Rock, can distract one's thoughts from the golf which at this stage is gaining in challenge.

The 7th, rather like the 8th at Luffness, offers an inviting drive down the hill; the 8th gives the chance of a three and the 9th is an engaging short hole where the eye wanders again across the popular beach to the less exposed setting of Muirfield; but then there are three very fine long holes with which to start the homeward half, the 11th and 12th being particularly satisfying to play well, if one can forget the view.

Another testing short hole in a crosswind follows, and two more long holes which can make or mar a medal round. These take us gradually back up the slope to the short 16th along the crest and, in sight of home, we prepare for the final descent to the clubhouse, outside which the legendary Babe Zaharias was once presented with the British Women's Championship Trophy.

That was over thirty years ago, but happily little has changed in the meantime; the starter's bell on the first tee is still a welcome sound; the little village street down which so many famous names have stepped has lost none of its charm, and golfers from all parts still converge upon Gullane, Luffness and the many other courses along that coast because they know the quality and fun of the golf never disappoint.

weekends).
Catering: lunch every day except Mon. Other meals by arrangement.
Hotels: Marine, N Berwick; Open Arms, Dirleton; Grey Walls; Golf Inn; Mallard & Queens all Gullane.

v24 Haddington
☎Haddington (062 082) 3627
Amisfield Course, Haddington, East Lothian.
17 miles E of Edinburgh on A1, cross Victoria Bridge on E edge of town, golf course is 500 yards on left.
Parkland course.
18 holes, 6280 yards, S.S.S.70
Club founded in 1865.
Visitors: welcome Mon-Fri anytime. Sat and Sun 10am-12am and 2pm-4pm.
Green fees: £4.50 per round, £6.50 per day weekdays; £5.75 per round, £8.50 per day weekends.
Society meetings: none.
Catering: lunch, bar snacks, bar meals, high tea.
Hotels: George; Mercat; Kings Arms; Railway.

v25 Harburn
☎Bo'ness (0506) 871256
West Calder, West Lothian EH55 8RS.
Turn S at West Calder off A70 Lanark to Edinburgh road.
Parkland course.
18 holes, 5843 yards, S.S.S.68
Club founded in 1933.
Visitors: welcome without prior notification.
Green fees: £6 per round, £8.50 per day weekdays; £7.50 per round, £10 per day weekends.
Society meetings: catered for by advance arrangements.
Catering: full facilities by arrangement, bar snacks etc, normally available.
Hotels: Meadowhead, West Calder; West End, West Calder.

v26 Hawick
☎Hawick (0450) 72293
Vertish Hill, Hawick, Roxburghshire. S of Hawick on A7.
Undulating course.
18 holes, 5929 yards, S.S.S.69
Club founded in 1876.
Visitors: no restriction if no competitions being held.
Green fees: £4 per round, £6 per day weekdays; £6 per day weekends.
Society meetings: welcome by pre-

booking.
Catering: full range of catering available.
Hotels: Kirklands; Elm House; Mansfield Park.

v27 Hirsel
☎Coldstream (0890) 2678
Kelso Road, Coldstream, Berwickshire TS12 4LG.
W end of Coldstream on A697, Edinburgh to Newcastle road.
Parkland course.
9 holes, 2828 yards, S.S.S.67
Club founded in 1948.
Visitors: anytime.
Green fees: £3.50 per day weekdays; £4.50 per day weekends.
Society meetings: by arrangement.
Catering: April-Sept or by arrangement.
Hotels: Tillmouth Park, Coldstream; Victoria, Coldstream; Newcastle Arms, Coldstream.

v28 Honourable Company of Edinburgh Golfers
☎Gullane (0620) 842123
Muirfield, Gullane, East Lothian EH31 2EG.
Last road on left leaving Gullane for North Berwick on A198, approximately 18 miles from Edinburgh.
Links course.
Medal 18 holes, 6941 yards, S.S.S.73
Course designed by Tom Morris.
Club founded in 1744.
Visitors: Tues, Thurs and Fri am. must be members of recognised golf club and have handicap of 18 or better if gentlemen, 24 if Ladies.
Green fees: £22 per round; £33 per day.
Society meetings: no reduced rates or packages. Same as for visitors.
Catering: morning coffee (45p) lunch (£8), afternoon tea (65p) (Ladies are not allowed in the clubhouse).
Hotels: Greywalls, Gullane; Open Arms, Dirleton.

v29 Jedburgh
☎Jedburgh (0835) 63587/63770 Sec.
Dunion Rd, Jedburgh.
Leave town by way of Castlegate, clubhouse about 0.5 mile on right.
Undulating parkland course.
9 holes, 5522 yards, S.S.S.67
Club founded in 1890.
Visitors: welcome except on competition days.

Green fees: on application.
Society meetings: welcome except on competition days.
Catering: bar meals available at weekends from June-Sept; at other times by arrangement.
Hotels: Royal, Canongate, Jedburgh; Jedforest, Jedburgh.

v30 Kelso
☎Kelso (0573) 23009
Racecourse Rd, Kelso, Roxburghshire TD5 7SL.
1 mile N of town centre within National Hunt Racecourse.
Flat parkland course.
18 holes, 6066 yards, S.S.S.69
Course designed by James Braid.
Club founded in 1887.
Visitors: welcome.
Green fees: on application.
Society meetings: welcome by prior arrangement.
Catering: facilities available during opening hours except Mon and Tues; societies catered for on these days by prior arrangement.
Hotels: many good hotels in area.

v31 Kilspindie
☎Aberlady (0875) 358 or 216
Aberlady, East Lothian EH32 0QD.
Immediately E of Aberlady village, private road to left leading to club.
Seaside course.
18 holes, 5410 yards, S.S.S.66
Course designed by Ross & Sayers - extended by Willie Park.
Club founded in 1867.
Visitors: subject to members' demands visitors are welcome but advisable to enquire in advance. Parties welcome if booked in advance.
Green fees: £7 per round, £10 per day weekdays; £9 per round, £12 per day weekends.
Society meetings: welcome weekdays.
Catering: full facilities.
Hotels: Kilspindie House, Aberlady; various hotels in Gullane and North Berwick.

v32 Kingsknowe
☎031-441 4030
326 Lanark Rd, Edinburgh EH14 2JD.
W of Edinburgh on A71.
Parkland course.
18 holes, 5979 yards, S.S.S.69
Course designed by J.C. Stutt.
Club founded in 1908.
Visitors: welcome weekdays.

Green fees: £5.50 per round, £7.50 per day; £7.50 per round weekends.
Catering: lunch and high tea served except Mon.
Hotels: many good hotels in Edinburgh.

V33 Kirkcudbright

☎Kirkcudbright (0557) 30542
Stirling Crescent, Kirkcudbright.
Left off A711 onto B727 in Kirkudbright.
Hilly parkland course.
18 holes, 5598 yards, S.S.S.67
Club founded in 1895.
Visitors: welcome except on competition days.
Green fees: on application.
Society meetings: catered for on first Mon of each month.
Catering: none.
Hotels: Mayfield; Arden House; Royal; Selkirk; Gordon House.

V34 Langholm

Whitaside, Langholm, Dumfriesshire DG13 0JR.
Between Carlisle and Hawick on A7, 400 metres from Market Place.
Hillside course.
9 holes, 5246 yards, S.S.S.66
Club founded in 1892.
Visitors: welcome weekdays and weekends without reservation.
Green fees: £3 per round/day; (£1.50 with member).
Society meetings: welcome to enquire.
Catering: can be arranged.
Hotels: Eskdale, Market Place, Langholm.

V35 Lauder

Galashiels Rd, Lauder.
Off A68, 0.5 mile from Lauder.
Undulating course.
9 holes, 6002 yards, S.S.S.70
Club founded in 1896.
Visitors: welcome.
Green fees: on application.
Society meetings: none.
Catering: none available.
Hotels: good hotels in Lauder.

V36 Liberton

☎031-664 3309
297 Gilmerton Rd, Edinburgh EH16 5UJ.
S of Edinburgh on A7.
Parkland course.
18 holes, 5299 yards, S.S.S.66
Club founded in 1920.
Visitors: welcome except after 5pm on Mon, Wed, Fri.

Green fees: on application.
Society meetings: welcome weekdays.
Catering: full facilities available.
Hotels: Kildonan Lodge; Minto; Suffolk.

V37 Linlithgow

☎Linlithgow (0505) 842585
Braehead, Linlithgow, West Lothian EH49 6QF.
M9 from Edinburgh, just SW of Linlithgow.
Undulating parkland course.
18 holes, 5858 yards, S.S.S.68
Club founded in 1913.
Visitors: welcome except Wed and Sat.
Green fees: £5 per round, £7.50 per day weekdays; £6.50 per round, £9 per day Sunday.
Society meetings: prices on application.
Catering: bar snacks weekdays, full catering weekends or by arrangement for parties.
Hotels: Star and Garter.

V38 Livingston G & C C

☎Livingston (0506) 38843
Carmondean, Livingston, West Lothian EH54 8PG.
Leave M8 at Livingston interchange, follow signposts to Knightsridge, club signposted from there.
Meadowland course.
18 holes, 6636 yards, S.S.S.72
Course designed by Charles Lawrie.
Club founded in 1978.
Visitors: welcome.
Green fees: on application.
Society meetings: welcome.
Catering: meals served.
Hotels: Houston House.

V39 Lochmaben

☎Lochmaben (0387) 810552
Castlehill Gate, Lochmaben, Dumfriesshire DG11 1NT.
On A709 between Dumfries and Lockerbie.
Undulating parkland course.
9 holes, 5304 yards, S.S.S.66
Course designed by James Braid.
Club founded in 1926.
Visitors: welcome except competition days.
Green fees: on application.
Society meetings: catered for on weekdays.
Catering: by arrangement for meetings.
Hotels: Balcastle, Lochmaben; Queens, Lockerbie.

V40 Lockerbie

☎Lockerbie (057 62) 3363
Currie Rd, Lockerbie, Dumfriesshire DG11 2ND.
A74 to Lockerbie, take road to Langholme and turn left at T-junction towards Corrie, club 0.5 mile on right.
Parkland course.
9 holes, 2614 yards, S.S.S.66
Course designed by James Braid.
Club founded in 1889.
Visitors: welcome weekdays and on Sun from 12 noon-3pm.
Green fees: on application.
Society meetings: catered for by arrangement.
Catering: limited service available by arrangement.
Hotels: Lockerbie House; Blue Bell.

V41 Longniddry

☎Longniddry (0875) 52141, 52228 Starter.
Links Rd, Longniddry, E Lothian EH32 0NL.
Take A1 from Edinburgh, at Wallyford roundabout take A198 to Longniddry, turn left at Lingniddry Inn down Links Rd.
Parkland/seaside course.
18 holes, 6210 yards, S.S.S.70
Course designed by Harry Colt.
Club founded in 1921.
Visitors: welcome excluding competition days and public holiday.
Telephone Starter.
Green fees: on application.
Society meetings: Mon-Thurs inclusive.
Catering: dining room excluding Fri, bar service, soup and sandwiches available.
Hotels: Marine; North Berwick; Kilspindie House, Aberlady.

V42 Lothianburn

☎031-445 2206 Clubhouse, 2288 Pro.
106 Biggar Rd, Edinburgh EH10 7DU.
S boundary of Edinburgh.
Hillside course.
18 holes, S.S.S.69
Course designed by James Braid.
Club founded in 1893.
Visitors: welcome weekdays only.
Green fees: £5.50 per round, £7 per day.
Society meetings: welcome by arrangement with Sec on weekdays.
Catering: lunch, bar meals and high tea available.
Hotels: numerous hotels in Edinburgh.

Green fees: on application.
Society meetings: welcome weekdays.

V43 Luffness New
☎Gullane (0620) 843114, 843336
Sec, 843376 Clubmaster.
Aberlady, East Lothian EH32 0QA.
E of Edinburgh, follow trunk road
A198 along coast, club lies between
Aberlady and Gullane.
Undulating seaside course.
18 holes, 6085 yards, S.S.S.69
Course designed by Willie Park
(1894).
Club founded in 1894.
Visitors: by members introduction or
by arrangement.
Green fees: on application.
Society meetings: weekday
bookings.
Catering: lunch, high tea and dinner
except Mon.
Hotels: Greywalls, Gullane; Marine,
North Berwick.

V44 Melrose
☎Melrose (089 682) 2655 or
2811 Sec.
Dingleton, Melrose, Rox.
0.5 mile S of Melrose at base of
Eildon Hills.
Parkland course.
9 holes, 5464 yards, S.S.S.68
Club founded in 1880.
Visitors: welcome weekdays and
Sun by arrangement with Sec.
Green fees: on application.
Society meetings: by arrangement
except Sat.
Catering: snacks available.
Hotels: numerous good hotels in
Melrose.

V45 Merchants of Edinburgh
☎031-447 1219
10 Craighill Gardens, Edinburgh
EH10 5PY.
S side of Edinburgh off A701.
Hilly parkland course.
18 holes, 4889 yards, S.S.S.65
Club founded in 1907.
Visitors: must be introduced by
member, but parties may apply in
writing for reservation to Sec.
Green fees: £4.50 per round, £6 per
round weekday parties.
Society meetings: welcome on
weekdays by arrangement with Sec.
Catering: meals ordered in advance
(except Wed and Thurs).
Hotels: Braid Hills.

V46 Minto
☎(0450) 87220
Minto Village, by Denholm, Hawick,
Roxburghshire.
5 miles NE of Hawick off A698, turn
left in Denholm for Minto.
Parkland course.
18 holes, 5460 yards, S.S.S.68
Club founded in 1926.
Visitors: welcome at all times.
Green fees: £5 weekdays; £6
weekends.
Society meetings: by prior
arrangement these are welcome.
Catering: bar and catering available.
Hotels: Elm House, Hawick;
Kirklands, Hawick.

V47 Moffat
☎Moffat (0683) 20020
Coateshill, Moffat DG10 9SB.
On A701/A74 between Beattock and
Moffat.
Hillside course.
18 holes, 5218 yards, S.S.S.66
Course designed by Ben Sayers.
Club founded in 1884.
Visitors: welcome without
introduction. Restricted play on Wed
- before 12 noon only for visitors.
Green fees: £5 per round; £7 per
day weekdays; £9 per day
weekends.
Society meetings: catered for at
weekends and during week except
Wed and Thur.
Catering: coffee, lunches each day
except Thurs.
Hotels: Moffat House; Balmorse;
Auchen Castle.

V48 Mortonhall
☎031-447 6974 Sec.
231 Braid Rd, Edinburgh EH10 6PB.
2 miles S of city centre on A702,
situated on S of Braid Hills.
Moorland course.
18 holes, 6557 yards, S.S.S.71
Course designed by James Braid &
Fred Hawtree.
Club founded in 1892.
Visitors: welcome weekdays.
Green fees: on application.
Society meetings: welcome by
arrangement on weekdays.
Catering: snacks and lunches
served.
Hotels: Braid Hills.

V49 Murrayfield
☎031-337 3478
Murrayfield Rd, Edinburgh
EH12 6EU.
2 miles W of city centre.
Parkland course.
18 holes, 5727 yards, S.S.S.68
Club founded in 1896.
Visitors: welcome weekdays with
letter of introduction.
Green fees: £2 per round visitors
and members; visiting clubs £15 per
day; £10 per round.
Society meetings: by arrangement.
Catering: meals served except Sun.
Hotels: Ellersly House; Murrayfield;
Post House.

V50 Musselburgh
☎031-665 2005
Monktonhall, Musselburgh,
Midlothian.
1 mile S off A1 at Musselburgh.
Parkland course.
18 holes, 6623 yards, S.S.S.72
Course designed by James Braid.
Club founded in 1938.
Visitors: on application.
Green fees: on application.
Society meetings: none.
Catering: full dining room facilities.
Hotels: Edinburgh (10 minutes).

V51 Newbattle
☎031-663 2123
Abbey Rd, Dalkeith, Midlothian.
7 miles SW of Edinburgh on A7, take
Newbattle exit at Esbank round-
about, go uphill opposite police
station, club 300 yards on right.
Undulating parkland course.
18 holes, 6012 yards, S.S.S.69
Club founded in 1934.
Visitors: Mon-Fri (incl) except Public
and Local Holidays up to 4pm.
Green fees: £6.50 per round; £9 per
day.
Society meetings: Mon-Fri
(inclusive) except holidays. 9am-
10am and 2pm-3pm (not weekends).
Catering: full facilities on request.
Hotels: Lugton Inn, Dalkeith; Stair
Arms, Pathhead; County; Dalkeith.

V52 New Galloway
☎New Galloway (064 42) 239
Castle Douglas, Kirkcudbrightshire
DG7 3RP.
Easily located on way out of village
on A762.
Hilly course.
9 holes, 5058 yards, S.S.S.65
Club founded in 1902.
Visitors: welcome except for open
competition days.
Green fees: £5 per day.
Society meetings: welcome by
arrangement with Sec.
Catering: available in village.
Hotels: Kenmure Arms, New

Galloway; Kenbridge, New Galloway.

V53 North Berwick
☎North Berwick (0620) 2135
Beach Rd, North Berwick EH39 4BB.
23 miles E of Edinburgh on A198.
Seaside course.
18 holes, 6298 yards, S.S.S.70
Course designed by Mackenzie Ross.
Club founded in 1832.
Visitors: unrestricted.
Green fees: £13 per day, £8.50 per round weekdays; £17 per day, £12.50 per round weekends.
Society meetings: unrestricted weekdays.
Catering: except Thurs.
Hotels: Marine; Royal; Point Gary; Nether Abbey.

V54 Newton Stewart
☎(0671) 2172
Kirroughtree Ave, Minnigaff, Newton Stewart, Dumfries & Galloway DG6.
Off A75.
Parkland course.
9 holes, 5500 yards, S.S.S.67
Club founded in 1981.
Visitors: welcome, lounge facilities.
Green fees: £3.50 weekdays; £4.50 weekends; members pay annual sub.
Society meetings: welcome.
Catering: meals and bar lunch all week.
Hotels: Kirroughtree (3 star).

V55 Peebles
☎Peebles (0721) 20197 Clubhouse, 20153 reservations.
Kirkland St, Peebles EH45 8EU.
NW of town off A72.
Undulating parkland course.
18 holes, 6137 yards, S.S.S.69
Course designed by James Braid, with alterations by H.S. Colt.
Club founded in 1892.
Visitors: welcome.
Green fees: £5 per round, £7 per day weekdays; £7 per round, £9 per day weekends.
Society meetings: catered for 32 maximum Sat. 40 maximum Sun.
Catering: meals, snacks served daily.
Hotels: Peebles; Hydro, Innerleithen Rd, Peebles; Park, Innerleithen Rd, Peebles; Kingsmuir, Glen Rd, Peebles.

V56 Portobello
☎031-669 4361
Stanley Rd, Portobello, Edinburgh

EH15.
E of Edinburgh on A1 to Milton Rd.
Parkland course.
9 holes, 2400 yards, S.S.S.32
Club founded in 1826.
Visitors: no restrictions.
Green fees: £1.10 (9 holes).
Society meetings: no restrictions.
Catering: none.
Hotels: Kings Manor, Milton Rd.

V57 Portpatrick (Dunskey)
☎Portpatrick (0776 81) 273
Portpatrick, Stranraer, Wigtownshire DG9 8TB.
A75 to Stranraer, follow signs to Portpatrick, fork right at War Memorial, 300 yards on right signpost to club.
Undulating meadowland/seaside course.
18 holes, 5644 yards, S.S.S.67
9 holes, 1442 yards, S.S.S.27
Course designed by Dunskey Estate.
Club founded in 1903.
Visitors: welcome unaccompanied best to book except competition days.
Green fees: £40 fortnightly; £30 weekly; £8 daily; £10 Sat & Sun. Per round after 2.30pm £6; Sat & Sun £7. Juniors with adult half price; 9 hole course £1.50 daily.
Society meetings: very welcome, must book in advance with D.R. Wilson, Norville Cairnryan Rd, Stranraer. (0776) 2307.
Catering: all meals except Mon.
Hotels: Fernhill; Portpatrick; Downshire; Roslin; Crown, all in Portpatrick.

V58 Powfoot
☎Annan (04612) 2866
Cummertrees, Annan, Dumfriesshire.
3 miles W of Annan, off B724.
Seaside course.
18 holes, 6283 yards, S.S.S.70
Course designed by James Braid.
Visitors: welcome weekdays.
Green fees: on application.
Society meetings: welcome weekdays only by arrangement.
Catering: lunch and tea by arrangement except Fri.
Hotels: Powfoot Golf; Richmond.

V59 Prestonfield
☎031-667 1273 or 667 9665.
6 Priestfield Rd N, Edinburgh EH16 5SH.
Near to Commonwealth Pool, Dalkeith Rd.
Parkland course.

18 holes, 6216 yards, S.S.S.70
Course designed by James Braid.
Club founded in 1920.
Visitors: welcome any weekday. Not between 12 noon-1.30pm Sat; not before 11.30am Sun.
Green fees: £8 per round, £10 per day.
Society meetings: weekdays starting from 9.30am and 2.00pm.
Catering: full except Mon - snacks only.
Hotels: Rosehall, Dalkeith Rd; March Hall, March Hall Crescent.

V60 Pumpherston
☎Livingston (0506) 32869
Drumshoreland Rd, Pumpherston, Livingston EH53 0LF.
1 mile S of Uphall off A89.
Undulating parkland course.
9 holes, 5154 yards, S.S.S.65
Club founded in 1910.
Visitors: only when accompanied by a member.
Green fees: £3 weekdays; £4.50 weekends.
Society meetings: maximum number of players - 24, weekdays only.
Catering: bar snacks.
Hotels: Houston House, Uphall, West Lothian.

V61 Ratho Park
☎031-333 1752 Sec, 1252 Clubhouse.
Ratho, Newbridge, Midlothian EH28 8NX.
8 miles W of Edinburgh on A71 or A8.
Parkland course.
Course designed by Harry Vardon and James Braid.
Club founded in 1928.
Visitors: unlimited, societies Tues, Wed and Thurs.
Green fees: £8 per round, £12 per day; £15 weekends.
Society meetings: on application.
Catering: morning coffee, snacks, lunch, high tea and dinner (except Mon).
Hotels: Norwood House, Glasgow Rd, Edinburgh.

V62 Ravelston
☎031-332 3486
Ravelston Dykes Rd, Blackhall, Edinburgh EH4 3NZ.
Off A90 Queensferry Rd, at Blackhall.
Parkland course.
9 holes, 5200 yards, S.S.S.66

Course designed by James Braid. Club founded in 1912.
Visitors: with members preferred.
Green fees: on application.
Catering: light snacks served.
Hotels: Dragonara.

V63 **Royal Burgess**
☎031-339 2075
181 Whitehouse Rd, Edinburgh EH4 6BY.
W side of Edinburgh on Queensferry Rd, 100 metres N of Barton roundabout.
Parkland course.
18 holes, 6604 yards, S.S.S.72
Course designed by Tom Morris.
Club founded in 1735.
Visitors: weekdays only.
Green fees: on request.
Society meetings: weekdays only.
Catering: lunch and bar snacks.
Hotels: Barnton; Royal Scot.

V64 **Royal Musselburgh**
☎Prestonpans (0875) 810276
Clubhouse, 810139 Pro.
Prestongrange House, Prestonpans, East Lothian.
7 miles E of Edinburgh, 1 mile from

Wallyford roundabout on A1, take A198 North Berwick road.
Parkland course.
18 holes, 6237 yards, S.S.S.70
Course designed by James Braid.
Club founded in 1774.
Visitors: weekdays welcome.
Green fees: £7 per round, £11 per day weekdays; £8.50 per round, £15 per day weekends.
Society meetings: by arrangement, book in advance.
Catering: coffee, lunch, high tea, snacks except Tues.
Hotels: Drummore; Woodside; Ravelston House; Kings Manor.

V65 **St Boswells**
☎St Boswells (0835) 22359
St Boswells, Roxburghshire TD6 0AT.
0.25 mile off A68 Newcastle-Edinburgh road, junction with B6404.
Meadowland course.
9 holes, 2527 yards, S.S.S.65
Course designed by John Shade.
Club founded in 1899.
Visitors: welcome, unrestricted except for club competitions.
Green fees: £3.00 per round/day

weekdays; £4 per round/day weekends.
Society meetings: arrange through Sec.
Catering: only by arrangement.
Hotels: Buccleuch Arms; Dryburgh Abbey;.

V66 **St Medan**
☎Port William (098 87) 358
Monreith, Port William, Wigtownshire DG8 8NJ.
3 miles S of Port William on A747.
Seaside course.
9 holes, 4454 yards, S.S.S.62
Club founded in 1905.
Visitors: welcome 7 days.
Green fees: £5 per round (18 holes); £6.50 per day; £25 weekly (7 days).
Society meetings: catered for any day.
Catering: full licence and catering 11am-11pm except Tues.
Hotels: Monreith Arms, Port William; Corsemalzie, Port William.

V67 **Sanquhar**
☎Sanquhar (065 92) 577
Old Barr Rd, Sanquhar, Dum-friesshire DG4 6JZ.

Off A76 0.5 mile from Sanquhar.
Parkland course.
9 holes, 2572 yards, S.S.S.68.
Club founded in 1894.
Visitors: welcome.
Green fees: on application.
Society meetings: by prior
arrangement.
Hotels: Blackaddie House;
Glendyne; Nithsdale, Mennock
Lodge.

v68 **Selkirk**
☎Selkirk (0750) 20621
The Hill, Selkirk.
1 mile S of Selkirk on A7 to Hawick.
Moorland course.
9 holes, 5640 yards, S.S.S.67
Club founded in 1883.
Visitors: welcome.
Green fees: £6 weekends; £4
weekdays.
Society meetings: by arrangement.
Catering: none available.
Hotels: Woodburn House, Selkirk.

v69 **Silverknowes**
☎031-336 5359
Silverknowes, Parkway, Edinburgh
EH4 5ET.
W end of Edinburgh, off Cramond
Foreshore.
Municipal course.
18 holes, 6210 yards, S.S.S.70
Club founded in 1958.
Visitors: welcome, with reservation
only.
Green fees: £3 weekdays; £3.20
weekends.
Society meetings: none.
Catering: none available.
Hotels: Commodore, adjacent to
course.

v70 **Southerness**
☎Kirkbean (0387 66) 677
Southerness, Dumfries DG2 8AZ.
16 miles SW of Dumfries off A710.
Links course.
18 holes, 6554 yards, S.S.S.72
Course designed by Mackenzie
Ross.
Club founded in 1947.
Visitors: no restrictions.
Green fees: £10 per day, £40 per
week.
Society meetings: apply to Sec.
Catering: full bar and catering
facilities available.
Hotels: Baron's Craig, Rockcliffe,
Dalbeattie; Abbey Arms, New Abbey,
Dumfries; Criffel Inn, New Abbey,
Dumfries; Station, Dumfries;
Cairndale, Dumfries.

v71 **Stranraer**
☎Stranraer (0776) 87245
Creachmore, Stranraer DG9 0LF.
Take A718 from Stranraer towards
Leswalt, golf club is well signposted
on right.
Parkland course.
18 holes, 6300 yards, S.S.S.71
Course designed by James Braid.
Club founded in 1905.
Visitors: welcome.
Green fees: £7.50 weekdays; £12
weekends.
Society meetings: catered for.
Catering: not Mon.
Hotels: Nort West Castle, Stranraer;
Fernhill, Portpatrick.

v72 **Swanston**
☎031-445 2239
111 Swanston Rd, Edinburgh EH10
SE side of city.
Hillside course.
18 holes, 5024 yards, S.S.S.65
Course designed by Herbert More.
Club founded in 1927.
Visitors: welcome weekdays and
with restrictions at weekends.
Green fees: on application.
Society meetings: by arrangement.
Catering: meals served except
Tues.
Hotels: Pentland Hills.

v73 **Thornhill**
☎(0848) 30546
Blacknest, Thornhill, Dumfries.
14 miles N of Dumfries on A76 to
Thornhill village, turn right at cross,
1 mile on right.
Moorland/parkland course.
18 holes, 6011 yards, S.S.S.69
Club founded in 1893.
Visitors: welcome.
Green fees: £3 weekdays;
£4 weekends; £25 weekly.
Society meetings: catered for by
arrangement.
Catering: full facilities available.
Hotels: Buccleuch, Thornhill.

v74 **Torphin Hill**
☎031-441 1100
Torphin Rd, Colinton, Edinburgh
EH13 0PG.
SW of Colinton village.
Hillside course.
18 holes, 5030 yards, S.S.S.66
Club founded in 1895.
Visitors: no restrictions except when
competitions being played.
Green fees: £4 weekdays;
£7 weekends.
Society meetings: welcome except

weekends.
Catering: full bar and catering except
Tues.
Hotels: Braid Hill.

v75 **Torwoodlee**
☎Galashiels (0896) 2660
Galashiels, Selkirkshire.
On A7 Galashiels to Edinburgh road,
1 mile from town centre.
Parkland course.
9 holes, 5800 yards, S.S.S.68
Course designed by James Braid.
Club founded in 1895.
Visitors: welcome with restrictions
on Sat.
Green fees: on application.
Society meetings: catered for on
weekdays.
Catering: full facilities except Tues.
Hotels: Burts, Melrose; George and
Abbotsford, Melrose.

v76 **Turnhouse**
☎031-339 1014
154 Turnhouse Rd, Edinburgh
EH12 0AD.
W of city on A9080 near airport.
Parkland/heathland course.
18 holes, 6171 yards, S.S.S.69
Club founded in 1909.
Visitors: only visiting clubs. Not at
weekends. Visitors from Hotel -
contact Pro.
Green fees: £6 per round,
£9 per day.
Catering: lunch, high tea served
except Mon.
Hotels: Royal Scott, Glasgow Rd.

v77 **Uphall**
☎Broxburn (0506) 856404
Uphall, W Lothian.
Off M8, 14 miles W of Edinburgh.
Meadowland course.
18 holes, 6250 yards, S.S.S.68
Visitors: welcome.
Green fees: £6 weekdays;
£10 weekends.
Society meetings: by arrangement.
Catering: bar snacks, meals by
arrangement.
Hotels: Houston House, Uphall;
Golden Circle, Bathgate.

v78 **West Linton**
☎West Linton (0968) 60463
West Linton, Peeblesshire.
15 miles from Edinburgh on A702.
Moorland course.
18 holes, 6024 yards, S.S.S.69
Club founded in 1890.
Visitors: welcome weekdays.
Green fees: £6 per round, £8 per day.

Society meetings: catered for weekdays except Tues.
Catering: full facilities except Tues.
Hotels: Gordon Arms, Linton; Raemartin.

V79 West Lothian

☎Bo'ness (0506) 826030 Clubhouse, 826049 Pro Shop Airngath Hill, Linlithgow, West Lothian.
On hill separating Bo'ness and Linlithgow, marked by Hope Monument.
Undulating meadowland course.
18 holes, 6578 yards, S.S.S.71
Course designed by Fraser Middleton.
Club founded in 1892.
Visitors: no restrictions mid-week, by arrangement at weekends.
Green fees: £5 per round, £7 per day weekdays; £6 per round, £9 per day weekends.
Society meetings: catered for weekdays and at weekends.
Catering: meals as requested.

Hotels: Mr & Mrs J. Walker, Earl O'Murray Hotel, Bonsyde, Linlithgow.

V80 Wigtown & Bladnoch

☎Wigtown (0671) 9243354 Lightlands Ave, Wigtown, Wigtownshire.
Turn right at town square, turn left at Agnew Crescent 400 yards on right.
Parkland course.
9 holes, 2712 yards, S.S.S.67
Club founded in 1960.
Visitors: unlimited.
Green fees: £3.50 weekdays; £4.50 weekends.
Society meetings: welcome.
Catering: none.
Hotels: Forobank, Wigtown.

V81 Wigtownshire County

☎Glenluce (058 13) 420 Mains of Park, Glenluce, Newton Stewart, Wigtownshire DG8 0QN.
8 miles E of Stranraer on A75, 2 miles W of Glenluce.
Links course.
9 holes, 5715 yards, S.S.S.68

Course designed by Gordon Cunningham.
Club founded in 1894.
Visitors: unrestricted.
Green fees: £6 per day weekdays; £7 per day weekends.
Society meetings: catered for.
Catering: April-Sept inclusive.
Hotels: North West Castle, Stranraer.

V82 Winterfield

☎(0368) 62280 North Rd, Dunbar, E Lothian.
W side of Dunbar.
Seaside course.
18 holes, 5035 yards, S.S.S.65
Club founded in 1935.
Visitors: welcome.
Green fees: on application.
Society meetings: welcome by arrangement with Pro.
Catering: meals served except Thurs.
Hotels: in Dunbar.

W Strathclyde

There are almost one hundred and thirty courses in the area of Strathclyde which includes Glasgow, Arran, the remoter courses of Islay and the Mull of Kintyre and a seemingly endless chain along the Firth of Clyde as far south as Girvan.

Foremost among them are the championship links of Prestwick, Royal Troon and Turnberry and serious disciples of the game would never dream of passing them by. Prestwick, the home of championship golf, is, in many ways, a reminder of the days of jiggers and Norfolk jackets but its place in the modern world is every bit as genuine. The Amateur championship returned there in 1987, one of the greatest compliments that could be paid.

Royal Troon, with something for every golfing taste, has been on active Open service since 1923 while Turnberry is a place that, once seen, is never forgotten. On a fair day, it is impossible to beat but for golfing neighbourliness there is nothing to match the string of courses north of Troon that takes in Barassie, Glasgow Gailes, Irvine and Western Gailes, home of the 1972 Curtis Cup match.

Heading up into Glasgow, East Renfrewshire occupies a lonely spot on the moors long before the city boundary is reached. Another landmark is Whitecraigs but, for those making for the airport with time to spare, Renfrew and the delightful course of Bridge of Weir lie within easy reach.

The city itself is well served but Strathclyde has its remote corners as well including the Isle of Arran which is such a central, scenic feature of the area. I confess that I still have not managed to get there but I learned early of the spell it casts over its admirers. A late lamented Scottish golf writer was recounting to me the tale of his annual holiday there when I made the innocent mistake of asking him if it was nice. "Nice", he spluttered, "Nice? It's paradise".

W1 **Airdrie**
☎Airdrie (023 64) 62195
Rochsoles, Airdrie ML6 SDZ.
From Airdrie Cross in centre of town travel N on Glenmavis Rd.
Parkland course.
18 holes, S.S.S.69
Course designed by James Braid.
Club founded in 1877.
Visitors: welcome with introduction from own Sec.
Catering: meals and snacks served; parties should contact Mrs Linde at club.
Hotels: Tudor, Alexander St; Kenilworth, Motherwell St.

W2 **Alexandra**
☎041-556 3711
Alexandra Park, Alexandra Parade, Glasgow G31 8SE.
Parkland course.
9 holes, 5000 yards
Course designed by Graham

McArthur.
Club founded in 1818.
Visitors: welcome.
Green fees: on application.
Society meetings: by arrangement.
Catering: catering facilities available.
Hotels: Holiday Inn, Glasgow Central; Trust House, Glasgow.

W3 **Annanhill**
☎Kilmarnock (0563) 21644
Irvine Rd, Kilmarnock KA3 1DW.
Off main Kilmarnock to Irvine road.
Parkland course.
18 holes, 6118 yards, S.S.S.70
Course designed by J. McLean.
Club founded in 1957.
Visitors: welcome all days except Sat.
Green fees: £3.20 per round, £4.50 per day weekdays; £7.20 per day/round weekends.
Society meetings: catering any day

by arrangement.
Catering: snacks at weekends, breakfast, lunch, dinner or high tea by arrangement.
Hotels: Howard Park, Glasgow Rd, Kilmarnock.

W4 **Ardeer**
☎Stevenston (0294) 64542
Greenhead, Stevenston, Ayrshire.
Follow A78 (signs for Largs and Greenock), on High Rd by passing Stevenston, turn right into Kerelaw Rd and continue for 1 mile.
Parkland course.
18 holes, 6630 yards, S.S.S.72
Club founded in 1880.
Visitors: welcome except Sat.
Green fees: £9 per day; Sunday £11.
Society meetings: catered for Mon-Sat.
Catering: full facilities available.
Hotels: on application.

W5 **Ayr Belleisle**
☎Alloway (0292) 41258
Belleisle Park, Doonfoot Rd, Ayr.
1.5 miles S of Ayr on A719.
Parkland course.
18 holes, 6540 yards, S.S.S.71
Course designed by James Braid &
Stutt.
Club founded in 1927.
Visitors: welcome.
Green fees: on application.
Society meetings: apply to Course
Administrator at address above.
Catering: meals and snacks
available in hotel.
Hotels: Belleisle House; Balgarth,
Dunure Rd, Ayr; Old Racecourse,
Victoria Park, Ayr.

W6 **Ayr Dalmilling**
☎Ayr (0292) 263893
Westwood Ave, Ayr, Strathclyde.
1.5 miles from town centre on NE
boundary off A77.
Meadowland course.

18 holes, 5401 yards, S.S.S.66
Club founded in 1960.
Visitors: unrestricted.
Green fees: £3.80 per round, £6 per
day; £7 weekends.
Society meetings: catered for.
Catering: tea or coffee, lunch, high
tea every day except Tues.
Hotels: Racers, Whitletts Rd, Ayr.

W7 **Ayr Seafield**
☎Alloway (0292) 41258
Belleisle Park, Doonfoot Rd, Ayr.
1.5 miles S of Ayr on A719.
Parkland/seaside course.
18 holes, 5244 (or 4889) yards,
S.S.S.66 (or 64)
Club founded in 1927.
Visitors: welcome.
Green fees: on application.
Society meetings: apply to Course
Administrator at address above.
Catering: meals and snacks in hotel.
Hotels: Belleisle House; Balgarth,
Dunure Rd, Ayr; Old Racecourse,

Victoria Park, Ayr.

W8 **Ballochmyle**
☎Mauchline (0290) 50469
Ballochmyle, Mauchline, Ayrshire
KA5 6RR.
Adjoining A76(T) Kilmarnock to
Dumfries road, 1 mile S of Mauchine
village.
Parkland course.
18 holes, 5952 yards, S.S.S.69
Club founded in 1937.
Visitors: welcome weekdays.
Green fees: £9 per day weekdays;
£11 per day weekends (subject to
review).
Society meetings: catered for
weekdays.
Catering: morning coffee, lunch,
high tea.
Hotels: Balgarth, Ayr, Annefield, Ayr;
Sorn, Sorn Ayrshire.

W9 **Balmore**
☎Balmore (0360) 20240

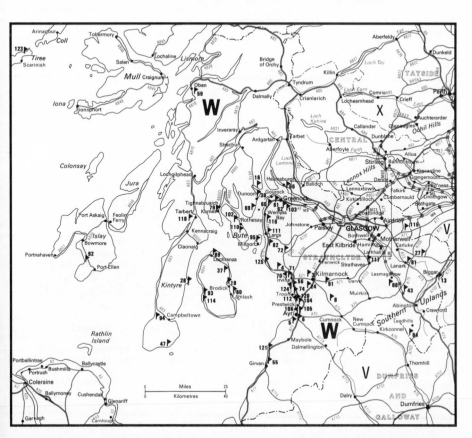

Balmore, Torrance, Stirlingshire.
2 miles N of Glasgow on A803 and
then A807.
Parkland course.
18 holes, 5516 yards, S.S.S.67
Course designed by James Braid.
Club founded in 1906.
Visitors: welcome with introduction
from member.
Green fees: £1 with member.
Catering: full catering facilities.
Hotels: Black Bull, Milngavie.

W10 **Barshaw**
☎041-889 2908, 884 2533 Sec,
889 5400 Mr Garrow
Barshaw Park, Glasgow Rd, Paisley,
Renfrewshire.
A737 from Glasgow W to Paisley,
1 mile before Paisley Cross.
Meadowland municipal course.
18 holes, 5673 yards, S.S.S.67
Club founded in 1920.
Visitors: welcome all week without
member.
Green fees: £2.30 per round.
Catering: none.
Hotels: Water Mill, Paisley; Bablock,
Paisley.

W11 **Bearsden**
☎041-942 2351
Thorn Rd, Bearsden, Glasgow.
1 mile from Bearsden Cross on
Thorn Rd.
Parkland course.
9 holes, 5977 yards, S.S.S.68
Club founded in 1891.
Visitors: introduced by member or
letter of introduction.
Green fees: £1 weekdays; £2
weekends.
Society meetings: none.
Catering: meals and snacks
available at all times.
Hotels: Black Bull, Milngavie,
Glasgow; Burnbrae, Bearsden.

W12 **Beith**
☎Beith (05055) 3166
Threepwood Rd, Bigholm, Beith.
Situated about 1 mile E of Beith.
Hilly course.
9 holes, 5488 yards, S.S.S.67
Club founded in 1896.
Visitors: Mon-Fri, Sun am.
Green fees: £4; £2 juniors under 18.
Society meetings: committee
meetings monthly, functions

welcome.
Catering: snacks 7 days.
Hotels: Mossend, Lochwinnoch.

W13 **Biggar**
☎Biggar (0899) 20618
The Park, Broughton Rd, Biggar,
Lanarkshire.
1 mile E of Biggar on Broughton Rd,
opposite police station.
Parkland course.
18 holes, 5416 yards, S.S.S.67
Course designed by Willie Park.
Club founded in 1895.
Visitors: unrestricted but telephone
(0899) 20319.
Green fees: £3.50 weekdays;
£5 weekends and Bank Holidays.
Society meetings: welcome, 36
maximum, advance booking
essential.
Catering: all day licence and
catering except Mon.
Hotels: Toftcombs; Elphinstone,
Biggar; Tinto, Symington.

W14 **Bishopbriggs**
☎041-772 1810
Brackenbrae Rd, Bishopbriggs,

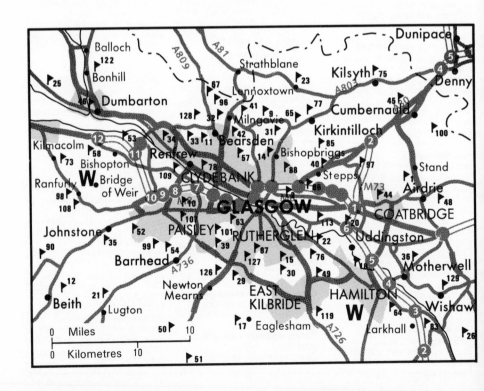

Glasgow G64 1QX.
4 miles N of Glasgow on A803, turn left 200 yards short of Bishopbriggs Cross.
Parkland course.
18 holes, 6041 yards, S.S.S.69
Club founded in 1906.
Visitors: welcome with member or by application to Committee.
Green fees: on application.
Catering: meals and snacks served except Wed.
Hotels: many good hotels in Glasgow.

W15 **Blairbeth**
☎041-634 3555
Fernhill, Rutherglen, Glasgow.
2 miles S of Rutherglen via Stonelaw Rd.
Parkland course.
18 holes, 5448 yards, S.S.S.67
Visitors: welcome with member.
Green fees: £1 per day weekdays; £3 weekends.
Catering: by arrangement.
Hotels: Kings Park, Rutherglen.

W16 **Blairmore & Strone**
☎Blairmore (036 984) 217
Strone, By Dunoon, Argyll PA23 8TJ.
0.75 mile N of Strone on A880.
Undulating parkland/moorland course.
9 holes, 2112 yards, S.S.S.62
Club founded in 1896.
Visitors: welcome.
Green fees: £3 per round/day. Some delays Sat afternoons and Mon evenings.
Catering: none.
Hotels: Blairmore House, Blairmore by Dunoon, Argyll.

W17 **Bonnyton**
☎Eaglesham (035 53) 2781
Eaglesham, Glasgow G76 0QA.
Eaglesham is on B764, 3 miles SW of East Kilbride.
Moorland course.
18 holes, 6252 yards, S.S.S.71
Club founded in 1957.
Visitors: welcome weekdays.
Green fees: £10 weekdays.
Society meetings: catered for by prior arrangement.
Catering: weekdays and Sunday lunch and high tea. Saturday lunch and dinner. Bar lunch every day.

W18 **Bothwell Castle**
☎Bothwell (0698) 853177
Blantyre Rd, Bothwell, Glasgow.

On A74 3 miles N of Hamilton.
Meadowland course.
18 holes, 6426 yards, S.S.S.71
Club founded in 1922.
Visitors: welcome weekdays 8am-3.30pm.
Green fees: £7.50 per round, £10 per day.
Society meetings: courtesies arranged, by written application during weekdays.
Catering: snacks, lunch, high tea, dinner daily.
Hotels: Silvertrees; Bothwell; Bothwell Bridge, Bothwell.

W19 **Brodick**
☎Isle of Arran (0770) 2349
Brodick, Isle of Arran.
0.5 mile from Brodick pier.
Seaside course.
18 holes, 4404 yards, S.S.S.62
Club founded in 1897.
Visitors: welcome all week.
Green fees: £3.50 per round restricted times. £5.50 per day.
Society meetings: by letter to Sec catered for at all times.
Catering: light lunch, contact Steward.
Hotels: contact Isle of Arran Tourist Information, The Pier, Brodick, Isle of Arran (0770) 2140/2401.

W20 **Calderbraes**
☎Uddingston (0698) 813425
57 Roundknowe Rd, Uddingston, Lanarkshire G71 7TS.
Start of M74, 4 miles from Glasgow.
Parkland course.
9 holes, 5046 yards, S.S.S.67
Club founded in 1890.
Visitors: introduced by member only.
Grees fees: on application.
Catering: snacks, lunch, dinner etc.
Hotels: Redstones, Uddingston.

W21 **Caldwell**
☎Uplawmoor (050 585) 329
Clubhouse, 616 Pro.
Uplawmoor, Renfrewshire.
Off A736 5 miles SW of Barrhead, 12 miles NE of Irvine.
Moorland course.
18 holes, 6102 yards, S.S.S.69
Club founded in 1903.
Visitors: welcome weekdays but advisable to check in advance.
Green fees: £8.05 per round, £11.50 per day.
Society meetings: catered for on weekdays.
Catering: welcome weekdays.

Hotels: Uplawmoor, Uplawmoor; Dalmeny, Barrhead.

W22 **Cambuslang**
☎041-641 3130
30 Westburn Drive, Cambuslang, Glasgow.
Off main Glasgow-Hamilton road at Cambuslang.
Parkland course.
9 holes, 6072 yards, S.S.S.69
Club founded in 1891.
Visitors: introduced.
Green fees: £5.
Society meetings: weekdays only.
Catering: full.
Hotels: Cambus Court, Cambuslang.

W23 **Campsie**
☎Lennoxtown (0360) 310244
Crow Rd, Lennoxtown, Glasgow G65 7HX.
N of Lennoxtown on B822.
Hillside course.
18 holes, 5517 yards, S.S.S.67
Club founded in 1897.
Visitors: welcome weekdays and by prior arrangement at weekends.
Green fees: on application.
Society meetings: catered for by arrangement with Sec.
Catering: bar snacks available; meals served by prior arrangement.
Hotels: Glazertbank, Kincaid House.

W24 **Caprington**
☎Kilmarnock (0563) 23702
Ayr Rd, Kilmarnock KA1 4UW.
S of Kilmarnock on Ayr Rd.
Parkland course.
18 holes, S.S.S.68
Visitors: welcome.
Green fees: on request (municipal course).
Hotels: Golden Sheaf.

W25 **Cardross**
☎Cardross (0389) 841754 Sec, 841213 Club, 841350 Pro.
Main Rd, Cardross, Dumbarton E82 5LB.
Between Dumbarton and Helensburgh on A814.
Parkland course.
18 holes, 6466 yards, S.S.S.71
Course designed by Willie Fernie of Troon and James Braid.
Club founded in 1895.
Visitors: welcome weekdays, weekends introduced by member.
Green fees: £8.50 per round, £12.50 per day.
Society meetings: by arrangement

with Sec (weekdays only).
Catering: bar snacks, tea except Mon.
Hotels: Dumbuck, Dumbarton; Commodore, Helensburgh; Lomond Castle, Alexandria.

W26 Carluke
☎Carluke (0555) 71070
Hallcraig, Mauldslie Rd, Carluke ML8 5HG.
About 1.5 miles from traffic lights at town centre on road to Hamilton and Larkhall.
Undulating parkland course.
18 holes, 5800 yards, S.S.S.68
Club founded in 1894.
Visitors: weekdays only until 4.30pm. except Tues.
Green fees: £9 per day (£1 with member).
Society meetings: by written request to Sec.
Catering: full except Tues.
Hotels: Popinjay (has 3 memberships).

W27 Carnwath
☎Carnwath (0555) 840251
1 Main St, Carnwath.
5 miles NE of Lanark.
Undulating course.
18 holes, 5860 yards, S.S.S.68
Club founded in 1907.
Visitors: welcome Mon, Wed, Fri and Sun.
Green fees: on application.
Society meetings: catered for.
Catering: meals served except Tues and Thurs.
Hotels: Tinto, Symington.

W28 Carradale
☎Carradale (05833) 624
Carradale, Campbeltown, Argyll PA28 6QX.
Off B842 from Campbeltown to Caradale.
Undulating course.
9 holes, 2392 yards, S.S.S.63 (18 holes)
Club founded in 1888.
Visitors: welcome at all times, no introduction necessary.
Green fees: £4 per (18 holes); £5 per day; weekly terms etc. available on application.
Catering: available at both hotels.
Hotels: Carradale, situated on course; Ashbank, 50 yards.

W29 Cathcart Castle
☎041-638 9449
Mearns Rd, Clarkston, Glasgow

G76 7YL.
On A77, 7 miles from Glasgow.
Undulating parkland course.
18 holes, 5832 yards, S.S.S.68
Club founded in 1895.
Visitors: introduction by member.
Green fees: on application.
Society meetings: by arrangement.
Catering: snacks, meals.
Hotels: Redhurst, Giffnock; McDonald, Giffnock.

W30 Cathkin Braes
☎041-634 6605
Cathkin Rd, Rutherglen, Glasgow G73 4SE.
SE of Glasgow off road to E Kilbride.
Moorland course.
18 holes, 6266 yards, S.S.S.71
Course designed by James Braid.
Club founded in 1888.
Visitors: Mon-Fri prior arrangement.
Green fees: £10 per round, £15 per day.
Society meetings: none.
Catering: full catering to order except Mon.
Hotels: Stuart, East Kilbride; Bruce, East Kilbride; Burnside, Rutherglen.

W31 Cawder
☎041-772 5167
Cadder Rd, Bishopbriggs, Glasgow G64 3QD.
0.5 mile W of Bishopbriggs off A803.
Parkland course.
Cawder-18 holes, 6229 yards, S.S.S.71
Keir-18 holes, 5877 yards, S.S.S.68
Course designed by Donald Steel (Cawder course), and James Braid (Keir course).
Club founded in 1933.
Visitors: welcome on weekdays by arrangement with Sec.
Green fees: on application.
Society meetings: welcome weekdays by arrangement with Sec.
Catering: full catering facilities.
Hotels: Black Bull, Milngavie; Glazertbank, Lennoxtown.

W32 Clober
☎041-956 1685
Craigton Rd, Milngavie G62 7HP.
7 miles NW of Glasgow.
Parkland course.
18 holes, 5068 yards, S.S.S.65
Course designed by Lyle Family.
Club founded in 1952.
Visitors: weekdays before 4.30pm.
Green fees: £5 per round.
Society meetings: by prior arrangement midweek.

Catering: available Tues, Wed, Fri, Sat and Sun; snacks Mon and Thurs.
Hotels: Black Bull; Thistle; Milngavie.

W33 Clydebank & District
☎Duntocher (0389) 72389
Hardgate, Clydebank, Dunbartonshire G81 5QY.
8 miles NW of Glasgow via Great Western Rd.
Parkland course.
18 holes, 5825 yards, S.S.S.68
Club founded in 1905.
Visitors: welcome weekdays, weekends with member only.
Green fees: £8 per day.
Society meetings: by arrangement.
Catering: meals served.
Hotels: Cameron House; Boulevard; Pine Trees.

W34 Clydebank Overtoun
☎041-952 6372 Pro Shop.
Overtoun Rd, Clydebank, Dunbartonshire.
5 minutes from Dalmuir station.
Parkland municipal course.
18 holes, 5643 yards, S.S.S.66
Club founded in 1928.
Visitors: municipal rules apply.
Green fees: £2 Mon-Sat; £2.20 Sun.
Society meetings: first Mon evening of every month.
Catering: café attached to Pro Shop.
Hotels: Boulevard, Great Western Rd; Radnor, Kilbowie Rd.

W35 Cochran Castle
☎Johnstone (0505) 20146
Craigston, Scott Ave, Johnstone PA5 0HF.
0.25 mile off Johnstone-Beith road to S of town, Bird in the Hand Hotel is good landmark near turning to club.
Undulating moorland course.
18 holes, 6123 yards, S.S.S.70
Course designed by Charles Hunter of Prestwick, altered by James Braid.
Club founded in 1895.
Visitors: introduced by member £1.30; visiting parties weekends excluded.
Green fees: £10 per day, £7 per round.
Society meetings: maximum 32 players.
Catering: full catering facilities except Mon.
Hotels: Lynhurst, Park Rd, Johnstone.

W36 Colville Park
☎Motherwell (0698) 63017

Jerviston Estate, Motherwell,
Strathclyde ML1 4UG.
On left hand side of A723, 1 mile N
of Motherwell town centre.
Parkland course.
18 holes, 6208 yards, S.S.S.70
Course designed by James Braid.
Club founded in 1922.
Visitors: party bookings mid-week
only by prior arrangement.
Green fees: party bookings £8 per
day VAT inclusive.
Society meetings: welcome
weekdays.
Catering: full catering facilities
available.
Hotels: Old Mill, Motherwell; Garrion,
Merry St, Motherwell.

w37 Corrie
☎Corrie (077 081) 223
Sannox, Isle of Arran.
By A84 coast road from Brodick.
Undulating course.
9 holes, 3896 yards, S.S.S.61
Club founded in 1892.
Visitors: welcome.
Green fees: £3 per day, £1.50 juniors.
Catering: light meals and snacks
served.
Hotels: Corrie.

w38 Cowal
☎Dunoon (0369) 5673 or 2216
Ardenslate Rd, Kirn, Dunoon, Argyll
PA23 8LT.
0.25 mile from A815 at Kirn.
Moorland course.
18 holes, 6250 yards, S.S.S.70
Course designed by James Braid.
Club founded in 1890.
Visitors: welcome.
Green fees: £5.75 per round, £7.50
per day weekdays; £9 per round,
£11.50 per day weekends; weekly
£28.75; (subject to review).
Society meetings: catered for at
special rates. Details from Sec.
Catering: full catering available
during season.
Hotels: Rosscairn, Hunter St, Kirn,
Dunoon; Lyall Cliff, East Bay,
Dunoon; Mayfair, Clyde St, Kirn,
Dunoon; Slatefield, Marine Parade,
Kirn, Dunoon.

w39 Cowglen
☎041-632 0556
301 Barrhead Rd, Glasgow G43.
S side of Glasgow, following signs to
Burrell Collection, opposite Pollok
golf club.
Undulating parkland course.
18 holes, 6006 yards, S.S.S.69

Club founded in 1906.
Visitors: by introduction from
member or by letter to Sec.
Green fees: £7 per round including
VAT; £10 per day including VAT.
Society meetings: request should
be made to Sec.
Catering: lunch, dinner and bar
snack.
Hotels: Tinto Firs, Kilmarnock Rd,
Glasgow.

w40 Crow Wood
☎041-779 1943
Garnkirk Estate, Muirhead, Chryston,
Glasgow G69 9JF.
1 mile N of Stepps on A80.
Parkland course.
18 holes, 6209 yards, S.S.S.70
Course designed by James Braid.
Visitors: with member only.
Green fees: subject to review.
Society meetings: by arrangement.
Catering: meals served except Mon.
Hotels: Garfield, Crow Wood Road
House.

w41 Douglaston
☎041-956 5750
Strathblane Rd, Milngavie, Glasgow
G62.
7 miles N of Glasgow city centre on
A879 and A81.
Parkland course.
18 holes, 6683 yards, S.S.S.72
Course designed by John Harris.
Club founded in 1976.
Visitors: open to public.
Green fees: £4 weekdays; £6
weekends and Bank Holidays.
Society meetings: party bookings of
any kind.
Catering: all types of catering.
Hotels: Burnbrae, 1 mile.

w42 Douglas Park
☎041-942 2220, 331 1837 Sec.
Hillfoot, Bearsden, Glasgow.
Next to Hillfoot Station.
18 holes, 5957 yards, S.S.S.68
Visitors: welcome with member
only.
Green fees: on request.
Society meetings: by arrangement
with Sec.
Catering: meals served by
arrangement.

w43 Douglas Water
☎Lanark (0555) 2295
Ayr Rd, Rigside, Lanark.
7 miles SW of Lanark on A70, 2
miles E of A74, signposted Rigside.
Undulating parkland course.

9 holes, 2947 yards, S.S.S.69
Course designed by striking coal
miners in 1921.
Club founded in 1922.
Visitors: welcome.
Green fees: £2.50 per day
weekdays; £3.50 weekends and
Bank Holidays.
Society meetings: none.
Catering: by arrangement.
Hotels: 7 miles to Lanark, 5 miles to
Douglas.

w44 Drumpellier
☎Coatbridge (0236) 24139 Pro,
28723 Clubmaster.
Drumpellier Ave, Coatbridge
ML5 1RX.
8 miles E of Glasgow on A89, 1 mile
from Coatbridge.
Parkland course.
18 holes, 6227 yards, S.S.S.70
Course designed by W. Fernie.
Club founded in 1894.
Visitors: welcome weekdays
excluding Bank Holidays.
Green fees: £15 per day, £10 per
round.
Society meetings: catered for on
weekdays.
Catering: full catering except Thurs.
Hotels: Coatbridge, Glasgow Rd,
Coatbridge.

w45 Dullatur
☎Cumbernauld (023 67) 23230
Dullatur, Glasgow.
1.5 miles from Cumbernauld village.
Undulating moorland course.
18 holes, 6195 yards, S.S.S.70
Club founded in 1897.
Visitors: welcome weekdays by
arrangement.
Green fees: £7.50 per day, £5 per
round; weekdays only.
Society meetings: catered for on
weekdays.
Catering: full facilities available.
Hotels: many hotels in Glasgow.

w46 Dumbarton
☎Dumbarton (0389) 32830
Broadmeadows, Dumbarton,
Dumbartonshire G82 2BQ.
15 miles NW of Glasgow.
Meadowland course.
18 holes, 5981 yards, S.S.S.69
Club founded in 1888.
Visitors: welcome weekdays.
Green fees: £8 per day.
Society meetings: by arrangement.
Catering: lunch, snacks etc except
Tues.
Hotels: Dumbuck, Dumbarton.

W47 Dunaverty

Southend, Campbeltown, Argyll
PA28 6RF.
On B842, 10 miles S of Campeltown.
Undulating seaside course.
18 holes, 4597 yards, S.S.S.63
Visitors: welcome.
Green fees: on request through
Cambeltown Courier office.
Catering: snacks available.
Hotels: Keil.

W48 Easter Moffat

☎Caldercruix (0236) 842289
Mansion House, Plains, by Airdrie,
Lanarkshire.
Course is situated 2 miles E of Air-
drie on the old Edinburgh-Glasgow
road.
Moorland/parkland course.
18 holes, 6221 yards, S.S.S.70
Club founded in 1922.
Visitors: welcome.
Green fees: on application.
Society meetings: welcome week-
days.
Catering: during playing season
(Mar-Sept) otherwise by arrange-
ment.
Hotels: Easter Croft, Caldercruix.

W49 East Kilbride

☎East Kilbride (03552) 20913
Chapelside Rd, Nerston, East
Kilbride G74 4PF.
On Glasgow-East Kilbride road turn
off at Nerston village by Borlands
Cars.
Undulating meadowland course.
18 holes, 6384 yards, S.S.S.71
Course designed by Fred Hawtree.
Club founded in 1900.
Visitors: accompanied by members.
Green fees: £5 per round, £8 per
day.
Society meetings: catered for on
Mon and Fri.
Catering: full catering except Tues
and Thurs pm.
Hotels: Bruce, East Kilbride; Stuart,
East Kilbride.

W50 East Renfrewshire

☎(03555) 206
Loganswell, Pilmuir, Newton Mearns,
Glasgow.
A77, 1 mile from Mearns Cross.
Moorland course.
18 holes, 6100 yards, S.S.S.70
Course designed by Tom Dobson.
Club founded in 1926.
Visitors: welcome with member
only.
Green fees: £9 per round, £14 per
day weekdays.

Society meetings: by arrangement.
Catering: meals served.
Hotels: MacDonalds.

W51 Eastwood

☎Loganswell (035 55) 261
Muirshield, Loganswell, Newton
Mearns, Glasgow G77 6RX.
On A77 from Glasgow, 3 miles S of
Newton Mearns Cross at junction of
Old Mearns Rd.
Moorland course.
18 holes, 5886 yards, S.S.S.68
Course designed by J. Moon.
Club founded in 1893.
Visitors: parties welcome by prior
appointment with Sec, C.B. Scouler.
Green fees: £9 per round, £14 per
day.
Society meetings: by arrangement.
Catering: full - snacks, lunch, dinner.
Hotels: Redhurst, Giffnock.

W52 Elderslie

☎Johnstone (0505) 22835 or 23956
63 Main Rd, Elderslie, Renfrewshire
PA5 9AZ.
On A737 between Paisley and
Johnstone.
Undulating parkland course.
18 holes, 6004 yards, S.S.S.69
Club founded in 1909.
Visitors: full facilities Mon-Fri only.
Green fees: £7 per round, £10 per
day.
Society meetings: catered for by
arrangement.
Catering: full licensed facilities.
Hotels: Excelsior, Glasgow Airport.

W53 Erskine

☎Bishopton (0505) 863327
Bishopton, Renfrewshire PA7 5PH.
N of M8 leave Erskine Toll Bridge
and turn left along B815 for 1.5
miles.
Parkland course.
18 holes, 6287 yards, S.S.S.70
Club founded in 1903.
Visitors: welcome if introduced by or
playing with a member.
Green fees: on application.
Society meetings: by arrangement.
Catering: meals served to members
and guests only, or by arrangement.
Hotels: Bishopton; Crest.

W54 Fereneze

☎041-881 1519, 221 6394 Sec,
881 7058 Pro.
Fereneze Ave, Barrhead, Glasgow
G78 1HJ.
9 miles SW of Glasgow.
Moorland course.
18 holes, 5821 yards, S.S.S.68

Club founded in 1904.
Visitors: by application to Pro, Sec
or accompanied by member.
Green fees: £9 per round/day, (£2
with member).
Society meetings: weekdays only,
apply to Sec fees as above.
Catering: lunch, bar snacks, evening
meals. Please book.
Hotels: Dalmeny Park, Barrhead.

W55 Girvan

☎0465 4346
Girvan, Ayrshire KA26 9HW.
Off A77.
Seaside/meadowland course.
18 holes, 5078 yards, S.S.S.65
Visitors: welcome.
Green fees: £3.80 per round, £6 per
day weekdays; £4.80 per round,
£7.60 per day weekends.
Society meetings: welcome by
arrangement.
Catering: meals served by
arrangement.
Hotels: many in area.

W56 Glasgow (Ayr)

☎0294 311347
Gailes, By Irvine, Ayrshire.
2 miles S of Irvine on road to Troon.
Links course.
18 holes, 6500 yards, S.S.S.71
Course designed by Willie Park Jr.
Club founded in 1787.
Visitors: on application.
Green fees: £16 per round.
Society meetings: on application.
Catering: lunch served except Mon.
Hotels: Hospitality Inn, Irvine.

W57 Glasgow

☎041-942 2340
Killermont, Bearsden, Glasgow
G61 2TW.
6 miles NW of Glasgow near Killer-
mont Bridge.
Parkland course.
18 holes, 5968 yards, S.S.S.69
Course designed by Tom Morris Sr.
Club founded in 1787.
Visitors: catered for by application.
Green fees: £16 per round.
Society meetings: on application.
Catering: lunch, high tea served ex-
cept Mon.
Hotels: Grosvenor.

W58 Gleddoch G & CC

☎Langbank (047 554) 304, 704 Pro.
Langbank, Renfrewshire PA14 6YE.
M8 to Greenock, first turning to
Langbank Houston.
Parkland/moorland course.

18 holes, 5661 yards, S.S.S.67
Course designed by Hamilton Stutt.
Club founded in 1975.
Visitors: welcome by arrangement
with Pro Keith Campbell.
Green fees: £8 per round, £12 per
day; weekends £15.
Society meetings: welcome.
Catering: meals and snacks.
Hotels: Gleddoch House.

W59 Glencruitten
☎Oban (0631) 62868
Glencruitten Rd, Oban.
1 mile from town centre off A816.
Hilly parkland/moorland course.
18 holes, 4452 yards, S.S.S.63
Course designed by James Braid.
Club founded in 1908.
Visitors: welcome weekdays, with
restrictions on Thurs and Sat.
Green fees: £5.50 per round, £7 per
day weekdays; £7 per round, £8 per
day weekends.
Society meetings: limited number of
societies accepted.
Catering: meals and snacks available.
Hotels: numerous good hotels in
area.

W60 Gourock
☎Gourock (0475) 31001
Cowal View, Gourock, Renfrewshire
PA19 6HD.
2 miles SW from Gourock station via
Victoria Rd, Golf Rd and Cowal
View.
Moorland course.
18 holes, 6492 yards, S.S.S.71
Course designed by Henry Cotton.
Club founded in 1896.
Visitors: weekdays, weekends with
members
Green fees: £7 per round, £9 per
day.
Society meetings: on application to
Sec.
Catering: bar lunch, high tea, dinner
by arrangement.
Hotels: Queens; Ashton; Gantock;
Castle Levan.

W61 Greenock
☎Greenock (0475) 20793
Forsyth St, Greenock, Renfrewshire
PA16 8RE.
1 mile SW of town centre, main road
to Gourock away from River Clyde.
Moorland course.
27 holes, 5346 yards, S.S.S.68
Club founded in 1890.
Visitors: welcome except Sat.
Green fees: on application.
Catering: full service except Thurs.

Hotels: Tontine, 6 Ardgowan
Square, Greenock.

W62 Greenock Whinhill
☎0475 24694
Beith Rd, Greenock, Renfrewshire.
23 miles W of Glasgow, Ren-
frewshire.
Moorland course.
18 holes, 5454 yards, S.S.S.68
Club founded in 1908.
Visitors: welcome.
Green fees: on application.
Society meetings: by arrangement.
Catering: meals by arrangement.
Hotels: Tontine.

W63 Haggs Castle
☎041-427 1157.
70 Dumbreck Rd, Glasgow
GW1 4SN.
SW of Glasgow near Ibrox Stadium
and Bellahouston Park.
Parkland course.
18 holes, 6464 yards, S.S.S.71
Course designed by Peter Allis &
Dave Thomas.
Club founded in 1910.
Visitors: only if accompanied by
member.
Green fees: £9 per round, £15 per
day.
Society meetings: by arrangement,
Wed only.
Catering: all types of catering available.
Hotels: Bellahouston, 517 Paisley
Rd West, Glasgow.

W64 Hamilton
☎Hamilton (0698) 282872,
286131 Sec
Riccarton, Ferniegair, Hamilton,
Lanarkshire.
Off A74 between Larkhill and
Hamilton.
Parkland course.
18 holes, 6264 yards, S.S.S.70
Course designed by James Braid.
Visitors: welcome with member,
others by arrangement.
Green fees: on request.
Society meetings: by arrangement
with Sec.
Catering: snacks daily, meals
served by arrangement.
Hotels: Royal, Hamilton;
Avonbridge.

W65 Hayston
☎041-776 1244
Campsie Rd, Kirkintilloch, Glasgow
G66 1RN.
NE from Glasgow via Bishopbriggs
and Kirkintilloch, 1 mile N of

Kirkintilloch.
Undulating course.
18 holes, 6042 yards, S.S.S.69
Course designed by James Braid.
Club founded in 1926.
Visitors: welcome weekdays prior to
4.30pm otherwise introduced by
members.
Green fees: £7 per round, £12 per
day.
Society meetings: acceptable Tues
and Thurs.
Catering: full service available from
9am until closing. Lunch, bar snacks,
high tea, dinner (if ordered in
advance).

W66 Helensburgh
☎Helensburgh (0436) 4173
25 Abercromby St, Helensburgh,
Dunbartonshire G84 9JD.
Abercromby St, off Sinclair St.
Moorland course.
18 holes, 6053 yards, S.S.S.69
Course designed by Tom Morris.
Club founded in 1893.
Visitors: welcome weekdays.
Green fees: £8 per round, £10 per
day.
Society meetings: welcome by
arrangement.
Catering: bar, lunch.
Hotels: Commodore.

W67 Hilton Park
☎041-956 4657
Aulmarroch Estate, Stockiemuir Rd,
Milngavie, Glasgow G62 9HB.
8 miles N of Glasgow on A809.
Moorland courses.
Allander-18 holes, 5361 yards,
S.S.S.69
Hilton-18 holes, 5489 yards,
S.S.S.70
Course designed by James Braid.
Club founded in 1927.
Visitors: welcome weekdays by
prior arrangement.
Green fees: £6 (1 round), £9 (2
rounds).
Society meetings: weekdays.
Catering: full catering.
Hotels: Kirkhouse, Blanefield; Black
Bull, Milngavie.

W68 Hollandbush
☎Lesmahagow (0555) 893484
Acretophead, Lesmahagow.
Off A74 between Lesmahagow and
Coalburn.
Parkland/moorland course.
18 holes, 6110 yards, S.S.S.70
Course designed by Ken Pate.
Club founded in 1954.
Visitors: welcome.

Green fees: on application.
Catering: full catering facilities.
Hotels: Station, Coalburn.

W69 **Innellan**
☎Innellan (0369) 3546
Knockamillie Rd, Innellan, Argyll.
Directions at Innellan Pier.
Undulating parkland course.
9 holes, 4878 yards, S.S.S.63
Club founded in 1895.
Visitors: anytime except Mon
evenings. See club notice board.
Green fees: £3 per round.
Society meetings: catered for
weekdays.
Catering: by arrangement for
parties.
Hotels: Esplanade, West Bay,
Dunoon.

W70 **Irvine**
☎Irvine (0294) 75626
Bogside, Irvine KA12 8SN.
On road from Irvine to Kilwinning,
turn left after Ravenspark Academy,
and carry straight on for 0.5 mile
over railway bridge.
Links course.
18 holes, 6454 yards, S.S.S.71
Course designed by James Braid.
Club founded in 1887.
Visitors: welcome weekdays except
Fri.
Green fees: on application.
Catering: meals and snacks served.
Hotels: Hospitality Inn; Redburn;
Eglinton Arms.

W71 **Irvine Ravenspark**
☎Irvine (0294) 76983
Kidsneuk, Irvine, Ayrshire.
On A78 midway between Irvine and
Kilwinning.
Meadowland course.
18 holes, 6496 yards, S.S.S.71
Club founded in 1907.
Visitors: welcome every day.
Green fees: £2.70 weekdays; £3.50
weekends.
Society meetings: catered for on
weekdays and Sunday.
Catering: lunch and high tea.
Hotels: Hospitality Inn; Annfield;
Redburn.

W72 **Kilbirnie Place**
☎Kilbirnie (050 582) 683398
Langs Rd, Kilbirnie, Ayrshire.
On outskirts of Kilbirnie, Ayrshire.
Parkland course.
18 holes, 5479 yards, S.S.S.67
Club founded in 1922.
Visitors: welcome weekdays and
Sun.

Green fees: on application.
Catering: meals only at weekends.
Hotels: Milton, Kilbirnie.

W73 **Kilmacolm**
☎Kilmalcolm (050 587) 2978
Porterfield Rd, Kilmacolm,
Renfrewshire PA13 3PD.
A740 to Linwood, then A761 to
Bridge of Weir.
Moorland course.
18 holes, 5964 yards, S.S.S.68
Course designed by James Braid.
Club founded in 1890.
Visitors: weekdays; weekends
accompanied by member.
Green fees: £9 per round, £13 per
day.
Society meetings: welcome by
arrangement.
Catering: available.
Hotels: Gryffe, Bridge of Weir.

W74 **Kilmarnock (Barassie)**
☎Troon (0292) 311077
29, Hillhouse Rd, Barassie, Troon,
Ayrshire KA10 6SY.
Off A78 2 miles N of Troon.
Seaside course.
18 holes, 6473 yards, S.S.S.71
Course designed by Matthew
M Monie.
Club founded in 1887.
Visitors: accepted Mon, Tues, Thurs
and Fri only.
Green fees: on application.
Society meetings: Tues and Thurs
by prior arrangement.
Catering: full catering facilities
available.
Hotels: Marine, Troon.

W75 **Kilsyth Lennox**
☎Kilsyth (0236) 822190
Tak-Ma-Doon Rd, Kilsyth, Glasgow
G65 0HX.
12 miles from Glasgow on A80.
Moorland/parkland course.
9 holes, 5944 yards, S.S.S.69
Club founded in 1907.
Visitors: welcome without
introduction until 5pm weekdays,
after 4pm Sat and after 2pm on Sun.
Green fees: £4 per day weekdays;
£4 per round weekends.
Society meetings: catered for on
weekdays.
Catering: lunch served except
Thurs, high tea served at weekends
from June-Sept.
Hotels: Coachman, Kilsyth.

W76 **Kirkhill**
☎041-641 3083
Greenlees Rd, Cambuslang,

Glasgow G72 8YN.
Follow East Kilbride road from
Burnside, take first turning on left
past Cathkin by-pass roundabout.
Meadowland course.
18 holes, 5862 yards, S.S.S.69
Course designed by James Braid.
Club founded in 1910.
Visitors: by arrangement with Sec.
Green fees: £7 per round, £10 per
day.
Society meetings: welcome by prior
arrangement in writing.
Catering: bar snacks and full meals
by arrangement with Clubmistress.
Hotels: Kings Park, Mill St,
Rutherglen; Burnside, East Kilbride
Rd, Burnside.

W77 **Kirkintilloch**
☎041-776 1256
Todhill, Campsie Rd, Kirkintilloch,
Glasgow G66 1RN.
1 mile from Kirkintilloch on road from
Kirkintilloch-Lennoxtown.
Meadowland course.
18 holes, 5900 yards, S.S.S.66
Course designed by James Braid.
Club founded in 1893.
Visitors: only if accompanied by a
member.
Green fees: on application.
Society meetings: catered for only if
sponsored by member.
Catering: full catering except Mon
and Tues.
Hotels: Garfield, Stepps, Glasgow.

W78 **Knightswood**
☎041-959 2131
Lincoln Ave, Knightswood, Glasgow.
Off Dumbarton Rd from city centre.
Parkland course.
9 holes, 2717 yards, S.S.S.64
Club founded in 1920s.
Visitors: welcome.
Green fees: £1.30 UB4O, juniors,
OAPs, weekends; £1, 50p juniors,
30p OAPs, 50p UB40 weekdays;
Passport 30p.
Society meetings: welcome by
arrangement.
Catering: none.
Hotels: Pond, Great Western Rd,
Glasgow.

W79 **Kyles of Bute**
☎Tighnabruaich (0700) 811355
Tighnabruaich, Argyll.
B836 from Dunoon to Tighnabruaich,
through village to Kanes Cross, then
B8000 to Millhouse, club entrance on
left at top of first rise.
Undulating moorland course.
9 holes, 2389 yards, S.S.S.32

Club founded in 1907.
Visitors: welcome except Sun am.
Green fees: £4 per day, £2 under 18.
Society meetings: by individual arrangement.
Catering: tea, coffee and snacks only.
Hotels: Royal; Kames; Kyles of Bute, all in Tighnabruaich.

W80 **Lamlash**
☎Lamlash (07706)296
Lamlash, Brodick, Isle of Arran KA27 8JU.
3 miles S of Brodick on Lamlash to Whiting Bay road.
Undulating moorland course.
18 holes, 4681 yards, S.S.S.63
Club founded in 1889.
Visitors: welcome.
Green fees: on application.
Society meetings: welcome.
Catering: licenced bar, tearoom.
Hotels: Bay; Marine; Glenisle.

W81 **Lanark**
☎Lanark (0555) 3219
The Moor, Whitelees Road, Lanark ML11 7RX.
Off A73 or A72, turn left in Lanark into Whitelees Rd, for 0.5 mile.
Moorland course.
18 holes, 6423 yards, S.S.S.71
Course designed by Ben Sayers and James Braid.
Club founded in 1851.
Visitors: welcome weekdays.
Green fees: on application.
Society meetings: catered for weekdays.
Catering: full catering by resident Chef.
Hotels: Tinto, Symington; The Popinjay, Rosebank.

W82 **Largs**
☎Largs (0475) 673594
Irvine Rd, Largs, Ayrshire KA30 8EU.
1 mile S of Largs on A78.
Parkland/seaside course.
Club founded in 1891.
Visitors: welcome.
Green fees: £12 per day, £8 per round.
Society meetings: Tues and Thurs.
Catering: full catering available.
Hotels: Elderslie; Glen Eldon.

W83 **Larkhall**
☎Larkhall (0698) 88113
Burnhead Rd, Larkhall, Lanarkshire SW on B7019.
9 holes, 6236 yards, S.S.S.70

Visitors: Municipal course, all welcome.
Green fees: on application.
Society meetings: by arrangement.

W84 **Leadhills**
☎Biggar (065 94) 222
Leadhills, Biggar, Lanarkshire ML12 6XR.
6 miles on A74 from Abington, course within village at rear of hotel.
Moorland course.
9 holes, 4100 yards, S.S.S.62
Club founded in 1935.
Visitors: welcome anytime.
Green fees: £1.50 weekdays; £2 weekends.
Society meetings: welcome.
Catering: none available.
Hotels: Hopetoun Arms, Leadhills.

W85 **Lenzie**
☎041-776 1535
19 Crosshill Rd, Lenzie, Glasgow G66 3DA.
A80 to Stepps, Lenzie road turn left at Traffic lights.
Moorland course.
18 holes, 5982 yards, S.S.S.69
Club founded in 1889.
Visitors: welcome with member.
Green fees: on application.
Society meetings: welcome weekdays.
Catering: meals and snacks available except Mon.

W86 **Lethamhill**
☎041-770 6220
Cumbernauld Rd, Glasgow G33 1AH.
On A80 adjacent to Hogganfield Loch.
Municipal course.
18 holes, 6073 yards, S.S.S.69
Visitors: welcome.
Green fees: £1 juniors, UB40's, £2 adults, weekdays; 60p OAPs, £2.60 adults, weekends.
Catering: tea room at club April-Sept.

W87 **Linn Park**
☎041-637 5871
Simshill Rd, Glasgow G44.
Off B766, S of Glasgow on road to Carnmunnock.
Parkland course.
18 holes, 4832 yards, S.S.S.64
Course designed by Glasgow Parks.
Club founded in 1925.
Visitors: welcome.
Green fees: £2.60 per round.
Society meetings: none.
Catering: tea and snacks.

Hotels: Kings Park.

W88 **Littlehill**
☎041-772 1916
Auchinairn Rd, Bishopbriggs, Glasgow.
3 miles N of city centre.
Parkland course.
18 holes, 6199 yards, S.S.S.69
Course designed by James Braid.
Club founded in 1924.
Visitors: no restrictions.
Green fees: £2 per round OAPs/ juniors weekdays; £2.60 per round OAPs/juniors weekends; (unemployed half price).
Society meetings: check with Glasgow Corp. Parks Dept.
Catering: lunch served except Mon.

W89 **Lochranza**
☎Lochranza (077 083) 273
Brodick, Isle of Arran GA27 8HJ.
Off 'the road'.
9 holes, 3580 yards, S.S.S.40
Visitors: welcome.
Green fees: £10 weekly; £1 junior; £1.50 per round.
Society meetings: by arrangement.
Catering: cold snacks available.
Hotels: 3 in area.

W90 **Lochwinnoch**
☎Lochwinnoch (0505) 842153
Burnfoot Rd, Lochwinnoch, Renfrewshire.
On A760 about 10 miles SW of Paisley, first on right after Struthers Garage, 400 yards along Burnfoot Rd.
Parkland course.
18 holes, 6202 yards, S.S.S.70
Club founded in 1897.
Visitors: weekdays until 4pm, weekends by arrangement.
Green fees: £8 per day.
Society meetings: catered for by arrangement.
Catering: full meals except Mon.
Hotels: Lindhurst, Johnstone.

W91 **Loudoun**
☎Galston (0563) 821993 Sec, 820551 Clubhouse.
Galston, Ayrshire KA4 8PA.
From Kilmarnock, take the Edinburgh road, A71, E towards Galston. Club lies on main road between Galston and Newmilns.
Parkland course.
18 holes, 5824 yards, S.S.S.68
Club founded in 1909.
Visitors: welcome weekdays.
Green fees: £12 per round.
Society meetings: welcome.

The Machrie Hotel & Golf Course

MACHRIE ISLE OF ISLAY ARGYLL PA42 7AN   TELEPHONE: 0496 2310

The original Machrie Golf Course, laid out by Willie Campbell in 1891 as a Championship Course, has recently been updated to conform to modern golfing requirements while remaining a stern test of any golfers ability. Free, unlimited golf for residents of hotel and cottages.

* Golf on our own 18 hole course.
* Fish for sea trout/salmon on the Machrie River.
* Ride at the local schools—novice or expert.
* Wander the hill trails and paths.
* Relax on uncrowded sandy beaches.
* Clay pigeon shooting at hotel.
* Bird watching in an ornithologist's paradise.
* Shooting and stalking arranged.
* Visit the local distilleries.
* Simply listen to the Peace.

Hotel rooms and cottage suites with baths, tea and coffee making facilities and colour T.V. Special flight arrangements can be made by the hotel for flights with Loganair and British Midland, special breaks and conferences also available on request.

Tourist Board commended 🏆🏆 **Ashley Courtenay recommened.**
R.A.C. ' Best places to stay and dine in Great Britain'.

Catering: facilities available.
Hotels: Broomhill, Kilmarnock; Foxbar, Kilmarnock.

W92 **Machrie**
☎(0496) 2310
Machrie Hotel, Port Ellen, Isle of Islay, Argyll PA42 7AN.
By plane from Glasgow or ferry from Kennacraig, on A846 S of Airfield.
Seaside links course.
18 holes, 6226 yards, S.S.S.71
Course designed by Willie Campbell, redesigned by Donald Steel.
Club founded in 1891.
Visitors: welcome.
Green fees: £8 per round, £12 per day.
Society meetings: by arrangement.
Hotels: Machrie.

W93 **Machrie Bay**
☎Machrie (077 084) 267
c/o Sec, Camus Ban, Machrie, by Brodick, Isle of Arran KA27 8DZ.
Ferry to Brodick and via String Rd to Machrie.
Fairly flat seaside course.
9 holes, 2123 yards, S.S.S.32
Course designed by William Fernie.
Club founded in 1900.

Visitors: welcome.
Green fees: on application.
Catering: snacks available in June, July and Aug.
Hotels: many good hotels on island.

W94 **Machrihanish**
☎Machrihanish (0586 81) 213
Machrihanish, Campbeltown, Argyll.
5 miles W of Campbeltown on B843.
Links seaside course.
18 holes, 6275 yards, S.S.S.70
Also 9 hole course.
Club founded in 1876.
Visitors: welcome at all times.
Green fees: £7.50 per round, £9.50 per day weekdays; £10 per day weekends.
Society meetings: welcome, certain weekends available also.
Catering: full catering and bar facilities.
Hotels: White Hart, Campbeltown; Ardell, Machrihanish; Ardshiel, Campbeltown.

W95 **Millport**
☎Millport (0457) 530485/530311
Golf Rd, Millport, Isle of Cubrae KA28 0BA.
Seaside/moorland course.

18 holes, 5831 yards, S.S.S.68
Club founded in 1888.
Visitors: welcome.
Green fees: on application.
Society meetings: welcome except at peak periods.
Catering: meals served.
Hotels: Royal George; Westbourne.

W96 **Milngavie**
☎041-956 1619
Laighpark, Milngavie, Glasgow G62 8EP.
Off A809 NW of Glasgow.
Moorland course.
18 holes, 5818 yards, S.S.S.68
Club founded in 1895.
Visitors: only with member at anytime.
Green fees: £11 per day.
Society meetings: catered for weekdays except Wed.
Catering: for parties by arrangement.
Hotels: Black Bull, Milngavie; Burnbrae, Bearsden.

W97 **Mount Ellen**
☎Glenboig (0236) 782277
Johnston House, Johnston Rd,

Gartcosh, Glasgow.
1 mile S of A80 Glasgow-Stirling road, between Muirhead village and Coatbridge.
Undulating meadowland course.
Club founded in 1905.
Visitors: by appointment.
Green fees: £8 per day weekdays; £9 weekends.
Society meetings: none.
Catering: full facilities.
Hotels: Garfield, Moodiesburn.

W98 **Old Ranfurly**
☎Bridge of Weir (0505) 613612
Ranfurly Place, Bridge of Weir, Renfrewshire PA11 3DE.
7 miles W of Paisley.
Moorland course.
18 holes, 6266 yards, S.S.S.70
Club founded in 1905.
Visitors: welcome weekdays by introduction and weekends with member.
Green fees: on application.
Society meetings: catered for by special arrangement.
Catering: snack lunch and high tea available.
Hotels: Gryffe Arms, Bridge of Weir.

W99 **Paisley**
☎041-884 2292
Braehead, Paisley PA2 8TZ.
From Glasgow, A737 to Paisley, 3 miles S of Paisley centre.
Moorland course.
18 holes, 6424 yards, S.S.S.71
Club founded in 1895.
Visitors: mid-week before 4pm.
Letter of introduction or prior arrangement with Sec.
Green fees: £8 per round; £12 per day.
Society meetings: by prior arrangement. No weekend or Bank Holidays.
Catering: full catering available.
Hotels: Watermill; Excelsior.

W100 **Palacerigg**
☎Cumbernauld (0236) 734969
Palacerigg Country Park, Cumbernauld G67 3HU.
Take A80 to Cumbernauld, follow signs to Country Park.
Parkland course.
18 holes, 6408 yards, S.S.S.71
Club founded in 1976.
Visitors: welcome weekdays.

Green fees: £4 weekdays; £5 weekends.
Society meetings: none.
Catering: lunch and high tea except Mon, Tues.
Hotels: Castlecary.

W101 **Pollok**
☎041-632 1080
90 Barrhead Rd, Glasgow G43 1BG.
On A736, 4 miles S of city centre.
Parkland course.
18 holes, 6257 yards, S.S.S.70
Club founded in 1892.
Visitors: men only Mon-Fri.
Green fees: £12 per round, £15 per day.
Society meetings: by letter to Sec.
Catering: full dining facilities.
Hotels: Tinto Firs; Albany; Macdonalds; Holiday Inn.

W102 **Port Bannatyne**
☎Isle of Bute (0700) 2009
Bannatyne Mains Rd, Port Bannatyne, Isle of Bute.
2 miles N of Rothesay on A845.
Hilly seaside course.
13 holes, 4654 yards, S.S.S.63
Course designed by James Braid.

Machrie and Machrihanish

As their names suggest, Machrie and Machrihanish sound related and can, in fact, be described as close cousins, separated only by a few miles of sea. Machrihanish is on the mainland of Kintyre in Argyll, Machrie on the Isle of Islay, the southernmost of Scotland's charming outer isles.

The charm of both lies in their remote setting, a pace to life that is appealingly unhurried and, for the golfer, two courses in the finest traditions of British seaside links. Machrihanish, situated on the west coast of the Mull of Kintyre, a feature of the famous view from Turnberry, is marginally better known perhaps because it can be approached entirely on dry land.

In fact, it takes a long, circuitous drive from Glasgow which passes through Tarbert, the port from which the ferries depart for Islay, which makes the scheduled air service from Glasgow decidedly more convenient. You can chat to the pilot and improve your geography on a clear day by being able to see every inch of the journey. There are no interminable waits for your baggage and no stream of inaudible announcements from the tiny terminal buildings at the other end.

In the old days, your next door neighbour on the flight was quite likely to have been a box of kippers but the other great joy is that you can survey the golf courses as you land and be on the first tee within minutes. On Islay, it is a question of a quick flip down the Bowmore road and turn left into the Machrie Hotel whose rooms and adjacent cottages make a perfect base.

Those who haven't seen the course for ten or so years will notice significant changes, the land which used to house the 2nd, 3rd and 4th being replaced by some new holes out at the far end. The 1st, a gentle opener, has a raised tee from which the whole scenic panorama is apparent, but the new 2nd quickly gets down to the real golfing business, a par 5 doglegging sharply left along the path of a fast flowing stream.

The 5th is a fine short hole and the 6th typical of Machrie's natural blessings, a drive on the left providing the correct approach as well as a view of the green in a dell. In its early days in the last century, the drive at the 7th over a vast sandhill was rather more formidable than it is now. Its dimensions were similar to those of the Maiden at Sandwich but, once cleared, the course follows the line of a glorious sandy beach. Unlike many other seaside courses, here is the opportunity of really seeing the sea.

The 10th tee is another wonderful lookout point although the mind has to concentrate on the task ahead, the introduction to the new golfing country and a scenic change to the hills and lonely peat moors. After a spell of stout hitting for four or five holes, the finish is not quite as severe but it immediately commands an affection both genuine and lasting.

Machrihanish is remembered with similar enthusiasm. From the moment that you tee up by the professional's shop, wondering just how much of the sandy bay you dare cut off, the prospects are invigorating. A notice for non-golfers proclaims "Danger. First tee above, please move further along the beach". Another might say, "Next stop to the west, Long Island" but after the Machrihanish Burn and the shot over the crest to the 2nd green have been negotiated, the true duneland character of a fine outward half is apparent.

This is the true heartland of Machrihanish, a course that has tested the Scottish Women and the Scottish Professionals in their championships a time or two but is essentially a holiday course with a combination of challenge and surroundings ‑are even in a country where spectacular golf abounds.

In common with many seaside links, Machrihanish, founded as the Kintyre Club and more than a century old, goes out and back but it follows the curve of the great bay just enough to make sure the wind isn't constantly facing or behind. The greens, generally large, are thoroughly in keeping with a course whose founders would still happily recognise it.

The one exception perhaps is the background to the 9th where the guide post is mixed up with the landing lights for the airfield which has the second longest runway in Europe; but the terrain for the homeward half, moving inland, heralds a change of character. The journey back to the row of houses by the clubhouse which looks out on the ever-changing moods of the ocean is some contrast but there is nothing much wrong with the 10th and

12th, the two par fives. The 11th and 15th greens can be elusive targets. The 13th green is subtly raised and there is the unusual feature of successive short holes, the 15th and 16th. Cypress Point, West Sussex, Royal Jersey and Sandy Lodge are other examples, but if short holes, in theory, should help the score, the 17th strikes danger.

With out of bounds along the left, the fairway is alarmingly narrow but elsewhere there is plenty of opportunity to open the shoulders.

Club founded in 1968.
Visitors: unrestricted, parties welcome.
Green fees: £3 weekdays; £4 weekends; £15 weekly. Juniors £1 weekdays; £2 weekends; £7 weekly.
Society meetings: welcome.
Catering: by arrangement.
Hotels: Royal, Rothesay; Aldmory House, Aldmory Rd, Rothesay; Glenburn, Rothesay.

w103 **Port Glasgow**
☎Port Glasgow (0475) 704181
Devol Farm Industrial Estate, Port Glasgow, Renfrewshire PA14 5XE.
W of Glasgow on M8 towards Greenock. In town of Port Glasgow.
Undulating course.
18 holes, 5712 yards, S.S.S.68
Club founded in 1895.
Visitors: weekdays until 3.55 pm if unintroduced, at all other times introduced.
Green fees: £5 per round, £8 per round.
Society meetings: catered for on non competition days (ie Sun-Fri unless competition on calendar).
Catering: meals served on request.
Hotels: Clune Brae; Star.

w104 **Prestwick**
☎Prestwick (0292) 77404
2 Links Rd, Prestwick, Ayrshire KA9 1QG.
1 mile from Prestwick Airport adjacent to Prestwick station.
Seaside links course.
18 holes, 6544 yards, S.S.S.72
Club founded in 1851.
Visitors: by arrangement. Prior booking essential.
Green fees: on application.

Society meetings: by arrangement.
Catering: dining room - male only; Cardinal room - mixed, casual dress, light lunches.
Hotels: Maring, Troon; Turnberry.

w105 **Prestwick St Cuthbert**
☎Prestwick (0292) 77101
East Rd, Prestwick, Ayrshire KA9 2SX.
Off main Ayr-Prestwick road, at Bellevue Rd.
Parkland course.
18 holes, 6470 yards, S.S.S.71
Course designed by Stutt & Co.
Club founded in 1899.
Visitors: weekdays welcome, weekends providing introduced by member.
Green fees: £7 per round, £10 per day.
Society meetings: by arrangement, not weekends or Bank Holidays.
Catering: lunch, bar lunch, dinner.
Hotels: Carlton; St Nicholas; Parkstone.

w106 **Prestwick St Nicholas**
☎Prestwick (0292) 77608
Grangemuir Rd, Prestwick, Ayrshire KA9 1SN.
Off A79, from Main St turn into Grangemuir Rd which runs down to sea.
Links course.
18 holes, 5926 yards, S.S.S.68
Course designed by C. Hunter.
Club founded in 1851.
Visitors: welcome weekdays.
Green fees: £15 per day, £10 per round weekdays.
Society meetings: catered for on weekdays.
Catering: lunch and high tea served.

Hotels: Parkstone; St Ninians; Links.

w107 **Ralston**
☎041-882 1349
Strathmore Ave, Ralston, Paisley, Renfrewshire PE1 3EP.
Off main Paisley to Glasgow road.
Parkland course.
18 holes, 6100 yards, S.S.S.69
Visitors: organised parties only.
Green fees: by arrangement.
Catering: meals served.

w108 **Ranfurly Castle**
☎Bridge of Weir (0505) 612609
Golf Rd, Bridge of Weir, Renfrewshire PA11 3HN.
Off M8 at sign for Linwood.
Undulating moorland course.
18 holes, 6284 yards, S.S.S.70
Club founded in 1889.
Visitors: weekdays by introduction.
Green fees: on application.
Society meetings: certain weekdays.
Catering: snacks, lunch, high tea.
Hotels: Gryffe Arms, Bridge of Weir.

w109 **Renfrew**
☎041-886 6692
Blythswood Estate, Inchinnan Rd, Renfrew.
Off A8 at Normandy Hotel.
Parkland course.
18 holes, 6818 yards, S.S.S.73
Course designed by John Harris.
Club founded in 1894.
Visitors: introduced by a member only. Parties by arrangement.
Green fees: £9 per round visitors, £13 per day.
Society meetings: welcome by arrangement, maximum 30.
Catering: full catering.

Hotels: Normandy, Renfrew; Excelsior, Glasgow Airport.

W110 **Rothesay**
☎Rothesay (0700)2244
Canada Hill, Rothesay, Isle of Bute
PA20 7HN.
Undulating course.
18 holes, 5440 yards, S.S.S.67
Course designed by James Braid.
Club founded in 1892.
Visitors: welcome, virtually no restrictions.
Green fees: £6 per day; £8 weekends; £24 fortnightly.
Society meetings: by arrangement.
Catering: full catering all week.
Hotels: various hotels adjacent to course.

W111 **Routenburn**
☎Largs (0475) 673230
Largs, Ayrshire KA30 9AH.
1 mile N of Largs, first major left turn coming into Largs from Greenock.
Seaside hill course.
18 holes, 5650 yards, S.S.S.67
Club founded in 1914.
Visitors: welcome on weekdays.
Green fees: £2.60 per round; £19 weekly; £3.70 per day.
Society meetings: party bookings during weekdays.
Catering: full catering facilities except Thurs.
Hotels: Charleston, Charles St, Largs.

W112 **Royal Troon & Portland**
☎Troon (0292) 311555
Craigend Rd, Troon, Ayrshire
KA10 6EP.
3 miles from Prestwick Airport.
Seaside courses.
Portland - 18 holes, 6641 yards, S.S.S.73
Old - 18 holes, 6274 yards, S.S.S.71
Course designed by Cotton, Pennink, Lawrie & Partners.
Club founded in 1878.
Visitors: Mon-Thurs only with starting time restriction. Maximum handicap 18. No ladies on old course.
Green fees: £30 Old; £20 Portland daily.
Society meetings: by application as per visitors.
Catering: full restaurant service and bar snacks by arrangement.
Hotels: Marine; Sun Court; Piersland all Troon.

W113 **Sandyhills**
☎041-778 1179
223 Sandyhills Rd, Glasgow
G32 9NA.
E side of Glasgow, from Tollcross Rd, left at Killin St and right into Sandyhills Rd.
Parkland course.
18 holes, 6253 yards, S.S.S.70
Visitors: welcome by arrangement.
Green fees: £7 per round, £10 per day.
Society meetings: welcome by arrangement.
Catering: full catering except Mon.
Hotels: good hotels in Glasgow.

W114 **Shiskine**
☎Isle of Arran (077 086) 293 Sec, 346 Treasurer.
Blackwaterfoot, Isle of Arran
KA27 8HA.
300 yards off A841 in Blackwaterfoot.
Seaside course.
12 holes, 3000 yards, S.S.S.42
Club founded in 1896.
Visitors: welcome.
Green fees: £3.50 per round, £4.50 per day.
Society meetings: catered for, write or telephone Hon Sec or Hon Treasurer.
Catering: Clubhouse, snacks, June-Sept.
Hotels: Kinloch; Blackwaterfoot; Rock.

W115 **Shotts**
☎Shotts (0501) 20431
Blairhead, Shotts ML7 5BJ.
2 miles from M8 off Benhar Rd.
Moorland course.
18 holes, 6125 yards, S.S.S.70
Course designed by James Braid.
Club founded in 1895.
Visitors: unlimited during week.
Green fees: £7 per day.
Society meetings: only weekdays.
Catering: full catering from April-Oct.
Hotels: Station, Shotts.

W116 **Skelmorlie**
☎(0475) 520152
Skelmorlie, Ayrshire PA17 5ES.
1 mile from Wemyss Bay station.
Parkland/moorland course.
13 holes, 5104 yards, S.S.S.65
Course designed by James Braid.
Club founded in 1891.
Visitors: welcome except Sat from Mar-Oct.
Green fees: £4 per day weekdays; £6 weekends.
Society meetings: welcome except Sat.
Catering: lunch, dinner and tea served.
Hotels: Manor Park; Heywood; Wemyss Bay; Redcliffe.

W117 **Strathaven**
☎Strathaven (0357) 20539 or 20421
Overton Ave, Glasgow Rd, Strathaven ML10 6NF.
Situated on outskirts of town on A726.
Parkland course.
18 holes, 6226 yards, S.S.S.70
Course designed by William Fernie of Troon and extended to 18 holes by J.R. Stutt.
Club founded in 1908.
Visitors: weekdays, parties Mon and Tues.
Green fees: on request.
Society meetings: Mon and Tues.
Catering: available all day.
Hotels: Strathaven, Strathaven.

W118 **Tarbert**
☎Tarbert (088 02) 565
Kilberry Rd, Tarbert, Argyll.
1 mile on A83 to Campbeltown from Tarbert, turn right onto B8024 for 0.25 mile.
Hilly seaside course.
9 holes, 2230 yards, S.S.S.64
Visitors: welcome with restriction.
Green fees: £2 per (9 holes); £3 per (18 holes); £5 per day.
Society meetings: by arrangement.
Catering: limited.
Hotels: Stonefield Castle, Tarbert, West Loch.

W119 **Torrance House**
☎E Kilbride (035 52) 33451
Strathaven Rd, E Kilbride, Glasgow
G75 0QZ.
On A726 on outskirts of E Kilbride.
Parkland course.
18 holes, 6640 yards, S.S.S.71
Course designed by Hawtree & Sons.
Club founded in 1969.
Visitors: welcome by reservation.
Green fees: on appliction.
Catering: meals served.
Hotels: Stuart; Bruce; Torrance; Crutherland.

W120 **Troon Municipal**
☎Troon (0292) 312464
Harling Drive, Troon, Ayrshire

KA10 6NE.
100 yards from railway station.
Links course.
Lochgreen-18 holes, 6687 yards,
S.S.S.72
Darley-18 holes, 6327 yards,
S.S.S.70
Fullerton-18 holes, 4784 yards,
S.S.S.63
Club founded in 1905.
Visitors: welcome.
Green fees: Lochgreen and Darley:
£4.40 per round, £7.60 per day
weekdays; £5.80 per round, £9.20
per day weekends; Fullerton: £3.45
per round, £5.40 day weekdays; £4
per round, £6.40 per day weekends.
Society meetings: welcome.
Catering: full catering.
Hotels: Ardneil; South Beach.

W121 **Turnberry Hotel**
☎Turnberry (0655) 31000
Turnberry Hotel, Turnberry, Ayrshire
KA26 9LT.
Off A77 from Glasgow just before
Girvan.
Seaside courses.
Ailsa-18 holes, 6408 yards, S.S.S.71
Arran-18 holes, 6276 yards,
S.S.S.70
Course designed by Mackenzie
Ross.
Visitors: welcome by prior
arrangement, and day visitors
welcome.
Green fees: hotel residents £18.50
Ailsa; £11 Arran; day visitors £27.50
Mon-Fri; £32.50 Sat/Sun; Arran
course only £17.
Society meetings: by prior
arrangement.
Catering: restaurant and bar
facilities available 8am-10pm.
Hotels: Turnberry.

W122 **Vale of Leven**
☎Alexandria (0389) 52351
Northfield Course, Bonfield,
Alexandria, Dunbartonshire.
Off A82 at Bonhill.
Moorland course.
18 holes, 5962 yards, S.S.S.66
Club founded in 1907.
Visitors: weekdays only unless
introduced during months April-Oct,
anytime other months.
Green fees: £5 per day weekdays;
£8 per day weekends.
Society meetings: welcome except
Sat.
Catering: full catering except Mon.
Hotels: Balloch, Balloch; Tulli-

chewan, Balloch; Riverside, Balloch;
Lomond Park, Balloch; Alexandria,
Alexandria.

W123 **Vaul**
☎Scarinish (087 92) 566
Scarinish, Isle of Tiree, Argyll.
Seaside course.
9 holes, 6246 yards, S.S.S.70
Club founded in 1920.
Visitors: welcome. No Sun golf.
Green fees: £3 per day; £10 per
week.
Society meetings: by arrangement.
Hotels: Lodge; Scarinish.

W124 **Western Gailes**
☎Irvine (0294) 311354
Gailes, by Irvine, Ayrshire
KA11 5AE.
5 miles N of Troon on A78.
Seaside course.
18 holes
Club founded in 1897.
Visitors: welcome on weekdays
except Thurs and Sat (no lady
visitors on Tues); advisable·to book
in advance.
Green fees: on application.
Society meetings: welcome by
arrangement on weekdays except
Thurs and Sat.
Catering: lunch and snacks
available.
Hotels: many hotels in Troon and
Ayr.

W125 **West Kilbride**
☎West Kilbride (0294) 823911
33-35, Fullerton Drive, Seamill,
West Kilbride, Ayrshire KA23 9HS.
On main Ardrossan to Largs road at
Seamill.
Seaside/links course.
18 holes, 6247 yards, S.S.S.70
Course designed by Tom Morris.
Club founded in 1893.
Visitors: welcome weekdays with
introduction. Not Bank Holidays or
weekends.
Green fees: on application.
Society meetings: Tues and Thurs.
Catering: lunch, high tea and dinner.
Hotels: Seamill Hydro, West
Kilbride; Hospitality Inn, Irvine.

W126 **Whitecraigs**
☎041-639 4530
72 Ayr Rd, Giffnock, Glasgow
G46 6SW.
7 miles S of Glasgow on A77.
Parkland course.

18 holes, 6230 yards, S.S.S.70
Club founded in 1905.
Visitors: by introduction only.
Green fees: £15 per round (£1 with
member).
Society meetings: Wed only.
Catering: lunch except Mon.
Hotels: Macdonald, Giffnock.

W127 **Williamwood**
☎041-637 1783
Clarkston Rd, Netherlee, Glasgow
G44
5 miles S of Glasgow.
Wooded parkland course.
18 holes, 5808 yards, S.S.S.68
Course designed by James Braid.
Visitors: by introduction only, unless
resident over 40 miles away.
Green fees: on application.
Society meetings: weekdays by
arrangement.
Catering: lunches and evening
meals served.
Hotels: MacDonald, Giffnock;
Bedhurst, Clarkston.

W128 **Windyhill**
☎041-942 7157
Baljaffray Rd, Bearsden, Glasgow
G61 4QQ.
Take A739 from Glasgow, after 8
miles turn right onto A809, after 1
mile turn left onto A810, club 1 mile
on right.
Undulating moorland course.
18 holes, 6254 yards, S.S.S.70
Club founded in 1908.
Visitors: welcome on weekdays.
Green fees: on application.
Catering: full facilities available.
Hotels: Burnbrae, Bearsden; Black
Bull, Milngavie.

W129 **Wishaw**
☎Wishaw (0698) 372869
55 Cleland Rd, Wishaw, Lanarkshire
ML2 7PH.
SE of Glasgow off M74, 3 miles S of
Motherwell.
Parkland course.
18 holes, 6160 yards, S.S.S.69
Course designed by James Braid.
Club founded in 1897.
Visitors: welcome weekdays. No
visitors allowed on Sat.
Green fees: £5 per round, £7 per
day; £10 Sunday.
Society meetings: by arrangement.
Catering: lunch, high tea, dinner if
ordered before 6pm.
Hotels: Wishaw Town.

X Tayside, Central Region and Fife

St Andrews may be the jewel in the crown but the central and eastern part of Scotland glitters with other rare delights. Carnoustie, Gleneagles and Blairgowrie feature on nearly all golfing itineraries and no form of recommendation is necessary by way of introduction. They are all now within easy reach of Edinburgh or Glasgow but that doesn't mean that they should be the subject of a flying visit.

Like Venice, St Andrews' secrets take a lifetime to untie and golfers should acknowledge the fact. Carnoustie is essentially a place to appreciate the golf, a place where in 1953 Ben Hogan prepared more meticulously for the Open than perhaps any other championship for which he entered. It is hallowed ground with the golfer cast more in the role of a pilgrim but the Americans are more inclined to swoon at the sight of Gleneagles with its hotel and five star scenery to match. This spectacular seam runs through the whole of the golf to the west and north of Perth, a city with an historical golfing gem in King James VI on the banks of the Tay.

Close by golf has probably been played on the North Inch since 1502 but the East of Scotland is full of clubs and courses with distinguished family trees and lengthy pedigrees. Monifieth and Montrose are cases in point and, between Dundee and Carnoustie, we must not forget Panmure at Barry. Moving inland, Downfield (modern by comparison), Edzell and Forfar all have their protagonists but so do the other Fife courses which have to live in the shadow of St Andrews.

Leven, Lundin Links and Ladybank more or less rub shoulders with each other, Scotscraig is another Open championship qualifying course while Elie and Crail are ancient reminders of the natural environment in which the game was founded and has always thrived.

X1 **Aberdour**
☎Aberdour (0383) 860256, 860688
Clubmaster.
Seaside Place, Aberdour, Fife
KY3 0TX.
Right off A92 in Aberdour village travelling from Inverkeithing. By coast route to Burntisland.
Parkland/seaside course.
18 holes, 5469 yards, S.S.S.67
Course designed by Peter Robertson & Joe Anderson.
Club founded in 1897.
Visitors: welcome weekdays.
Casual visitors should telephone Pro for tee reservation.
Green fees: £6 per round, £9 per day weekdays.
Society meetings: visiting clubs by prior booking with Sec, except Sat.
Catering: by arrangement with Clubmaster, except Tues.
Hotels: Aberdour.

X2 **Aberfeldy**
☎Aberfeldy (0887) 20535
Taybridge Rd, Aberfeldy, Perthshire

PH15 2BH.
10 miles off A9 at Ballinluig.
Parkland course.
9 holes, 2733 yards, S.S.S.67
Visitors: welcome.
Green fees: on application.
Society meetings: small society meetings could be arranged.
Catering: snacks available.
Hotels: Weem; Cruachan; Breadalbane; Ailean Chraggan; Station.

X3 **Aberfoyle**
☎Aberfoyle (087 72) 441
Braeval, Aberfoyle, Stirling FK8 3RL.
1 mile from Aberfoyle on A81, Stirling road.
Hillside course.
18 holes, 5205 yards, S.S.S.66
Course designed by James Braid.
Club founded in 1892.
Visitors: welcome.
Green fees: £7.50 per day.
Society meetings: none.
Catering: at weekends only.
Hotels: numerous in area.

X4 **Alloa**
☎Alloa (0259) 722745
Schawpark, Sauchie,
Clackmannanshire FK10 3AX.
On A908 1 mile N of Alloa.
Parkland course.
18 holes, 6230 yards, S.S.S.70
Course designed by James Braid.
Club founded in 1891.
Visitors: welcome.
Green fees: £7 per round, £11 per day.
Society meetings: weekdays only.
Catering: full catering facilities.
Hotels: Bruce; Royal Oak, Alloa.

X5 **Alva**
☎Alva (0259) 60431
Beauclerc St, Alva,
Clackmannanshire.
On A91 3 miles N of Alloa.
Undulating course.
9 holes, 4574 yards, S.S.S.64
Club founded in 1900.
Visitors: welcome.
Green fees: on application.
Catering: none.

Hotels: Glen; Johnstone.

x6 Alyth

☎Alyth (082 83) 2268
Pitcrocknie, Alyth, Perthshire.
On B954 Alyth to Glenisla road about
0.5 mile from major roundabout on
A926 Blairgowrie-Kirriemuir road.
Moorland course.
18 holes, 6226 yards, S.S.S.70
Course designed by James Braid.
Club founded in 1894.
Visitors: welcome.
Green fees: on application.
Society meetings: welcome by
arrangement with Sec.
Catering: full catering facilities.
Hotels: Alyth, Commercial St; Lands
of Loyal, Loyal Rd.

x7 Anstruther

☎Anstruther (0333) 310224 Sec.
Marsfield, Shore Rd, Anstruther, Fife
KY10 3DZ.
Turn S off main road at Craw's Nest
Hotel.
Seaside course.
9 holes, 4120 yards, S.S.S.63
Club founded in 1890.

Visitors: welcome except on
competition days.
Green fees: £4 per day weekdays;
£4 per day weekends; £2.50-£3
juniors.
Caatering: snacks and lunch served.
Hotels: Craws Nest; Royal;
Smugglers Inn.

x8 Arbroath

☎Arbroath (0241) 72272
Elliot, Arbroath, Angus.
On A92, 2 miles S of Arbroath.
Seaside course.
18 holes, 6078 yards, S.S.S.69
Visitors: welcome.
Green fees: on application.
Society meetings: by arrangement.
Catering: snacks, meals by
arrangement.
Hotels: in Arbroath.

x9 Auchterarder

☎Auchterarder (0764) 62804
Orchil Rd, Auchterarder, Perthshire.
Off A9 to SW of town, about 400
yards up A824, hidden entrance to
club.
Parkland course.

18 holes, 5737 yards, S.S.S.68
Course designed by Bernard Sayers.
Club founded in 1892.
Visitors: any day of week and at
weekends unless Open Competitions
are being held.
Green fees: under review.
Society meetings: recognised
Golfing societies welcome if previous
arrangement made with Sec.
Catering: bar snacks, lunch and
dinner (notification for latter is
advisable).
Hotels: Gleneagles plus many in
Auchterarder.

x10 Auchterderran

☎(059) 721 579
Woodend Rd, Cardenden, Fife
KY5 0NH.
N of Auchterderran High School on
Glenrothes-Cardenden road.
Undulating moorland/parkland
course.
9 holes, 5250 yards, S.S.S.66
Club founded in 1906.
Visitors: welcome.
Green fees: on application.
Society meetings: welcome by

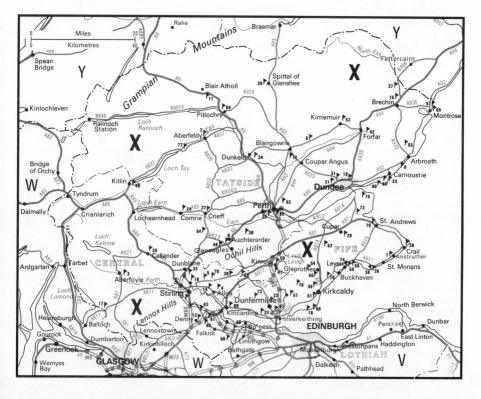

advance booking.
Catering: bar facilities available.
Hotels: Bowhill; Central.

x11 Blair Atholl

☎Blair Atholl (0796 81) 274
Blair Atholl, Perthshire.
On A9 6 miles N of Pitlochry.
Flat parkland course.
9 holes, 5710 yards, S.S.S.69
Club founded in 1890.
Visitors: welcome.
Green fees: £5 per day/round.
Revised every November.
Society meetings: catered for.
Catering: bar snacks and meals.
Club for hire.
Hotels: Atholl Arms; Glen Tilt.

x12 Blairgowrie

☎Blairgowrie (0250) 2594/2622.
Rosemount, Blairgowrie, Perthshire
PH10 6LG.
A93 from Perth.
Moorland course.
Rosemount-18 holes, 6588 yards,
S.S.S.72
Lansdowne-18 holes, 6895 yards,
S.S.S.73
Wee-9 holes, 2307 yards, S.S.S.32.5
Course designed by James Braid,
Thomas/Alliss, Peter Chalmers.
Club founded in 1889.
Visitors: advance booking Mon,
Tues, Thurs. Through starter Wed,
Sat, Sun. No parties Wed, Sat, Sun.
Green fees: £14 per round, £20 per
day weekdays; weekends £16.
Society meetings: Mon, Tue, Thurs
book through (0250) 2622.
Catering: full facilities.
Hotels: Kinloch House; Rosemount
Golf; Altamount House.

x13 Bonnybridge

☎Bonnybridge (0324) 812645
Larbert Rd, Bonnybridge, Stirling-
shire.
On B816, 3 miles W of Falkirk.
Undulating moorland course.
9 holes, 6060 yards, S.S.S.69
Club founded in 1925.
Visitors: welcome with member
only.
Green fees: on application.
Society meetings: none.
Catering: meals served, limited in
winter.
Hotels: Norwood (adjacent to
course).

x14 Braehead

☎Alloa (0259) 722078
Cambus, by Alloa.
On A907 on Stirling to Alloa road,
about 1.5 miles from Alloa.
Part parkland/part meadowland
course.
18 holes, 6013 yards, S.S.S.69
Club founded in 1896.
Visitors: welcome unrestricted, but
telephone for starting time.
Green fees: £5 flat rate weekdays;
£5 per round, £7 day weekends.
Society meetings: none.
Catering: weekend only.
Hotels: Royal Oak, Alloa; Dunmar
House, Alloa.

x15 Brechin

☎Brechin (035 62) 2383
Trinity, by Brechin, Angus DD9 7PD.
Take B966 out of Brechin toward
Aberdeen, course is 1 mile from
Brechin and is clearly signposted.
Parkland/meadowland course.
18 holes, 5267 yards, S.S.S.66
Course designed by James Braid.
Club founded in 1893.
Visitors: welcome at any time.
Parties welcome by prior arrange-
ment. Restricted on Weds (Ladies
Day).
Green fees: £5 per day; £7 per
week; £6 Sat; £9 Sun.
Society meetings: write to Club
Sec.
Catering: full catering and bar.
Hotels: Northern; Brechin &
Glenesk, Edzell; Panmure, Edzell;
Central, Edzell.

x16 Bridge of Allan

☎Bridge of Allan (0786) 832332
Sunnlaw, Bridge of Allan, Stirling.
3 miles N of Stirling, at bridge over
River Allan turn up hill to golf course
for 1 mile.
Undulating course.
9 holes, 4932 yards, S.S.S.65
Club founded in 1895.
Visitors: welcome weekdays and
Sun.
Green fees: £5 weekdays; £7 Sun.
Catering: bar snacks at weekends
and after 7.30pm weekdays.
Hotels: Royal, Bridge of Allan.

x17 Buchanan Castle

☎Drymen (0360) 60369
Drymen, Glasgow.
Off A809, 17 miles NW of Glasgow.
Parkland course.
18 holes, 6032 yards, S.S.S.69
Course designed by James Braid.
Club founded in 1936.
Visitors: by arrangement (limited).
Green fees: £12 per round, £16 per
day.

Society meetings: by arrangement
Drymen (0360) 60307
Catering: by arrangement with
Clubmaster.
Hotels: Buchanan Arms, Drymen.

x18 Burntisland

☎Burntisland (0592) 874093
Manager,
873247 Starter and Pro.
Dodhead, Burntisland, Fife.
On B923, 0.5 mile E of Burntisland.
Moorland course.
18 holes, S.S.S.68
Course redesigned by James Braid.
Club founded in 1897.
Visitors: welcome, contact Pro for
starting time.
Green fees: on application.
Catering: snacks and meals served
except Tues.
Hotels: many good hotels in area.

x19 Caird Park

☎Dundee (0382) 453606
Mains Loan, Dundee, Tayside
DD4 9BX.
Via Kingsway to NE of town.
Parkland course.
18 holes, 6303 yards, S.S.S.70
Club founded in 1926.
Visitors: welcome.
Green fees: on application.
Catering: by arrangement.
Hotels: many good hotels in area.

x20 Callander

☎Callander (0877) 30090
Clubhouse, 30975 Pro.
Aveland Rd, Callander, Perthshire
FK17 8EN.
A84 from Stirling, turn right at Roman
Camp Hotel about 0.5 mile from
Main St, car park and clubhouse
signposted.
Parkland course.
18 holes, 5125 yards, S.S.S.66
Course designed by Tom Morris.
Club founded in 1890.
Visitors: welcome any time.
Green fees: £6 per round, £8 per
day weekdays; £7 per round, £10 per
day weekends.
Society meetings: welcome any
time, contact Sec telephone 10am-
2pm (0877) 30090; 7pm-9pm 30866.
Catering: full catering every day, bar
open all day.
Hotels: Abbotsford Lodge; Roman
Camp; Dalgair House; The Coppice.

x21 Camperdown (Municipal)

☎Dundee (0832) 62715
Camperdown Park, Dundee.

Coupar Angus Rd, at Kingsway junction.
Championship parkland course.
18 holes, 6305 yards, S.S.S.72
Course designed by Eric Brown.
Club founded in 1959.
Visitors: all enquiries to General Manager of Parks, 353 Clepington Rd, Dundee.
Green fees: £5.70.
Society meetings: by arrangement.
Catering: by arrangement telephone (0832) 621993.
Hotels: Park.

x22 Canmore
☎Dunfermline (0383) 724969
Venturefair Ave, Dunfermline, Fife.
On A823, 1 mile N of Dunfermline.
Undulating parkland course.
18 holes, 5474 yards, S.S.S.66
Club founded in 1897.
Visitors: welcome weekdays and Sat after 4pm.
Green fees: on application.
Society meetings: welcome by arrangement.
Catering: full catering.
Hotels: King Malcolm.

x23 Carnoustie
☎Carnoustie (0241) 53249
Links Parade, Carnoustie, Angus DD7 6JE.
On A630, 12 miles E of Dundee.
Seaside course.
Championship-18 holes, 6931 yards, S.S.S.74
Burnside-18 holes, 5935 yards, S.S.S.69
Buddon Links-18 holes, 6445 yards, S.S.S.71
Visitors: welcome with reservation.
Green fees: on application.
Society meetings: by arrangement.
Catering: available.
Hotels: Brax; Glencoe; Bruce; Station; Kinloch; Aran.

x24 Comrie
☎ Comrie (0764) 70544
c/o Sec, Donald C McGlashan, 10 Polinard, Comrie, Perthshire.
On A85 6 miles W of Crieff.
Highland course.
9 holes, 5962 yards, S.S.S.69
Club founded in 1894.
Visitors: welcome at all times.
Green fees: £4 weekdays; £5 weekends.
Society meetings: by arrangement with Sec.
Catering: coffee, light snacks during summer season.

Hotels: Comrie; Royal, Comrie.

x25 Craigie Hill
☎Perth (0738) 22644 Sec/Pro 24377 Club.
Cherrybank, Perth PH2 0NE.
About 1 mile W of Perth, easy access from Stirling-Perth road.
Hilly course.
18 holes, 5739 yards, S.S.S.66
Club founded in 1911.
Visitors: Mon-Fri unlimited; weekends telephone bookings.
Green fees: £4 per round, (£1.50 with member) £6 per day, juniors £1.25 weekdays; £8 per day, after 4pm £4.75 weekends. All inclusive of VAT.
Society meetings: available weekdays and Sun.
Catering: full except Thurs.
Hotels: see Tourist Association.

x26 Crail
☎Crail (0333) 50278, 50686 Sec.
Balcomie Clubhouse, Fifeness, Crail KY10 3XN.
2 miles E of Crail.
Seaside links/parkland course.
18 holes, 5720 yards, S.S.S.68
Course designed by Tom Morris.
Club founded in 1786.
Visitors: welcomed, restrictions only on main competition days and members priority times.
Green fees: £7 per round, £10.50 per day weekdays; £9.50 per round, £13.50 per day weekends.
Society meetings: entertained as for visitors excepting second half July and first half Aug.
Catering: full service of quality catering.
Hotels: Balcomie Links; Marine, Crail; Craws Nest, Anstruther.

x27 Crieff
☎Crieff (0764) 2397, 2909 booking.
Perth Rd, Crieff, Perthshire PH7 3LR.
Take A85 Perth-Crieff road for 17.5 miles, course is at 40 mile per hour limit entering Crieff.
Parkland course.
Ferntower-18 holes, 6419 yards, S.S.S.71
Dornock-9 holes, 2386 yards, S.S.S.63
Club founded in 1891.
Visitors: welcome, advance booking advisable, must book for weekends.
Green fees: on application.
Society meetings: welcome but must book well in advance.

Catering: full restaurant facilities - advisable to book. Bar meals also available.
Hotels: Crieff; Murray Park; Arduthie.

x28 Cupar
☎Cupar (0334) 53549
Hilltarvit, Cupar.
10 miles from St Andrews off A91.
9 holes, 5300 yards, S.S.S.65
Club founded in 1855.
Visitors: welcome weekdays.
Green fees: £4 weekdays; £5 weekends per (18 holes).
Society meetings: catered for on weekdays and Sun.
Catering: lunch and high tea by arrangement.
Hotels: many good hotels in area.

x29 Dalmunzie
☎Glenshee (025 085) 226
Spittal Of Glenshee, Blairgowrie, Perthshire PH10 7QE.
On A93 Blairgowrie-Braemar road, 22 miles N of Blairgowrie, adjacent to Dalmunzie Hotel.
Undulating course.
9 holes, 2035 yards, S.S.S.62
Course designed by Alister Mackenzie.
Club founded in 1922.
Visitors: welcome any day.
Green fees: £3 per day, £2.50 per round.
Society meetings: please book, all welcome.
Catering: facilities in hotel.
Hotels: Dalmonzie House.

x30 Dollar
☎Dollar (02594) 2400
Brewlands House, Dollar, Clackmannanshire.
On A91, 13 miles E of Stirling.
Hillside course.
18 holes, 5144 yards, S.S.S.66
Club founded in 1896.
Visitors: welcome weekdays, with member only at weekends.
Green fees: on application.
Society meetings: by arrangement.
Catering: meals served by arrangement.

x31 Downfield
☎Dundee (0382) 825595
Turnberry Ave, Dundee DD2 3QP.
Turn off Kingsway into A923, 100 yards from roundabout turn right into Harrison Rd, 0.5 mile to clubhouse.
Parkland course.
18 holes, 6899 yards, S.S.S.73

Course designed by C.K. Cotton.
Club founded in 1932.
Visitors: weekdays between 9.30am-11.48am and 2.18pm-3.48pm.
Green fees: £10 per round, £15 per day.
Society meetings: accepted at Committee's discretion.
Catering: facilities available, book in advance.
Hotels: many in area.

x32 Dunblane New
☎Dunblane (0786) 823711
Perth Rd, Dunblane, Perthshire FK15.
On A9 6 miles N of Stirling.
Undulating parkland course.
18 holes, 5876 yards, S.S.S.68
Club founded in 1923.
Visitors: Mon-Fri (advisable to pre-book by telephone).
Green fees: £8 per round, £12 per day.
Society meetings: by prior arrangement with Match Sec.
Catering: full catering service,
Hotels: Stakis Dunblane Hydro.

x33 Dunfermline
☎Dunfermline (0383) 723534
Pitfirrane, Crossford, Dunfermline KY12 8QV.
4 miles W of Dunfermline on road to Kincardine Bridge.
Parkland course.
18 holes, 6244 yards, S.S.S.69
Course designed by J.R. Stutt & Sons.
Club founded in 1887.
Visitors: Mon-Fri.
Green fees: £11.50 per day, £7.50 per round .
Society meetings: none.
Catering: morning coffee, lunch, high tea.
Hotels: Keavil; Pitfirran Arms.

x34 Dunkeld & Birnam
☎Dunkeld (035 02) 524
Fungarth, Dunkeld, Perthshire.
1 mile N of Dunkeld on Blairgowrie road.
Moorland course.
9 holes, 5264 yards, S.S.S.66
Club founded in 1910.
Visitors: welcome.
Green fees: £4 per round, £5 per day weekdays; £6 per day weekends.
Society meetings: catered for.
Catering: full facilities.
Hotels: Royal Dunkeld; Hillhead

House; Stakis Dunkeld House.

x35 Dunnikier Park
☎Kirkcaldy (0592) 261599
Dunnikier Way, Kirkcaldy, Fife KY1 3LP.
N boundary of town.
Parkland course.
18 holes, 6601 yards, S.S.S.72
Club founded in 1963.
Visitors: no restrictions.
Green fees: £2.65 per round weekdays; £3.75 per round weekends.
Society meetings: on application to Sec.
Catering: full catering facilities.
Hotels: Dunnikier House.

x36 Dunning
☎Dunning (076 484) 398 Treasurer.
Rollo Park, Dunning, Perth.
Off A9, 9 miles SW of Perth.
Parkland course.
9 holes, 4836 yards, S.S.S.64
Visitors: welcome.
Green fees: on application.
Society meetings: by arrangement.
Catering: at Dunning Hotel.
Hotels: Dunning; Kirk Style; Thorntree.

x37 Edzell
☎Edzell (035 64) 235
High St, Edzell, by Brechin, Angus DD9 7TF.
A94 Forfar-Aberdeen road, turn onto B966 at end of Brechin by-pass, golf course on left past arch at entrance to village.
Undulating moorland course.
18 holes, 6299 yards, S.S.S.70
Club founded in 1895.
Visitors: welcome.
Green fees: £7 per round, £10 per day weekdays; £9 per round, £12 per day weekends.
Society meetings: by arrangement with Sec.
Catering: full meal service, full bar service.
Hotels: Glenesk; Central; Panmure Arms.

x38 Elie
☎Elie (0333) 330301 Sec, 330327 Club.
Golf House Club, Elie Leven, Fife KY9 1AS.
12 miles from St Andrews on A915, 6 miles from Leven on A917.
Seaside links course.
18 holes, 6241 yards, S.S.S.70
Club founded in 1875.

Visitors: welcome.
Green fees: £9 per round, £14 per day weekdays; £12 per round, £18 per day weekends.
Society meetings: by arrangement with Sec not July, Aug or Public Holidays.
Catering: lunch, soups, sandwiches, high teas by arrangement with Steward.
Hotels: Golf, Elie; Craw's Nest, Anstruther; Old Manor, Lundin Links.

x39 Elie Sports Club
☎Elie (0333) 330955
Elie, Fife KY9 1AG.
10 miles S of St Andrews.
Seaside course.
9 holes, 5800 yards, S.S.S.66
Visitors: welcome.
Gren fees: on application.
Society meetings: by arrangement.
Catering: meals served.
Hotels: Golf, Elie; New Queens.

x40 Falkirk
☎Falkirk (0324) 23457
Stirling Rd, Falkirk.
1.5 miles W of Falkirk town centre on A9.
Parkland course.
18 holes, 6202 yards, S.S.S.70
Club founded in 1922.
Visitors: weekdays only to 4pm unaccompanied. With member at any time.
Green fees: £6 per round, £9 per day.
Society meetings: Mon, Tues, Thurs, Fri prior written arrangement with Sec.
Catering: full catering, lunches, bar snacks available.
Hotels: Cladhan, Kemper Ave, Falkirk; Norwood, Larbert Rd, Bonnybridge.

x41 Falkirk Tryst
☎Larbert (0324) 562415
86 Burnhead Rd, Stenhousemuir, Larbert FK5 4BD.
2 miles from Falkirk, 0.75 mile from Larbert Station.
Flat links course.
18 holes, 6053 yards, S.S.S.69
Club founded in 1885.
Visitors: visitors by introduction only Sat and Wed.
Green fees: £5.50 per round, £8 per day.
Society meetings: Mon, Tues, Thurs and Fri only.
Catering: full catering facilities available.

Hotels: Park, Falkirk.

X42 **Forfar**
☎Forfar (0307) 62120
Cunninghill, Arbroath Rd, by Forfar, Angus DD8 2RL.
1 mile from town on road to Arbroath.
Undulating moorland course.
18 holes, 6255 yards, S.S.S.69
Course designed by James Braid.
Club founded in 1871.
Visitors: welcome.
Green fees: £8.50 weekdays, £10.50 weekends.
Society meetings: welcome except Sat.
Catering: meals served.
Hotels: Royal; Benholm House.

X43 **Glenbervie**
☎Larbert (0324) 562605
Stirling Rd, Larbert, Stirlingshire FK5 4SJ.
On A9 between Falkirk and Stirling.
Parkland course.
18 holes, 6469 yards, S.S.S.71
Course designed by James Braid.
Club founded in 1932.
Visitors: no visitors at weekends.

Green fees: £10 per round, £16 (2 rounds).
Society meetings: Tues and Thurs.
Catering: lunches, high tea, dinner.
Hotels: Park, Falkirk.

X44 **Gleneagles Hotel**
☎Auchterarder (076 46) 3543
Auchterarder, Perthshire PH3 1NF.
Halfway between Perth and Stirling on A9.
Undulating moorland courses.
King's-18 holes, 6452 yards, S.S.S.71
Queen's-18 holes, 5964 yards, S.S.S.69
Glendevon-18 holes, 5719 yards, S.S.S.68
Prince's-18 holes, 4664 yards, S.S.S.64
King's and Queen's courses designed by James Braid.
Club founded in 1908.
Visitors: welcome with written application.
Green fees: on application to Golf Office.
Society meetings: welcome subject to availability of courses.

Catering: meals and snacks available.
Hotels: Gleneagles.

X45 **Glenrothes**
☎(0592) 758686
Golf Course Rd, Glenrothes, Fife KY6 2LA.
W end of town 8 miles from M90.
Undulating parkland course.
18 holes, 6449 yards, S.S.S.71
Course designed by J.R. Stutt.
Club founded in 1958.
Visitors: no restrictions but parties of 12 and more to book in advance through Sec (one months notice).
Green fees: £2.65 per round weekdays; £3.75 per round weekends.
Society meetings: catered for by arrangement with Sec one month in advance, minimum 15 maximum 40.
Catering: all types of catering available 7 days.
Hotels: Rothes Arms, South Parks Rd, Glenrothes; Forum, Town Centre, Glenrothes; Stakis Albany, Rescobie, Valley Gardens, Leslie.

X46 Grangemouth Municipal

☎Polmont (0324) 714355
Polmont, Falkirk, Stirlingshire.
M9, junction 4, follow signpost at
roundabout to Polmont Hill.
Parkland course.
18 holes, subject to alteration as
under construction since 1986.
6,300-6,400 yards, S.S.S.71
Visitors: welcome.
Green fees: on application.
Society meetings: by arrangement.
Catering: meals by arrangement, 24
hours in advance.
Hotels: Inchrya Grange.

X47 Green Hotel

☎Kinross (0577) 63467 Hotel,
62237 Club.
Green Hotel, Kinross KY13 7AS.
On M90 between Edinburgh and
Perth.
Parkland course.
18 holes, 6339 yards, S.S.S.71
Visitors: welcome.
Green fees: on application.
Society meetings: by arrangement.
Catering: meals served.
Hotels: Green.

X48 Killin

☎Killin (056 72) 312
Killin, Perthshire FK21.
On outskirts of village on Aberfeldy
road going E.
Parkland course.
9 holes, 2508 yards, S.S.S.65
Course designed by J. Anderson.
Club founded in 1913.
Visitors: welcome weekdays and
weekends.
Green fees: £4 per day.
Society meetings: April, May, June,
Sept.
Catering: light meals provided.
Hotels: Bridge of Lochay; Killin; Falls
of Dochart.

X49 Kinghorn

☎Kinghorn (0592) 890345
Macduff Crescent, Kinghorn, Fife
Off A92 3 miles W of Kirkcaldy.
Undulating links course.
18 holes, 5146 yards, S.S.S.67
Course layout recommended by Tom
Morris.
Club founded in 1887.
Visitors: municipal course, parties
by arrangement.
Green fees: £2.75 weekdays; £3.75
weekends.
Society meetings: as for visiting

parties.
Catering: by arrangement.
Hotels: Kingswood, Burntisland;
Cuinzie Weuk, Kinghorn.

X50 King James VI

☎Perth (0738) 32460 and 25170
Moncreiffe Island, Perth PH2 8NR.
On an island in centre of Perth,
(River Tay). Access by footbridge
(15 minutes walk).
Inland parkland course.
18 holes, 6026 yards, S.S.S.69
Club founded in 1858.
Visitors: welcome.
Green fees: £5.50 per round, £8.50
per day weekdays; £11.50 per day,
£5.50 after 4pm Sunday.
Society meetings: by arrangement.
Catering: bar meals available.
Hotels: Salutation, South St, Perth.

X51 Kirkcaldy

☎Kirkcaldy (0592) 260370
Balwearie Rd, Kirkcaldy, Fife
KY2 5LT.
On A907 at W end of town.
Parkland course.
18 holes, 6004 yards, S.S.S.70
Club founded in 1904.
Visitors: welcome any day except
Sat.
Green fees: £5 per round, £8 per
day weekdays; £6 per round, £10 per
day weekends.
Society meetings: anyday except
Tues and Sat.
Catering: full catering available
everyday.
Hotels: Parkway, Abbotshall Rd,
Kirkcaldy.

X52 Kirriemuir

☎Kirriemuir (0575) 72729 Sec,
72144 Club, 73317 Pro.
23 Bank St, Kirriemuir, Angus
DD8 4BE.
1 mile N of town centre.
Moorland/parkland course.
18 holes, 5591 yards, S.S.S.67
Course designed by James Braid.
Club founded in 1907.
Visitors: during week, at weekends
if accommodated by members only.
Green fees: £7.50 per day, £5 per
round after 4pm, £23 weekly.
Children half price.
Society meetings: parties can be
booked for week days.
Catering: full catering available at
clubhouse.
Hotels: Dykehead, Cortachy; Ogilvy
Arms; Airlie Arms, Kirriemuir.

X53 Ladybank

☎Ladybank (0337) 30814 Sec,
30725 Starter.
Annsmuir, Ladybank, Fife KY7 7RA.
6 miles W of Cupar on main
Edinburgh-Dundee road.
Moorland course.
18 holes, 6617 yards, S.S.S.72
Course designed by Tom Morris.
Club founded in 1879.
Visitors: at any time (Sat excepted)
Green fees: £10 per round, £15 per
day weekdays; £12 per round, £18
per day weekends.
Society meetings: by arrangement
with Sec.
Catering: full catering services
provided.
Hotels: Fernie Castle, Letham, Fife;
Lomond Hills, Freuchie, Fife.

X54 Leslie

Balsillie, Leslie, Fife
On A911, E of M90 at junction 5 or 6.
Undulating course.
9 holes, 4670 yards, S.S.S.63
Visitors: welcome.
Green fees: on application.
Society meetings: no Clubhouse.
Hotels: Rothes Oak; Station;
Greenside.

X55 Letham Grange G & CC

☎Gowanbank (0241 89) 373
Letham Grange, Colliston, by
Arbroath, Angus.
1 mile E of Colliston village church;
Colliston is 3 miles N of Arbroath on
Brechin road.
Undulating parkland course.
18 holes, 6789 yards, S.S.S.72
Course designed by Donald Steel &
G.K. Smith.
Club founded in 1985.
Visitors: welcome.
Green fees: weekdays £9.50, (£4.50
with member), £4.50 hotel resident,
£14 all day; weekends £12, (£6 with
member), £6 hotel resident; £10 all
day.
Society meetings: welcome by
arrangement with Sport Sec or Pro.
Catering: all day service, lunch,
dinner both à la carte.
Hotels: Letham Grange, Colliston,
by Arbroath.

X56 Leven

☎Leven (0333) 26397
Links Rd, Leven, Fife KY8 4HS.
Travel E along Promenade, turn left
into Church Rd, turn right into Links

LETHAM GRANGE

At this tastefully resorted Victorian Mansion set in 350 acres of a mature woodland estate, with its own Championship Golf Course, known as "The Augusta of Scotland" and incorporating its own Village with various designs of houses and various plots for sale.

You'll enjoy a choice of eating styles featuring Cuisine freshly prepared from local produce.

The area is rich in History & Romance; Visit Glamis Castle and the picturesque Fife Fishing Villages, or play golf on Scotland's Historic Links Courses.

PAR BREAKS: nights/price
(2) £87 (3) £127 (4) £164 (5) £199 (6) £232 (7) £263
EAGLE BREAKS: nights/price
(2) £99 (3) £145 (4) £187 (5) £227 (6) £264 (7) £299
LINKS BREAK: as Eagle plus £10. For round of Golf at Carnoustie Championship Links.
Each of the three breaks include unlimited Golf, Dinner, Bed and Breakfast. Societies Welcome.
LETHAM GRANGE
Colliston, by Arbroath, Angus, Scotland. DD11 4RL
Telephone: 024189 373   Fax: 024189

Rd, clubhouse at end of road on right.
Seaside course.
18 holes, 6434 yards, S.S.S.71
Club founded in 1867.
Visitors: welcome at all times, but courtesy times limited at weekends. For booking telephone (0333) 21390 (up to 12 players) large parties should contact Mr Innes, Clydebank Buildings, Durie St, Leven.
Green fees: £6.50 per round, £10 per day weekdays; £8 per round, £12 per day weekends.
Society meetings: see above.
Catering: breakfasts, lunch, dinner, high tea, bar snacks available.
Hotels: Old Manor, Lundin Links; Caledonian, Leven.

X57 Lochgelly
☎Lochgelly (0592) 480174
Cartmore Rd, Lochgelly, Fife
On A910 2 miles NE of Cowden-beath.
Parkland course.
18 holes, 5768 yards, S.S.S.67
Club founded in 1911.
Visitors: welcome.
Green fees: on application.

Catering: catering facilities available.
Hotels: many good hotels in area.

X58 Lundin
☎Lundin Links (0333) 320202
Golf Rd, Lundin Links, Fife KY8 6BA.
On A915, 3 miles NE of Leven.
Seaside course.
18 holes, 6377 yards, S.S.S.71
Course designed by James Braid.
Club founded in 1857.
Visitors: allowed Mon-Fri all day, Sat afternoon only after 2.30pm.
Green fees: £8 per round, £12 per day weekdays; £10 per round Saturday.
Catering: no catering Mon.
Hotels: Old Manor, Lundin Links.

X59 Milnathort
☎Milnathort (0577) 64069
South St, Milnathort KY13 2AW.
Off M90 1.5 miles N of Kinross.
Parkland course.
9 holes, 5411 yards, S.S.S.68
Club founded in 1890.
Visitors: welcome except on competition days.
Green fees: £5 weekdays; £6

weekly.
Society meetings: welcome by prior arrangement with Hon Sec.
Catering: meals and snacks available.
Hotels: Royal, South St, Milnathort; Thistle, New Rd, Milnathort.

X60 Monifieth
☎Monifieth (0382) 532767
c/o Sec, I.F. Baxter, 45 Ferry Rd, Monifieth DD5 4NG.
6 miles N of Dundee between Broughty Ferry and Carnoustie.
Seaside courses.
Medal-18 holes, 6657 yards, S.S.S.72
Ashludie-18 holes, 5123 yards, S.S.S.66
Visitors: welcome by arrangement with Starter except on Sat.
Green fees: Medal- £8 per round, £12 per day. Ashludie- £6 per round, £9 per day. Medal- £9 per round, £13 per day Sun. Ashludie- £7 per round, £10 per day Sun.
Society meetings: welcome by arrangement with Sec usually on weekdays.
Catering: every day except Tues.

X61 Montrose Links Trust

☎Montrose (0674) 72932
Starters Box, East Links, Trail Drive,
Montrose, Angus DD10 8SW.
Off A92 Dundee to Aberdeen road,
1 mile from town centre.
Seaside courses.
Medal-18 holes, 6451 yards,
S.S.S.71
Broomfield-18 holes, 4815 yards,
S.S.S.66
Club founded in 1810.
Visitors: welcome.
Green fees: Medal- £8.50 per day,
£6 per round weekdays; £9.50 per
day, £6.75 per round weekends;
Broomfield- £4.75 per day, £5.50 per
round weekdays; £3.75 per round,
£4.75 per day weekends.
Society meetings: welcome.
Catering: can be arranged in one of
the member Golf Clubs.
Hotels: Park, John St, Montrose -
offer golfing package holidays.

X62 Muckhart

☎Muckhart (025 981) 423
Drumburn Rd, Muckhart, Dollar,
Clackmannanshire FK14 7JH.
Lies between A91 and A823 S of
Muckhart, signposted off above
roads.
Undulating moorland course.
18 holes, 6115 yards, S.S.S.70
Club founded in 1908.
Visitors: welcome, telephone call
advisable at weekends.
Green fees: £5 per round, £8 per
day weekdays; £8 per round, £10 per
day weekends.
Society meetings: every day
contact Clubmaster.
Catering: lunches every day,
evening meals by arrangement.
Hotels: bed and breakfast
accommodation on perimeter of
course.

X63 Murrayshall

☎Scone (0738) 52784
Murrayshall, by Scone, Perthshire
PH2 7PH.
A94 from Perth turning right before
New Scone.
Undulating parkland course.
18 holes, 6416 yards, S.S.S.71
Course designed by J. Hamilton
Stutt.
Club founded in 1981.
Visitors: welcome weekdays and
weekends.
Green fees: £8 per day, £15 per
round weekdays; £10 per round, £18
per day weekends.
Society meetings: welcome

weekdays and weekends by prior
arrangement.
Catering: full clubhouse catering.
Hotels: Murrayshall House on golf
course.

X64 Muthill

☎Crieff (0764) 3319 Sec.
Peat Rd, Muthill, Crieff PH5 2AL.
500 yards off Stirling-Crieff road
A822, signposted at foot of road.
Parkland course.
9 holes, 2371 yards, S.S.S.63
Club founded in 1935.
Visitors: restricted evenings and
days when club matches are taking
place.
Green fees: £3 per day weekdays;
£3.50 per day weekends.
Society meetings: not encouraged.
Catering: none, changing room and
toilets only.
Hotels: Drummond Arms, Muthill.

X65 Panmure

☎(0241) 53120
Barry, Angus DD7 7RT.
Off A930, 2 miles W of Carnoustie.
Seaside course.
18 holes, 6301 yards, S.S.S.70
Club founded in 1845.
Visitors: welcome except Sat.
Green fees: £9 per round, £14 per
day weekdays (Sun-Fri).
Society meetings: by arrangement.
Catering: snacks served, meals
except Mon.
Hotels: Bruce.

X66 Pitlochry

☎Pitlochry (0796) 2792 Pro and
Starter.
Golf Course Rd, Pitlochry.
A9 to Pitlochry, then via Atholl Rd,
Larchwood Rd, and Golf Course Rd.
Hill course.
18 holes, 5811 yards, S.S.S.68
Course designed by Willie Fernie of
Troon and modernised by Major
Cecil Hutchinson.
Club founded in 1908.
Visitors: welcome.
Green fees: on application.
Society meetings: welcome by
arrangement with Estate Office
(0796) 2114.
Catering: meals and snacks served
- breakfast and dinner by arrange-
ment with Steward (0796) 2334.
Hotels: many good hotels in area.

X67 Pitreavie (Dunfermline)

☎Dunfermline (0383) 722591,

723151 Pro.
Queensferry Rd, Dunfermline, Fife
KY11 5PR.
From A90(M) turn off for Dunfermline
to join A823, course halfway
between Rosyth and Dunfermline on
E side of duel carriageway.
Undulating parkland course.
18 holes, 6086 yards, S.S.S.69
Course designed by Dr Mackenzie of
Leeds.
Club founded in 1923.
Visitors: welcome every day. Parties
and Societies must reserve in
advance. Small party can reserve
tees through Pro.
Green fees: £5 per round, £7.50 per
day weekdays; £10 per day
weekends.
Society meetings: must be
reserved in advance through Sec.
Catering: full catering facilities,
parties to be booked in advance.
Hotels: King Malcolm (Thistle Inns),
Dunfermline; Pitbauchlie House,
Dunfermline.

X68 Polmont

☎Polmont (0324) 711277
Manuelrigg Maddiston, by Falkirk,
Stirlingshire.
4 miles S of Falkirk, first right after
Central Region Fire Brigade HQ.
Undulating parkland course.
9 holes, 3044 yards, S.S.S.69
Club founded old 1904, new 1976.
Visitors: unlimited, and after 1pm
Sat.
Green fees: £3 weekdays; £4 Sat;
£5 Sun; round ticket with member
£1.50.
Society meetings: by arrangement.
Catering: full catering, by arrange-
ment with Sec.
Hotels: Inchyra Grange; Polmont.

X69 Royal Albert

☎Montrose (0674) 72376
Dorward Rd, Montrose, Angus.
Seaside courses.
18 holes, 4863 yards, S.S.S.66
18 holes, 6442 yards, S.S.S.71
Visitors: welcome.
Green fees: on request.
Catering: lunches served.
Hotels: Park; Corner House.

X70(A) St Andrews Balgrove Course

☎St Andrews (0334) 75757
St Andrews, Fife KY16 9JA.
A91 to St Andrews.
Seaside course.
9 holes

Club founded in 1974.
Visitors: welcome.
Green fees: on application.
Society meetings: welcome in Links Room.
Catering: full facilities available.
Hotels: in St Andrews.

x70(B) St Andrews Eden Course
☎St Andrews (0334) 75757
Golf Place, St Andrews, Fife KY16 9JA.
A91 to St Andrews.
Seaside course.
18 holes, 5971 yards, S.S.S.69
Visitors: welcome.
Green fees: on application.
Society meetings: welcome in Links Room.
Catering: full facilities available.
Hotels: in St Andrews.

x70(C) St Andrews Jubilee Course
☎St Andrews (0334) 75757
St Andrews, Fife KY16 9JA.
A91 to St Andrews.
Seaside course.
18 holes, 6284 yards, S.S.S.70
Visitors: welcome.
Green fees: on application.
Society meetings: welcome in Links Room.
Catering: full facilities available.
Hotels: in St Andrews.

x70(D) St Andrews New Course
☎St Andrews (0334) 75757
St Andrews, Fife KY16 9JA.
A91 to St Andrews.
Seaside course.
18 holes, 6604 yards, S.S.S.72
Visitors: welcome.
Green fees: on application.
Society meetings: welcome in Links Room.
Catering: full facilities available.
Hotels: in St Andrews.

x70(E) St Andrews Old Course
☎St Andrews (0334) 75757
St Andrews, Fife KY16 9JA.
A91 to St Andrews.
Seaside course.
18 holes, 6566 yards, S.S.S.72
Visitors: welcome (except Sun) and only with letter of introduction or handicap certificate.
Green fees: on application.
Society meetings: welcome in Links

Room.
Catering: full facilities available.
Hotels: in St Andrews.

x71 St Fillans
☎St Fillans (0764) 85312
St Fillans, Perthshire PH6 2NF.
On A85 between Crieff and Lochearnhead, at E end of Loch Earn.
Parkland course.
9 holes, 5268 yards, S.S.S.66
Club founded in 1903.
Visitors: welcome any day.
Green fees: £3.50 per day weekdays; £4.50 per day weekends.
Society meetings: catered for any day.
Catering: unlicensed, snacks and light meals available.
Hotels: Achray House; Drummond Arms.

x72 St Michaels
☎Leuchars (033 483) 365
Leuchars, St Andrews, Fife.
On A919 6 miles from St Andrews and Dundee at W end of Leuchars village turn over rail bridge. Course is about 200 yards out of village.
Undulating parkland course.
9 holes, 5510 yards, S.S.S.67
Club founded in 1903.
Visitors: welcome except Sun before 1pm.
Green fees: £3.50 per round, £6 per day weekdays; £4 per round weekends; juniors (under 16) half price.
Society meetings: welcome except Sun before 1pm.
Catering: bar and lounge facilities, meals available by prior arrangement with Sec.
Hotels: numerous in area.

x73 Saline
☎Saline (0383) 852591
Kinneddar Hill, Saline, Fife KY12 9UN.
4.5 miles NW of Dunfermline, signposted off A907 Dunfermline-Stirling road.
Undulating moorland course.
9 holes, 5302 yards, S.S.S.66
Club founded in 1912.
Visitors: welcome without restriction except competition Sats.
Green fees: £3 weekdays; £4 Sunday.
Society meetings: catered for weekdays and Sun.
Catering: bar, snacks, full catering by prior arrangement.

Hotels: Saline, Saline; Pitbauchlie, Crossford, Dunfermline.

x74 Scoonie
North Links, Leven, Fife.
10 miles SW of St Andrews.
Parkland course.
18 holes, 4931 metres, S.S.S.66
Club founded in 1951.
Visitors: welcome.
Green fees: on application.
Society meetings: welcome at weekends, minimum 15 and maximum 30.
Catering: snacks available.
Hotels: Caledonian.

x75 Scotscraig
☎Tayport (0382) 552515
Golf Rd, Tayport, Fife DD6 9DZ.
On B946 3 miles from S end of Tay Road Bridge, turn left third street past petrol station.
Links/seaside course.
18 holes, 6486 yards, S.S.S.71
Club founded in 1817.
Visitors: welcome weekdays and by arrangement at weekends.
Green fees: on application.
Society meetings: welcome by arrangement.
Catering: meals served except Tues.
Hotels: Seymour, Newport on Tay; Pinewoods, St. Michaels.

s76 Stirling
☎Stirling (0786) 64098 Sec (to book in advance), 71490 Pro (to book on day).
Queens Rd, Stirling FK8 2QY.
0.5 mile W of town centre on A811 on left hand side.
Parkland course.
18 holes, 5976 yards, S.S.S.69
Club founded in 1896.
Visitors: welcome weekdays and Sun.
Green fees: £7.50 per round, £12 per day weekdays; £8.50 per round, £13 per day weekends.
Catering: lunch and high tea available by arrangement.
Hotels: Garfield; Kingsgate; Golden Lion; Station.

x77 Taymouth Castle
☎Kenmore (088 73) 228
Kenmore, by Aberfeldy, Tayside PH15 2NT.
6 miles W of Aberfeldy, large sign by castle gates on right of road.
Fairly flat parkland course.
18 holes, 6066 yards, S.S.S.69

St Andrews

Golfers go to St Andrews as Moslems flock to Mecca, Mormons descend on Salt Lake City and Roman Catholics gather in St Peter's Square. It is as much a shrine as any of the religious centres; indeed, its symbolic importance grows more not less.

Every golf course in the world owes something to the Old course because, whether by accident or design, it embraces nearly all the elements upon which sound, traditional, golf-course architecture is based. In discussing the qualifications for an architect long ago, Tom Simpson said that, 'Above everything else, he must understand the message of the Old course'.

Some architects have gone to the lengths of building replicas of some of the holes. Charles Blair Macdonald, a figure of enormous influence in shaping golf in America, repaid his genuine love of St Andrews by building a course on the lines of the old, classic links at The National Golf Links of America, situated on Long Island.

Among the holes which he built were copies of St Andrews 11th and 17th. Augusta's 4th hole also bears more than passing resemblance to St Andrews' 11th. They are all fine holes but, however much of a compliment they may be to St Andrews, the best holes are always those which owe nothing to imitation and everything to Nature.

Modern machinery has simplified golf course architecture in the sense that nothing is now impossible. However it has its drawbacks: in addition to escalating costs, it has allowed some architects to drift (sometimes alarmingly) away from the age-old tenets which St Andrews holds dear.

This syndrome is typified by greens in the middle of lakes, huge carries to greens, enormous bunkers shaped like eccentric jig-saw pieces, and railway sleepers by the train load. Television and resort developers are largely to blame for what might be termed stadium golf. They are built in the hope that new courses can

be different, more shocking, more controversial.

Horror-provoking stretches of water, roller-coaster fairways, wildernesses and penal hollows make only the publicity men happy - they have all their glamorous adjectives at the ready. Golf, even professional golf, is played for pleasure and there is no pleasure in losing ball after ball or feeling that the impossible is being attempted.

Many of these courses seem to be designed purely with the best players in mind, but there is a sign of sanity being restored. It came after the 1986 US Open at Shinnecock Hills which brought forth cris de coeur from such players as Lee Trevino, Hale Irwin, David Graham and Jack Renner. Shinnecock is one of the oldest courses in the America, the Club, in fact, being the first to be 'formalised' in the United States.

Everyone liked the course for different reasons. Trevino saw Shinnecock's greatness in the fact that it favoured no group of players in particular. Graham liked the idea that it allowed you to hit the ball low with the chance to run the ball on to the green, if you wanted to. It gave the player desirable options, and made a break from the all-or-nothing shots which are standard on many new courses.

Irwin revealed his support for an organisation aimed at preserving our great courses, a view endorsed a year or so later by Curtis Strange who, following his record breaking 62 over the Old course in the 1987 Dunhill Cup, declared 'They should come to St Andrews and be reminded what traditional design is all about'.

Maybe the developments in golf course architecture in the last few years are part of a passing phase. Fashion exists in golf course architecture just as it does in clothes, motor cars or buildings but golf courses are more permanent. It needs visits to St Andrews to understand that simplicity is the best basic art and that the game is better when the player has to formulate his strategy on the tee, choosing how to play a hole from as many as four or five options.

Often the fairways appear to have no limits but positional play is a vital ingredient at St Andrews. You must always think at least a shot ahead - although St Andrews offers a wide choice of courses, too. The New, the Eden and a Jubilee course, which has recently been substantially upgraded, are splendid foils for the Old. In a few years, there will be a Strathtyrum, a remodelled Balgove and excellent practice facilities which, alas have been lacking for too long.

St Andrews is planning for the future, not just living in the past, but it needs a shrewd mind to understand that what one might term traditional architecture is still the best and St Andrews is still its most faithful standard-bearer.

Course designed by James Braid. Club founded in 1923.
Visitors: unlimited, booking required.
Green fees: £8 per round, £12 per day weekdays; £10 round, £15 per day weekends.
Society meetings: welcome.
Catering: full catering, bar open from 11am.
Hotels: Kenmore; Fortingall; Weem; Coshieville.

x78 **Thornton**
☎Glenrothes (0592) 771111
Station Rd, Thornton, Fife KY1 4DW.
1 mile E of A92 through Thornton.
Parkland course.
18 holes, 6177 yards, S.S.S.69
Club founded in 1921.
Visitors: welcome.
Green fees: on application.
Society meetings: catered for.

Catering: lunch, snacks and high tea.
Hotels: Crown, Thornton; Albany Glenrothes.

x79 **Tillicoultry**
☎Tillicoultry (0259) 50124
Alva Rd, Tillicoultry.
9 miles E of Stirling on A91.
Undulating meadowland course.
9 holes, 5266 yards, S.S.S.66
Course designed by Peter Robertson,
Braids Hill G.C. Edinburgh.
Club founded in 1899.
Visitors: welcome weekdays, weekends by arrangement, restrictions on juniors (under 15).
Green fees: £3 per day weekdays; £5.50 per day weekends.
Society meetings: by arrangement contact Sec (0259) 51024,
R. Whitehead, 12 Stalker Ave, Tillicoultry, or (0259) 51337 (home).

Catering: bar meals April-Sept, catering for parties by prior arrangement.
hotels: Castle Craig, High Street, Tillicoultry.

x80 **Tulliallan**
☎Alloa (0259) 30396
Alloa Rd, Kincardine on Forth, by Alloa.
1.5 miles N of Kincardine Bridge on Alloa road, next to Police College.
Parkland course.
18 holes, 5982 yards, S.S.S.69
Club founded in 1902.
Visitors: welcome by arrangement with Pro.
Green fees: on application.
Society meetings: welcome by prior arrangement except Sat; weekdays maximum 40, Sun maximum 30.
Catering: meals and snacks served.
Hotels: Powfoulis Manor, Airk; Grange Manor, Grangemouth.

Y Highlands and Grampian

The availability of golf courses has, for some time now, been one of the most important factors in deciding where to take a holiday. All over the Continent, particularly in Spain and Portugal, the number of courses has increased spectacularly - more often than not as the centre of elaborate development projects embracing villas, apartments and hotels.

These are designed to attract the tourist arriving by the Jumbo package load and there is no doubt such holidays are extremely popular but there is equally no doubt that there is nothing to beat golf in Britain for quality, variety or cheapness.

Nowhere in Britain have new roads opened up previously inaccessible parts more dramatically than in the north of Scotland. You can now drive from Edinburgh to Inverness almost exclusively on motorway and dual carriageway and the improvements don't stop there. New bridges across the Firths have brought Royal Dornoch ever nearer, a factor that undoubtedly led to its selection for the 1985 Amateur championship.

It is the jewel of the north although it was recognised years ago as a favourite holiday haunt of Roger and Joyce Wethered and Sir Ernest Holderness, another British champion. In the days before you could fly to Aberdeen or Inverness, or put your car on the train to Perth, this was the greatest possible compliment it could be paid and one which really put it on the golfing map.

Dornoch has become an important port of call for connoisseurs from all over the world and, not surprisingly, some of the region's other courses suffer a little by comparison; but Golspie and Brora, further north still, should not be missed. Green fee figures are incredibly reasonable and, in the long summer evenings, it is light enough to be playing until approaching midnight.

As the golfing crow flies, Nairn is no great distance although the journey south by road is by way of Inverness and Culloden Moor: Nairn, where David Blair played much of his golf, lies on the Moray Firth and is another ideal centre with several good hotels, notably the aptly named Golf View.

Nairn has been used for a number of Scottish championships and has its first few holes along the water's edge but a little further inland lies Boat of Garten, and further along the coast right round to Aberdeen can be found a succession of appealing places to play. On the road south from Inverness, Newtonmore and Kingussie are particularly recommended.

The nearest to matching Nairn on the coastal stretch is Lossiemouth which I first remember seeing as a town from a windswept hockey pitch at Gordonstoun School; while a few miles to the east can be found a sporting course at Spey Bay, the pleasantest memory I have of a week in an Army camp at Fochabers.

Rounding Kinnaird's Head, we come to Cruden Bay, a few miles from Old Meldrum, the birthplace of George Duncan; and finally to the delights of Aberdeen with Balgowrie or Royal Aberdeen the pick. However, there is another easy drive along the banks of the Dee to Banchory, Aboyne, Ballater and Braemar.

Y1 Abernethy

☎Nethybridge (047 982) 350
Nethybridge, Inverness-shire. On
B970 Grantown on Spey-Coylum
Bridge road, 0.25 mile N of Nethybr-
idge.
Undulating course.
9 holes, 2484 yards, S.S.S.66
Club founded in 1895.
Visitors: welcome.
Green fees: on application.
Catering: meals served.
Hotels: Nethybridge; Mountview.

Y2 Aboyne

☎Aboyne (0339) 2328
Formaston Park, Aboyne, Aberdeen-
shire AB3 5HD.
Travelling W on A93 from Aberdeen,
take first turning on right after
entering village, signposted on A93.
Undulating parkland course.
18 holes, 5330 yards, S.S.S.66
Club founded in 1883.
Visitors: welcome.
Green fees: on application.

Society meetings: welcome except
Sun.
Catering: full catering service
available from April-Oct.
Hotels: Huntly Arms; Balnacoil
House; Birse Lodge.

Y3 Alness

☎Alness (0349) 883877
Ardross Road, Alness, Ross-shire.
On A9 10 miles N of Dingwall.
9 holes, 4718 yards, S.S.S.63
Course designed by John Suther-
land.
Club founded in 1904.
Visitors: welcome at any time.
Green fees: £2.50 weekdays; £3.50
weekends; juniors and OAP half
price.
Society meetings: none.
Catering: can be arranged.
Hotels: Morven, Alness; Station,
Alness.

Y4 Askernish

Askernish, South Uist, Western Isles.

5 miles NW of Lochboisdale, ferry
terminal from Oban.
9 holes, 5312 yards, S.S.S.67
Course designed by Tom Morris.
Club founded in 1891.
Visitors: welcome.
Green fees: on application.
Society meetings: welcome.
Catering: none.
Hotels: Borrodale, Daliburgh;
Lochboisdale, Lochboisdale.

Y5 Auchenblae

☎Auchenblae (0569) 407
Auchenblae, Laurencekirk, Kincardi-
neshire AB3 1JT.
2 miles off A94 at Fardom.
Parkland course.
9 holes, 2174 yards, S.S.S.30
Visitors: welcome anytime; restricted
Wed and Fri (competition nights for
members).
Green fees: £2.50 per day weekdays;
£3 per day weekends.
Society meetings: none.
Catering: local shop sells snacks etc.

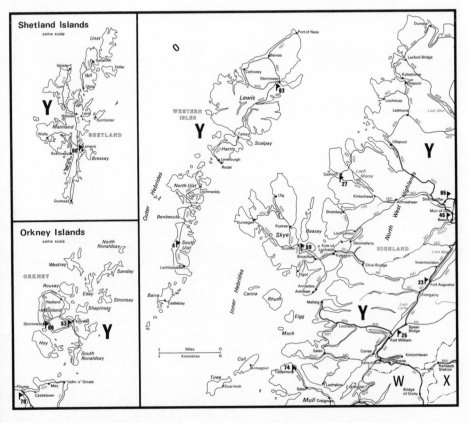

Hotels: Drumtochty Arms, Auchenblae.

Y6 Auchmill
☎Aberdeen (0224) 642121 (ask for
the Parks and Leisure Department)
Auchmill, Aberdeen.
5 miles N of Aberdeen.
9 holes, S.S.S.35
Visitors: municipal course, all
welcome.
Green fees: on application.
Hotels: in Aberdeen.

Y7 Ballater
☎Ballater (0338) 55567
Ballater, Aberdeenshire AB3 5QX.
A93 on Deeside, 40 miles W of
Aberdeen.
Flat, inland course.
18 holes, 5704 yards, S.S.S.67
Course designed by James Braid.
Club founded in 1892.
Visitors: welcome.
Green fees: £7 per day weekdays;
£9 per day weekends.
Society meetings: welcome by

arrangement with Sec.
Catering: full catering from 1 April-
15 Oct.
Hotels: Coach House; Invercauld;
Craigendarroch.

Y8 Banchory
☎Banchory (03302) 2365
Kinneskie, Banchory, Kincard-
ineshire AB3 3TA.
18 miles W of Aberdeenshire, on N
Deeside Rd.
Parkland course.

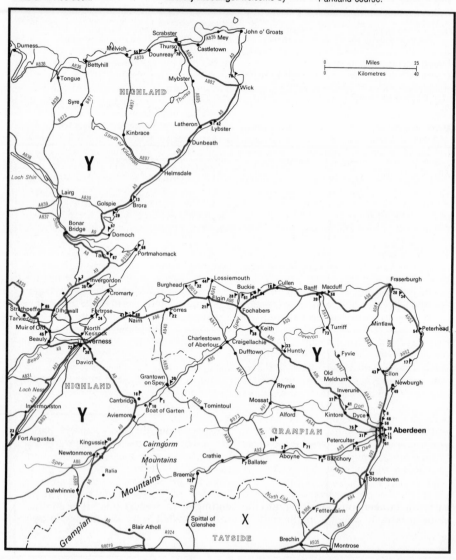

Brora

An integral part of the pleasure of golf at Brora is the drive to get there. From north or south, the road follows Sutherland's spectacular coastline overlooked by the brooding heather-clad hills which echo the call of rare birds. Dornoch is journey's end for most golfers to such distant parts but Golspie and Brora are only a few miles further on and both are authentic delights.

Brora is a seaside course without the dunes although few links get closer to the beach and the sea itself is always visible. There is a degree or two of latitude from the tee but there is urgent need for sound positional play in order to obtain the correct angle for the second shots and there is a definite spring in the turf.

As you might expect from the designing hand of James Braid, the greens are imaginatively shaped and contoured without being large targets and they complement the overall length which, with only one par five to bolster it, is still over 6,100 yards. With a wind from the north such as blew on the day that I stole away from Dornoch's first Amateur in 1985, it seemed altogether longer, many of the holes on the front nine being particularly demanding.

The 3rd and 5th, "Canal" and "Burn", 447 and 428 yards, left more than enough to do. The attractive 3rd green is guarded by bunkers left and right and the 5th possesses entirely natural defences. An inch the wrong side of a diagonally running sandy ridge on the green's approach and you are down the bank from where a daring chip is the only hope of rescuing par.

Brora is well in keeping with many of Britain's links which have the clubhouse at one end and the 9th green at the other but the 6th, turning right angles inland, provides a welcome touch of variety as well as being an absolutely first class short hole. The options from the tee are to carry the bunkers on the left set into the slope or bring in a shot from the right.

Brora's one par 5 is the 8th which favours an approach down the left to a green lying adjacent to the beach although not quite as alarmingly close as at the short 9th. Here, the local rule reminding you to treat the beach as a lateral water hazard is specially relevant. Boulders are, in fact, the main hazard but there is an unusual local rule which urges players "to treat cow droppings as casual water".

Local residents have certain grazing rights making necessary the presence of small electric fences round the greens but neither animals nor fences struck me as any inconvenience nor did anything to lessen the enjoyment.

My reservation as we turned for home was that the back nine, on the inland side, might suffer by comparison. Not so. The 10th, with its tee beside the railway line which sees only a handful of trains a week, immediately dispelled any doubt. It and the 11th, with its rippling apron to the green, are fine 4s and there follows another good two-shot hole along a gentle valley to a green backed by gorse.

The gorse is a hint of what to expect at the 13th, a short, short hole (125 yards) across a gentle stream, only a truly hit shot holding anywhere near the flat when it is situated at the front of the green. It is a reminder that a lack of length is no lack of quality and the same applies to a shortish par four like the 15th where the drive has to scale quite a slope to get a sight of the green.

The second shots at the 15th and 16th call for more judgment and precision but the 17th is the hole which will probably leave the most indelible memory. The prospect from the tee against a background of sea is superb and there is every inclination, and need, to flex your muscles on a drive to a fairway below. Another small, cleverly shaped green is no easy target and don't be fooled by ending with a short hole. It is another satisfying shot to try and master, invariably a long iron or wood.

In high summer, golf at Brora can also be a game for insomniacs as evening becomes twilight and twilight mingles with the dawn. The club has long been famous for its midnight competition in June but, whether you play four rounds a day or just one, Brora is emphatically worth the journey.

18 holes, 5271 yards, S.S.S.66
Club founded in 1905.
Visitors: welcome.
Green fees: on application.
Society meetings: welcome by arrangement.
Catering: meals served.
Hotels: Tornacoil; Burnett Arms; Banchory Lodge.

Y9 **Balnagask**
☎Aberdeen (0224) 642121 (ask for the Parks and Leisure Department).
St Fitticks Rd, Aberdeen.
2 miles SE of city centre.
Undulating seaside course.
9 holes,
18 holes, S.S.S.69
Course designed by Hawtree & Son.
Visitors: welcome.
Green fees: £4.20 per (18 hole); £2.10 per (9 hole); winter rates and junior rates on application.
Hotels: in Aberdeen.

Y10 **Boat of Garten**
☎Boat of Garten (047 983) 282
Shop, 351 Club
Boat of Garten, Inverness-shire
PH24 3BQ.
5 miles N of Aviemore on old A9 road, turn right onto B970.
Undulating parkland course.
18 holes, 5690 yards, S.S.S.68
Course designed by James Braid.
Club founded in 1898.
Visitors: welcome.
Green fees: £5 weekdays; £7 weekends.
Society meetings: must be booked in advance.
Catering: facilities available all day.
Hotels: Craigard; Moorfield; Boat.

Y11 **Bon-Accord**
☎Aberdeen (0224) 633464
19 Golf Rd, Aberdeen AB2 1QB.
Beside Pittodrie Stadium at beach.
Seaside course.
18 holes, 6384 yards, S.S.S.70
Club founded in 1872.
Visitors: municipal course.
Green fees: summer: £4.20 per round, juniors before 5pm £2.35;

winter: £2.80 per round juniors before 5pm £1.70.
Catering: by arrangement with Steward.
Hotels: Caledonian, Union Terrace.

Y12 **Braemar**
☎Braemar (033 83) 618
Cluniebank Rd, Braemar,
Aberdeenshire AB3 5XX.
Signposted from village of Braemar, club lies approximately 0.5 mile from village centre.
Parkland/moorland course.
18 holes, 4916 yards, S.S.S.64
Course designed by Joe Anderson.
Club founded in 1902.
Visitors: welcome.
Greeen fees: £5 per day, £4 per round weekdays; £7 per day, £5 per round weekends.
Society meetings: welcome, prior booking required.
Catering: available except Tues, Wed.
Hotels: Fife Arms, Mar Rd, Braemar; Braemar Lodge, Glenshee Rd, Braemar.

Y13 **Brora**
☎Brora (0408) 21417
Golf Rd, Brora, Sutherland
KW9 6QS.
75 miles N of Inverness on A9, signpost in middle of village giving direction.
Seaside links course.
18 holes, 6110 yards, S.S.S.69
Course designed by James Braid.
Club founded in 1889.
Visitors: welcome at any time, restrictions may occur on tournament days.
Green fees: £6 per round; £25 per week; £35 per fortnight; £40 per 3 weeks; £45 per month.
Society meetings: arrange on written application. Discount available over 15 in number.
Catering: available Jun, Jul, Aug. Also available on request from Societies and parties.
Hotels: Links, Golf Rd; Royal Marine, Golf Rd; Sutherland Arms,

Fountain Sq; Braes, Fountain Sq; Bay View, Golf Rd; all Brora.

Y14 **Buckpool**
☎Buckie (0542) 32236
Barhill Rd, Buckie, Banffshire
AB5 1DU.
Leave A98 towards Buckpool, 1 mile signposted Buckie, course at end of road.
Seaside links course.
18 holes, 6259 yards, S.S.S.70
Visitors: welcome, parties by arrangement.
Green fees: £4 per day weekdays; £6 per day weekends.
Society meetings: catered for by prior arrangement.
Catering: weekends and by arrangement.
Hotels: St Andrews, 1 mile.

Y15 **Caledonian**
☎Aberdeen (0224) 632443
20 Golf Rd, Aberdeen.
Adjacent to Pittodrie Stadium.
18 holes
Visitors: welcome.
Green fees: on application.
Society meetings: by arrangement.
Catering: snacks available.
Hotels: in Aberdeen.

Y16 **Carrbridge**
☎Carrbridge (047 986) 674 Hon Sec
Carrbridge, Inverness-shire
PH23 3AU.
About 200 yards from village on A938.
Parkland/moorland course.
9 holes, 2625 yards, S.S.S.66
Club founded in 1980.
Visitors: welcome except during tournament (usually in Sept).
Green fees: on application.
Catering: none.
Hotels: Carrbridge; Struan House.

Y17 **Cruden Bay**
☎Cruden Bay (0779) 812285
Aulton Rd, Cruden Bay, Peterhead
Aberdeenshire AB4 7NN.
23 miles N of Aberdeen on coastal

Boat of Garten

There is a wonderfully romantic ring about some of the more remote outposts of the British golfing empire. Westward Ho!, Machrihanish, Castletown and Lamlash, but most romantically named of all is Boat of Garten, named after the old ferry which used to carry passengers from the area around Loch Garten across the Spey.

In more recent times, publicity has centred more upon noble local efforts to save the osprey and it is against a background that varies from gentle greenness to rugged beauty that golfers enjoy a course that is almost as rare. The mountain heart of Scotland on the journey north from Pitlochry is one of the few parts of Britain where thoughts of golf are faraway and it is not until the road drops down from Drumochter into more fertile plains around Newtonmore and Kingussie that they are revived.

Even then, the relative sparseness of the population hardly matches the demand for the game that exists elsewhere, but the Boat of Garten, lying about six miles east of Aviemore, has an army of admirers. It only needs the briefest introduction to understand why.

It is a joy to find a course where the emphasis is not on length. Small greens and even smaller landing areas make the par of 69 highly elusive, imposing the vital need for precise striking and clear judgment. The fairways, nicely undulating though never severely so, are none too wide and liberally fringed by a mixture of birch, heather and broom.

There has been a course of some sort at Boat of Garten for almost a hundred years but it was the handiwork of James Braid which, by extending it to eighteen holes, really put it on the map. It was always said of Braid, five times Open champion, that he drove with "divine fury". Yet that is far from the main requirement. Controlled accuracy is a rather more important quality than fury, divine or ungodly.

The 1st hole is no guide to what follows, the chief danger to an opening short hole taking the form of out of bounds on the right. The 2nd is a much truer indication of the general character and the short 3rd an example of the difficulty of negotiating a successful route to the green if the shot is not all carry; but at the 4th, where twin crests have to be cleared, the power has to be turned up a notch or two.

As the only par 5, it has distinct novelty value although its name, "Birches", could equally be applied to many other holes. If it is not apparent by now, the awareness quickly increases that the course was originally a birch wood, the 6th, "The Avenue", a clue in itself, weaving a narrow path between the trees on one of three par fours over 400 yards.

In contrast to the blind second at the 7th, the raised 8th green poses an inviting prospect from the tee, as does the 10th, 265 yards. Played simply as a four, there are no great problems, but the tiger's line really is a tiger's line.

On a clear day when the highland air sparkles, the distant views provide an extra dimension to the golf with, it is hoped, inspiring results; but the drive at the 14th has got to be nailed and it has to be straight if a long second over a sharp brow is to reach the green. Some respite is found at the next four holes, three of which, modest fours, help to explain the overall yardage of 5,690.

The 15th, something of an old-fashioned hole, and none the worse for that, derives the name "Gully" from the situation and shape of its green but the 16th is the only par three on the back nine and, to dispel any complacency, there is a definite sting in the tail.

At the 18th, out of bounds lurks down the right; there is no great latitude to the left and the second shot has to take account of a long incline and an even steeper slope to the green itself. A glance to the right shows the smart new bridge that replaced the old chain ferry and, beside the clubhouse, two all-weather tennis courts are reminders of changing times. However, one thing that never changes is the grandeur of the setting and the infinite pleasure of the golf which is full of charm and subtle challenge.

route to Peterhead.
Seaside course.
9 holes, 4710 yards, S.S.S.62
18 holes, 6370 yards, S.S.S.71
Course designed by Tom Morris &
Archie Simpson.
Club founded in 1899.
Visitors: not on competition days
before 3.30pm. Restricted at
weekends.
Green fees: £9 per day weekdays;
£12 per day weekends.
Society meetings: on application.
Catering: full bar and restaurant
facilities.
Hotels: Kilmarnock Arms, Cruden
Bay; Waterside Inn, Peterhead; Udny
Arms, Newburgh; Atholl, Aberdeen.

Y18 Cullen
☎Cullen (0542) 40685
The Links, Cullen, Buckie,
Banffshire.
200 yards from A98 on W side of
Cullen.
Seaside course.
18 holes, 4610 yards, S.S.S.62
Visitors: welcome.
Green fees: £4 weekdays; £4.50
weekends.
Society meetings: none.
Catering: lunches from May-Sept.
Hotels: Royal Oak, Cullen; Seafields
Arms, Cullen.

Y19 Deeside
☎Aberdeen (0224) 867697
Bieldside, Aberdeen.
3 miles W of Aberdeen on A93 North
Deeside road.
Parkland course.
18 holes, 5972 yards, S.S.S.69
Club founded in 1903.
Visitors: welcome if recognised
members of golf clubs and with letter
of introduction from Sec.
Green fees: £12 per day weekdays;
£15 per day weekends and Bank
Holidays.
Society meetings: welcome on
Thurs only.
Catering: full facilities available.
Hotels: Cults, Cults, Aberdeen;
Bieldside Inn, Bieldside, Aberdeen.

Y20 Duff House Royal
☎Banff (026 12) 2062
The Barnyards, Banff AB4 3SX.
On A98 entering town from S.
Parkland course.
18 holes, 6161 yards, S.S.S.69
Course designed by Dr A.
Mackenzie.
Club founded in 1909.

Visitors: welcome without
introduction at all times, but tee times
restricted at weekends and Jul and
Aug.
Green fees: £6 per round, £8 per
day weekdays; £8 per round, £10 per
day weekends.
Society meetings: catered for at all
times but weekend dates fully
booked with waiting list operating.
Catering: full catering service
available.
Hotels: Banff Springs; County,
Banff; Fife Lodge, Banff.

Y21 Elgin
☎Elgin (0343) 2338 Sec, 2884 Pro.
Hardhillock, Elgin, Morayshire
IV30 3SX.
From centre of Elgin take A941
Rothes road to S side of New Elgin,
then left on to Birnie road for 1 mile
to clubhouse turning off A941
indicated at sign to golf course.
Undulating moorland/parkland
course.
18 holes, 6401 yards, S.S.S.71
Club founded in 1906.
Visitors: welcome after 9.30am
weekdays, 10am weekends.
Green fees: £6 per round, £9 per
day weekdays; £9 per round, £11 per
day weekends.
Society meetings: parties
welcomed by arrangement with Sec
or Pro.
Catering: full catering all days
except Tues and Thurs afternoons.
Full bar facilities all day.
Hotels: Eight Acres; Laich Moray;
Rothes Glen.

Y22 Forres
☎Forres (0309) 72949
Muiryshade, Forres IV36 0RD.
1 mile S of clock tower in town
centre, by St Leonards Rd and
Edgehill Rd.
Undulating parkland course.
18 holes, 5615 yards, S.S.S.69
Course designed by James Braid.
Club founded in 1889.
Visitors: bar and catering.
Green fees: £6 per day, £4 per
round.
Society meetings: welcome by
confirmation.
Catering: by arrangement.
Hotels: Royal; Ramnee; Park.

Y23 Fort Augustus
☎Fort Augustus (0320) 6460 Sec.
Markethill, Fort Augustus,
Inverness-shire.

Off A82, entrance beyond 30 mph
restriction S of village.
9 holes, 5454 yards, S.S.S.78
Course designed by Dr Lane.
Club founded in 1905.
Visitors: tickets at clubhouse,
minimum restrictions.
Green fees: £4 per day weekdays;
£6 per day weekends; £15 weekly
Mon-Fri.
Society meetings: apply Sec,
Glentarff, Fort Augustus.
Catering: self-catering facilities
available.
Hotels: Lovat Arms; Caledonian;
Brae.

Y24 Fortrose & Rosemarkie
☎Fortrose (0381) 20529 or 20140
Ness Rd East, Fortrose, Ross-shire
IV10 8SE.
Fortrose is on Cromarty road
branching off A9 out of Inverness,
about 16 miles N of Inverness.
Seaside links course.
18 holes, 5973 yards, S.S.S.69
Course re-designed by James Braid.
Club founded in 1888.
Visitors: welcome at all times.
Green fees: £6 per day weekdays;
£6 per round, £7 per day weekends.
Society meetings: catered for if
possible on written application.
Catering: available.
Hotels: Marine, Rosemarkie; Royal,
Fortrose.

Y25 Fort William
☎Fort William (0397) 4464
North Rd, Torlundy, Fort William
PH33 6RD.
On A82 Fort William to
Inverness road, 2 miles N of Fort
William.
Moorland course.
18 holes, 5640 yards, S.S.S.68
Course designed by J.R. Stutt.
Club founded in 1975.
Visitors: welcome any time.
Green fees: under review.
Society meetings: welcomed.
Catering: full licensed, bar snacks.
Hotels: several within reasonable
proximity.

Y26 Fraserburgh
☎Fraserburgh (0346) 28287
Philarth, Fraserburgh AB4 5TL.
1 mile SE of Fraserburgh, on A92
Aberdeen-Fraserburgh road, turn off
right on road to Cairnbulg.
Undulating seaside course.
18 holes, 6217 yards, S.S.S.70
Course designed by James Braid.

A Perfect Highland Interlude

For many years the name of Dornoch meant no more to me than the fact that, in my early school days, I shared a desk with a boy who lived there. Like all good young Scotsmen he played golf, and often used to speak of his course, adding with a typical youthful boast that I ought to go and see it for myself.

I never took him very seriously because I knew from the atlas that Dornoch was 620 miles from home and there was no reason to justify a trip. But, as time passed, more and more people confirmed what he had said; and as I listened one day at St Andrews to an enthusiastic description by Billy Joe Patton of a recent visit he had made, on the firm recommendation of his Walker Cup captain, Dick Tufts, I decided that I must go after all at the first opportunity.

Shortly afterwards, ambition was at last fulfilled. It was a perfect Highland interlude, and for three days my partner and I were caught in Dornoch's enchanting spell, playing round after round with an eagerness that is rare on a new course. Here was a traditional links, set amid gentle dune country, never out of sight or sound of the sea, and untouched by the centuries.

According to local records, golf was played at Dornoch as early as 1616, which would make it, according to some golfing authorities, the second oldest golfing nursery in the world after St Andrews. It was not until 1877 that the Royal Dornoch Golf Club was founded and old Tom Morris was commissioned to come up from St Andrews to lay out nine holes.

Another nine were added and, shortly after the turn of the century, they were transformed into a championship links by John Sutherland, who for over fifty years was club secretary.

Dornoch used not to be widely known as a championship test because its remoteness made it impractical for such occasions; but the 1980 Home Internationals were played there three years after the club's centenary and final recognition came with the staging of the 1985 Amateur championship, won by Garth McGimpsey. So the course held by men close to the heart of the game to be one of the finest in the world was well and truly on the map.

First impressions are often the best and I still remember my initial visit. I became more than ever convinced of Dornoch's unmistakable quality of greatness and, to be fair, that opinion has been amply confirmed subsequently. It would be hard to think of a course that ranks above it as a pure test of golf or one that is more enjoyable to play.

For the Amateur championship, the weather held no hint of June. A cold wind from the north or north-west made the outward half unduly severe; but more than twenty years before, we experienced unusual contrasts, each time the links proving itself fair, challenging and rewarding for every class of player.

For years, the holes stayed firmly in the memory and I can see again the long, gradual curve at two levels of the first eight moving out to the point towards Embo where the 9th fairway turns for home along the shore.

The thrill of the drive from the 3rd tee to a narrow fairway on a shelf below; the pitch to the pulpit green at the 5th; the splendour of four superb short holes and the succession of good shots that are demanded from the turn if a score is not to get out of hand - that is the essence of Dornoch.

The tees are angled and the course slightly crescent shaped, so that the wind is not constantly in the face or the back, and the greens are so guarded or raised as to ensure that the ill-judged and ill-conceived second or approach is unlikely to succeed even from turf where the lies are seldom less than good.

The 12th (500 yards) is a classic of its length and the 14th, "Foxy", an admirable illustration of a hole where bunkers need have no place, the second to a plateau green depending entirely on the placing of the drive.

These were one's special impressions,

but when all thoughts of golf were forgotten, the matchless beauty of the setting remained. The massive, brooding hills of Sutherland, the golden stretch of sand that borders the huge sweep of the Dornoch Firth, and the lighthouse on its lonely distant point, give an added inspiration that make the world at large seem a thousand miles away.

Club founded in 1881.
Visitors: no restrictions, all welcome.
Green fees: £5 weekdays; £7 weekends; both per round/day.
Society meetings: no restrictions weekdays and most Sun - small parties on Sat subject to Club commitments.
Catering: bar lunches daily, evening meals to order.
Hotels: Station; Royal; Alexandra; Saltoun.

Y27 Gairloch
☎Gairloch (0445) 2407
Gairloch, Ross-shire IV21 2BE.
On A832, 72 miles NW of Inverness.
Seaside course.
9 holes, 2093 yards, S.S.S.63
Course designed by Captain Burgess.
Club founded in 1898.
Visitors: welcome, no Sunday golf.
Green fees: £5 per day; £15 per week; £3 per round.
Society meetings: none.
Catering: small kiosk during summer.
Hotels: Gairloch; Craig Mor.

Y28 Garmouth & Kingston
☎Spey Bay (034 387) 388
Garmouth, Fochabers, Moray IV32 7LU.
Off A96 8 miles E of Elgin.
Seaside course.
18 holes, 5649 yards, S.S.S.67
Club founded in 1929.
Visitors: welcome.
Green fees: £5 per day; £6 weekends; £3 after 6.30pm.
Society meetings: by arrangement with Sec.
Catering: by arrangement with Sec.
Hotels: Gordon Arms, Laichmoray; Fochabers, Elgin.

Y29 Golspie
☎Golspie (040 83) 3266
Ferry Rd, Golspie, Sutherland.
First right in Golspie off A9 from Inverness.
Links/heathland/seaside/meadowland course.
Club founded in 1889.
Visitors: unrestricted.
Green fees: £6 per day; £30 weekly; £45 fortnightly.
Society meetings: welcome subject to tee reservations for competitions and tournaments.
Catering: licensed restaurant.
Hotels: Golf Links, Golspie.

Y30 Grantown-on-Spey
☎Grantown-on-Spey (0479) 2079
Golf Course Rd, Grantown-on-Spey.
Leave A9 at Aviemore, take A939 to Grantown, situated at end of town.
Moorland/parkland course.
18 holes, 5745 yards, S.S.S.67
Course designed by Willie Park, some holes by James Braid.
Club founded in 1890.
Visitors: welcome at anytime.
Green fees: £5 weekdays; £6 weekends.
Society meetings: catered for.
Catering: morning coffee, lunch, high tea.
Hotels: Grant Arms; Ben Mohr; Garth.

Y31 Hazlehead
☎Aberdeen (0224) 642121 (ask for the Parks and Leisure Department).
Hazlehead Park, Aberdeen.
4 miles W of city centre.
Moorland courses.
18 holes, 6045 yards, S.S.S.68
18 holes, 6205 yards, S.S.S.70
Visitors: municipal course, all welcome.
Green fees: £4.20 per (18 holes), £2.10 per (9 holes); winter and junior rates on application.
Hotels: in Aberdeen.

Y32 Hopeman
☎(0348) 830578
Hopeman, Moray IV30 2SS.
8 miles N of Elgin.
Seaside course.
18 holes, 5439 yards, S.S.S.66
Visitors: welcome at all times.
Green fees: £3.50 weekdays; £4.50 weekends.

Society meetings: welcome.
Catering: snacks and bar facilities.
Hotels: Station; Neuk.

Y33 Huntly
☎Huntly (0466) 2643
Cooper Park, Huntly. Aberdeenshire.
On A96 half mile from town centre.
Parkland course.
18 holes, 5399 yards, S.S.S.66
Club founded in 1900.
Visitors: welcome except Thurs and Wed.
Green fees: £6 per day weekdays; £7 per day weekends; £20 weekly.
Society meetings: by arrangement with Sec.
Catering: facilities by arrangement.
Hotels: Castle, Huntly; Huntly, The Square; Gordon Arms, The Square.

Y34 Inverallochy
☎Inverallochy (034 65) 2324
Inverallochy, Nr Fraserburgh.
3 miles S of Fraserburgh on B9033.
Seaside links course.
18 holes, 5137 yards, S.S.S.65
Club founded in 1888.
Visitors: welcome every day.
Green fees: £3 per day.
Society meetings: none.
Catering: limited catering available.
Hotels: Tufred Duch, St Combs, Fraserburgh.

Y35 Invergordon
☎Invergordon (0349) 852116
Cromlet Drive, Invergordon, Ross-shire IV18 0EU - (Clubhouse).
King George Street, Invergordon - (Course).
Off High St, Invergordon.
Parkland course.
9 holes, 3014 yards, S.S.S.69
Course designed by Mr J. Urquhart.
Club founded in 1940.
Visitors: welcome at any time. (Mon and Wed evenings Ladies competitions); (Tues and Thurs evenings Mens competitions). (All day Sat Mens competitions).
Green fees: £3 weekdays; £3.50 weekends; Under 18's, 50p weekdays; £1.50 weekends.

Society meetings: by arrangement.
Catering: bar lunches on Sat.
Hotels: Marine; Kincraig, Invergordon.

Y36 Inverness
☎Inverness (0463) 239882 Sec,
231989 Pro.
Culcabock Rd, Inverness IV2 3XQ.
1 mile from town centre on S side of
River Ness.
Parkland course.
18 holes, 6226 yards, S.S.S.70
Club founded in 1883.
Visitors: welcome, restricted Sat.
Green fees: £8 per round, £10 per
day weekdays; £10 per round, £13
per day weekends.
Society meetings: yes - limited and
early bookings required. Not Sat or
Sun.
Catering: available, except Thurs.
Hotels: Kingsmill, Kingsmill Rd,
Inverness; Craigmonie; Caledonian,
Church St, Inverness.

Y37 Inverurie
☎Inverurie (0467) 24080
Blackhall Rd, Inverurie, Aberdeen-
shire.
On A96 Aberdeen-Inverness road.
Parkland/wooded course.
18 holes, 5703 yards, S.S.S.68
Course designed by G. Smith and
J.M. Stutt.
Club founded in 1923.
Visitors: welcome but prior booking
on (0467) 20193 advisable.
Green fees: £5 per day weekdays;
£7 per day weekends.
Society meetings: welcome by prior
arrangement.
Catering: available daily.
Hotels: Kintore Arms, Inverurie;
Gordon Arms, Inverurie; Pittodrie
House, Pitcaple, Inverurie.

Y38 Keith
☎Keith (054 22) 2469, 2831 Sec.
Fife-Keith, Keith, Banffshire.
0.5 mile off A96 on Dufftown Rd.
Undulating parkland course.
18 holes, S.S.S.68
Club founded in 1965.
Visitors: welcome.
Green fees: on appliction.
Society meetings: by arrangement.
Catering: by arrangement.
Hotels: Gordon Arms.

Y39 Kings Links
☎Aberdeen (0224) 632269
Kings Links, Aberdeen.
E of city centre.

Seaside course.
Visitors: municipal course, all
welcome.
Green fees: £4.20 per (18 hole);
£2.10 per (9 hole); Winter and Junior
rates on application.
Hotels: in Aberdeen.

Y40 Kingussie
☎Kingussie (054 02) 600 Sec,
374 Club.
Gynack Rd, Kingussie, Inverness-
shire PH21 1LR.
Leave A9 at N end of village, drive
into village, turn right at Duke of
Gordon Hotel and continue to end of
road.
Hill course.
18 holes, 5504 yards, S.S.S.67
Course designed by Vardon & Herd.
Club founded in 1890.
Visitors: unrestricted.
Green fees: £4.50 per round, £5.50
per day weekdays; £5 per round, £6
per day weekends.
Society meetings: by arrangement.
Catering: for societies.
Hotels: many good hotels in area.

Y41 Kintore
☎0467 32631
Balbithan Road, Kintore, Inverurie,
Aberdeenshire.
Off A96, 12 miles N of Aberdeen.
Undulating moorland course.
9 holes, 2650 yards, S.S.S.66
Club founded in 1911.
Visitors: welcome, course open to
visitors daily except Mon, Wed and
Fri after 4pm.
Green fees: £4 per day weekdays;
£6 per day weekends.
Society meetings: welcome
weekdays.
Catering: provided if booked in
advance.
Hotels: Kintore Arms; Crown;
Torryburn.

Y42 Lybster
Main St, Lybster, Caithness
KW1 6BL.
13 miles S of Wick on A9, turn down
village main street, golf course
entrance opposite football pitch.
Moorland course.
9 holes, 1898 yards, S.S.S.62
Club founded in 1926.
Visitors: welcome, pay before play
in money box provided.
Green fees: £2 per day - limited
number of rounds; £1 Ladies and
Juniors.
Society meetings: any group

welcome anytime except Sat
evenings (club competitions).
Catering: none.
Hotels: Portland Arms; Bayview;
Commercial, all within village.

Y43 McDonald
☎Ellon (0358) 22891
Hospital Rd, Ellon, Aberdeenshire
AB4 9AW.
Leave Ellon by A948 Auchnagatt
road and take first turning on left.
Parkland course.
18 holes, 5986 yards, S.S.S.69
Club founded in 1927.
Visitors: welcome.
Green fees: £5 weekdays; £6 Sat,
£8 Sun. Reductions after 4 pm.
U18's halfprice.
Society meetings: welcome.
Catering: full catering facilities daily.
Hotels: Buchan, Bridge St, Ellon;
New Inn, Market St, Ellon.

Y44 Moray
☎Lossiemouth (034 381) 2018
Stotfield Rd, Lossiemouth, Moray
IV31 6QS.
From Elgin on A96 Aberdeen-
Inverness road, travel on A941 Elgin-
Lossiemouth road.
Links courses.
Old-18 holes, 6643 yards, S.S.S.72
New-18 holes, 6044 yards, S.S.S.69
Club founded in 1889.
Visitors: no restriction.
Green fees: Old: £7 per round, £10
per day; New: £5 per round; £6 per
day.
Catering: full during summer,
weekend Oct-Mar.
Hotels: Stotfield; Laverock Bank.

Y45 Muir of Ord
☎Muir of Ord (0463) 870825
Great Northern Rd, Muir of Ord,
Ross and Cromarty IV6 7SX.
15 miles N of Inverness on A862.
Moorland/parkland course.
18 holes, 5129 yards, S.S.S.65
Course part designed by James
Braid.
Club founded in 1875.
Visitors: welcome unrestricted.
Green fees: Oct-Mar £4 weekdays;
£5 weekends; £20 per week; £1
Juniors; April-Sept £5 weekdays; £6
weekends; £20 per week; £1 Juniors.
Society meetings: welcome book in
advance.
Catering: snacks, bar lunches, full
meals.
Hotels: Ord Arms, Muir of Ord; Prior,
Beauly.

Y46 **Murcar**
☎Aberdeen (0224) 704354
Bridge of Don, Aberdeen AB2 8BD.
3 miles from Aberdeen on A92,
Fraserburgh road.
Seaside course.
18 holes, 6240 yards, S.S.S.71
Course designed by Archie Simpson.
Club founded in 1909.
Visitors: welcome weekdays.
Green fees: £7 per round before
11.30am, £12 per day weekdays.
Society meetings: catered for on
weekdays.
Catering: snacks, lunches, dinners.
Hotels: numerous in Aberdeen.

Y47 **Nairn**
☎Nairn (0667) 53208
Seabank Rd, Nairn IV12 4HB.
1 mile N of A96, W of Nairn, turn off
onto Seabank Rd at church.
Seaside links course.
18 holes, 6556 yards, S.S.S.71
Course designed by Tom Morris and
James Braid.
Club founded in 1887.
Visitors: welcome.
Green fees: on application.
Society meetings: catered for.
Catering: summer: full catering
except Thurs; winter: restricted
catering.
Hotels: Golf View; Royal Marine;
Windsor; Newton; Alton Burn.

Y48 **Nairn Dunbar**
☎Nairn (0667) 52741
Lochloy Rd, Nairn IV12 5AE.
On A96, 0.5 mile E of town.
Seaside course.
18 holes, 6431 yards, S.S.S.71
Club founded in 1899.
Visitors: welcome.
Green fees: £6 weekdays; £7
weekends.
Society meetings: welcome.
Catering: available.
Hotels: Royal Marine; Ramleh;
Windsor; Sunnybrae Guest House.

Y49 **Newburgh-on-Ythan**
☎Newburgh (035 86) 389
c/o 1 Millend, Newburgh, Aberdeenshire AB4 0AW.
14 miles N of Aberdeen on
Peterhead road, on entering village
of Newburgh turn right at Ythan
Hotel.
Seaside links course.
9 holes, 6404 yards, S.S.S.71
Club founded in 1912.
Visitors: welcome except Tues after
4pm from May-Sept.

Green fees: on application.
Society meetings: on application to
Sec.
Catering: no facilities at club.
Hotels: Ythan; Goveran House;
Udny.

Y50 **Newtonmore**
☎Newtonmore (054 03) 328
Golf Course Rd, Newtonmore,
Inverness-shire PH20 1AP.
Leave A9 2 miles S of Newtonmore,
road to golf course in centre of
village 150 yards away.
Moorland/parkland course.
18 holes, 5890 yards, S.S.S.68
Course designed by James Braid.
Club founded in 1896.
Visitors: welcome.
Green fees: on application.
Society meetings: welcome.
Catering: meals and snacks served.
Hotels: Craigerne; Alvey; Balavil;
Braeriach; Mains.

Y51 **Nigg Bay**
☎Aberdeen (0224) 871286
St Fitticks Rd, Balnagask,
Aberdeenshire
SE of city centre.
Seaside course.
18 holes, 5984 yards, S.S.S.69
Club founded in 1955.
Visitors: welcome.
Green fees: £2.80.
Society meetings: by arrangement.
Hotels: in Aberdeen.

Y52 **Northern**
☎Aberdeen (0224) 636440
Golf Rd, Kings Links, Aberdeen.
E of city centre.
Seaside course.
18 holes, 6700 yards, S.S.S.69
Visitors: welcome (municipal
course).
Green fees: on application.
Society meetings: by arrangement.
Catering: at weekends, by
arrangement during week.
Hotels: in Aberdeen.

Y53 **Orkney**
☎Kirkwall (0856) 2457
Grainbank, St Ola, By Kirkwall,
Orkney.
0.5 mile W of Kirkwall.
Parkland course.
18 holes, 5406 yards, S.S.S.68
Club founded in 1889.
Visitors: welcome any day.
Green fees: £4 per day; £15 per
week.
Society meetings: none.

Catering: none - bar in evenings
during summer months.
Hotels: Ayre; Ayre Rd, Kirkwall.

Y54 **Peterhead**
☎Peterhead (0779) 72149
Craigewan Links, Peterhead,
Aberdeenshire AB4 6LT.
A92 and A975, 30 miles N of
Aberdeen.
Seaside links course.
18 holes, 6100 yards, S.S.S.69
Club founded in 1841.
Visitors: welcome any time.
Green fees: £4.50 weekdays; £7.50
weekends.
Society meetings: any day except
Sat or tournament days (by
appointment, telephone or letter).
Catering: by prior arrangement with
Steward.
Hotels: Caledonian; Palace;
Waterside; all in Peterhead.

Y55 **Reay**
☎Reay (0847 81) 288
by Thurso, Caithness KE14 7RE.
W from Thurso towards Bettyhill,
11 miles.
Undulating seaside course.
18 holes, 5865 yards, S.S.S.68
Club founded in 1892.
Visitors: welcome any non
competition days.
Green fees: £5 per day; £18 weekly;
juniors half rate.
Catering: none.
Hotels: Forss House, Forss,
Caithness; Meluich, Meluich,
Sutherland.

Y56 **Royal Aberdeen**
☎Aberdeen (0224) 702571
Balgownie, Bridge of Don, Aberdeen
AB2 8AT.
2 miles N of Aberdeen on A92,
cross River Don, turn right at first set
of traffic lights and then along Links
Rd to course.
Links courses.
18 holes, 4033 yards, S.S.S.60
18 holes, 6372 yards, S.S.S.71
Course designed by Robert
Simpson of Carnoustie.
Club founded in 1780.
Visitors: welcome with letter of
introduction.
Green fees: £15 per day, £11 per
round weekdays; £15 per day, £15
per round weekends.
Society meetings: welcome by
arrangement with Sec.
Catering: full facilities available.
Hotels: Atholl, Kings Gate,

Aberdeen; Caledonian, Elvan Terrace, Aberdeen; Holiday Inn, Dyce, Aberdeen.

Y57 Royal Dornoch
☎Dornoch (0862) 810219
Golf Rd, Dornoch, Sutherland IV25 3LW.
A9 from Inverness, take A949 for Dornoch, signposted in town.
Seaside course.
18 holes, 6577 yards, S.S.S.72
Course designed by Tom Morris and John Sutherland.
Club founded in 1877.
Visitors: welcome weekdays and weekends tee reservations in advance.
Green fees: £18 per day, £13 per round weekdays; £25 per day Sat; £18 per day Sun; £13 per round Sun; £65 weekly.
Society meetings: catered for except in July or Aug; early reservations required.
Catering: catering facilities available except Mon.
Hotels: Burghfield House; Carling Bank; Dornoch Castle; Dornoch; Royal Golf.

Y58 Royal Tarlair
☎Macduff (0261) 32897
Buchan St, Macduff AB4 1TA.
On A98 48 miles from Aberdeen.
Undulating seaside course.
18 holes, 5866 yards, S.S.S.68
Course designed by George Smith.
Club founded in 1923.
Visitors: welcome any day.
Green fees: £6 per day weekdays; £7 per day weekends.
Society meetings: catered for by arrangement.
Catering: served every day and weekends.
Hotels: Knowes, Market St; Fife Arms, Shore St.

Y59 Sconser
☎Portree (0478) 2364
Sconser, Isle of Skye, Inverness.
Between Broadford and Portree (on main road).
Seaside course.
9 holes, 4798 yards, S.S.S.63
Course designed by Dr F. Deighton.
Club founded in 1964.
Visitors: welcome at all times.
Green fees: £4 per round, £6 per day weekdays; £12 per week.
Hotels: Sconser Lodge.

Y60 Shetland
☎Gott (059 584) 369
Dale, Shetland.
N road from Lerwick, 3 miles.
Undulating moorland course.
18 holes, 5900 yards, S.S.S.71
Course designed by Fraser Middleton.
Visitors: welcome.
Green fees: on application.
Society meetings: by arrangement.
Hotels: Lerwick; Grand; Queens.

Y61 Spey Bay
☎Fochabers (0343) 820424
Spey Bay, Fochabers, Moray.
Turn off A96 near Fochabers Bridge, follow B9104 Spey Bay road as far as coast.
Links course.
18 holes, 6059 yards, S.S.S.68
Visitors: welcome.
Green fees: on application.
Catering: meals served.
Hotels: Spey Bay.

Y62 Stonehaven
☎Stonehaven (0569) 62124
Cowie, Stonehaven AB3 2RH.
On A92 1 mile N of town, new roundabout at Commodore Hotel, take second exit on left, pass Leisure Centre on right.
Seaside/parkland course.
18 holes, 5103 yards, S.S.S.65
Course designed by A. Simpson.
Club founded in 1888.
Visitors: welcome except Sat and Sun forenoons.
Green fees: £6 weekdays; £7.50 weekends.
Society meetings: usually each month (last Sat).
Catering: full.
Hotels: Commodore; St Leonards; Heugh; Royal.

Y63 Stornoway
☎Stornoway (0851) 2240
Castle Grounds, Stornoway, Isle of Lewis PA87 0XP.
5 minutes walk from town centre, just within main entrance to castle grounds.
Parkland/moorland course.
18 holes, 5119 yards, S.S.S.66
Course designed by J.R. Stutt.
Club founded in 1890.
Visitors: welcome from Mon-Sat.
Green fees: £6 per day, £4 per round; £20 per week; £30 per fortnight.
Society meetings: catered for by

arrangement.
Catering: catering facilities available by arrangement.
Hotels: Caberfeigh; County; Seaforth.

Y64 Strathlene
☎Buckie (0542) 31798
Portessie, Buckie, Banffshire AB5 2DJ.
On A942, 2 miles E of Buckie Harbour, from main Banff to Inverness Rd, take turning to Strathlene 3 miles E of Buckie Rd sign.
Undulating moorland/seaside course.
18 holes, 6180 yards, S.S.S.69
Course designed by Alex Smith.
Club founded in 1877.
Visitors: welcome.
Green fees: £4 weekdays; £6 weekends.
Society meetings: welcome.
Catering: by arrangement.
Hotels: Commercial.

Y65 Strathpeffer Spa
☎Strathpeffer (0997) 21219
Strathpeffer, Ross-shire IV14 9AS.
5 miles W of Dingwall, 0.25 mile N of village square (signposted).
Undulating upland course.
18 holes, 4792 yards, S.S.S.65
Club founded in 1888.
Visitors: welcome without reservation.
Green fees: £5 per day; £20 per week.
Society meetings: by arrangement.
Catering: licensed, meals, snacks. No catering Mon.
Hotels: Highland; Holly Lodge; Coul House, Contin, Strathpeffer..

Y66 Stromness
☎Stromness (0856) 850772
Ness, Stromness, Orkney K16 3DU.
Adjacent to Point of Ness, S extremity of Stromness.
Seaside course.
18 holes, 4600 yards, S.S.S.64
Club founded in 1922.
Visitors: any day.
Green fees: £4 per day.
Society meetings: Stromness open 36hrs, 1st Sat Aug.
Catering: no, bar facilities.
Hotels: Stromness; Braes.

Y67 Tain
☎Tain (0862) 2314
Tain, Ross-shire IV19 1PA.
A9 N of Inverness, 0.5 mile from

town centre.
Seaside/parkland course.
18 holes, 6222 yards, S.S.S.70/68
Course designed by Tom Morris.
Club founded in 1890.
Visitors: welcome.
Green fees: on application.
Society meetings: welcome.
Catering: by arrangement with Club
Steward.
Hotels: Royal, Tain; Morangie, Tain;
Mansfield, Tain.

Y68 **Tarbat**
☎Portmahomack (086 287) 519
Portmahomack, Ross-shire
IV20 1YQ.
B9165 off A9, 7 miles E of Tain.
Seaside links course.
9 holes, 2329 yards, S.S.S.63
Course designed by J. Sutherland.
Club founded in 1910.
Visitors: welcome except Sun.
Green fees: £2 daily.
Society meetings: welcome,
contact Sec.
Catering: none available.
Hotels: Castle; Caledonian,
Portmahomack.

Y69 **Tarland**
☎Tarland (033 981) 413
Tarland, Aboyne, Aberdeenshire
AB3 4YL.
On A93, 31 miles W of Aberdeen
and 11 miles NE of Ballater.
Undulating parkland course.
9 holes, 2660 yards, S.S.S.68
Course designed by Tom Morris.
Club founded in 1908.
Visitors: no restrictions, advise
telephoning first due to club
competitions.
Green fees: £4 weekdays; £6
weekends.
Society meetings: 14 days advance
notice for Sat. No Society meetings
on Sun.
Catering: yet to be arranged.
Hotels: Aberdeen Arms; Commer-
cial.

Y70 **Thurso**
☎Thurso (0847) 63807
Newlands of Geise, Thurso,
Caithness.
2 miles SW from centre of Thurso on
B870.
Parkland course.
18 holes, 5841 yards, S.S.S.69

Course designed by W. Stuart.
Club founded in 1964.
Visitors: no restrictions.
Green fees: £4 per day.
Society meetings: none.
Catering: Tues, Thurs evenings, Sat
and Sun lunches during summer
season.
Hotels: Portland; Princes St, Thurso;
St Clair, St Clair St, Thurso; Weigh
Inn, Thurso.

Y71 **Torphins**
☎Torpins (033 982) 493
Golf Rd, Torphins.
Mail c/o: 26 Beltie Rd, Torphins,
Banchory AB3 4JT.
6 miles W from Banchory on A980.
Undulating heathland course.
9 holes, 2330 yards, S.S.S.63
Club founded in 1896.
Visitors: unrestricted except during
competitions.
Green fees: £3 per day weekday; £5
weekend.
Catering: snacks only at present.
Hotels: Learney Arms, Torphins.

Y72 **Torvean**
☎Inverness (0463) 237543 Starter,
225651 Club
Glenurquhart Rd, Inverness.
On A82 1 mile W of city centre, on W
side of Caledonian Canal.
Parkland municipal course.
18 holes, 4308 yards, S.S.S.62
Club founded in 1962.
Visitors: welcome.
Green fees: on application.
Society meetings: welcome by
arrangement with Inverness District
Council.
Catering: very limited facilities.
Hotels: Loch Ness House.

Y73 **Turriff**
☎Turriff (0888) 62745
Rosehall, Turriff, Aberdeenshire
AB5 7H.
On Aberdeen side of town, about 1
mile up Huntly Rd on B9024.
Meadowland/parkland course.
18 holes, 6105 yards, S.S.S.69
Club founded in 1899.
Visitors: welcome, golf societies by
arrangement with Sec.
Green fees: £5 per round, £6 per
day weekdays; £6 per round, £8 per
day weekends.
Society meetings: by arrangement

with Sec.
Catering: by arrangement.
Hotels: Union, Turriff; Banff Spring,
Banff.

Y74 **Western Isle**
☎Tobermory (0688) 2020
c/o Sec, Stronsaule, Tobermory, Isle
of Mull PA75 6PR.
A848 to Tobermory, course near
Western Isle Hotel.
9 holes, 4921 yards, S.S.S.64
Club founded in 1898.
Visitors: welcome.
Green fees: on application.
Society meetings: welcome.
Catering: none available.
Hotels: Western Isle, Tobermory.

Y75 **Westhill**
☎Aberdeen (0224) 740159
Westhill Heights, Westhill, Skene,
Aberdeenshire AB3 6TY.
6 miles from Aberdeen on A944
Aberdeen-Alford road, course to N of
town overlooking it.
Undulating parkland/moorland
course.
Course designed by Charles Lawrie.
Club founded in 1977.
Visitors: weekdays except 4.30-7pm
Sun, Sat after 3.30pm.
Green fees: £5 per round, £7 per
day weekdays; £6 per round, £9 per
day weekends and Bank Holidays.
Society meetings: weekdays and
Sun.
Catering: by arrangement.
Hotels: Westhill Inn.

Y76 **Wick**
☎Wick (0955) 2726
Reiss, Wick, Caithness KW1 4RW.
2.5 miles N of Wick on A9, turn right
at signpost, 0.75 mile to clubhouse.
Seaside links course.
18 holes, 5976 yards, S.S.S.69
Course designed by McCulloch.
Club founded in 1870.
Visitors: welcome, subject to club
and open competitions.
Green fees: £4 per day; £12 per
week; £24 per fortnight.
Society meetings: by arrangement.
Catering: none.
Hotels: Queens; Nethercliffe;
Station; Mackays; Rosebank;
Ladbroke Mercury; all in Wick.

Z Northern Ireland

Z1 Ardglass
☎Ardglass (0396) 841219 or
841755
Castle Place, Ardglass.
On B176 7 miles from Downpatrick.
Seaside course.
18 holes, 5215 metres, S.S.S.68
Club founded in 1896.
Visitors: welcome.
Green fees: £5 weekdays; £8
weekends.
Society meetings: welcome.
Catering: meals served except Mon.
Hotels: Abbey Lodge, Downpatrick;
Arms, Ardglass.

Z2 Ballycastle
☎Ballycastle (026 57) 62536
Cushendall Rd, Ballycastle, Co
Antrim BT54 6QP.
About 50 miles along coast road,
W of Larne Harbour.
Undulating seaside course.
18 holes, 5882 yards, S.S.S.69
Club founded in 1890.
Visitors: welcome weekdays.
Green fees: £6, (£5 with member)
weekdays; £8, (£6 with member)
weekends.
Society meetings: catered for
throughout the year except Jul-Aug
(bookable).
Catering: light snacks available.
Hotels: Antrim Arms; The Diamond,
Ballycastle.

Z3 Ballyclare
☎Ballyclare (096 03) 22696
Springfield Rd, Ballyclare, Co Antrim
14 miles N of Belfast.
Parkland course.
18 holes, 6708 yards, S.S.S.71
Course designed by T.J. McAuley.
Club founded in 1923.
Visitors: welcome.
Green fees: £5 per day weekdays;
£8 weekends.
Society meetings: by prior
arrangement.
Catering: meals served daily.
Hotels: Chimney Corner, Newtonab-
bey.

Z4 Ballymena
☎Broughshane (0266) 861207
128 Raceview Rd, Ballymena,
Co Antrim BT42 4HY.
2.5 miles E of town on A42 to Brough

Shane and Carnlough.
Parkland course.
18 holes, 5168 yards, S.S.S.67
Club founded in 1902.
Visitors: welcome weekdays and
Sunday. Not Saturday.
Green fees: £6.50 weekdays; £9
weekends and Bank Holidays.
Society meetings: recognised
golfing societies by arrangement with
Hon Sec.
Catering: available except Mon.
Hotels: Adair Arms; Tullyglass
House; Leighinmohr; The Country
House.

Z5 Balmoral
☎Belfast (0232) 381514
518 Lisburn Rd, Belfast BT9 6GX.
Clubhouse is immediately beside the
King's Hall on Belfast's Lisburn Rd,
and Balmoral Halt railway station is
just on other side of road.
Parkland course.
18 holes, 5679 metres, S.S.S.70
Club founded in 1914.
Visitors: welcome except Sat.
Green fees: £6 per round; £9 per
day.
Society meetings: as per
arrangement.
Catering: yes.
Hotels: Conway.

Z6 Banbridge
☎Banbridge (082 06) 25211 and
22342
Huntly Rd, Banbridge, Co Down
BT32 3UR.
About 0.5 mile from town along
Huntly Rd, River Bann on right all the
way.
Parkland course.
12 holes, 5376 metres, S.S.S.68
Club founded in 1913.
Visitors: welcome most days,
Ladies preference Tues, Mens
competitions Sat.
Green fees: £5 weekdays; £7
weekends.
Society meetings: welcome
summer months, green fees for
societies.
Catering: can be arranged on
request.
Hotels: Bannville House, Lurgan Rd;
Belmont, Rathfriland Rd; Downshire,
Newry Street.

Z7 Bangor
☎Bangor (0247) 270922
Broadway, Bangor, Co Down
BT20 4RH.
0.75 mile from town centre.
Undulating parkland course.
18 holes, 6450 yards, S.S.S.71
Course designed by James Braid.
Club founded in 1903.
Visitors: welcome weekdays.
Green fees: £7.50 per day (£4 with
member) weekdays; £10 per day (£5
with member) weekends and Bank
Holidays.
Society meetings: Mon, Wed, Fri
(£6 per head).
Catering: available.
Hotels: Royal; Sands.

Z8 Belvoir Park
☎Belfast (0232) 491693 Office,
641159 Catering, 692817 Bar,
692817 Pro.
73 Church Rd, Newtonbreda, Belfast
BT8 4AN.
About 4 miles from centre of Belfast,
off Ormean Rd which is main road to
Saintfield and Newcastle.
Parkland course.
18 holes, 6276 yards, S.S.S.70
Course designed by H.S. Colt.
Club founded in 1927.
Visitors: welcome.
Green fees: £8 weekdays except
Wed; £10 weekends, Wed and Bank
Holidays.
Society meetings: council permit 5
outings per month April/Sept, 24 or
more £6 green fee.
Catering: excellent facilities by
'Skillets'
Hotels: Drumkeen; Stormont.

Z9 Bushfoot
☎Bushmills (026 57) 31317
50 Bushfoot Rd, Portballintrae,
Bushmills, Co Antrim BT57 8RR.
4 miles E of Portrush on coast.
Seaside course.
9 holes, 5572 yards, S.S.S.67
Club founded in 1890.
Visitors: welcome on weekdays and
at weekends if no official club
competitions.
Green fees: £4 per day, (£3 with
member) weekdays; £5 per day, (£4
with member) weekends and Bank
Holidays; Under 18 - £2, (£1.50 with

member) weekdays; £3, (£2 with member) weekends and Bank Holidays.
Society meetings: welcome by arrangement.
Catering: snacks served.
Hotels: Bayview; Beach; Causeway.

z10 Cairndhu

☎Ballygally (0574) 83324
192 Coast Rd, Ballygally, Larne BT40 2QC.
On Antrim coast road, 3.5 miles from Larne.
Parkland course.
18 holes, 6112 yards, S.S.S.69
Course designed by John S.F. Morrison.
Club founded in 1929.
Visitors: welcome except Sat.
Green fees: Men - £5 weekdays, £7.50 weekends; Ladies - £2.50 weekdays, £3.75 weekends.
Society meetings: welcome.
Catering: meals and snacks available on weekdays (8pm-10pm), Sat (11.30am-6pm) and Sun (2pm-9pm); other meals available by arrangement.
Hotels: Ballygally Castle, Coast Rd, Ballygally; Halfway House, Coast Rd, Ballygally.

z11 Carnalea

☎Bangor (0247) 270368
Station Rd, Bangor, Co Down BT19 1EZ.
Adjacent to Carnalea railway station 1.5 miles from Bangor.
Seaside meadowland course.
18 holes, 5548 yards, S.S.S.67
Club founded in 1927.
Visitors: welcome 7 days.
Green fees: £5, (£3.60 with member) weekdays; £8, (£5 with member) weekends and Bank Holidays.
Society meetings: catered for weekdays only.
Catering: full catering except Mon.
Hotels: Royal; Crawfordsburn Inn; Tedworth.

z12 Carrickfergus

☎Carrickfergus (096 03) 63713
Sec, 62203 Clubhouse
North Rd, Carrickfergus BT38 8LP.
Off A2, 9 miles NE of Belfast.
Parkland/meadowland course.
18 holes, 5752 yards, S.S.S.68
Club founded in 1926.
Visitors: welcome except Sat.
Green fees: £5, (£3.50 with member) weekdays; £7, (£4 with

member) weekends and Bank Holidays.
Society meetings: Mon or Fri only.
Catering: lunch and evening meal.
Hotels: Coast Road, Carrickfergus; Dobbins Inn, Carrickfergus.

z13 Castlerock

☎Castlerock (0265) 848215
Members, 848314 Office
65 Circular Rd, Castlerock, Co Londonderry BT51 4TJ.
On A2, 6 miles W of Coleraine.
Seaside course.
9 holes, 2457 metres, S.S.S.34
18 holes, 6121 metres, S.S.S.72
Course designed by Ben Sayers.
Club founded in 1900.
Visitors: welcome.
Green fees: £8, (£5 with member) weekdays; £11, (£7 with member) weekends and Bank Holidays.
Society meetings: weekdays; weekends 10am-11am.
Catering: franchise at club.
Hotels: Golf, Castlerock.

z14 City of Derry

☎Londonderry (0504) 46369
49 Victoria Rd, Londonderry BT47 2PU.
On main Londonderry to Strabane Rd, 3 miles from Craigavon Bridge.
Parkland course.
Dunhugh-9 holes, 4708 yards, S.S.S.63
Prehen-18 holes, 6362 yards, S.S.S.71
Club founded in 1912.
Visitors: welcome on weekdays before 4.30pm unless with member and at weekends by arrangement with Pro. Dunhugh course open at all times.
Green fees: on application.
Society meetings: catered for on weekdays and possibly at weekends.
Catering: full catering facilities available.
Hotels: Everglades, Prehen Rd, Londonderry; Broomhill House, Limavady Rd, Londonderry; White Horse Inn, Campsie Rd, Londonderry; Glen House, Eglinton, Londonderry.

z15 Clandeboye

☎Bangor (0247) 465767
Tower Rd, Conlig, Newtownards BT23 3TN.
On main Bangor to Newtonards Rd, 2 miles from Bangor into Conlig village.
Ava - moorland/meadowland course.

Dufferin - parkland/woodland course.
Ava-18 holes, 5634 yards, S.S.S.67
Dufferin-18 holes, 6000-7000 yards, S.S.S.70-73
Ava course designed by W.R. Robinson; Dufferin course designed by Limburger, McAuley, Alliss and Thomas.
Club founded in 1933.
Visitors: welcome.
Green fees: on application.
Society meetings: by arrangement.
Catering: meals served.
Hotels: Royal, Bangor; Culloden, Craigavad; Crawfordsburn Inn, Crawfordsburn; Strangford Arms, Newtownards.

z16 Cliftonville

☎Belfast (0232) 744158
44 Westland Rd, Belfast BT14 6NH.
From centre of Belfast take Antrim road, about 2 miles from centre.
Meadowland course.
9 holes, 3120 yards, S.S.S.70
Club founded in 1922.
Visitors: welcome except Sat and Tues afternoons.
Green fees: £5.20, (£2.60 with member) weekdays; £7, (£3.50 with member) Sunday.
Society meetings: by arrangement with Council through Sec.
Catering: meals served by arrangement.
Hotels: Lansdowne Court, Antrim Rd, Belfast.

z17 County Armagh

☎Armagh (0681) 522501
Demesne, Newry Rd, Armagh, Co Armagh.
Off Newry Rd, 0.25 mile from city centre.
Parkland course.
18 holes, 6147 yards, S.S.S.69
Club founded in 1893.
Visitors: welcome except between 12 noon and 2pm Sat and 12 noon and 3pm Sun.
Green fees: £5 weekdays; £7.50 weekends.
Society meetings: catered for except on Sat.
Catering: full facilities available.
Hotels: Charlemont Arms, Armagh; Drumsill House, Armagh.

z18 Cushendall

☎Cushendall (0266) 71318
Shore Rd, Cushendall, Ballymena, Co Antrim BT44 0QQ.
Turn right at Curfew Tower in village, proceed 0.25 mile to Strand.

Seaside/parkland course.
9 holes, 2193 metres, S.S.S.63
Course designed by Daniel Delargy.
Club founded in 1938.
Visitors: welcome.
Green fees: £4 per day weekdays;
£6 per day weekends and Bank
Holidays.
Society meetings: weekdays.
Catering: summer, weekends
winter.
Hotels: Thornlea, Coast Rd,
Cushendall.

Z19 Donaghadee
☎Donaghadee (0247) 883624 or
888697
84 Warren Rd, Donaghadee,
Co Down BT21 0PQ.
On A2 18 miles E of Belfast.
Seaside/meadowland course.
18 holes, 5576 metres, S.S.S.69
Club founded in 1899.
Visitors: welcome except Sat when
must be with member.
Green fees: £6.50 per day
weekdays; £7.50 weekends and
Bank Holidays.
Society meetings: Mon, Wed,
Thurs.
Catering: every day except Mon.
Hotels: Copelands, Warren Rd,
Donaghadee; Groomsport House,
Groomsport, Co Down.

Z20 Downpatrick
☎Downpatrick (0396) 2773
Saul Rd, Downpatrick, Co Down
BT30 6PA.
A24 and A7 23 miles SE of Belfast.
Parkland course.
18 holes, 5823 yards, S.S.S.68
Visitors: welcome.
Green fees: on application.
Society meetings: by arrangement.
Catering: full facilities, limited
evenings.
Hotels: Denvir's; Abbey Lodge.

Z21 Dungannon
☎Dungannon (08687) 22098
Dungannon, Co Tyrone.
0.5 mile out of town on Dunaghmore
Rd.
Parkland course.
18 holes, 5818 yards, S.S.S.68
Visitors: welcome anytime.
Green fees: £3 weekdays; £5
weekends.
Society meetings: welcome by
arrangement.
Catering: by arrangement.
Hotels: Dunowen; Inn on the Park.

Z22 Dunmurry
☎Belfast (0232) 610834
91 Dunmurry Lane, Dunmurry,
Belfast BT17 9JS.
Situated between Dunmurry village
and Upper Malone Rd, Belfast.
Parkland course.
18 holes, 5832 yards, S.S.S.68
Course designed by T.J. McAuley.
Club founded in 1905.
Visitors: not before 5pm Sat, after
5pm Tues and Thurs.
Green fees: £6 weekdays; £7
weekends and Bank Holidays.
Society meetings: not Fri or Sat,
11am-12 noon Sun.
Catering: every day except Mon.
Hotels: Conway; Beechlawn.

Z23 Enniskillen
☎Enniskillen (0365) 25250
Castle Coole, Enniskillen,
Co Fermanagh.
1 mile from Enniskillen.
Parkland course.
9 holes, 5476 metres, S.S.S.69
New 9 holes due to open end of
1988.
Course designed, first 9 holes by
Dr Dixon & George Mawhinney, and
second 9 holes by T.J. McAuley.
Club founded in 1896.
Visitors: unrestricted.
Green fees: £5 per day.
Society meetings: golfing societies
welcome if previous arrangements
made with Sec.
Catering: bar snacks daily, full
catering by prior arrangement.
Hotels: Killyhevlin; Fort Lodge;
Railway, all within 1 mile of club.

Z24 Fintona
☎Fintona (0662) 841480
Ecclesville Demesne, Fintona,
Co Tyrone.
9 miles SW of Omagh.
Parkland course.
9 holes, 6251 yards, S.S.S.70
Club founded in 1896.
Visitors: welcome.
Green fees: on application.
Society meetings: catered for on
weekdays.
Catering: available by prior
arrangement.
Hotels: Royal Arms, Omagh;
Silverbirgh,Omagh; Valley,
Fivemiletown.

Z25 Fortwilliam
☎Belfast (0232) 370770
Downview Ave, Belfast B15 4EZ.

On A2 3 miles N of Belfast.
Meadowland course.
18 holes, 5796 yards, S.S.S.67
Course designed by Mr Buchart.
Club founded in 1903.
Visitors: welcome except Sat.
Green fees: £8, (£4 with member)
weekdays; £10, (£5 with member)
weekends.
Society meetings: welcome by
arrangement with Sec.
Catering: full catering service
available.
Hotels: Lansdowne Court, Antrim
Rd, Belfast.

Z26 Greenisland
☎Whiteabbey (0232) 862236
156 Upper Rd, Greenisland,
Carrickfergus BT38 8RW.
About 9 miles N of Belfast.
Meadowland course.
9 holes, 5887 yards, S.S.S.68
Course re-designed by H. Middleton.
Club founded in 1894.
Visitors: welcome except Sat.
Green fees: £4.50 weekdays; £6
Sunday.
Society meetings: welcome by prior
arrangement.
Catering: full facilities.
Hotels: Glenavna, Whiteabbey;
Newtown Abbey.

Z27 Helen's Bay
☎Bangor (0247) 852601
Golf Rd, Helen's Bay, Bangor, Co
Down BT19 1TL.
Off A2, 9 miles E of Belfast.
9 holes, 5154 metres, S.S.S.67
Club founded in 1896.
Visitors: welcome, but with member
only on Sat.
Green fees: £6, (£4 with member)
weekdays; £9, (£5 with member)
weekends.
Society meetings: catered for on
Tues, Wed and Fri.
Catering: full catering facilities.

Z28 Holywood
☎Holywood (023 17) 5503
Nuns Walk, Demesne Rd, Holywood,
Co Down BT18 9DX.
On A2 6 miles E of Belfast.
Undulating course.
18 holes, 5885 yards, S.S.S.69
Club founded in 1904.
Visitors: welcome except on
competition days.
Green fees: £6.50 weekdays; £8.25
weekends.
Society meetings: catered for on

Mon, Tues and Wed.
Catering: catering facilities except
Mon.
Hotels: Culloden; Cultra Holywood.

Z29 **Kilkeel**
☎Kilkeel (0679 37) 62296
Mourne Park, Ballyardle, Newry,
Co Down BT34 4LB.
3 miles from Kilkeel on main road to
Newry.
Parkland course.
9 holes, 5623 metres, S.S.S.69
Course designed by Lord Justice
Babbington.
Club founded in 1949.
Visitors: welcome at all times.
Green fees: £5 per round weekdays;
£6 weekends and Bank Holidays.
Society meetings: special
concessions to registered golf
societies.
Catering: full catering facilities
available.
Hotels: Kilmorey Arms, Kilkeel;
Cranfield House, Cranfield.

Z30 **Killymoon**
☎Cookstown (064 87) 62254

200 Killymoon Rd, Cookstown,
Co Tyrone BT80 8TW.
Parkland course.
18 holes, 5498 metres, S.S.S.69
Course designed by Hugh Adair.
Club founded in 1889.
Visitors: all week except Sat, club
competition day.
Green fees: £5, (£3 with member)
weekdays; £6, (£4 with member)
Sun.
Society meetings: Mon, Tues, Wed,
Fri, Sun.
Green fees: Mon-Fri £4; Public
Holidays and Sun £6 (if over 20 in
society).
Catering: for catering telephone.
Hotels: Glenavon, Drum Rd,
Cookstown.

Z31 **Kirkistown Castle**
☎Portavogie (024 77) 71233 or
71353
142 Main Rd, Cloughey, Newtownards, Co Down BT22 1HZ.
A20 from Belfast to Kircubbin, follow
signs to Newtownards and
Portaferry, then B173 to Cloughey.
Links course.

18 holes, 6157 yards, S.S.S.70
Course designed by B. Polley.
Club founded in October 1902.
Visitors: welcome.
Green fees: on application.
Society meetings: welcome on
weekdays, except Bank Holidays.
Catering: full facilities available.
Hotels: The Roadhouse, 204 Main
Rd, Cloughey.

Z32 **The Knock**
☎Dundonald (023 18) 3251 Sec.
Summerfield, Upper Newtownards
Rd, Dundonald, Belfast BT16 0QX.
On A2 main Newtownards road to
East Belfast (across Queens or
Albert Bridges from Belfast city
centre), 4 miles on left hand side 0.5
mile beyond Stormont Houses of
Parliament.
Parkland course.
18 holes, 5845 metres, S.S.S.71
Course designed by Colt, McKenzie
& Allison Ltd.
Club founded in 1895.
Visitors: weekdays except Sat and
Wed pm.
Green fees: £8, (£4 with member);

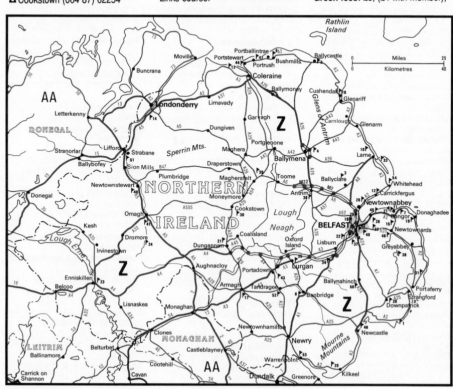

£12 (£4 with member) Sun and Bank Holidays.
Society meetings: Mon and Thurs.
Catering: full facilities throughout week, except Sun pm.
Hotels: Stormont, within 1 mile.

z33 Larne
☎Islandmagee (096 03) 82228
54 Ferris Bay Rd, Islandmagee, Larne BT40 3RT.
From Belfast, N to Carrickfergus and 6 miles from Whitehead, from Larne S along coast road to Islandmagee.
Seaside course.
9 holes, 6082 yards, S.S.S.69
Course designed by Babington.
Club founded in 1894.
Visitors: weekdays - not Sat.
Green fees: £4 weekdays; £6 weekends.
Society meetings: open - not Sat.
Catering: available.
Hotels: Magheramorne House.

z34 Lisburn
☎Lisburn (0846) 677216
68 Eglantine Rd, Lisburn, Co Antrim BT27 5RQ.
3 miles S of Lisburn, 200 yards from BBC radio transmitter mast.
Meadowland/parkland course.
18 holes, 5708 metres, S.S.S.72
Course designed by Hawtree & Sons.
Club founded in 1905.
Visitors: at specified times.
Green fees: £9 weekdays; £11 weekends.
Society meetings: Mon and Thurs.
Catering: 7 days.
Hotels: White Gables, Hillsborough.

z35 Lurgan
☎Lurgan (0762) 322087
The Demesne, Lurgan, Co Armagh BT67 9BN.
Centre of Lurgan to Windsor Ave and proceed past castle gates.
Parkland course.
18 holes, 5836 metres, S.S.S.70
Course designed by Pennink.
Club founded in 1894.
Visitors: welcome.
Green fees: on application.
Society meetings: welcome.
Catering: available except Mon.
Hotels: Silverwood.

z36 Mahee Island
☎Killinchy (0727) 541234
Comber, Newtownards, Co Down.
Killinchy Rd, signposted 6 miles from Comber.

9 holes, 5588 yards, S.S.S.67
Club founded in 1929.
Visitors: welocme. Mon-Ladies competition day. No visitors before 4.30pm Sat.
Green fees: £5 weekdays; £8 weekends.
Society meetings: by arrangement with Hon Sec.
Catering: by arrangement.
Hotels: La Mon (approx 10 miles).

z37 Malone
☎Belfast (0232) 612758
240 Upper Malone Rd, Dunmurry, Belfast BT17 9LB.
5 miles from Belfast centre, take Upper Malone Rd.
Parkland course.
18 holes, 6433 yards, S.S.S.71
Course designed by Fred Hawtree.
Club founded in 1895.
Visitors: welcome except Wed after 2pm and Sat before 5pm.
Green fees: on application.
Society meetings: catered for Mon and Thurs.
Catering: full catering facilities available except Sun after 2pm.
Hotels: Conway, Dunmurry; Beechlawn, Dunmurry.

z38 Massereene
☎Antrim (084 94) 62096
51 Lough Rd, Antrim.
1 mile S of town, 3.5 miles from Aldergrove Airport.
Parkland course.
18 holes, 6614 yards, S.S.S.73
Course designed by F.W. Hawtree.
Club founded in 1895.
Visitors: welcome weekdays & weekends, Sat competition day.
Green fees: April-Sept £7.50; Oct-Mar £5 weekdays; April-Sept £9; Oct-Mar £6 weekends.
Society meetings: Tues, Thurs 9am-12am & 2pm-3.30pm; Wed 9am-11.30am.
Catering: all catering provided for from snacks to dining room meals.
Hotels: Dunadry; Deerpark.

z39 Moyola Park
☎Castledawson (0648) 68392/ 68468
Shanemullagh, Castledawson, Magherafelt, Co Londonderry BT45 8DG.
Turn right half way through Castledawson village, along Curran Rd, entrance 400 yards on right, to left of Curran Rd.
Parkland course.

18 holes, 6517 yards, S.S.S.71
Course designed by Don Patterson.
Green fees: on application.
Society meetings: welcome at all times.
Catering: weekends all day, weekdays by arrangement with Steward.
Hotels: The Arches, Market St, Magherafelt; Myola Lodge, Broagh Rd, Castledawson.

z40 Newtownstewart
☎Newtownstewart (066 26) 61466/ 61829.
38 Golf Course Rd, Newtownstewart, Co Tyrone BT78 4HU.
2 miles SW of Newtownstewart via B84 from Newtownstewart to Drumquin.
Undulating parkland course.
18 holes, 5448 metres, S.S.S.69
Course designed by Frank Pennink.
Club founded in 1914.
Visitors: welcome but advance booking advisable.
Green fees: £4 weekdays; £5 weekends.
Society meetings: catered for by prior arrangement.
Catering: meals served by arrangement.
Hotels: Hunting Lodge, Letterbin, Baronscourt, Co Tyrone; Royal Arms, High St, Omagh; Silverbirch, Gortin Rd, Omagh; Fir Trees Lodge, Melmount Rd, Strabane.

z41 Omagh
☎Omagh (0662) 3160
Dublin Rd, Omagh, Co Tyrone BT78 1HX.
On A5 in outskirts of Omagh.
Undulating parkland course.
18 holes, 5051 metres, S.S.S.67
Club founded in 1910.
Visitors: welcome except on Sat or major competition days.
Green fees: £4 per day weekdays; £5 per day weekends.
Society meetings: welcome weekdays.
Catering: catering available for societies.
Hotels: Royal Arms; Knock na Moe; Silverbirch.

z42 Ormeau
☎Belfast (0232) 641069
Ravenhill Rd, Belfast BT6 0BN.
2 miles from city centre.
Parkland course.
9 holes, 2653 yards, S.S.S.65
Club founded in 1893.

The Courses of Ireland

Golfing tours of Ireland require a special kind of stamina. By that, I don't mean that every fairway is as soft as a peat bog or that the winds down Killarney way are any stronger than those that blow at Muirfield or Machrihanish. The locals may try to convince you they are but then the Irish are a persuasive race.

They also have an idiosyncratic logic. "You've a strong crosswind against you", I was once told, and Michael Bonallack had an Irish caddie who advised him that the putt facing him was "slightly straight". What I mean by special stamina is that you have to pace your day in the certain knowledge that what precedes and follows the golf will be more exhausting. I was initiated as to what to expect during a cricket tour long ago. Well after midnight, I enquired tentatively what time the bars closed, thinking (correctly) it would be the only way of breaking up the party "About October, I think", came the reply.

It is not that the Irish don't take their golf seriously but simply, as I found at cricket, that they have no set hours of play. They ply you with Guinness, regale story after story about Carr, Bruen, Bradshaw and O'Connor and, by the time you leave, you will have sung every conceivable Irish ballad. However, in your few waking moments, you will also remember their courses. They more than live up to all the talk.

To summarise their delights in one short commentary is akin to devoting a single day to the historical wonders of Rome. Each area deserves a holiday in itself but the purpose of this exercise is to whet an appetite that may take a life time to satisfy fully.

However, the important thing is that the seeds are easy to sow and it matters not where you begin particularly as the North and South are united as one golfing country. Portrush, scene of Max Faulkner's victory in the 1951 Open championship, and Royal County Down at Newcastle are undoubtedly the pride of the North. Each claims an enchanting setting, Portrush not far from the Giant's Causeway and Newcastle watched over by the Mountains of Mourne.

As a combination of beauty and superb tests of golf, they have few equals; but it is a combination that tends to be applicable all over Ireland. A journey from Newcastle to Dublin must include County Louth at Baltray, the handiwork of Tom Simpson, a course whose praises are not sung as loudly as they should be.

Dublin is only about thirty miles by road where Portmarnock - the most widely used course for international occasions - is there to savour. Royal Dublin is a few steps nearer the centre of a city that is well served by courses. Cork has Little Island, and Carlow, in its lovely old deer park, is an ideal stopping place on the way to the West, Eire's golfing pride.

Killarney, host to the 1973 European team championship, like Gleneagles, has a beautiful inland setting but the real flavour of Irish golf centres upon Ballybunion, Lahinch, County Sligo at Rosses Point, Waterville and, more recently, Tralee. All possess true greatness in the most wonderfully natural coastal settings.

Ballybunion now has a second course designed by Robert Trent Jones; Lahinch attracts a huge entry each year for the South of Ireland championship and was host to the Home Internationals in 1987, while Rosses Point, deep in the heart of the country made famous by the poetry of W.B. Yeats, is another delight.

Visitors: welcome weekdays.
Green fees: £4, (£3 with member) weekdays; £5 weekends.
Society meetings: by arrangement.
Catering: none.
Hotels: Drumkeen, Newtownards, Belfast.

z43 Portadown

☎Portadown (0762) 355356
192 Gilford Rd, Carrickblacker, Portadown, Co Armagh BT63 5LF.
On A59 SE of Portadown, proceed for 2 miles and entrance to clubhouse is 400 yards beyond Metal Box factory on right.
Parkland course.
18 holes, 5621 metres, S.S.S.70
Club founded in 1905.
Visitors: welcome except Sat (Ladies day Tues).
Green fees: £5 weekdays; £7 weekends and Bank Holidays.
Society meetings: Sun, Mon, Fri. Other days by special arrangement.
Catering: all days by arrangement.
Hotels: Seagoe; Carngrove, Portadown.

z44 Portstewart

☎Portstewart (026 583) 2015 or 3839.
117 Strand Rd, Portstewart, Co Londonderry BT55 7PG.
4 miles W of Portrush.
Links course.
Strand-18 holes, 6784 yards, S.S.S.72
Town-18 holes, 4733 yards, S.S.S.62
Club founded in 1894.
Visitors: welcome.
Green fees: Strand - £8 (£5 with member) weekdays; £11 (£7 with member) weekends and Bank Holidays. Town - £3 weekdays; £5 weekends and Bank Holidays.
Society meetings: welcome weekdays, if over 15, green fees £7. Must book by telephone.
Catering: every day.
Hotels: Edgewater, Portstewart.

z45 Royal Belfast

☎Holywood (0232) 428165
Station Rd, Craigavad, Holywood, Co Down BT18 0BT.
Parkland course.
18 holes, 6205 yards, S.S.S.69
Course designed by H.S. Colt.
Club founded in 1881.
Visitors: except Thurs & Sat. by introduction or letter from Club Sec.

Green fees: £10 weekdays; £15 weekends and Bank Holidays.
Society meetings: by arrangement.
Catering: full catering.
Hotels: Culloden.

z46 Royal County Down

☎Newcastle (039 67) 23314
Newcastle, Co Down BT33 0AN.
From Belfast take A24 to Carryduff, A7 to Ballynahinch and A2 to Newcastle, about 30 miles.
Links course.
18 holes, 6968 yards, S.S.S.74
Course designed by Tom Morris Sr.
Club founded in 1898.
Visitors: welcome Mon, Tues and Fri.
Green fees: £12 per day weekdays; £15 weekends.
Society meetings: by arrangement only.
Catering: by arrangement only.
Hotels: Slieve Donard; Burrendale.

z47 Royal Portrush

☎Portrush (0265) 822311
Bushmills Rd, Portrush, Co Antrim BT56 8JQ.
1 mile from Portrush town off A1.
Links course.
Valley-18 holes, 6273 yards, S.S.S.71
Dunluce-18 holes, 6784 yards, S.S.S.73
Course designed by H.S. Colt.
Club founded in 1888.
Visitors: welcome weekdays and Sun, telephone booking recommended.
Green fees: Dunluce - £10 weekdays; £15 Sat; £12 Sun. Valley - £7 weekdays; £10 weekends.
Society meetings: catered for weekdays and Sun.
Catering: full catering available every day, snacks, high tea and à la carte.
Hotels: Bayview, Portballatrae, Bushmills; Macherabudy House, Coleraine Rd, Portrush.

z48 Scrabo

☎Newtownards (0247) 812355 and 815048
233 Scrabo Rd, Newtownards, Co Down BT23 4SL.
Off A20 10 miles E of Belfast.
Undulating course.
18 holes, 5699 metres, S.S.S.71
Club founded in 1907.
Visitors: welcome except Sat and Wed.

Green fees: £6 weekdays; £9 Sun and Bank Holidays.
Society meetings: except Wed and Sat.
Catering: every day except Mon.
Hotels: Strangford Arms, Newtownards.

z49 Shandon Park

☎Belfast (0232) 793730
73 Shandon Park, Belfast BT5 6NY.
3 miles from city centre via Knock dual carriageway.
Parkland course.
18 holes, 6252 yards, S.S.S.70
Club founded in 1926.
Visitors: welcome on weekdays and Sun.
Green fees: £7, (£4 with member) weekdays; £9 weekends.
Society meetings: catered for by arrangement.
Catering: meals and snacks available.
Hotels: Stormont; Drumkeen.

z50 Spa

☎Ballynahinch (0238) 562365
20 Grove Rd, Ballynahinch, Co Down BT24 8PN.
A24, exit at sign for Spa or Dromara, 1 mile from Ballynahinch.
Parkland course.
9 holes, 5770 yards, S.S.S.70
Course designed by R.R. Bell and A. Mathers.
Club founded in 1907.
Visitors: welcome weekdays.
Green fees: on application.
Society meetings: weekdays and some Sun.
Catering: meals available.
Hotels: Millbrook Lodge, Ballynahinch; White Horse.

z51 Strabane

☎Strabane (0504) 382271
Ballycolman, Strabane, Co Tyrone BT82 9PH.
1 mile from Strabane on Dublin road beside church and three schools.
Parkland course.
18 holes, 5865 yards, S.S.S.69
Course designed by Eddie Hackett.
Club founded in 1909.
Visitors: welcome.
Green fees: £3 per round, £4 per day weekdays; £5 per round, £6 per day weekends.
Society meetings: by arrangement with Sec.
Catering: by arrangement.

Hotels: Fir Trees Lodge.

z52 Tandragee
☎Tandragee (0762) 841272
Markethill Rd, Tandragee, Craigavon
BT62 2ER.
5 miles from Portadown on Newry
Rd.
Parkland course.
18 holes, 6084 yards, S.S.S.69
Course designed by F. Hawtree.
Club founded in 1922.
Visitors: weekends must be
accompanied by a member. Mon-Fri
after 4pm accompanied by member.
Green fees: £7 weekdays; £10
weekends and Bank Holidays.
Society meetings: application to
Sec.
Catering: 12.30am until 9pm.
Hotels: Seagoe, Portadown;

Gosford House, Markethill.

z53 Warrenpoint
☎Warrenpoint (069 37) 72371
Lower Dromore Rd, Warrenpoint, Co
Down BT34 3LN.
Situated on A4 Newry road, 0.5 mile
W of Warrenpoint.
Parkland course.
18 holes, 5626 metres, S.S.S.70
Club founded in 1893.
Visitors: welcome except Sat.
Green fees: on application.
Society meetings: catered for
except on Sat.
Catering: full catering facilities.
Hotels: Osborne.

z54 Whitehead
☎Whitehead (096 03) 53631 Sec,
53792 Clubhouse

McCrae's Brae, Whitehead,
Co Antrim BT38 9NZ.
Take turning into Whitehead off main
Carrickfergus to Larne road then
Islandmagee road, signpost at
bottom of McCrae's Brae to golf club.
Undulating parkland course.
18 holes, 6426 yards, S.S.S.71
Club founded in 1904.
Visitors: any day except Sat.
Green fees: £5, £4 for parties 20
plus weekdays; £6.50, £5.50 for
parties 20 plus Sun, Bank Holidays.
Society meetings: before 4.30pm
Mon to Thurs, before 3.30pm Fri;
10.30am to 12 noon Sun. Tee off
not Sat.
Catering: can be arranged with
Steward.
Hotels: Magheramorne House,
Magheramorne, Coast Road,
Carrickfergus.

AA North Eire

When dialling outside Eire, dial 0001-353, delete 'O' and proceed e.g. County Sligo (071) 77186 Dial 0001-353-71-77186 (Dublin numbers have already been prefixed).

AA1 Achill Island
☎(098) 45197 Sec.
Keel, Achill, Co Mayo.
Via Castlebar or Westport.
Seaside course.
9 holes, 2705 yards, S.S.S.67
Course designed by P. Skerrit.
Club founded in 1951.
Visitors: welcome.
Green fees: £2 per day, £10 per week.
Society meetings: monthly (approx).
Catering: none at club.
Hotels: Achill Sound; Wavecrest; Atlantic; McDowell's

AA2 Ardee
☎Ardee (041) 53227
Town Parks, Ardee, Co Louth.
0.25 mile N of town.
Parkland course.
18 holes, 6100 yards, S.S.S.69
Club founded in 1911.
Visitors: welcome at all times.
Green fees: £6 weekdays; £7 weekends and Bank Holidays; (half price with member).
Society meetings: Sat mornings.
Catering: available, must be ordered before play.
Hotels: Gables B & B; Nuremore.

AA3 Athenry
☎(091) 94466
Palmerstown, Oranmore,
Co Galway.
5 miles from Athenry on main road to Galway.
Parkland course.
9 holes, 5448 yards, S.S.S.67
Club founded in 1957.
Visitors: welcome Mon-Sat, Sun with member.
Green fees: £4 weekdays; £5 weekends.
Society meetings: welcome if booked in advance.
Catering: by arrangement.
Hotels: in Galway and Athenry.

AA4 Athlone
☎Athlone (0902) 2073

Hodson Bay, Athlone.
3 miles from Athlone on Roscommon road on shores of Lough Ree.
Undulating parkland course.
18 holes, 6000 yards, S.S.S.70
Course designed by Fred Hawtree.
Club founded in 1892.
Visitors: welcome weekdays and by arrangement on Sat.
Green fees: on application.
Society meetings: catered for on weekdays.
Catering: full catering facilities except Mon.
Hotels: Hodson Bay; Prince of Wales; Royal Hoey; Shamrock Lodge.

AA5 Balbriggan
☎Dublin (0001) 412173/412229
Sec/Manager.
Blackhall, Balbriggan, Co Dublin.
0.5 mile S of town on main Belfast-Dublin road, 17 miles from Dublin.
Meadowland course.
18 holes, 5717 metres, S.S.S.70
Course designed by B. Browne.
Club founded in 1945.
Visitors: welcome weekdays.
Green fees: £7 weekdays; £8 weekends and Bank Holidays.
Society meetings: weekdays.
Catering: bar snacks.
Hotels: Holmpatrick House, Skerries, Co Dublin; El Molino, Julianstown, Co Meath.

AA6 Ballina
☎(096) 21050
Mossgrove, Shanaghy, Ballina, Co Mayo.
On outskirts of town on road to Bonniconlon.
Undulating course.
9 holes, 5702 yards, S.S.S.66
Club founded in 1924.
Visitors: welcome.
Green fees: £5 daily.
Society meetings: by arrangement with Sec.
Catering: available.
Hotels: Downhill; Bartra House.

AA7 Ballinamore
☎Ballinamore (078) 44346
Creevy, Ballinamore, Co Leitrim.
1 mile from town centre, sign at bridge.
Moorland course.

9 holes, 5680 yards, S.S.S.67
Club founded in 1923.
Visitors: welcome.
Green fees: on application.
Society meetings: welcome.
Catering: soup and sandwiches available.
Hotels: Slieve-an-Iaraim; Commercial; McAllisters.

AA8 Ballinasloe
☎Ballinasloe (0905) 42126
Ballinasloe, Co Galway.
2 miles from Ballinasloe on Ballinasloe-Portumna road.
Parkland/meadowland course.
18 holes, 5850 yards, S.S.S.65
Course designed by Eddie Hackett.
Club founded in 1905.
Visitors: welcome.
Green fees: on application.
Society meetings: welcome.
Catering: snacks and bar facilities available.
Hotels: Haydens; East County.

AA9 Ballybofey & Stranorlar
☎Ballybofey (074) 31093
Ballybofey, Co Donegal.
14 miles from Strabane, club signposted on Strabane road.
Parkland course.
18 holes, 5922 yards, S.S.S.69
Course designed by P.C. Carr.
Club founded in 1958.
Visitors: welcome all times except major competitions.
Green fees: £6.
Society meetings: welcome all times except major competitions.
Catering: snacks, meals by prior arrangement.
Hotels: Kee's, Stranorlar; Jackson's Ballybofey.

AA10 Ballyhawnis
☎Ballyhawnis (0907) 30014
Coolnaha, Ballyhawnis, Co Mayo.
1 mile from Ballyhawnis on Sligo road.
Undulating course.
10 holes, 2866 yards, S.S.S.69
Club founded in 1929.
Visitors: welcome except on Sun.
Green fees: £4 per day (£3 with member).
Society meetings: catered for by Ladies Committee.

Hotels: Central, Ballyhawnis; Westway, Kiltimagh.

AA11 **Ballyliffin**
☎Clonmany 13
Ballyliffin, Clonmany, Co Donegal.
8 miles from Buncrana, 6 miles from Cardonagh.
Seaside links course.
18 holes, 6611 yards, S.S.S.71
18 holes, 6229 yards, S.S.S.69
Club founded in 1947.
Visitors: welcome.
Green fees: on application.
Society meetings: welcome.
Hotels: Strand; Ballyliffin.

AA12 **Belmullet**
☎Belmullet (097) 81266
Belmullet, Co Mayo.
Turn right at Binghaustown Church.
Seaside links course.
9 holes, 2857 yards, S.S.S.67
Club founded in 1923.
Visitors: welcome.
Green fees: £2 per day.
Catering: none.
Hotels: Western Strands Hotel.

AA13 **Belturbet**
☎Belturbet (049) 22287
Erne Hill, Belturbet, Co Cavan.
0.5 mile on Cavan Rd from Belturbet, on left.
Parkland course.
9 holes, 5230 yards, S.S.S.65
Club founded in 1950.
Visitors: welcome weekdays and weekends.
Green fees: £3, (£2 with member).
Society meetings: most welcome at all times.
Catering: snacks available, meals by prior arrangement.
Hotels: Seven Horseshoes, Main St; Rosevilla; The Diamond.

AA14 **Boyle**
☎(010 353) 796294
Boyle, Co Roscommon.
1.5 miles from Boyle on Roscommon Rd.
Undulating parkland course.
9 holes, 5450 yards, S.S.S.66
Course designed by Eddie Hackett.
Club founded in 1911.
Visitors: welcome.
Green fees: £4.
Society meetings: welcome.
Catering: none except for special occasions.
Hotels: Royal, Boyle; Forest Park, Boyle.

AA15 **Bundoran**
☎Bundoran (072) 41302
Bundoran, Co Donegal.
32 miles W of Enniskillen, 25 miles N of Sligo.
Undulating links parkland course.
Course designed by Harry Vardon.
Club founded in 1894.
Visitors: welcome at all times, time sheet at weekends.
Green fees: £7 daily; £8 weekends; half green fees for societies 16 or more.
Society meetings: welcome but advance booking required.
Catering: snacks only, meals in hotel.
Hotels: Great Northern on course; Holyrood; Imperial; Maghery; Atlantic.

AA16 **Carrickmines**
☎Dublin (0001) 895676
Carrickmines, Co Dublin.
T43, 7 miles S of Dublin, left at Sandyford.
9 holes, 6026 yards, S.S.S.69
Visitors: welcome weekdays and with member on Sat and Bank Holidays.
Green fees: on application.

AA17 **Carrick-on-Shannon**
☎Carrick-on-Shannon (079) 67015
Woodbrook, Carrick-on-Shannon, Co Leitrim.
Between Carrick-on-Shannon and Boyle, on Dublin-Sligo road, 3 miles from station.
Undulating parkland course.
9 holes, 2792 yards, S.S.S.68
Course designed by Eddie Hackett.
Club founded in 1910.
Visitors: welcome.
Green fees: £5 daily, £20 weekly.
Society meetings: on request.
Catering: available.
Hotels: Bush; County.

AA18 **Castle**
☎Dublin (0001) 904207
Woodside Drive, Rathfarnham, Dublin 14.
From city turn left after Terenure and second right.
Parkland course.
18 holes, 6240 yards, S.S.S.69
Course designed by H.S. Colt.
Club founded in 1913.
Visitors: welcome weekdays.
Green fees: £10 per round.
Society meetings: applications considered.
Catering: full lunch and dinner served.
Hotels: Orwell Lodge, Rathgar, Dublin 6.

AA19 **Castlebar**
☎Castlebar (094) 21649
Rocklands, Castlebar, Co Mayo.
1.25 miles from town centre.
Parkland course.
18 holes, 6109 yards, S.S.S.69
Club founded in 1910.
Visitors: welcome weekdays.
Green fees: £5 per day.
Society meetings: welcome.
Catering: catering available with 3 hours notice.
Hotels: Welcome Inn; Breaffy House; Travellers Friend; Imperial.

AA20 **Castlerea**
☎Castlerea (0907) 20068
Clonalis, Castlerea, Co Roscommon.
On main Dublin-Castlebar road, course just outside town on Castlebar side.
Parkland course.
9 holes, 4974 yards, S.S.S.67
Club founded in 1905.
Visitors: welcome except Sun or competition days.
Green fees: £3 per day weekdays; £5 per day weekends.
Society meetings: welcome by arrangement.
Catering: available by arrangement for societies.
Hotels: Don Arms; Tulleys.

AA21 **Claremorris**
☎Claremorris (094) 71527
Rushbrook, Castlemaggaret, Claremorris, Co Mayo.
On Galway road coming from Claremorris town, 1.5 miles from town.
Parkland course.
9 holes, 5898 yards, S.S.S.69
Club founded in 1927.
Visitors: welcome.
Green fees: £3 per day.
Society meetings: catered for on weekdays.
Catering: facilities available by arrangement.
Hotels: Western; Imperial; Central, all in Claremorris.

AA22 **Clones**
☎Scotshouse (047) 56017
Hilton Park, Clones, Co Monaghan.
3 miles S of Clones towards Scotshouse.
Parkland course.
9 holes, 5570 yards, S.S.S.67

Club founded in 1913.
Visitors: welcome.
Green fees: £3 weekdays; £4 weekends.
Society meetings: welcome.
Catering: meals served except Mon.
Hotels: Creighton, Clones; Hibernian, Clones; Lennard Arms, Clones; White Horse, Cootehill.

AA23 Clontarf
☎Dublin (0001) 315085
Donnycarney House, Malahide Rd, Dublin 3.
NE of city centre, 3 miles on main road to Malahide.
Parkland course.
18 holes, 5447 metres, S.S.S.68
Club founded in 1912.
Visitors: welcome weekdays, check with Sec for times.

Green fees: £10.
Society meetings: Tues and Fri.
Catering: full facilities.
Hotels: Skylon.

AA24 Connemara
☎(095) 21153
Ballyconneely, Co Galway.
4 miles from Ballyconneely.
Undulating seaside links course.
Championship-18 holes, 6604 metres, S.S.S.73
Medal-18 holes, 6186 yards, S.S.S.71
Course designed by Eddie Hackett.
Club founded in 1972.
Visitors: welcome.
Green fees: £8 per day.
Society meetings: welcome.
Catering: meals served.
Hotels: Allbeyglen Castle, Clifden;

Rockglen, Clifden; Eadiseask, Ballyconneely; Clifden Bay, Clifden.

AA25 Corballis
☎Dublin (0001) 450583
Donabate, Co Dublin.
T1 N from Dublin, right down L91, 2 miles beyond Swords.
Seaside course.
18 holes, 4898 yards, S.S.S.64
Visitors: welcome by arrangement.
Green fees: on application.
Society meetings: welcome by arrangement except Sat afternoon and Sun.
Catering: by arrangement.
Hotels: many good hotels in area.

AA26 County Cavan
☎Cavan (049) 31283
Arnmore House, Drumelis, Cavan.

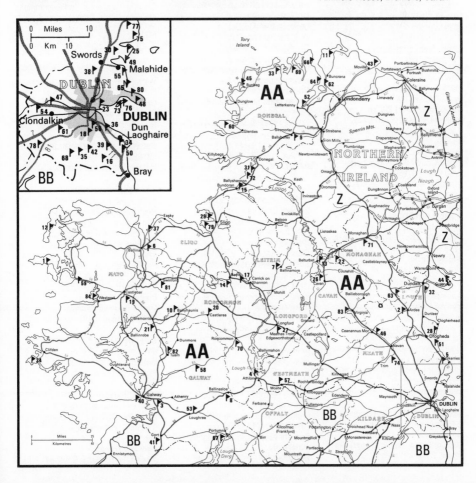

Located within 1 mile from Cavan town on Killeshandra road. Parkland course.
18 holes, 6030 yards, S.S.S.69
Club founded in 1894.
Visitors: welcome 7 days a week, restricted times, Wed and Sun.
Green fees: £6 per day, (£3 with member).
Society meetings: catered for.
Catering: full catering.
Hotels: Hotel Kilmore, Dublin Rd, Cavan; Farnham Arms, Main St, Cavan.

AA27 County Longford
☎(43) 46310
Glack, Longford.
Off Dublin-Sligo Rd, (N4) E of town, signposted.
Undulating course.
18 holes, 6028 yards, S.S.S.68
Course designed by Eddie Hackett.
Club founded in 1894.
Visitors: welcome.
Green fees: £5.
Society meetings: welcome by arrangement.
Catering: meals served.
Hotels: Annally; Longford Arms.

AA28 County Louth
☎Drogheda (041) 22329 Sec
Baltray, Drogheda, Co Louth.
5 miles E of Drogheda, take road along N bank of River Boyne to Baltry village.
Championship links course.
18 holes, 6728 yards, S.S.S.72
Course designed by Tom Simpson.
Club founded in 1892.
Visitors: on application.
Green fees: on application.
Society meetings: on application.
Catering: full facilities.
Hotels: Co Louth Golf Club.

AA29 County Sligo
☎Sligo (071) 77186
Rosses Point, Co Sligo.
5 miles from Sligo.
Seaside links course.
18 holes, 6646 yards, S.S.S.71
Course designed by Colt & Alison.
Club founded in 1894.
Visitors: welcome every day, wise to check before arrival.
Green fees: £10 per day, (half price with member).
Society meetings: welcome by arrangement with Sec/Manager.
Catering: snacks during day, à la carte after 6pm, Dining Room closed Thurs. Other catering by arrangement.

Hotels: Yeats Country Ryan, Rosses Point, Co Sligo; Ballincar House, Ballincar, Sligo.

AA30 Donabate
☎Dublin (0001) 45035
Donabate, Balcarrick, Co Dublin.
1st right 1 mile N of Swords on Dublin-Belfast road.
Parkland course.
18 holes, 5679 metres, S.S.S.69
Visitors: welcome.
Green fees: on application.
Society meetings: welcome by arrangement.
Catering: meals served.
Hotels: Crofton Airport.

AA31 Donegal
☎Ballintra (073) 34054
Murvagh, Laghey PO, Co Donegal.
About 1 mile off main Ballyshannon-Donegal Town road, halfway between towns.
Seaside links course.
Championship 18 holes, 7271 yards, S.S.S.73
Course designed by Eddie Hackett.
Club founded in 1960.
Visitors: welcome every day.
Green fees: £6 per day weekdays; £8 weekends.
Society meetings: catered for every day.
Catering: full catering facilities.
Hotels: Hyland Central, Donegal; Abbey, Donegal.

AA32 Dundalk
☎(042) 21731 Office, 22102 Pro, 21379 Members.
Blackrock, Dundalk, Co Louth.
Off T1 3 miles S of Dundalk on Dundalk Bay.
Parkland course.
18 holes, 6740 yards, S.S.S.72
Course designed by Tom Shannon.
Club founded in 1905.
Visitors: welcome except Sun (competition day).
Green fees: £8 weekdays; £10 weekends and Bank Holidays.
Society meetings: welcome, booking essential.
Catering: full catering. Dinners, snacks every day.
Hotels: Fairways; Imperial; Ballymascanlon; Derryhale; Carrickdale; Lorne.

AA33 Dunfanaghy
Dunfanaghy, Co Donegal.
Off main road 0.25 mile E of Dunfanaghy.

Seaside links course.
18 holes, 5066 metres, S.S.S.66
Club founded in 1906.
Visitors: welcome at all times.
Green fees: £4, (£3 with member) weekdays; £5, (£4 with member) weekends.
Catering: local hotels.
Hotels: Arnold's; Shandon; Carrig Rua; Portnablagh.

AA34 Dun Laoghaire
☎Dublin (0001) 803916
Eglinton Park, Dun Laoghaire, Co Dublin.
7 miles from Dublin, 0.5 mile from Dun Laoghaire town centre and ferry port.
Parkland course.
18 holes, 6059 yards, S.S.S.69
Club founded in 1910.
Visitors: Sun-Fri. Thurs 11.30am-1pm and 3.30pm-5pm.
Green fees: £13 weekdays; £16 Sun.
Society meetings: prior bookings only.
Catering: full service during golfing season.
Hotels: Royal Marine, Dun Laoghaire; Fitzpatricks; Castle, Killiney.

AA35 Edmondstown
☎Dublin (0001) 932461 Clubhouse, 931082 Office.
Edmondstown, Rathfarnham, Dublin 16.
T42 S of Dublin, Rathfarnham, 1 mile.
Parkland course.
18 holes, 6195 yards, S.S.S.69
Course designed by Eddie Hackett.
Club founded in 1944.
Visitors: welcome weekdays.
Green fees: £10 weekdays; £12 weekends.
Society meetings: available, weekdays except Tues.
Catering: full catering.
Hotels: City Centre.

AA36 Elm Park
☎Dublin (0001) 693438, 693014 or 694505.
Nutley Lane, Donnybrook, Dublin 4.
2 miles from city centre beside Montrose television studios and St Vincents Hospital.
Parkland course.
18 holes, 5485 yards, S.S.S.68
Course designed by Fred Davies.
Club founded in 1927.
Visitors: welcome but telephone in

County Louth

There are certain courses throughout Britain and Ireland where a sense of expectancy reaches a peak at a specific point near journey's end, when turning off the main road at Wadebridge for St Enodoc, for instance, or when a long drive nears its end along the only road to Southerness, a superb links on the Solway Firth, which in 1985 hosted the Scottish Amateur for the first time.

A similar sense of anticipation accompanies the last lap to Brancaster which takes you past the church and down through the marsh lined by tall rushes; and there is a less glamorous approach beyond the level crossing to the Royal Cinque Ports Golf Club at Deal. The twisty conclusion to the journey to Rye is another example. But there are few sights as thrilling as the links of County Louth at Baltray at last coming into view.

It is a fine, challenging course in the traditional mould of dunes, undoubtedly one of my favourites and one whose rating within Ireland is not as high as it should be. It is worthy of the best, full of variety and contrast with always the magnificence of its distant views.

Although there have been modifications, one or two made necessary by moving the clubhouse some years ago, there is still an authentic touch of Tom Simpson about it that bears the unmistakable mark of quality. If I had to exemplify it, I would point to the long 3rd which, after a reasonably straightforward drive, reveals hidden talents once the brow of dunes has been scaled. Beautifully natural humps and hollows make careful placing of the second shot essential and, for those attempting to get home in two, there is only a narrow path between salvation and ruin. An attractive small green is not easy to hit.

The curving 1st and testing 2nd make a nice introduction but the 4th, a short par 4, offers some relief before the first of four first class short holes. The 5th and 7th, sandwiched around another fine par 5,

demand well-controlled, truly hit iron shots while the 8th and 9th are no easy 4s.

A sense of space becomes more apparent on the second half which, having begun with a hole alongside the clubhouse, works its way towards the sea by means of the dogleg par 5 11th. It is then that a special character is lent by the 12th, 13th and 14th which, from a combination of factors, comprise a notable trio. They emphasise the merit of great par 4s, not perhaps daunting in terms of yardage but rewarding in the satisfaction they give by being played properly, as they must be if they are to yield a par or a birdie.

Changes to the course have resulted in two short holes in the last four but the 16th is appealing and the 18th the last of five par 5s. Baltray, as the course is more conveniently called after the local fishing village, has a championship cloak without a doubt and it has its less forbidding side which makes it so popular for a day out.

Harry Bradshaw's winning aggregate of 291 in the 1947 Irish Professional championship tells a tale or two about its full blown potential. It is also rare among Irish clubs in having two legendary Irish women golfers as members. Val Reddan, as Clarrie Tiernan, won the Irish title twice and was also the first Irish woman to play in the Curtis Cup. After the war, she was confronted by her new local rival Philomena Garvey in the final of the Irish; not, as would have been most appropriate, at Baltray, but at Lahinch. After the longest final, Garvey won at the 39th, the first of her 15 victories.

Continuing the feminine influence, Mrs Josephine Connolly founded the East of Ireland men's championship played annually at Baltray, an event by which Irish golfers set great store. It can claim father and son winners in Joe and Roddy Carr, but when you speak of the course you speak of distinction. Its list of champions is no more than it deserves.

advance.
Green fees: £10, (£4 with member)
weekdays; £14, (£4.50 with member)
weekends and Bank Holidays.
Society meetings: catered for Tues
only.
Catering: full catering facilities
available.
Hotels: many good hotels in area.

AA37 Enniscrone
☎(096) 36297, Sec 36243/21472.
Enniscrone, Co Sligo.
8 miles N of Allina, 0.5 mile from
Enniscrone.
Seaside course.
18 holes, 6487 yards, S.S.S.72
Course designed by Eddie Hackett.
Club founded in 1931.
Visitors: unrestricted.
Green fees: £7 per day; weekly and
society rates on request.
Society meetings: welcome if
arrangement made in advance.
Catering: light snacks, meals must
be ordered in advance.
Hotels: Atlantic; Castle Arms;
Dartragh House; Benhulben;
Downhill.

AA38 Forest Little
☎Dublin (0001) 401763 or 401183
Forest Little, Cloghran, Co Dublin.
0.5 mile beyond Dublin Airport on
Dublin-Belfast road, take first turn
left.
Parkland course.
18 holes, 5844 metres, S.S.S.70
Course designed by Fred Hawtree.
Club founded in 1940.
Visitors: welcome weekdays.
Green fees: £10 per day.
Society meetings: catered for on
Mon and Thurs afternoons.
Catering: snacks always available;
à la carte menu from 5pm daily.
Hotels: Dublin Airport; Hawthorn.

AA39 Foxrock
☎Dublin (0001) 893992 or 895668
Torquay Rd, Dublin 18.
Club is situated about 6 miles from
Dublin, turn right off T7 just past
Stillergan on to Leopardstown Rd,
then left into Torquay Rd.
Parkland course.
9 holes, 5439 metres, S.S.S.69
Club founded in 1893.
Visitors: welcome Mon, Wed am,
Thurs, Fri. May play Sun only with
member.
Green fees: £10 per day, (£4.50 with
member) weekdays; (£5 with
member) Sun.

Society meetings: catered for Mon
and Thurs.
Catering: soup, sandwiches, coffee.
Hotels: Killiney Court; Killiney
Castle.

AA40 Galway
☎Galway (091) 22169 Sec/Man,
23038 Pro, 21827 Catering.
Blackrock, Salthill, Galway.
On L100 2 miles W of Galway.
Seaside course.
18 holes, 5858 metres, S.S.S.72
Club founded in 1895.
Visitors: not Sun, limited availability
Tues and Sat.
Green fees: £12.
Society meetings: accepted
advance booking (Green fees £8).
Catering: full facilities.
Hotels: club within 1 mile radius of
several hotels.

AA41 Gort
☎Gort (091) 31336
Laughty Shaughnessy, Gort,
Co Galway.
24 miles S of Galway on County
Road No 363 Gort-Tubber.
Parkland course.
9 holes, 5473 yards, S.S.S.66
Course designed by Matt Hackett.
Club founded in 1924.
Visitors: welcome all week.
Green fees: £5 per day, (£3 with
member).
Society meetings: catered for
weekdays.
Catering: salads and sandwiches
served.
Hotels: Sullivans Royal, Gort;
Glynn's, Gort.

AA42 Grange
☎Dublin (0001) 932832 or 932889
Grange Rd, Rathfarnham, Dublin 16.
7 miles S from city centre, near
Rathfarnham village.
Parkland course.
18 holes, 5517 yards, S.S.S.69
Course designed by James Braid.
Club founded in 1910.
Visitors: welcome weekdays except
Tues and Wed afternoons.
Green fees: on application.
Society meetings: welcome Mon
and Thurs.
Catering: full catering facilities
available.
Hotels: Marlay, Rathfarnham, Dublin
14.

AA43 Greencastle
☎Greencastle (077) 81013

Greencastle, via Lifford, Co Donegal.
On L85 23 miles NE of Londonderry
through Moville.
Seaside course.
9 holes, 5386 yards, S.S.S.65
Club founded in 1892.
Visitors: welcome.
Green fees: £3 weekdays; £5
weekends.
Society meetings: except Sun.
Catering: available at all times.
Hotels: McNamaras, Moville; Foyle,
Moville; Fort, Greencastle.

AA44 Greenore
☎(042) 73212
Greenore, Co Louth.
15 miles N of Dundalk on
Carlingford Rd.
Seaside course.
18 holes, 6140 yards, S.S.S.69
Course designed by Eddie Hackett.
Club founded in 1896.
Visitors: welcome weekdays and
most weekends.
Green fees: £6 weekdays;
£8 weekends and Bank Holidays.
Society meetings: catered for
weekends and other days except
Tues.
Catering: except Tues.
Hotels: Ballymascomlon; Village,
Carlingford.

AA45 Gweedore
☎Gweedore (075) 31140
Derrybeg, Letterkenny, Co Donegal.
L82 from Letterkenny or T72 from
Donegal.
Seaside course.
18 holes, 6873 yards, S.S.S.73
Course designed by Eddie Hackett.
Club founded in 1923.
Visitors: always welcome,
reasonable rates, excellent service.
Green fees: £5 per day;
£6 weekends.
Society meetings: catered for
weekends.
Catering: lunch served at weekends.
Hotels: Sea View, Gweedore;
Glenveagh, Gweedore.

AA46 Headfort
☎(046) 40146
Kells, Co Meath.
0.25 mile from Kells on main Kells-
Dublin road.
Parkland course.
18 holes, 6393 yards, S.S.S.70
Club founded in 1930.
Visitors: welcome Mon, Wed, Thurs,
Fri. Limited weekends.
Green fees: £8 weekdays; £10

weekends and Bank Holidays.
Society meetings: catered for
weekdays.
Catering: bar snacks, other by prior
arrangement.
Hotels: Headfort Arms, Kells.

AA47 **Hermitage**
☎Dublin (0001) 268491 or 265049
Lucan, Co Dublin.
T3 W from Dublin, 1 mile from Lucan
Village.
Championship 18 holes, 6034
metres, S.S.S.71
Medal-18 holes, 5668 metres,
S.S.S.70
Green Pegs-18 holes, 5470 yards,
S.S.S.69
Club founded in 1905.
Visitors: welcome Mon, Thurs, Fri
most mornings.
Green fees: £14, (£5 with member)
weekdays; £18, (£9 with member)
weekends.
Society meetings: catered for
weekdays.
Catering: every day.
Hotels: Ashling; Spa; Springfield.

AA48 **Howth**
☎Dublin (0001) 323055
Carrickbrack Rd, Sutton, Dublin.
9.5 miles NE of city centre, 1.5 miles
from Sutton Cross towards Howth
summit.
Heathland course.
18 holes, 6168 yards, S.S.S.69
Course designed by James Braid.
Club founded in1916.
Visitors: welcome weekdays.
Green fees: £10 weekdays only.
Society meetings: catered for
weekdays except Wed.
Catering: snacks and bar service.
Hotels: Marine, Sutton; Howth
Lodge, Howth.

AA49 **Island**
☎Dublin (0001) 452205 Sec, 45095
Club.
Corballis, Donabate, Co Dublin.
From Dublin leave T1 approx 1 mile
beyond Swords, then L91 for 3 miles
and turn right.
Seaside course.
18 holes, 5746 metres, S.S.S.71
Course designed by F Hawtree &
Eddie Hackett.
Club founded in 1890.
Visitors: mid-week.
Green fees: £10 weekdays.
Society meetings: Mon, Tues, Fri.
Catering: available.
Hotels: Grand, Malahide.

AA50 **Killiney**
☎Dublin (0001) 851983
Killiney, Co Dublin.
3 miles from Dun Laoghaire town
centre.
Parkland course.
9 holes, 3046 yards, S.S.S.69
Club founded in 1903.
Visitors: no visitors Thurs, Sat, Sun.
Green fees: £10.
Society meetings: none.
Catering: snacks only.
Hotels: Fitzpatrick Castle, Killiney;
The Court, Killiney Bay; The Victor,
Killiney.

AA51 **Laytown &**
Bettystown
☎Drogheda (041) 27170/27563.
Bettystown, Co Meath.
On L125 off T1, 25 miles N of Dublin,
4 miles from Drogheda.
Seaside links course.
18 holes, 6200 yards, S.S.S.69
Club founded in 1909.
Visitors: welcome weekdays.
Green fees: on application.
Society meetings: catered for on
weekdays, bookable 1 year in
advance.
Catering: meals and snacks served.
Hotels: Neptune, Bettystown; Boyne
Valley, Stameen, Drogheda;
Rosnaree, Dublin Rd, Drogheda;
Mosney Holiday Centre, Mosney.

AA52 **Letterkenny**
☎Letterkenny 144.
Barnhill, Letterkenny, Co Donegal.
On T72, 2 miles N of Letterkenny.
18 holes, 6299 yards, S.S.S.69
Course designed by Eddie Hackett.
Visitors: welcome.
Green fees: on application.
Society meetings: welcome.
Catering: snacks served, meals by
arrangement.
Hotels: Ballymaine; Three Ways;
Gallagher's; McCawy's.

AA53 **Loughrea**
☎(091) 41049
Loughrea, Co Galway.
On L11, 1 mile N of Loughrea.
Meadowland course.
9 holes, 5578 yards, S.S.S.67
Club founded in 1924.
Visitors: unrestricted.
Green fees: £4 weekdays; £5
weekends.
Society meetings: welcome.
Catering: by prior arrangement.
Hotels: O'Deas, Loughrea.

AA54 **Lucan**
☎Dublin (0001) 282106 or 280246
Celbridge Rd, Lucan, Co Dublin.
Take Galway road from Dublin, turn
left at traffic lights after passing
through village of Lucan, club is on
left of road 0.5 mile towards
Celbridge.
Parkland course.
9 holes, 6300 yards, S.S.S.70
Club founded in 1897.
Visitors: weekdays only up to 3pm.
Green fees: £8, (£4 with member, 1
only).
Society meetings: Mon & Tues £7
for 20 or over.
Catering: full services available.
Hotels: Spa, Lucan.

AA55 **Malahide**
☎Dublin (0001) 450248
Coast Rd, Malahide, Co Dublin.
8 miles N of Dublin, follow Malahide
road.
Parkland course.
9 holes, 2674 yards, S.S.S.67
Course designed by Nathaniel Hone.
Club founded in 1892.
Visitors: welcome except on Sun
and Wed.
Green fees: on application.
Catering: simple meals available.
Hotels: Grand, Malahide; Stuart,
Malahide; Grove.

AA56 **Milltown**
☎Dublin (0001) 976090
Lower Churchtown Rd, Dublin 14.
3 miles S of city centre, via Ranelagh
village.
Parkland course.
18 holes, 5703 metres, S.S.S.70
Club founded in 1907.
Visitors: welcome except Tues and
Wed pm.
Green fees: £10, (£5 with member)
weekdays; £12, (£7 with member)
weekends.
Society meetings: by arrangement.
Catering: lunch and dinner served.
Hotels: Orwell Lodge, Orwell Rd,
Dublin 6.

AA57 **Moate**
☎(0902) 81271
Moate, Co Westmeath.
On T4, 8 miles E of Athlone.
Parkland course.
9 holes, 5348 yards, S.S.S.66
Club founded in 1942.
Visitors: welcome.
Green fees: £4 weekdays; £5
weekends; (reduction of £1 with
member).

Society meetings: catered for.
Catering: meals by arrangement.
Hotels: Grand; Kilcleagh Park.

AA58 Mountbellew
☎(0905) 79259
Shankhill, Mountbellew, Co Galway.
On T4, 28 miles E of Galway.
Undulating meadowland course.
9 holes, 5649 yards, S.S.S.66
Club founded in 1927.
Visitors: welcome.
Green fees: £3 weekdays;
£4 weekends.
Society meetings: by arrangement
with Sec.
Catering: tea, soup, sandwiches, full
meals on notification.
Hotels: Guest houses, hotels in
Ballinasloe, 16 miles, and Tuam, 16
miles.

AA59 Mulrany
☎Mulrany (098) 36107
Mulrany, Westport, Co Mayo.
N59, 10 miles from Newport.
Undulating seaside course.
9 holes, 6380 yards, S.S.S.70
Visitors: welcome.
Green fees: £3 per day; £15 per
week.
Society meetings: welcome.
Catering: none.
Hotels: Mulrany Bay.

AA60 Narin & Portnoo
☎Clooney 21.
Portnoo, Co Donegal.
8 miles W of Glenties via T72 and
L81.
Seaside course.
18 holes, 5700 yards, S.S.S.68
Visitors: welcome.
Green fees: on application.
Society meetings: by arrangement.
Hotels: Lake House, Portnoo;
Nesbitt Arms, Highlands.

AA61 Newlands
☎Dublin (0001) 593157 and 593498
Clondalkin, Co Dublin 22.
6 miles from city centre on main
southern Cork road.
Parkland course.
18 holes, 6275 yards, S.S.S.70
Course designed by James Braid.
Club founded in 1926.
Visitors: welcome weekdays.
Green fees: £12, (£5 with member).
Society meetings: welcome
weekdays.
Catering: full catering facilities.
Hotels: Skylon.

AA62 North West
☎Buncrana (077) 61027
Lisfannon, Fahan, Co Donegal.
12 miles from Derry on main
Buncrana road.
Seaside links course.
18 holes, 6203 yards, S.S.S.69
Club founded in 1890.
Visitors: welcome every day.
Green fees: £6 per day; special
weekly rates.
Society meetings: weekdays,
limited to two at weekends (special
rates).
Catering: available Wed, Thurs, Sat
Sun and at other times by arrange-
ment.
Hotels: White Strang, Buncrana;
Roneragh House, Fahan.

AA63 Nuremore
☎(042) 61438
Carrickmacross, Co Monaghan.
On main Dublin-Derry road about 1
mile from Carrickmacross on Dublin
side.
Parkland course.
9 holes, 5466 metres, S.S.S.69
Course designed by Eddie Dunne.
Club founded in 1964.
Visitors: welcome.
Green fees: £3 weekdays;
£4 weekends.
Society meetings: catered for by
prior arrangement through hotel.
Catering: meals and snacks served
at hotel.
Hotels: Nuremore.

AA64 Otway
Rathmullan, Co Donegal.
On W shore of Loch Swilly.
Seaside course.
9 holes, 4134 yards, S.S.S.60
Visitors: welcome.
Green fees: on application.
Hotels: Fort Royal; Rathmullan
House; Pier.

AA65 Portmarnock
☎Dublin (0001) 323082
Portmarnock, Co Dublin.
From Dublin along coast road to
Baldoyle, on to Portmarnock, turn
right at Jet Garage, 1 mile up private
road.
Green-18 holes, 6064 yards,
S.S.S.73
White-18 holes, 6276 yards,
S.S.S.74
Yellow-18 holes, 6489 yards,
S.S.S.75
Course designed by W.G. Pickeman
& George Ross.

Club founded in 1894.
Visitors: welcome (no Ladies
weekends or Bank Holidays).
Green fees: on application.
Society meetings: by arrangement,
maximum 50.
Catering: full facilities.
Hotels: Grand, Malahide; Marnie
Sutton.

AA66 Portsalon
☎Portsalon 11
Portsalon, Co Donegal.
L78 from Letterkenny.
Seaside course.
18 holes, 5522 yards, S.S.S.67
Visitors: welcome.
Green fees: on application.
Hotels: Portsalon.

AA67 Portumna
☎Portumna (0509) 41059
Portumna, Co Galway.
1.5 miles from Portumna on
Woodfood road.
Woodland/parkland course.
9 holes, 5566 yards, S.S.S.68
Course designed by P. O'Brien.
Club founded in 1913.
Visitors: welcome.
Green fees: on application.
Society meetings: welcome.
Catering: by arrangement only.
Hotels: Westpark, Portumna;
Clonwyn House, Portumna; Portland
House, Portumna.

AA68 Rathfarnham
☎Dublin (0001) 931201
Newtown, Rathfarnham, Dublin 16.
2 miles from Rathfarnham village.
Parkland course.
9 holes, 3173 yards, S.S.S.70
Club founded in 1899.
Visitors: not Tues and Sat.
Green fees: £9, (£5.50 with
member).
Society meetings: weekdays.
Catering: lunch and dinner by
arrangement with Club Steward.
Hotels: Marley Park, Marley Grange,
Rathfarnham, Dublin 6.

AA69 Rosapenna
☎(074) 55301
Downings, Letterkenny, Co Donegal.
22 miles from Letterkenny via Milford
and Carrigart.
Seaside course.
18 holes, 6254 yards, S.S.S.71
Course designed by Tom Mitchell
(1893) and re-designed by James
Braid & Harry Vardon (1906).
Visitors: welcome.

Green fees: on application.
Catering: at Rosapenna Hotel.
Hotels: Rosapenna; Carrigart.

AA70 Roscommon
☎(0903) 6283
Mote Park, Roscommon, Co Roscommon.
On T15, 96 miles W of Dublin.
Meadowland course.
9 holes, 6340 yards, S.S.S.70
Visitors: welcome.
Green fees: on application.
Society meetings: by arrangement.
Catering: none available.
Hotels: Abbey; Royal.

AA71 Rossmore
☎(047) 81316
Rossmore Park, Monaghan.
About 2 miles from Monaghan on Monaghan-Cootehill road.
Undulating parkland course.
9 holes, 5859 yards, S.S.S.68
Club founded in 1920.
Visitors: welcome.
Green fees: £4 weekdays; £5 weekends.
Society meetings: catered for.
Catering: available by arrangement.
Hotels: Hillgrove; Four Seasons; Westenra.

AA72 Rossnowlagh
☎Bundoran (072) 65343
Sand House Hotel, Rossnowlagh, Co Donegal.
Seaside course.
9 holes
Visitors: welcome only during holiday season.
Green fees: on application.
Catering: lunch served.
Hotels: Sand House.

AA73 Royal Dublin
☎Dublin (0001) 336346 or 331262.
Bull Island, Dollymount, Dublin 3.
4 miles NE of city centre on coast road to Howth.
Seaside links course.
18 holes, 6810 yards, S.S.S.73
Course designed by H.S. Colt.
Club founded in 1885.
Visitors: welcome weekdays; weekends and Bank Holidays by arrangement with Sec/Manager.
Green fees: £18 per day weekdays; £20 per day weekends.
Society meetings: weekdays except Wed.
Catering: full catering service.
Hotels: Marine, Sutton; Howth Lodge.

AA74 Royal Tara
☎Navan (046) 25244
Bellinter, Navan, Co Meath.
30 miles N of Dublin.
Parkland course.
18 holes, S.S.S.70
Club founded in 1923.
Visitors: welcome by arrangement.
Green fees: £6 weekdays; £7 weekends.
Society meetings: welcome by arrangement.
Catering: full catering facilities.
Hotels: good hotels in area.

AA75 Rush
☎Dublin (0001) 437548, 438177 Office.
Rush, Co Dublin.
Dublin-Belfast road, turn right at Blakes Cross.
Seaside links course.
9 holes, 5598 metres, S.S.S.69
Club founded in 1943.
Visitors: avoid Wed, Thurs, Sat, Sun and Bank Holidays, not totally excluded.
Green fees: £7.
Society meetings: catered for.
Catering: full facilities.
Hotels: Pier House, Skerries; Argyle Lodge, B & B, Rush.

AA76 **St Annes**
☎Dublin (0001) 332797,
336471 Sec.
Bull Island, Clontarf, Dublin 5.
4 miles NE of Dublin.
Seaside course.
9 holes, 5940 yards, S.S.S.68
Club founded in 1921.
Visitors: Thurs only by appointment.
Green fees: £10.
Society meetings: Thurs by
appointment.
Catering: facilities at club by
arrangement.
Hotels: in Dublin.

AA77 **Skerries**
☎Dublin (0001) 491567 or 491204
Hacketstown, Skerries, Co Dublin.
Take Belfast road N out of Dublin,
past Airport and Swords, fork right
for Lusk and Skerries after end of
Swords by-pass.
Undulating parkland course.
18 holes, 5852 yards, S.S.S.70
Club founded in 1906.
Visitors: welcome.
Green fees: £12, (£9 with member)
weekdays; £8, (£3.50 with member)
weekends.
Society meetings: catered for Mon,
Thurs and Fri.
Catering: full catering facilities
available.
Hotels: Pier House, Harbour Rd,
Skerries; Anna Villa, Convent Lane,
Skerries.

AA78 **Slade Valley**
☎Dublin (0001) 582207 or 582183
Lynch Park, Brittas, Co Dublin.
Off N7 Dublin-Naas road.
Undulating course.
Championship 18 holes, 5462
metres, S.S.S.69
18 holes, 5337 metres, S.S.S.68
Course designed by W.D. Sullivan &
D. O'Brien.
Club founded in 1971.
Visitors: welcome by arrangement
with Sec.
Green fees: £12, (£6 with member)
weekdays; £12, (£8 with member)
weekends.

Society meetings: by arrangement
with Sec.
Catering: meals available at
weekends and also Tues and Wed
during summer.
Hotels: Green Isle; Downshire
House, Blessington.

AA79 **Strandhill**
☎Sligo (071) 68188
Strandhill, Co Sligo.
5 miles W of Sligo city, course is
situated in resort of Strandhill and is
well signposted.
Seaside links course.
18 holes, 5950 yards, S.S.S.69
Club founded in 1931.
Visitors: welcome weekdays and
most weekends.
Green fees: £5 weekdays; £6
weekends and Bank Holidays.
Society meetings: welcome.
Catering: snacks available and
meals by arrangement.
Hotels: Ocean View, Strandhill; The
Southern, Sligo; Silver Swan, Sligo.

AA80 **Sutton**
☎Dublin (0001) 323013
Cush Point, Sutton, Dublin 13.
7 miles NE of city centre.
Seaside links course.
9 holes, 5522 yards, S.S.S.67
Club founded in 1890.
Visitors: welcome except
competition days (Tues and Sat).
Green fees: £8, (£2 with member)
weekdays; £10, (£3 with member)
weekends and Bank Holidays.
Society meetings: by arrangement
only.
Catering: by arrangement only.
Hotels: Marine; Howth Lodge; Royal
Howth.

AA81 **Swinford**
☎(094) 51378
Brabazon Park, Swinford, Co Mayo.
Beside town, opposite Western
Health Board complex.
Parkland course.
9 holes, 2725 yards, S.S.S.67
Club founded in 1922.

Visitors: welcome.
Green fees: £3 per day; £10 per
week; £20 per month.
Society meetings: enquiries
welcome.
Catering: catering facilities available
by arrangement.
Hotels: O'Connors, Swinford;
Westway, Kiltinagh.

AA82 **Tuam**
☎Tuam (093) 24354
Barnacurragh, Tuam, Co Galway.
1.5 miles from town on the Athenry
road which is off Dublin road.
Parkland course.
18 holes, 6321 yards, S.S.S.70
Club founded around 1910.
Visitors: welcome weekdays.
Green fees: £5 per person.
Society meetings: catered for on
weekdays and Sat by arrangement.
Catering: snacks available.
Hotels: Imperial, Tuam; Hermitage,
Tuam.

AA83 **Virginia**
☎Virginia, Co Cavan.
50 miles N of Dublin on main Cavan
-Dublin road, within Park Hotel, by
Lough Ramor.
Meadowland course.
9 holes, 4083 metres, S.S.S.62
Club founded in 1946.
Visitors: welcome.
Green fees: £3 weekdays; £4
weekends and Bank Holidays.
Catering: meals and snacks
available in hotel.
Hotels: Park.

AA84 **Westport**
☎Westport 547
Carrowholly, Westport, Co Mayo.
2 miles from Westport.
Parkland course.
18 holes, 6706 yards, S.S.S.71
Course designed by Hawtree & Son.
Visitors: welcome.
Green fees: on application.
Society meetings: welcome.
Catering: snacks and meals served.
Hotels: Clew Bay; Castlecourt;
Westport.

BB Southern Eire

BB1 Abbeyleix
☎(0502) 31450
Abbeyleix, Co Laois.
Within 0.5 mile of Main St on Strad-
bally Rd.
Parkland course.
9 holes, S.S.S.68
Visitors: welcome.
Green fees: £3 weekdays; £5 week-
ends.
Society meetings: catered for
usually on Sat.
Catering: catering by arrangement
for Societies.
Hotels: Hibernian, Abbeyleix;
Killeshin, Porthoise; Montague,
Porthoise.

BB2 Adare Manor
☎(061) 86204
Adane, Co Limerick.
10 miles from Limerick city on main
Killarney road.
Parkland course.
9 holes, 5700 yards, S.S.S.67
Club founded in 1900.
Visitors: welcome weekdays up to
4.30pm. Other times with member or
by prior arrangement.
Green fees: £8 per day, (£4 with
member).
Society meetings: on club notice
board. Book well in advance.
Catering: limited to chicken, fish etc.
served in basket with french fries.
Sandwiches, tea, coffee etc
available.
Hotels: Dunranen Arms, Adare;
Woodlands, Adare.

BB3 Arklow
☎Arklow (0402) 2492
Abbeylands, Arklow, Co Wicklow.
0.5 mile from Arklow.
Seaside course.
18 holes, 5963 yards, S.S.S.68
Course designed by Hawtree &
Taylor.
Visitors: welcome except Sun.
Green fees: on application.
Society meetings: welcome except
Sun.
Catering: by arrangement.
Hotels: Arklow Bay; Royal; Bridge.

BB4 Athy
☎Athy (0507) 31729
Geraldine, Athy, Co Kildare.
On T6, 2 miles N of Athy.

Undulating parkland course.
9 holes, 3079 yards, S.S.S.69
Club founded in 1906.
Visitors: welcome weekdays.
Green fees: £4, (£3 with member)
weekdays; £6, (£4 with member)
weekends and Bank Holidays.
Society meetings: catered for Sat
mornings.
Catering: by arrangement with Club
Steward. Ring after 7.30pm.
Hotels: Leinster Arms, Athy, Co
Kildare; Kilkea Castle, Castle
Dermot, Co Kildare.

BB5 Ballybunion
☎Ballybunion (068) 2714
Sandhill Rd, Ballybunion, Co Kerry.
Seaside course.
Old-18 holes, 6542 yards, S.S.S.72
New-18 holes, 6477 yards, S.S.S.72
Club founded in 1896.
Visitors: welcome.
Green fees: £4 weekdays;
£6 weekends.
Society meetings: welcome.
Catering: snacks and meals served.
Hotels: Ambassador; Marine.

BB6 Baltinglass
☎(0508) 81350
Baltinglass, Co Wicklow.
40 miles S of Dublin.
Parkland course.
9 holes, 6070 yards, S.S.S.69
Course designed by Dr. W.G. Lyons,
Hugh Dark and Col. Mitchell.
Club founded in 1928.
Visitors: welcome.
Green fees: on application.
Society meetings: 3 outings
allowed per month.
Catering: meals by arrangement.
Hotels: good hotels in area.

BB7 Bandon
☎Bandon (023) 41111/42224
Castlebernard, Bandon, Co Cork.
1.5 miles W of Bandon town.
Parkland course.
18 holes, 5496 yards, S.S.S.69
Club founded in 1909.
Visitors: welcome every day.
Green fees: £6 weekdays;
£8 weekends.
Society meetings: £6 weekends
always welcome.
Catering: available.
Hotels: Munster Arms, Bandon,
Co Cork.

BB8 Berehaven
☎Castletown Bear 24
Berehaven, Castletown Bear,
Co Cork.
9 holes, 4950 yards, S.S.S.64
Green fees: on application.
No other facilities.

BB9 Birr
☎Birr (0509) 20082
Glenns, Birr, Co Offaly.
2 miles from Birr on road to Banager.
Undulating parkland course.
18 holes, 6262 yards, S.S.S.70
Club founded in 1896.
Visitors: welcome, but should check
on Sun.
Green fees: £6 weekdays; £6
weekends, (£4 with member).
Society meetings: catered for every
day except Sun.
Catering: available by arrangement
except Tues.
Hotels: County Arms, Birr; Doolys,
Birr; Shannon, Banagher.

BB10 Blainroe
☎Wicklow (0404) 68168
Blainroe, Co Wicklow.
3 miles S of Wicklow town on coast
road.
Seaside course.
18 holes, 6681 yards, S.S.S.72
Course designed by Hawtree &
Sons.
Club founded in 1978.
Visitors: ring for times.
Green fees: £7 weekdays; £12
weekends.
Society meetings: catered for on
weekdays and at weekends.
Catering: lunch and dinner and bar
food.
Hotels: Arklow Bay; Grand, Wicklow.

BB11 Borris
☎Carlow (0503) 73143
Deer Park, Borris, Co Carlow.
Drive S from Carlow via Begenals-
town; drive E from Kilkenny via
Gowran and Goresbridge.
Parkland course.
10 holes, 6041 yards, S.S.S.69
Visitors: welcome weekdays and
with member on Sun.
Green fees: £5 weekdays; £6
weekends.
Society meetings: catered for on
weekdays and Sat mornings

between 10am and 12am.
Catering: catering available for societies by arrangement.
Hotels: Newport, Kilkenny; Springhill, Kilkenny; Clubhouse, Kilkenny; Rose Hill, Kilkenny; Royal, Carlow; Seven Oaks, Carlow.

BB12 **Bray**
☎Bray 862484 Sec, 862092 Public.
Ravenswell Rd, Bray, Co Wicklow.
L29 from Dublin, turn left at bridge entering town.
Parkland course.
9 holes, 2866 metres, S.S.S.70
Club founded in 1897.
Visitors: welcome weekdays except Mon.
Green fees: £6 per day.
Society meetings: societies affiliated to Golfing Union catered for.
Catering: limited catering available.
Hotels: many good hotels in area.

BB13 **Cahir Park**
☎(052) 41474
Kilcommon, Cahir, Co Tipperary.
1 miles out of Cahir on Clogheen road.
Parkland course.

9 holes, 5696 metres, S.S.S.69
Course designed by Eddie Hackett.
Club founded in 1968.
Visitors: welcome.
Green fees: on application.
Society meetings: catered for except on Sun.
Hotels: Cahir House; Galtee; Cahir; The Wishing Well, Cahir.

BB14 **Callan**
☎Callan (056) 25136
Geraldine, Callan, Co Kilkenny.
From Kilkenny to Callan, 1 mile from Callan to course.
Meadowland course.
9 holes, 5444 yards, S.S.S.68
Club founded on 30th April 1929.
Visitors: welcome.
Green fees: £4 per day.
Society meetings: welcome except on Sun.
Catering: by prior arrangement only.
Hotels: many good hotels in area.

BB15 **Carlow**
☎Carlow (0503) 31695 Bar, 42599 Office.
Deerpark, Dublin Rd, Carlow, Co Carlow.

1 mile from Carlow station, take Naas road from Dublin.
Undulating parkland course.
18 holes, 6247 yards, S.S.S.70
Course designed by Tom Simpson.
Club founded in 1899.
Visitors: welcome.
Green fees: £7 weekdays; £10 weekends and Bank Holidays; (half appropriate rate playing with member).
Society meetings: catered for on weekdays or Sat mornings.
Catering: full catering available.
Hotels: Seven Oaks, Athy Rd, Carlow; Royal, Dublin St, Carlow.

BB16 **Carrick-on-Suir**
☎Carrick-on-Suir (051) 40047
Garravoone, Co Tipperary.
Course is situated approx 2 miles from town of Carrick-on-Suir, on main Carrick-on-Suir to Dungarvan road; there is a signpost on right side of road.
Undulating parkland course.
9 holes, 5948 yards, S.S.S.68
Course designed by Edward Hackett.
Club founded in 1939.
Visitors: welcome all days except

Sun.
Green fees: £5, (£3 if playing with member).
Society meetings: welcome all days except Sun.
Catering: available if booked in advance.
Hotels: Bessborough Arms, Carrick-on-Suir; Cedarfield House, Carrick-on-Suir.

BB17 **Castlecomer**
☎(056) 41139
Drumgoole, Castlecomer,
Co Kilkenny.
On N7 10 miles from Kilkenny.
Parkland course.
9 holes, 6238 yards, S.S.S.71
Course designed by Pat Ruddy.
Club founded in 1935.
Visitors: welcome Mon to Sat.
Green fees: £4 weekdays; £5 weekends, (£3 with member).
Society meetings: Mon to Sat.
Catering: lunches to order, snacks served.
Hotels: Newpark, Kilkenny.

BB18 **Castletroy**
☎Limerick (061) 335261
Castletroy, Limerick.
3 miles from Limerick city on Dublin road, turn at signpost in Castletroy, course 300 yards on left.
Parkland course.
18 holes, 6340 yards, S.S.S.71
Club founded in 1937.
Visitors: weekdays unlimited, weekends with member only.
Green fees: £9, (£6 with member).
Society meetings: Mon, Wed, Fri by arrangement.
Catering: full catering service.
Hotels: Two Mile Inn; Cruises; Royal George.

BB19 **Charleville**
☎Charleville (063) 81257
Ardmore, Charleville, Co Cork.
About 35 miles from Cork and 25 miles from Limerick.
Parkland course.
18 holes, 6407 yards, S.S.S.70
Club founded in 1947.
Visitors: welcome weekdays.
Green fees: £5 per person.
Society meetings: any day except Sun.
Catering: soup and sandwiches, cold plates.
Hotels: Deerpark, Limerick Rd, Charleville.

BB20 **Cill Dara**
☎ Kildare (045) 21433

Kildare, Co Kildare.
1 mile E of Kildare.
Moorland course.
9 holes, 6196 yards, S.S.S.66
Visitors: welcome.
Green fees: on application.
Catering: meals served by arrangement.
Hotels: Derby House, Kildare; Kaedeen, Newbridge.

BB21 **Clonmel**
☎Clonmel (052) 21138/21508
Lyranearla, Clonmel, Co Tipperary.
On mountain road on way to Comeragh mountains, 3 miles SE of Clonmel.
Parkland course.
18 holes, 6365 yards, S.S.S.70
Course designed by Eddie Hackett.
Club founded in 1911.
Visitors: contact Mary Lynch Sec/Manager. Ring for details.
Green fees: £6 weekdays; £8 weekends.
Society meetings: welcome.
Catering: full catering facilities.
Hotels: Manilla; Clonmel Arms, Clonmel.

BB22 **Cork**
☎Cork (021) 353451, 353037 or 353263
Little Island, Co Cork.
5 miles due E of Cork city, 0.5 mile off Cork-Rosslare road at Little Island railway station.
Undulating parkland course.
Course designed by Dr Alexander Mackenzie.
Club founded in 1888.
Visitors: welcome.
Green fees: £9 per day weekdays; £10 per day; (£5 with member) weekends.
Society meetings: welcome except on competition days and Thurs.
Catering: full catering facilities.
Hotels: Silver Springs, Tivoli, Cork; Ashbourne House, Glounthaune; John Barleycorn, Riverstown; Commodore, Cosh, Co Cork.

BB23 **Courtown**
☎Gorey (055) 25166
Kiltennel, Gorey, Co Wexford.
3 miles from Gorey on Dublin-Rosslare road.
Parkland course.
18 holes, 6398 yards, S.S.S.70
Course designed by Harris & Associates
Club founded in 1936.
Visitors: welcome except on major competition days.

Green fees: £6 weekdays; £9 weekends.
Society meetings: accepted except during June, July, Aug.
Catering: snacks and full catering available.
Hotels: Bayview, Courtown, Taravie; Marlfield House, Gorey.

BB24 **Curragh**
☎Curragh (045) 41238
Curragh, Co Kildare.
28 miles from Dublin, signposted from Newbridge, Co Kildare.
Parkland course.
18 holes, 6505 yards, S.S.S.71
Course designed by David Ritchie (1852).
Club founded in 1883.
Visitors: welcome.
Green fees: £5 weekdays; £7 weekends and Bank Holidays.
Society meetings: welcome from 1 Jan to mid-Oct by prior arrangement.
Catering: lunches and snacks served.
Hotels: Kaedeen; Derby; Lumville.

BB25 **Delgany**
☎Dublin (0001) 874536
Delgany, Co Wicklow.
Adjacent to village of Delgany off main road to Wexford.
Parkland course.
18 holes, 5454 metres, S.S.S.69
Club founded in 1908.
Visitors: welcome except on competition days.
Green fees: on application.
Society meetings: welcome.
Catering: full catering facilities.
Hotels: Wicklow Arms; Glenview.

BB26 **Doneraile**
☎Doneraile (022) 24137
Doneraile, Co Cork.
Off T11, 28 miles N of Cork, 9 miles from Mallow.
Parkland course.
9 holes, 5528 yards, S.S.S.66
Visitors: welcome.
Green fees: on application.
Society meetings: welcome.
Catering: meals served.
Hotels: Central; Hibernian; Mallow.

BB27 **Dooks**
☎(066) 68205 Office, 68200 Members.
Dooks, Killorglin, Co Kerry.
Off T66, 8 miles W of Killorglin, at bridge between Killorglin and Glenbeigh.
Seaside course.

18 holes, 5135 metres, S.S.S.68
Course designed by Eddie Hackett.
Club founded in 1889.
Visitors: welcome, check at
weekends.
Green fees: £8.
Society meetings: welcome.
Catering: snacks.
Hotels: Bianconi Inn, Killonglin;
Towers, Glenbeigh.

BB28 **Douglas**
☎Cork (021) 291086
Douglas, Co Cork.
Within 3 miles of Cork city, 0.5 mile
beyond Douglas village.
Parkland course.
18 holes, 5294 metres, S.S.S.68
Club founded in 1910.
Visitors: welcome with reservation
at weekends.
Green fees: on application.
Society meetings: catered for by
arrangement before start of season.
Catering: snacks and meals served.
Hotels: several hotels within 3 miles
of course.

BB29 **Dromoland Castle**
☎(061) 71144 extn 618.

Newmarket-on-Fergus, Co Clare.
On main Limerick-Galway road, 1.5
miles through Newmarket-on-Fergus.
Undulating parkland course.
18 holes, 6098 yards, S.S.S.71
Course designed by Whittaker
(USA).
Club founded in 1964.
Visitors: full facilities available, two
hotels within grounds.
Green fees: £10 per day; £5 hotel
guests.
Society meetings: welcome any
day (fees negotiable).
Catering: none; hotels below, both
in grounds of course for meals.
Hotels: Dromoland Castle; Clare
Inn.

BB30 **Dungarvan**
☎ (058) 41605
Ballinacourty, Dungarvan,
Co Waterford.
About 3 miles E of Dungarvan, from
Dungarvan take course road to
Tramore, first right turn leads to club.
Meadowland course.
9 holes, 5615 metres, S.S.S.69
Club founded in 1924.
Visitors: Mon-Fri £4 per player.

Green fees: £5 per day.
Society meetings: Mon-Fri - apply
in advance.
Catering: none.
Hotels: Clonea Strange; Gold Coast
Holiday Homes, entrance to club.

BB31 **East Cork**
☎Cork (021) 631687
Goatacrue, Midleton, Co Cork.
On main Cork to Waterford road 10
miles E of Cork city, turn left at
roundabout in Midleton, signposted
from same roundabout about 1.5
miles.
Parkland course.
Yellow-18 holes, 4874 yards,
S.S.S.65
Red (Ladies)-18 holes, 4510 yards,
S.S.S.69
Blue-18 holes, 5207 yards, S.S.S.67
Course designed by Edward Hackett.
Club founded in 1970.
Visitors: welcome anytime.
Green fees: £6.
Society meetings: details from
clubhouse.
Catering: lunches served except
Sun.
Hotels: Sherwood House, Midleton;

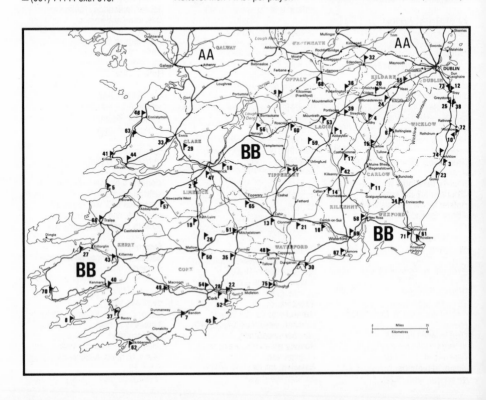

Commodore, Cobh.

BB32 Edenberry
☎Edenberry (0405) 31072
Edenberry, Co Offaly.
0.75 mile outside town.
Parkland/moorland course.
9 holes, 5900 yards, S.S.S.67
Course designed by Havers.
Club founded in 1947.
Visitors: welcome.
Green fees: £4 weekdays; £5
weekends.
Society meetings: welcome on Sat.
Catering: catering only on special
occasions and for societies.

BB33 Ennis
☎Ennis (065) 21070
Dumbiggle, Ennis, Co Clare.
1 mile W of Ennis.
Parkland course.
18 holes, 5890 yards, S.S.S.66
Visitors: welcome.
Green fees: on application.
Society meetings: by arrangement.
Catering: snacks served, meals by
arrangement.
Hotels: Queens; West Country Inn;
Old Ground.

BB34 Enniscorthy
☎Enniscorthy (054) 33191
Knockmarshal, Enniscorthy,
Co Wexford.
1.5 miles from town on New Rose
Rd.
Parkland course.
9 holes, 6220 yards, S.S.S.70
Course designed by E. Hackett.
Club founded in 1924.
Visitors: welcome except weekends
where prior arrangement is
desirable.
Green fees: £4 weekdays; £5
weekends.
Society meetings: most welcome.
Catering: full catering.
Hotels: Murphy Floods, Town
Centre, Enniscorthy.

BB35 Fermoy
☎(025) 31472
Fermoy, Co Cork.
2 miles from Fermoy off Cork-Dublin
road.
Undulating course.
18 holes, 5550 yards, S.S.S.70
Course designed by Commander
Harris.
Club founded in 1892.
Visitors: welcome weekdays.
Green fees: £6 per day.
Society meetings: weekdays and

Sat am.
Catering: snacks served.
Hotels: Grand, Fermoy.

BB36 Garryhinch
☎Portarlington (0502) 23115
Portarlington, Co Offaly.
6 miles from Monasterevin.
Parkland course.
9 holes, 5598 yards, S.S.S.66
Visitors: welcome.
Green fees: on application.
Society meetings: welcome except
Sun.
Catering: meals by prior arrange-
ment.
Hotels: Hazel, Monasterevin;
Montague, Portlaoise.

BB37 Glengarriff
☎(027) 63150
Glengarriff, Co Cork.
On T65, 55 miles W of Cork.
Seaside course.
9 holes, 2042 metres, S.S.S.62
Club founded in 1936.
Visitors: welcome.
Green fees: on application.
Society meetings: special rates for
societies.
Hotels: 6 hotels within 1 mile.

BB38 Greystones
☎Dublin (0001) 876624
Greystones, Co Wicklow.
25 miles S of Dublin.
Undulating parkland course.
18 holes, 5227 yards, S.S.S.67
Club founded in 1895.
Visitors: welcome weekdays except
Thurs.
Green fees: £8.
Society meetings: Mon and Fri.
Catering: by prior arrangement.
Hotels: La Touche, Greystones;
Royal, Bray.

BB39 Heath
☎Portlaoise (0502) 26533
The Heath, Portlaoise, Co Laois.
5 miles NE of Portlaoise, just off
main Dublin, Cork and Limerick road.
Heathland course.
18 holes, 5766 metres, S.S.S.70
Club founded in 1930.
Visitors: welcome on weekdays and
by arrangement with Hon Sec at
weekends.
Green fees: £5, (£3.50 with
member) weekdays; £7, (£5 with
member) weekends.
Society meetings: welcome by
arrangement.
Catering: full catering facilities

available by arrangement with
Steward.
Hotels: Killeshin, Portlaoise;
Montague, Emo.

BB40 Kenmare
☎(064) 41291
Kenmare, Killarney, Co Kerry.
On T65, 20 miles S of Killarney,
100 yards out of town.
Parkland course.
9 holes, 2410 yards, S.S.S.63
Club founded in 1904.
Visitors: welcome.
Green fees: £5.
Society meetings: weekdays, Sat.
Catering: bar and snacks available.
Hotels: hotels in town, wide choice
of Guest Houses, B & B.

BB41 Kilkee
☎Kilkee 48
East End, Kilkee, Co Clare.
Within 400 metres of town.
Meadowland course.
9 holes
Course designed by McAllister.
Club founded in 1892.
Visitors: welcome.
Green fees: on application.
Society meetings: catered for in
May, June and from mid-Aug to end-
Sept.
Catering: snacks always available;
meals for societies available by
arrangement.
Hotels: Strand; Vistoria; Thomond.

BB42 Kilkenny
☎Kilkenny (056) 22125
Glendine, Kilkenny.
2 miles N of town off Castlecomer
Rd.
Parkland course.
18 holes, 6400 yards, S.S.S.70
Club founded in 1896.
Visitors: welcome very little
restrictions.
Green fees: £7 weekdays; £8
weekends and Bank Holidays.
Society meetings: mostly Sat
mornings.
Catering: at clubhouse.
Hotels: Newport; Hotel Kilkenny;
Springhill.

BB43 Killarney
☎(064) 31034
Mahonys' Point, Killarney, Co Kerry.
3 miles W of town off Killarney-
Killonglin road.
Undulating parkland course.
Kileen 18 holes, 6909 yards,
S.S.S.73

Lahinch

Tom Morris and Tom Dunn were the most modest and self-effacing of all golf course architects, dismissing their skills by claiming, "God obviously intended this for a golf course". Of Lahinch, which borders great beaches lashed by Atlantic rollers, Morris said the same thing in a different way, "the links is as fine a natural course as it has ever been my good fortune to play over".

After his extensive reconstruction in 1927, Dr Alister Mackenzie maintained that "Lahinch will make the finest and most popular course that I, or, I believe, anyone else, ever constructed". Divine intention could no longer be given all the credit although Mackenzie did pay tribute to the great number of natural hazards with which he had to work. One of the main contributions Mackenzie made to a profession he adopted after forsaking his medical practice was in the design, shaping and angling of greens.

In the early days, greens were simply regarded as hollows or artificial platforms on which to place the pin, but Colt, Fowler, Mackenzie and Ross believed that greens should be a study in themselves.

Mackenzie could make a dull piece of ground interesting just by his greens but nobody could label the land at Lahinch as anything other than full of variety. In places you might call it eccentric, if being critical, or highly individual, if being kind. The short 6th hole, the Dell, is unique, the green, unseen from the tee, nestling between two giant sandhills. Lahinch without the Dell would be like Pisa without the Leaning Tower. However the course, which housed the Home Internationals in 1987, has other glories by which to be judged.

Its popularity, measured by the army of visitors that necessitated a second course being built, is centred upon its unmistakable seaside character which is felt and appreciated from the opening, uphill drive towards a green silhouetted against the skyline to the par 5 18th which climaxes a finish over the last seven holes which has recently been significantly lengthened.

The direction of the drive at the 1st is more crucial than may initially be apparent and the same applies at the 2nd which offers an inviting second shot as the fairway plunges down to a flatter approach. Next comes a classic short hole followed by a challenging tee shot at the 4th where a large dune waits to be carried. The 5th, Klondyke, is another hole that is peculiarly Lahinch.

The one reassuring piece of news is that, like the 2nd, it is a par 5 but, with a wind off the sea, the 7th is a mighty two-shotter whatever the card might say. On calmer days, it has picture book qualities, the view from the crest of the fairway embracing a green far below set against a backcloth of ocean. There are thoughts of modifications to the 8th but a new tee has added a cubit or two to the stature of the 9th although one of Lahinch's best holes, the short 11th, is one that it would be a travesty to alter.

It is proof that short holes don't need to be a long iron or wood to be difficult; here it is more touch and skill that are required to hold a beautiful example of Mackenzie's green designing. A contrasting prospect greets players on the 12th which follows the line of the river estuary; but the old green has been restored and the hole is now a stern four. It is a modification that has led to the lengthening of the 13th as well, a change, combined with the others, that has made Lahinch perhaps a couple of strokes harder.

The last five holes lack the scenic beauty of some of the others but they command attention and have decided many a match in the South of Ireland championship, Lahinch's famous annual festival. The finish comprises two par fives, the 14th and 18th, two long par fours and the last of the short holes, the 16th. There are times when they seem quite a haul but there is nothing overbearing about Lahinch whatever the weather; and if you want advice about that, the club goats, which make up its emblem, are held to be the most reliable indicators. The danger signs are when they surround the clubhouse. On my first visit, on a day when it was unfit even for hardy goats, I was greeted with the sight of four intrepid souls, drenched to the skin, putting out in the dark on the 18th green. They must have got their weather forecast from the radio or they may have felt, if you will pardon the expression, that the goats were kidding.

Mahonys Point 18 holes, 6734 yards, S.S.S.71
Kileen course designed by Fred Hawtree and Mahonys course designed by Sir Guy Campbell.
Club founded in 1891.
Visitors: welcome.
Green fees: £15 per day.
Society meetings: catered for every day.
Catering: meals and snacks served.
Hotels: Castlerosse; Aghadoe; Europe.

BB44 **Kilrush**
☎Kilrush 138
Parknamoney, Kilrush, Co Clare.
On main road into town from Ennis, Co Clare.
Parkland course.
9 holes, 2793 yards, S.S.S.67
Club founded in 1934.
Visitors: welcome.
Green fees: £4 per day.
Society meetings: catered for by arrangement.
Catering: bar facilities only.
Hotels: Orchard, Kilrush.

BB45 **Kinsale**
☎Cork (021) 772197
Ringenane, Belgooly, Co Cork.
On main Cork-Kinsale road, 2 miles short of Kinsale and 10 miles from Cork Airport.
Parkland course.
9 holes, 5332 yards, S.S.S.68
Club founded in 1912.
Visitors: welcome Mon-Fri. No weekends.
Green fees: £6 per day.
Society meetings: welcome by appointment £5 per player.
Catering: full catering available.
Hotels: many grade A hotels in Kinsale.

BB46 **Lahinch**
☎(065) 81003

Lahinch, Co Clare
34 miles from Shannon Airport.
Seaside courses.
Old-18 holes, 698 yards, S.S.S.73
Castle-18 holes, 5265 yards, S.S.S.67
Course designed by Tom Morris & revised by Dr A MacKenzie.
Club founded in 1893.
Visitors: welcome weekdays; weekends except from 9am-10am and 1pm-2pm Sat; 9am-10.30am and 1pm-2pm Sun.
Green fees: Old: £12 per day weekdays; Castle: £9 per day weekdays; £15 weekends and Bank Holidays.
Society meetings: Old - Mon-Sat, Castle - everyday.
Catering: full catering facilities.
Hotels: Aberdeen Arms, Lahinch; Sancta Maria, Lahinch; Liscanner Golf, Liscanner; Atlantic, Lahinch; Claremont, Lahinch.

BB47 **Limerick**
☎(061) 44083
Ballyclough, Limerick.
Turn left off Limerick-Cork road at Punches Cross.
Parkland course.
18 holes, 6344 yards, S.S.S.70
Club founded in 1891.
Visitors: welcome before 4pm Mon, Wed, Thurs, Fri. No visitors weekends.
Green fees: £10 per day.
Society meetings: Mon, Wed, Fri.
Catering: full.
Hotels: Royal George; Glentworth.

BB48 **Lismore**
☎Lismore (058) 54026
Lismore, Co Waterford.
0.5 mile from Lismore on Killarney road.
Parkland course.
9 holes, 5127 metres, S.S.S.67
Course designed by Eddie Hackett.

Club founded in 1965.
Visitors: welcome all days, some Sundays reserved.
Green fees: £5 per day.
Society meetings: all days except Sun.
Catering: prior booking needed.
Hotels: Lismore, Lismore; Ballyraeter House, Lismore.

BB49 **Macroom**
☎(026) 41072
Lackaduve, Macroom, Co Cork.
On T29, 25 miles W of Cork.
Parkland course.
9 holes, 5439 metres, S.S.S.68
Club founded in 1924.
Visitors: welcome.
Green fees: £4 per day.
Society meetings: welcome by arrangement.
Catering: full catering available.
Hotels: Castle (adjacent with free golf for residents).

BB50 **Mallow**
☎Mallow (022) 21145
Ballyellis, Mallow, Co Cork.
1 mile E of N20 at Mallow Bridge, 20 miles N of Cork city.
Parkland course.
18 holes, 6461 yards, S.S.S.71
Course designed by John Harris.
Club founded in 1948.
Visitors: welcome weekdays.
Green fees: £7 any day; society groups £5 on weekdays.
Society meetings: catered for weekdays.
Catering: lunch every day.
Hotels: Longueville Houses; Central; Hibernian.

BB51 **Mitchelstown**
☎(025) 24072
Mitchelstown, Co Cork.
1 mile from Mitchelstown off N8 Dublin-Cork road.
Parkland course.

9 holes, 5057 metres, S.S.S.67
Course designed by Eddie Hackett.
Club founded in 1908.
Visitors: welcome.
Green fees: £4 weekdays; £5
weekends and Bank Holidays.
Society meetings: welcome except
Sun.
Catering: full catering facilities
available for societies by arrange-
ment.
Hotels: Clongibbon House, New
Square, Mitchelstown; Firgrove,
Mitchelstown.

BB52 **Monkstown**
☎Cork (021) 841225
Parkgariffe, Monkstown, Co Cork.
On L68 7 miles S of Cork.
Parkland course.
18 holes, 5669 metres, S.S.S.69
Club founded in 1908.
Visitors: welcome all week.
Green fees: £9 weekdays; £10
weekends.
Society meetings: welcome £8.
Catering: full meals all day.
Hotels: many good hotels in area.

BB53 **Mountrath**
☎(0502) 32558
Mountrath, Co Laois.
8 miles from Portlaoise on main
Dublin-Limerick road.
Undulating parkland course.
9 holes, 5500 yards, S.S.S.65
Club founded in 1929.
Visitors: welcome.
Green fees: £4, (£3 with member).
Society meetings: contact Sec.
Catering: only on request for events,
societies etc.
Hotels: Killeshin, Portlaoise.

BB54 **Muskerry**
☎Cork (021) 85104 Pro, 85297 Sec.
Carrickrohane, Co Cork.
7 miles W of city centre, near
Blarney village.
Parkland course.
18 holes, 5786 metres, S.S.S.70
Club founded in 1897.
Visitors: welcome on weekdays
except Wed afternoons and Thurs
mornings before 12.30am.
Green fees: on application.
Catering: snacks available; meals
by arrangement before play.
Hotels: Blarney.

BB55 **Naas**
☎(045) 97509
Kardiffstown, Salins, Naas,
Co Kildare.

Leave dual carriageway at
Johnstown Village, and take link road
N of carriageway to Salins.
18 holes, 6233 yards, S.S.S.68
Visitors: welcome.
Green fees: on application.
Society meetings: welcome Mon,
Wed and Fri.
Hotels: Lawlor's; Osbertown House;
Cill Dara; Town House.

BB56 **Nenagh**
☎(067) 31476
Beechwood, Nenagh, Co Tipperary.
4 miles from Nenagh Tam, well
signposted.
Inland course.
18 holes, 5181 metres, S.S.S.67
Course designed by E. Hackett.
Club founded in 1917.
Visitors: welcome every day except
Sat morning or Sun.
Green fees: £6 weekdays; £7
weekends.
Society meetings: Sat morning
10am-12.30pm.
Catering: full catering facilities at
club.
Hotels: many hotels in area.

BB57 **Newcastle West**
☎Newcastle West 76
Newcastle West, Co Limerick.
1 mile from town on Cork road.
Meadowland course.
9 holes, 5400 yards, S.S.S.65
Visitors: welcome.
Green fees: on application.
Society meetings: by arrangement.
Hotels: Central; Devon; River Room.

BB58 **New Ross**
☎New Ross (051) 21433
Tinneanny, New Ross, Co Wexford.
From town centre take Waterford Rd,
turn right at Albatros factory, about 1
mile.
Parkland course.
9 holes, 6133 yards, S.S.S.69
Club founded in 1904.
Visitors: welcome except Sun if
there is a competition.
Green fees: on application.
Society meetings: by arrangement.
Catering: snacks always available,
meals by arrangement.
Hotels: Five Counties; Royal.

BB59 **Rathdowney**
☎(0505) 46170
Rathdowney, Portlaoise.
Take N7 to Abbeyleix, turn left for
town of Rathdowney, follow
signposts from square in Ra-

thdowney, Co Laois.
Meadowland course.
9 holes, S.S.S.66
Course designed by Eddie Hackett.
Club founded in 1931.
Visitors: welcome.
Green fees: on application.
Society meetings: by arrangement.
Catering: by arrangement with Hon
Sec giving one week notice.
Hotels: Central, Rathdowney; Leix
Co, Borris in Ossory, Co Laoise.

BB60 **Roscrea**
☎(0505) 21130
Derry Vale, Dublin Rd, Roscrea,
Co Tipperary.
2 miles from Roscrea on Dublin side
of town, beside main road on right
hand side before railway bridge.
Meadowland course.
9 holes, 6059 yards, S.S.S.69
Club founded in 1911.
Visitors: welcome Mon to Sat.
Green fees: £5.
Society meetings: welcome am Sat
in groups of not more than 30.
Catering: by arrangement only.
Hotels: Racket Hall, 200 yards.

BB61 **Rosslare**
☎(053) 32203
Rosslare, Co Wexford.
Links seaside course.
18 holes, 6502 yards, S.S.S.71
Club founded in 1908.
Visitors: welcome.
Green fees: £8 weekdays; £10
weekends.
Society meetings: welcome.
Catering: available.
Hotels: Kellys Strand; Cedars; Golf.

BB62 **Skibbereen**
☎Skibbereen (028) 21227
Skibbereen, Co Cork.
Off T65, 47 miles SW of Cork.
Moorland course.
9 holes, 5890 yards, S.S.S.67
Visitors: welcome.
Green fees: on application.
Society meetings: welcome.
Hotels: Eldon; West Cork; Lissard
House.

BB63 **Spanish Point**
☎(065) 84198
Spanish Point, Miltown Malbay, Co
Clare.
9 miles from Lahinch Golf Club, 2
miles from Miltown Malbay on
seafront.
Seaside course.
9 holes, 6171 metres, S.S.S.54

Club founded in 1940.
Visitors: welcome.
Green fees: £3.50 weekdays.
Society meetings: welcome except on Sun.
Catering: only on special occasions.
Hotels: Central, Miltown Malbay, Co Clare.

BB64 **Thurles**
☎Thurles (0504) 21983
Turtulla, Thurles, Co Tipperary.
1 mile S of Thurles on Cork road.
Parkland course.
18 holes, 6300 yards, S.S.S.70
Club founded in 1911.
Visitors: welcome except on Sun.
Green fees: £6.
Society meetings: catered for on weekdays and Sat.
Catering: full catering available.
Hotels: Hayes, Thurles; Munster, Thurles.

BB65 **Tipperary**
☎(062) 51119
Rathanny, Tipperary
1 mile from town.
Parkland course.
9 holes, 6054 yards, S.S.S.68
Visitors: welcome except Mon.
Green fees: on application.
Society meetings: by arrangement.
Hotels: Glen; Royal; Aherlow House; Tipperary.

BB66 **Tralee**
☎(066) 36379
West Barrow, Ardfert, Co Kerry.
From Tralee through villages of Spa and Churchill to Barrow, narrow roads.
Links course.
18 holes, 6465 yards, S.S.S.71
Course designed by Arnold Palmer Design Co.
Club founded in 1904.
Visitors: welcome Mon-Sat by arrangement with Sec.
Green fees: £12 weekdays; £14 weekends, yet to be ratified.
Society meetings: £9 weekdays; £12 weekends, yet to be ratified.
Catering: full except Mon.
Hotels: Mount Brandon; Ballygarry House; Earl of Desmond, all in Tralee.

BB67 **Tramore**
☎(051) 81247
Newtown Hill, Tramore, Co Waterford.
Via Waterford, 1 mile beyond

Tramore.
Parkland course.
18 holes, 6408 yards, S.S.S.70
Course designed by Tibbett (1936/7).
Visitors: welcome.
Green fees: on application.
Society meetings: by arrangement.
Catering: meals served except Mon.
Hotels: Majestic; Grand; Sea View.

BB68 **Tullamore**
☎(0506) 21439
Brookfield, Tullamore, Co Offaly.
2.5 miles from town centre on Birr road.
Parkland course.
18 holes, 6314 yards, S.S.S.71
Course designed by James Braid.
Club founded in 1896.
Visitors: welcome except during club competitions on Sun.
Green fees: on application.
Society meetings: catered for on weekdays and Sat.
Catering: by prior arrangement.
Hotels: Phoenix Arms.

BB69 **Waterford**
☎Waterford (051) 76748/74182
New Rath, Waterford.
0.25 mile from city centre.
Parkland course.
18 holes, 6237 yards, S.S.S.69
Course designed by Cecil Barcroft and Willie Park.
Club founded in 1912.
Visitors: welcome weekdays.
Green fees: £6 weekdays; £9 weekends.
Society meetings: catered for on weekdays.
Catering: full catering facilities available.
Hotels: Ardree; Bridge; Granville; Dooleys; Tower.

BB70 **Waterville**
☎Waterville (0667) 4102/4133.
Waterville, Co Kerry.
N70 to Waterville, then coastal road for 1 mile W of town.
Seaside links course.
18 holes, 7241 yards, S.S.S.74
Course designed by J.A. Mulcahy and E. Hackett.
Club founded in 1970.
Visitors: welcome.
Green fees: £15 per day.
Society meetings: Tel H/O 021 775554.
Catering: snack lunch or full meals at Waterville Lake Hotel.
Hotels: Waterville Lake, Waterville, Co Kerry.

BB71 **Wexford**
☎Wexford (053) 42238
Mulganon, Wexford.
Within 0.5 mile from town.
Parkland course.
18 holes, 6038 yards, S.S.S.69
Course designed by J. Hamilton Stutt & Co.
Club founded in 1961.
Visitors: welcome.
Green fees: £6 weekdays; £7 weekends.
Society meetings: welcome.
Hotels: Talbot; Whites; Wexford; Kelly's Strand; Rosslare; Cedars, Rosslare.

BB72 **Wicklow**
☎(0404) 2361
Dunbur Rd, Wicklow, Co Wicklow.
On L29 32 miles from Dublin.
Seaside course.
9 holes, 2633 yards, S.S.S.67
Club founded in 1904.
Visitors: welcome weekdays.
Green fees: on application.
Catering: meals served except Tues.
Hotels: many good hotels in area.

BB73 **Woodbrook**
☎Dublin (01) 824799.
Bray, Co Wicklow.
From Dublin on main road to Bray, 1 mile outside Bray.
Parkland course.
18 holes, 6541 yards, S.S.S.71
Club founded in 1927.
Visitors: welcome on weekdays.
Green fees: £12 weekdays; £16 weekends.
Catering: bar snacks and full meals served.
Hotels: Royal, Bray; Victor, Dun Laoghaire; Killiney Castle, Killiney.

BB74 **Woodenbridge**
☎Arklow (0402) 5202
Woodenbridge, Avoca, Co Wicklow.
50 miles S of Dublin on route N11 to Arklow; town club 4 miles from Arklow.
Parkland course.
9 holes, 6104 yards, S.S.S.68
Club founded in 1884.
Visitors: welcome weekdays and most Sun.
Green fees: £6 weekdays; £8 weekends.
Society meetings: welcome weekdays by arrangement.
Catering: lunch and evenings meal available except Mon.

Hotels: Woodenbridge, Woodenbridge, Co Wicklow; Valley, Woodenbridge; Vale View, Avoca.

BB75 **Youghal**
☎(024) 92787
Knockaverry, Youghal, Co Cork.

Overlooking Youghal town and bay. Meadowland course. 18 holes, 6206 yards, S.S.S.69 Course designed by Commander Harris. Club founded in 1911.
Visitors: welcome.

Green fees: on application.
Society meetings: welcome.
Catering: coffee and sandwiches available at present; new clubhouse under construction.
Hotels: Hilltop; Devonshire Arms.

The
GOLF COURSE
Guide
TO BRITAIN & IRELAND

INDEX

Y

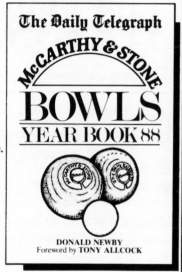

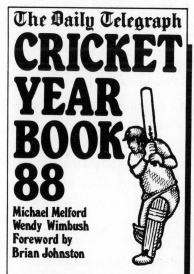